Instructor's Resource Manual

for

Kotz, Treichel, and Weaver's

Chemistry and Chemical Reactivity

Sixth Edition

Susan M. Young
Hartwick College

THOMSON

BROOKS/COLE

Australia • Canada • Mexico • Singapore • Spain • United Kingdom • United States

Printed in the United States of America
3 4 5 6 7 09 08 07 06

Printer: Thomson/West

ISBN: 0-534-99856-9

For more information about our products,
contact us at:
Thomson Learning Academic Resource Center
1-800-423-0563

For permission to use material from this text or
product, submit a request online at
http://www.thomsonrights.com.
Any additional questions about permissions can be
submitted by email to **thomsonrights@thomson.com.**

Thomson Higher Education
10 Davis Drive
Belmont, CA 94002-3098
USA

Asia (including India)
Thomson Learning
5 Shenton Way
#01-01 UIC Building
Singapore 068808

Australia/New Zealand
Thomson Learning Australia
102 Dodds Street
Southbank, Victoria 3006
Australia

Canada
Thomson Nelson
1120 Birchmount Road
Toronto, Ontario M1K 5G4
Canada

UK/Europe/Middle East/Africa
Thomson Learning
High Holborn House
50–51 Bedford Road
London WC1R 4LR
United Kingdom

Latin America
Thomson Learning
Seneca, 53
Colonia Polanco
11560 Mexico
D.F. Mexico

Spain (including Portugal)
Thomson Paraninfo
Calle Magallanes, 25
28015 Madrid, Spain

Table of Contents

PREFACE

This *Instructor's Resource Manual* for the sixth edition of *Chemistry and Chemical Reactivity* continues an attempt to help instructors make general chemistry courses more interesting, challenging, and relevant for their students. This edition of the *Resource Manual* therefore continues to emphasize the organization of the course as well as the important topic of lecture demonstrations. Also, since the authors of the textbook and this manual frequently use multimedia in the classroom, there are many references to appropriate videodisc segments, computer programs, and portions of the *General ChemistryNow CD-ROM.*

Answers to Study Questions

This *Instructor's Resource Manual* includes a complete set of solutions to all of the Study Questions in the sixth edition of *Chemistry & Chemical Reactivity.* The solutions, whenever possible, were written in a style that matches the format of the solved Example problems in the textbook. The answers were written assuming they would be used by faculty and posted for students. For this reason, the solutions are not as detailed as the answers to the blue, bold-faced numbered questions in the *Student Solutions Manual*, prepared by Alton Banks.

Instructor's Notes

In each chapter identifies the number of lectures roughly allocated to each topic and notes where the topics in the text may be placed as an alternate to the order in which they are presented in the text.

Lecture Demonstrations

It is the authors' hope that the textbook conveys a clear and organized view of chemistry as an interesting and useful subject. In order to further emphasize this representation, demonstrations are especially important. Therefore, each chapter of this *Manual* contains information on the demonstrations often used in typical lectures. Some of these demonstrations are pictured in the text since they are too dangerous to be done in the classroom.

Many of the photos in the book and the demonstrations are taken from the excellent series of books by Bassam Shakhashiri, *Chemical Demonstrations: A Handbook for Teachers of Chemistry.* Another excellent source of demonstrations and experiments is the *Journal of Chemical Education.* The journal can be searched on the web at http://jchemed.chem.wisc.edu.

Multimedia

The *Periodic Table Videodisc*, the *Periodic Table Live!* CD-ROM, and the *Redox Videodisc* have been distributed by *JCE: Software.* The *General ChemistryNOW* CD-ROM is included with the textbook, and Bill Vining wrote a description of the materials on the CD-ROM for this manual.

Personal Response System

A sample set of question sheets that can be used in lecture along with a Personal Response System are included in this edition of the manual, along with a description of the PRS system written by Jack Kotz. Additional question sheets can be found on the web site accompanying this textbook or by contacting your Thomson/Brooks-Cole representative. Information about one popular system, the InterWrite PRS, can be found on the web at http://www.gtcocalcomp.com/interwriteprs.htm.

Acknowledgments

I could not have completed this manual without the help of Andrew Jorgensen, University of Toledo, who revised the Instructor's Notes, and Stephania Messersmith, University of Toledo, who revised the Suggested Demonstrations. Jack Kotz, State University of New York College at Oneonta, wrote the PRS questions that are included at the end of this manual and Bill Vining, University of Massachusetts, Amherst, wrote the description of the *General ChemistryNOW* CD-ROM. Also, the advance copy of the *Student Solutions Manual* by Alton Banks, North Carolina State University, and the Appendix answers written by Jack Kotz were invaluable when checking the accuracy of the answers to the blue, bold-faced numbered questions.

Any errors that remain in this manual are the responsibility of the author of this manual, and you should contact me if you have corrections or comments. The *Instructor's Resource Manual* was prepared using a G4 PowerBook, Microsoft Word X for Mac, Microsoft Excel X for Mac, MathType 5.1, and ChemDraw Ultra 8.0.

As a final note, I would like to thank my husband John and the many friends whose support helped make this project possible.

Susan M. Young
Associate Professor of Chemistry
Hartwick College
youngs@hartwick.edu

November 2004

Chapter 1
Matter and Measurement

INSTRUCTOR'S NOTES

This chapter discusses a wide range of basic subjects needed for the study of chemistry. How you use the material will depend on the preparation level of your students. Essentially all of the topics in this chapter would be found in a typical high school chemistry class. However, if students took that course two or three years earlier, or if their performance at that time was inconsistent with their present goal of a professional study for science or engineering, an extensive review might be necessary. Such a review could take three to four lecture periods. If your class consists of students who have been screened by a placement exam or other process to reasonably ensure that they have good abilities in high school chemistry, you may assign most or even all of the chapter for outside reading with only a single class to review and stress key points. The chapter can stand on its own without direct instruction if your students learned the topics previously. For an intermediate approach you could assign sections 1.1-1.5 for student reading then take two to three lectures for the rest of the chapter. Section 1.8 reviews a wide range of mathematical topics that will be needed by the student in the course, so mastery of this material should be stressed.

The need for accurate measurement of physical quantities and the correct recording of this information can be characterized as necessary for reasons of safety using medical (drug dosage) and engineering examples (material composition and properties). Mistakes in this area can mean the difference between life and death.

A pre-quiz selected from Chapter 1 Study Questions could help establish what degree of review is needed for your students.

SUGGESTED DEMONSTRATIONS

1. Density
   - Kolb, K. E.; Kolb, D. K. "Method for Separating or Identifying Plastics," *Journal of Chemical Education* **1991**, *68*, 348.
   - Franz, D. A. "Densities and Miscibilities of Liquids and Liquid Mixtures," *Journal of Chemical Education* **1991**, *68*, 594.
   - Checkai, G.; Whitsett, J. "Density Demonstration Using Diet Soft Drinks," *Journal of Chemical Education* **1986**, *63*, 515.
   - Shakhashiri, B. Z. "Density and Miscibility of Liquids," *Chemical Demonstrations: A Handbook for Teachers of Chemistry;* University of Wisconsin Press, 1989; Vol. 3, pp. 229–233.

2. Properties of Elements
   - Pictures of the elements and their uses can be found on the *Periodic Table Videodisc* and on the *Periodic Table Live!* CD-ROM available from JCE Software.

3. Illustration of "Physical Change"

   - Liquid nitrogen is always a favorite of students. We freeze a banana, a hot dog, a flower, or similar object.

4. Illustration of "Chemical Change"

   - The first lecture in the course is often begun with a "bang" by setting off several hydrogen-filled balloons in a darkened lecture room. The demonstration is described in *Chemical Demonstrations: A Handbook for Teachers of Chemistry;* University of Wisconsin Press, 1983; Vol. 1, pp. 106–112. The reaction is also shown on the *General ChemistryNow CD-ROM*, the *Periodic Table Videodisc* and the *Periodic Table Live!* CD-ROM.

   - Other reactions could be done as well, depending on the facilities available. Possibilities include placing small pieces of potassium in water, the thermite reaction (Shakhashiri, Volume 1, page 85), or the reaction of zinc and ammonium nitrate (Shakhashiri, Volume 1, page 51). The latter reaction gives off a large amount of ZnO dust and other irritating fumes. It is not suitable for a room without good ventilation.

   - For fun, and to give some color, as well as talking about our future study of acid-base reactions, we add aqueous NH_3 to separate flasks containing (i) very dilute acid with phenolphthalein, (ii) $Al(NO_3)_3$, and (iii) dilute $CuSO_4$.

   - We often have a student contribute a penny to put into concentrated HNO_3. The reaction brings up a brief discussion of oxidation–reduction processes. The NO_2 gas generated prompts a discussion of air pollution problems, as well as the fuels used in the Lunar Lander and in the Space Shuttle. (CAUTION: NO_2 is a very corrosive gas. Use only in a well ventilated room. We do the reaction by putting the penny in a few milliliters of acid in a 2-L Erlenmeyer flask that is lightly stoppered. This effectively contains the gas.)

   - The *Periodic Table Videodisc* and the *Periodic Table Live!* CD-ROM can be used to explore reactions of the elements with air, water, acids, and bases. Examples include the reaction of potassium with water and the reaction of cobalt with HCl and HNO_3.

5. Energy

   - We have often noted that chemistry deals with energy and so some demonstrations in the first lecture are a thermite reaction or the use of light sticks.

6. Units of Measurement

   - Add a few drop of bromcresol green to a 2-L flask before the lecture. On filling with water during lecture, the water becomes blue. When the flask is almost full, it is topped off with dilute HCl, and the solution turns yellow. Next, the water is poured into an ordinary 1-L flask or beaker that already contains some dilute base, and the solution turns blue again. This is then poured into a graduated cylinder containing some phenolphthalein. We use this sequence to comment on the relative accuracies of the different types of glassware. We take some containers such as soda cans so students can connect metric units with familiar objects.

   - A weighed piece of fruit or some other solid gives some meaning to mass expressed in grams.

- Earley, C. W. "A Simple Demonstration for Introducing the Metric System to Introductory Chemistry Classes," *Journal of Chemical Education* **1999**, *76*, 1215.

7. Demonstrations Using Significant Figures

- Kirksey, H. G. "Significant Figures: A Classroom Demonstration," *Journal of Chemical Education* **1992**, *69*, 497.

- Abel, K. B.; Hemmerlin, W. M. "Significant Figures," *Journal of Chemical Education* **1990**, *67*, 213.

SOLUTIONS TO STUDY QUESTIONS

1.1   (a) C   Carbon   (c) Cl   Chlorine   (e) Mg   Magnesium

       (b) K   Potassium   (d) P   Phosphorus   (f) Ni   Nickel

1.2   (a) Mn   Manganese   (c) Na   Sodium   (e) Xe   Xenon

       (b) Cu   Copper   (d) Br   Bromine   (f) Fe   Iron

1.3   (a) barium   Ba   (d) lead   Pb

       (b) titanium   Ti   (e) arsenic   As

       (c) chromium   Cr   (f) zinc   Zn

1.4   (a) silver   Ag   (d) tin   Sn

       (b) aluminum   Al   (e) technetium   Tc

       (c) plutonium   Pu   (f) krypton   Kr

1.5   (a) NaCl is a compound; sodium is an element

       (b) Sugar is a compound; carbon is an element.

       (c) Gold chloride is a compound; gold is an element.

1.6   (a) $Pt(NH_3)_2Cl_2$ is a compound; Pt is an element

       (b) Copper is an element; copper(II) oxide is a compound

       (c) Silicon is an element; sand is a compound

1.7   (a) physical property

       (b) chemical property

       (c) chemical property

       (d) physical property

       (e) physical property

       (f) physical property

1.8   (a) chemical change

       (b) physical change

       (c) chemical change

       (d) physical change

1.9 (a) Physical properties: color (colorless), physical state (liquid)

Chemical property: reactivity (burns in air)

(b) Physical properties: color (shiny metal, orange), physical state (liquid)

Chemical property: reactivity (aluminum reacts readily with bromine)

1.10 (a) Physical properties: color (white), physical state (solid), density (2.71 g/cm^3)

Chemical properties: reactivity towards acid (reacts to produce gaseous carbon dioxide)

(b) Physical property: color (gray zinc, purple iodine, white compound)

Chemical property: reactivity (zinc and iodine react to give a white compound)

1.11 $500. \text{ mL} \cdot \dfrac{1 \text{ cm}^3}{1 \text{ mL}} \cdot \dfrac{1.11 \text{ g}}{1 \text{ cm}^3} = 555 \text{ g}$

1.12 $2.365 \text{ g} \cdot \dfrac{1 \text{ cm}^3}{10.5 \text{ g}} = 0.225 \text{ cm}^3$

1.13 $2.00 \text{ g} \cdot \dfrac{1 \text{ cm}^3}{0.718 \text{ g}} \cdot \dfrac{1 \text{ mL}}{1 \text{ cm}^3} = 2.79 \text{ mL}$

1.14 $1 \text{ cup} \cdot \dfrac{237 \text{ mL}}{1 \text{ cup}} \cdot \dfrac{1 \text{ cm}^3}{1 \text{ mL}} = 237 \text{ cm}^3$

$\dfrac{205 \text{ g}}{237 \text{ cm}^3} = 0.865 \text{ g/cm}^3$

1.15 $\dfrac{37.5 \text{ g}}{(20.2 - 6.9) \text{ mL}} \cdot \dfrac{1 \text{ mL}}{1 \text{ cm}^3} = 2.82 \text{ g/cm}^3$

The sample's density matches that of aluminum.

1.16 $\dfrac{23.5 \text{ g}}{(52.2 - 47.5) \text{ mL}} \cdot \dfrac{1 \text{ mL}}{1 \text{ cm}^3} = 5.0 \text{ g/cm}^3$

The sample's density matches that of fool's gold.

1.17 $(25 \text{ °C} + 273.15 \text{ °C}) \dfrac{1 \text{ K}}{1 \text{ °C}} = 298 \text{ K}$

1.18 $(5.5 \times 10^3 \text{ °C} + 273.15 \text{ °C}) \dfrac{1 \text{ K}}{1 \text{ °C}} = 5.8 \times 10^3 \text{ K}$

1.19 (a) 289 K   (b) 97 °C   (c) 310 K

1.20 (a) −196 °C   (b) 336 K   (c) 1180 °C

1.21 $42.195 \text{ km} \cdot \dfrac{1000 \text{ m}}{1 \text{ km}} = 4.2195 \times 10^4 \text{ m}$

$42.195 \text{ km} \cdot \dfrac{0.62137 \text{ miles}}{1 \text{ km}} = 26.219 \text{ miles}$

1.22 $19 \text{ cm} \cdot \dfrac{10 \text{ mm}}{1 \text{ cm}} = 190 \text{ mm}$

$19 \text{ cm} \cdot \dfrac{1 \text{ m}}{100 \text{ cm}} = 0.19 \text{ m}$

1.23 $2.5 \text{ cm} \times 2.1 \text{ cm} = 5.3 \text{ cm}^2$

$5.3 \text{ cm}^2 \cdot \left(\dfrac{1 \text{ m}}{100 \text{ cm}} \right)^2 = 5.3 \times 10^{-4} \text{ m}^2$

1.24 $\text{Area} = \pi \, r^2 = \pi \left(\dfrac{11.8 \text{ cm}}{2} \right)^2 = 109 \text{ cm}^2$

$109 \text{ cm}^2 \cdot \left(\dfrac{1 \text{ m}}{100 \text{ cm}} \right)^2 = 1.09 \times 10^{-2} \text{ m}^2$

1.25 $250 \text{ mL} \cdot \dfrac{1 \text{ cm}^3}{1 \text{ mL}} = 250 \text{ cm}^3$

$250 \text{ mL} \cdot \dfrac{1 \text{ L}}{10^3 \text{ mL}} = 0.25 \text{ L}$

$250 \text{ mL} \cdot \dfrac{1 \text{ cm}^3}{1 \text{ mL}} \cdot \left(\dfrac{1 \text{ m}}{100 \text{ cm}} \right)^3 = 2.5 \times 10^{-4} \text{ m}^3$

$250 \text{ mL} \cdot \dfrac{1 \text{ L}}{10^3 \text{ mL}} \cdot \dfrac{1 \text{ dm}^3}{1 \text{ L}} = 0.25 \text{ dm}^3$

1.26 $1.5 \text{ L} \cdot \dfrac{10^3 \text{ mL}}{1 \text{ L}} = 1.5 \times 10^3 \text{ mL}$

$1.5 \text{ L} \cdot \dfrac{10^3 \text{ mL}}{1 \text{ L}} \cdot \dfrac{1 \text{ cm}^3}{1 \text{ mL}} = 1.5 \times 10^3 \text{ cm}^3$

$1.5 \times 10^3 \text{ cm}^3 \cdot \left(\dfrac{1 \text{ dm}}{10 \text{ cm}} \right)^3 = 1.5 \text{ dm}^3$

1.27 $2.52 \text{ kg} \cdot \dfrac{10^3 \text{ g}}{1 \text{ kg}} = 2.52 \times 10^3 \text{ g}$

1.28 $2.265 \text{ g} \cdot \dfrac{1 \text{ kg}}{10^3 \text{ g}} = 2.265 \times 10^{-3} \text{ kg}$

$2.265 \text{ g} \cdot \dfrac{10^3 \text{ mg}}{1 \text{ g}} = 2.265 \times 10^3 \text{ mg}$

1.29

	Method A	Deviation	Method B	Deviation
	2.2	0.2	2.703	0.777
	2.3	0.1	2.701	0.779
	2.7	0.3	2.705	0.775
	2.4	0.0	5.811	2.331
(a) Average:	2.4	0.2	3.480	1.166

For method B the reading of 5.811 can be excluded because it is more than twice as large as all other readings. Using only the first three readings, average = 2.703 g/cm^3 and average deviation = 0.001 g/cm^3.

(b) Method A: Percent error = $\dfrac{2.702 - 2.4}{2.702} \times 100\% = 10\%$

Method B: Percent error = $\dfrac{2.703 - 2.702}{2.702} \times 100\% = 0.04\%$ (omitting data point)

(c) Before excluding a data point for B, method A is more accurate and more precise. After excluding data for B, this method gives a more accurate and more precise result.

1.30   (a) Student A: Average = 135 °C   Percent error = $\dfrac{135 - 135}{135} \times 100\% = 0\%$

Student B: Average = 138 °C   Percent error = $\dfrac{138 - 135}{135} \times 100\% = 2\%$

(b) Student B is more precise; Student A is more accurate

1.31   (a) Qualitative observations: blue-green color, solid physical state

Quantitative observations: density of 2.65 g/cm^3, mass of 2.5 g, length of 4.6 cm

(b) Mass and length are extensive properties, color, physical state, and density are intensive properties

(c) $2.5 \text{ g} \cdot \dfrac{1 \text{ cm}^3}{2.65 \text{ g}} = 0.94 \text{ cm}^3$

1.32.   Physical properties: Hydrogen and oxygen are colorless gases while iron and sodium are both solids at room temperature.

Chemical properties: Hydrogen and oxygen react to form water. Sodium reacts violently with water. Iron reacts with oxygen to form rust.

1.33   (a) Aluminum: Al   Silicon: Si   Oxygen: O

(b) Oxygen is a gas, while aluminum, silicon, and aquamarine are solids at room temperature. Oxygen is colorless, while aluminum and silicon are gray. The gemstone is a bluish color.

1.34   Observations (c), (e), and (f) identify physical properties.

1.35 $(-248.6 \,°C + 273.15 \,°C)\dfrac{1\,K}{1\,°C} = 24.6\,K$

$(-246.1 \,°C + 273.15 \,°C)\dfrac{1\,K}{1\,°C} = 27.1\,K$

1.36   density $= \dfrac{2.361\,g}{(2.35\,cm \times 1.34\,cm \times 0.105\,cm)} = 7.14\,g/cm^3$

The metal is (c) Zinc

1.37 $1.97\,Å \cdot \dfrac{10^{-10}\,m}{1\,Å} \cdot \dfrac{1\,nm}{10^{-9}\,m} = 0.197\,nm$

$1.97\,Å \cdot \dfrac{10^{-10}\,m}{1\,Å} \cdot \dfrac{1\,pm}{10^{-12}\,m} = 197\,pm$

1.38 $0.154\,nm \cdot \dfrac{10^{-9}\,m}{1\,nm} = 1.54 \times 10^{-10}\,m$

$1.54 \times 10^{-10}\,m \cdot \dfrac{1\,pm}{10^{-12}\,m} = 154\,pm$

1.39   (a) $7.5\,\mu m \cdot \dfrac{10^{-6}\,m}{1\,\mu m} = 7.5 \times 10^{-6}\,m$

(b) $7.5 \times 10^{-6}\,m \cdot \dfrac{1\,nm}{10^{-9}\,m} = 7.5 \times 10^{3}\,nm$

(c) $7.5 \times 10^{-6}\,m \cdot \dfrac{1\,pm}{10^{-12}\,m} = 7.5 \times 10^{6}\,pm$

1.40 $600\,g\,H_2O \cdot \dfrac{1\,cm^3}{0.995\,g} = 600\,cm^3$

$600\,g\,Pb \cdot \dfrac{1\,cm^3}{11.34\,g} = 50\,cm^3$

Given equal masses the less dense substance (water) will have a greater volume.

1.41 $1.53\,g\,cisplatin \cdot \dfrac{65.0\,g\,Pt}{100.0\,g\,cisplatin} = 0.995\,g\,Pt$

1.42 $250\,g\,solder \cdot \dfrac{67\,g\,Pb}{100\,g\,solder} = 170\,g\,Pb$

1.43 $0.50\,mL \cdot \dfrac{10.\,g\,procaine\,hydrochloride}{100\,mL\,solution} \cdot \dfrac{10^{3}\,mg}{1\,g} = 50.\,mg\,procaine\,hydrochloride$

1.44 $7.6\,g \cdot \dfrac{1\,cm^3}{2.70\,g} = 2.8\,cm^3$

cube edge $= \sqrt[3]{2.8\,cm^3} = 1.4\,cm$

1.45 $154 \text{ g} \cdot \dfrac{1 \text{ cm}^3}{8.56 \text{ g}} \cdot \dfrac{1 \text{ mL}}{1 \text{ cm}^3} = 18.0 \text{ mL}$

The water will rise 18.0 mL to a final volume of 68.0 mL.

1.46 $\dfrac{18.82 \text{ g}}{(15.3 - 8.5) \text{ mL}} \cdot \dfrac{1 \text{ mL}}{1 \text{ cm}^3} = 2.8 \text{ g/cm}^3$

The white solid's density matches that of (c) KBr.

1.47 $\dfrac{67 \text{ g}}{(26.0 - 22.5) \text{ mL}} \cdot \dfrac{1 \text{ mL}}{1 \text{ cm}^3} = 19 \text{ g/cm}^3$

The necklace's density matches that of gold. The necklace contains more than 2 troy ounces of gold, so $300 is a good price.

1.48   Calcium: Ca   Fluorine: F

The shape of the fluorite crystals can be described as interwoven cubes.

The overall shape of the crystals indicates that the ions in the solid matrix arrange themselves with alternating calcium and fluoride ions to produce the crystal appearance.

1.49   The non-uniform appearance of the mixture indicates that samples taken from different regions of the mixture would be different—a characteristic of a heterogeneous mixture. Recalling that iron is attracted to a magnetic field while sand is generally not attracted in this way suggests that passing a magnet through the mixture would separate the sand and iron.

1.50   Liquids: mercury and water   Solid: copper

Of the substances shown, mercury is most dense and water is least dense.

1.51   The plastic (with a much lower density than CCl_4) will float. The aluminum (which is more dense than CCl_4) will sink.

1.52   The large colorless block of salt represents the macroscopic view. The spheres represent the microscopic or particulate view. If one can imagine producing multiple "copies" of the particulate view, the macroscopic view will result.

1.53   Melting point. Sugar melts around 160–186 °C while salt melts at 800 °C.

1.54   Milk is mostly water. When water freezes its volume increases (its density decreases). When the milk froze, the increase in volume was so great that it pushed out of the bottle.

1.55   The normally accepted value for a human temperature is 98.6° F. On the Celsius scale, this corresponds to 37 °C. Gallium has a melting point of 29.8 °C, so the solid should melt in your hand.

1.56   The lab partner is on the right track in estimating the density to lie between that at 15 °C and that at 25 °C. If one assumes is it halfway between those densities, a better estimate would be 0.99810 g/cm^3. A more accurate analysis, however, shows that the decrease in density with increasing temperature is not linear. A more careful analysis would lead to a value of perhaps 0.99820 g/cm^3 (not far from the actual value of 0.99840 g/cm^3)

1.57   HDPE will float in liquids with a density higher than 0.97 g/mL, ethylene glycol, water, acetic acid, and glycerol.

1.58   The two liquids will be layered, with hexane floating on top of perfluorohexane. HDPE and PVC will lie at the bottom of the hexane layer (HDPE on top of the PVC). Teflon will sink to the bottom of the perfluorohexane layer.

1.59   (a) solid iron   (b) liquid water   (c) water vapor

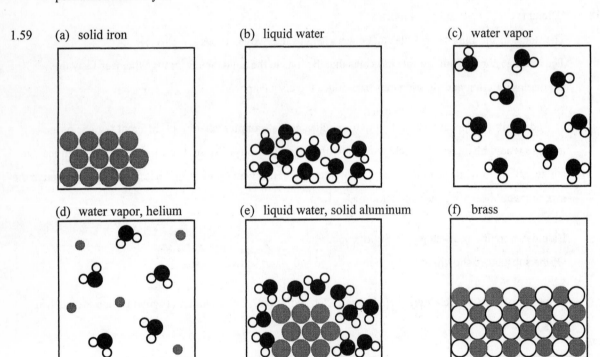

(d) water vapor, helium   (e) liquid water, solid aluminum   (f) brass

1.60   The sample's density and melting point could be compared with that of silver to prove whether or not the sample is silver.

1.61   One could check for an odor, check the boiling or freezing point, or determine the density. If the density is approximately 1 g/cm^3 at room temperature, the liquid could be water. If it boils at about 100 °C and freezes at about 0 °C, that would be consistent with water. To check for the presence of salt, boil the liquid away. If a substance remains, it could be salt, but further testing would be required.

1.62   The mass of the object is determined and then the volume is determined by submersion in a known volume of liquid. The increase in volume would be equal to the volume of the irregularly shaped object. The density could be calculated by dividing its mass by its volume.

1.63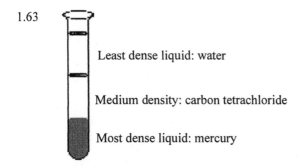

Least dense liquid: water

Medium density: carbon tetrachloride

Most dense liquid: mercury

1.64   If too much sugar is excreted, the density of urine will increase. If too much water is excreted, the density of urine will decrease.

1.65   (a) Solid potassium reacts with liquid water to produce gaseous hydrogen and a homogeneous mixture of potassium hydroxide in liquid water.

        (b) The reaction is a chemical change.

        (c) Potassium and water are reactants, hydrogen and potassium hydroxide are products.

        (d) Among the qualitative observations are (i) the reaction is violent; and (ii) heat and light (a purple flame) are produced.

1.66   A copper-colored metal could be copper, but it may also be an alloy of copper, for example, brass or bronze. Testing the material's density and melting temperature would be one way to find out if it is copper.

1.67   (a) The water could be evaporated by heating the solution, leaving the salt behind.

        (b) Use of a magnet would attract the iron filings away from the lead.

        (c) Mixing the solids with water would dissolve only the sugar. Filtration would separate the solid sulfur from the solution. Finally, the sugar could be separated from the water by boiling the solution.

1.68   Any balloon filled with a gas having a density less than 1.12 g/L will float in air. Helium and neon balloons will float.

1.69   One possible method is outlined on Screen 1.18. Separate the iron from a weighed sample of cereal by passing a magnet through a mixture of cereal and water after the flakes have disintegrated. Remove the iron flakes from the magnet and weigh them to determine the mass of iron in the mass of cereal.

11

1.70   When a hot object comes in contact with a cooler object, the more rapidly moving molecules in the hot object slow down while the slower molecules in the cooler object speed up. A transfer of molecular motion occurs.

1.71   (a) P_4 and Cl_2 are reactants, PCl_3 is the product

      (b) P_4 molecules are a tetrahedron (a four-sided polyhedron) and Cl_2 molecules consist of two chlorine atoms. PCl_3 molecules contain a phosphorus atom bonded to three chlorine atoms in a triangular pyramid.

1.72.   Physical change

1.73   (a) 5.4×10^{-2} (b) 5.462×10^3 (c) 7.92×10^{-4}

1.74   (a) 1620   (b) 0.000257   (c) 0.0632

1.75   (a) 9.44×10^{-3} (b) 5.69×10^3 (c) 11.9

1.76 2.44×10^8 (b) 4.85×10^{-2}(c)   0.133

1.77   (a) 3   (c) 5

      (b) 3   (d) 4

1.78   (a) 3   (c) 4

      (b) 2   (d) 3

1.79   0.122

1.80   0.0286

1.81

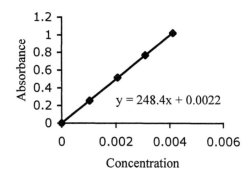

slope = 248.4

$0.635 = (248.4)(\text{concentration}) + 0.0022$

$\text{concentration} = 2.548 \times 10^{-3}$

1.82

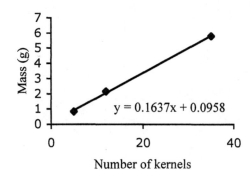

slope = 0.1637 g/kernel

$\text{mass} = (0.1637)(500) + 0.0958 = 81.9 \text{ g}$

$20.88 \text{ g} = (0.1637)(\text{number of kernels}) + 0.0958$

number of kernels = 127

1.83 (a) 0.21

(b) 5.6

(c) slope $= \dfrac{5.6 - 4.0}{0.30 - 0.21} = 18$; intercept $= 0.20$

(d) $y = 18x + 0.20 = (18)(1.0) + 0.20 = 18$

1.84 (a) slope $= \dfrac{20.00 - 4.00}{0.00 - 4.00} = -4.00$

(b) $y = -4.00x + 20.00 = (-4.00)(6.0) + 20.00 = -4.00$

1.85 $C = 0.0823$

1.86 $n = 1.63$

1.87 $T = 295$

1.88 $n = 1.5$ (the answer is 2 to 1 significant figure)

1.89 $1.50 \text{ carat} \cdot \dfrac{0.200 \text{ g}}{1 \text{ carat}} \cdot \dfrac{1 \text{ cm}^3}{3.513 \text{ g}} = 0.0854 \text{ cm}^3$

1.90   (a) $\text{Volume} = (0.563 \text{ nm})^3 = 0.178 \text{ nm}^3$

$0.178 \text{ nm}^3 \cdot \left(\dfrac{10^{-9} \text{ m}}{1 \text{ nm}} \right)^3 \cdot \left(\dfrac{100 \text{ cm}}{1 \text{ m}} \right)^3 = 1.78 \times 10^{-22} \text{ cm}^3$

(b) $\dfrac{2.17 \text{ g}}{1 \text{ cm}^3} \cdot 1.78 \times 10^{-22} \text{ cm}^3 = 3.86 \times 10^{-22} \text{ g}$

(c) $\dfrac{3.86 \times 10^{-22} \text{ g}}{4 \text{ NaCl formula units}} = 9.65 \times 10^{-23} \text{ g/formula unit}$

1.91 $\text{Volume} = (\pi)(\text{radius})^2(\text{thickness}) = (\pi)(2.2 \text{ cm}/2)^2(0.30 \text{ cm}) = 1.1 \text{ cm}^3$

$1.1 \text{ cm}^3 \cdot \dfrac{19.3 \text{ g}}{1 \text{ cm}^3} = 22 \text{ g}$

1.92 $57 \text{ kg} \cdot \dfrac{10^3 \text{ g}}{1 \text{ kg}} \cdot \dfrac{1 \text{ cm}^3}{8.96 \text{ g}} = 6.4 \times 10^3 \text{ cm}^3 \text{ copper}$

$\text{length of wire} = \dfrac{\text{volume}}{(\pi)(\text{radius})^2} = \dfrac{6.4 \times 10^3 \text{ cm}^3}{(\pi)(0.950/2 \text{ cm})^2} = 9.0 \times 10^3 \text{ cm}$

$9.0 \times 10^3 \text{ cm} \cdot \dfrac{1 \text{ m}}{100 \text{ cm}} = 90. \text{ m}$

1.93 $\dfrac{1.77 \text{ lb}}{1 \text{ L}} \cdot \dfrac{453.6 \text{ g}}{1 \text{ lb}} \cdot \dfrac{1 \text{ kg}}{10^3 \text{ g}} = 0.803 \text{ kg/L}$ (the correct conversion factor)

$\dfrac{0.803 \text{ kg}}{1 \text{ L}} \cdot 7682 \text{ L} = 6170 \text{ kg}$

$22,300 \text{ kg} - 6170 \text{ kg} = 16,130 \text{ kg additional fuel needed}$

$16,130 \text{ kg} \cdot \dfrac{1 \text{ L}}{0.803 \text{ kg}} = 20,100 \text{ L fuel needed}$

1.94   (a) $\dfrac{(0.125 - 0.106) \text{ g}}{0.125 \text{ g}} \cdot 100\% = 15\%$ of mass lost on popping

(b) $1 \text{ lb popcorn} \cdot \dfrac{453.6 \text{ g}}{1 \text{ lb}} \cdot \dfrac{1 \text{ kernel}}{0.125 \text{ g}} = 3630 \text{ kernels}$

1.95 $12 \text{ oz.} \cdot \dfrac{28.4 \text{ g}}{1 \text{ oz.}} \cdot \dfrac{1 \text{ cm}^3}{2.70 \text{ g}} = 126 \text{ cm}^3$

$75 \text{ ft}^2 \left(\dfrac{12 \text{ in}}{1 \text{ ft}} \right)^2 \left(\dfrac{2.54 \text{ cm}}{1 \text{ in}} \right)^2 = 7.0 \times 10^4 \text{ cm}^2$

$\text{thickness} = \dfrac{\text{volume}}{\text{area}} = \dfrac{126 \text{ cm}^3}{7.0 \times 10^4 \text{ cm}^2} = 1.8 \times 10^{-3} \text{ cm} = 1.8 \times 10^{-2} \text{ mm}$

1.96 $150{,}000 \text{ people} \cdot \dfrac{660 \text{ L water}}{1 \text{ day}} \cdot \dfrac{365 \text{ days}}{1 \text{ year}} \cdot \dfrac{10^3 \text{ mL}}{1 \text{ L}} \cdot \dfrac{1 \text{ cm}^3}{1 \text{ mL}} \cdot \dfrac{1.00 \text{ g}}{1 \text{ cm}^3} \cdot \dfrac{1 \text{ kg}}{10^3 \text{ g}}$

$\cdot \dfrac{1 \text{ kg fluoride}}{10^6 \text{ kg water}} \cdot \dfrac{100.0 \text{ kg NaF}}{45.0 \text{ kg fluoride}} = 8.0 \times 10^4 \text{ kg NaF/year}$

1.97 $0.5 \text{ acre} \cdot \dfrac{1.0 \times 10^4 \text{ m}^2}{2.47 \text{ acres}} \left(\dfrac{100 \text{ cm}}{1 \text{ m}} \right)^2 = 2 \times 10^7 \text{ cm}^2$

$\text{thickness} = \dfrac{\text{volume}}{\text{area}} = \dfrac{5 \text{ cm}^3}{2 \times 10^7 \text{ cm}^2} = 2 \times 10^{-7} \text{ cm}$

This is likely related to the "length" of oil molecules.

1.98 $500. \text{ mL} \cdot \dfrac{1 \text{ cm}^3}{1 \text{ mL}} \cdot \dfrac{1.285 \text{ g}}{1 \text{ cm}^3} \cdot \dfrac{38.08 \text{ g sulfuric acid}}{100.00 \text{ g solution}} = 245 \text{ g sulfuric acid}$

1.99 $0.546 \text{ g} \cdot \dfrac{1 \text{ cm}^3}{8.96 \text{ g}} \cdot \dfrac{1 \text{ mL}}{1 \text{ cm}^3} \cdot \dfrac{1 \text{ L}}{10^3 \text{ mL}} = 6.09 \times 10^{-5} \text{ L}$

1.100   (a) 1.97×10^{11}

(b) 74

(c) 18

1.101 $279 \text{ kg} \cdot \dfrac{10^3 \text{ g}}{1 \text{ kg}} \cdot \dfrac{1 \text{ cm}^3}{19.3 \text{ g}} = 1.45 \times 10^4 \text{ cm}^3$

volume = (area)(thickness)

$1.45 \times 10^4 \text{ cm}^3 = (\text{area}) \left(0.0015 \text{ mm} \cdot \dfrac{1 \text{ cm}}{10 \text{ mm}} \right)$

$\text{area} = 9.6 \times 10^7 \text{ cm}^2 \cdot \left(\dfrac{1 \text{ m}}{100 \text{ cm}} \right)^2 = 9.6 \times 10^3 \text{ m}^2$

1.102   (a) At 25 °C: $250. \text{ mL} \cdot \dfrac{1 \text{ cm}^3}{1 \text{ mL}} \cdot \dfrac{0.997 \text{ g}}{1 \text{ cm}^3} = 249 \text{ g water} (= 249 \text{ g ice when cooled})$

$249 \text{ g ice} \cdot \dfrac{1 \text{ cm}^3}{0.917 \text{ g}} \cdot \dfrac{1 \text{ mL}}{1 \text{ cm}^3} = 272 \text{ mL ice}$

(b) The ice cannot be contained in the can.

1.103   (a)   volume = (length)(width)(height) = $(18 \text{ ft})(15 \text{ ft})(8.5 \text{ ft}) \left(\frac{12 \text{ in}}{1 \text{ ft}} \right)^3 \left(\frac{2.54 \text{ cm}}{1 \text{ in}} \right)^3 \left(\frac{1 \text{ m}}{100 \text{ cm}} \right)^3 = 65 \text{ m}^3$

$$65 \text{ m}^3 \cdot \frac{1 \text{ L}}{10^{-3} \text{ m}^3} = 6.5 \times 10^4 \text{ L}$$

(b) $6.5 \times 10^4 \text{ L} \cdot \frac{1.2 \text{ g}}{1 \text{ L}} \cdot \frac{1 \text{ kg}}{10^3 \text{ g}} = 78 \text{ kg}$

$$78 \text{ kg} \cdot \frac{10^3 \text{ g}}{1 \text{ kg}} \cdot \frac{1 \text{ lb}}{454 \text{ g}} = 170 \text{ lb}$$

1.104   volume = $\left(^4/_3\right) \pi r^3 = \left(^4/_3\right) \pi \left(\frac{9.40 \text{ mm}}{2} \cdot \frac{1 \text{ cm}}{10 \text{ mm}} \right)^3 = 0.435 \text{ cm}^3$

density = $\dfrac{3.475 \text{ g}}{0.435 \text{ cm}^3} = 7.99 \text{ g/cm}^3$

1.105   (a)   density = $\dfrac{16.08 \text{ g} - 12.20 \text{ g}}{3.50 \text{ mL}} \cdot \dfrac{1 \text{ mL}}{1 \text{ cm}^3} = 1.11 \text{ g/cm}^3$ The liquid is ethylene glycol.

(b)   The calculated density would be 1.1 g/cm^3. While this value still suggests that the liquid is ethylene glycol, it is close to the value for acetic acid. Further testing should be done on the liquid.

1.106   (a)   density = $\dfrac{74.122 \text{ g}}{36.7 \text{ mL} - 28.2 \text{ mL}} \cdot \dfrac{1 \text{ mL}}{1 \text{ cm}^3} = 8.7 \text{ g/cm}^3$

(b)   The metal is probably cadmium, but the calculated density is close to that of cobalt, nickel, and copper. Further testing should be done on the metal.

1.107   (a)   density = $\dfrac{0.9360 \text{ g}}{7.50 \times 10^2 \text{ mL}} \cdot \dfrac{10^3 \text{ mL}}{1 \text{ L}} = 1.25 \text{ g/L}$

(b)   The gas could be N_2, C_2H_4, or CO.

(c)   density = $\dfrac{0.9360 \text{ g}}{7.496 \times 10^2 \text{ mL}} \cdot \dfrac{10^3 \text{ mL}}{1 \text{ L}} = 1.249 \text{ g/L}$

The gas could be N_2 or CO.

1.108   density of mixture = (0.6118)(2.8899 g/mL) + (0.3882)(1.4832 g/mL) = 2.344 g/mL

This density matches that of silicon.

1.109   3.416 g − 3.263 g = 0.153 g Hg

volume of Hg = $0.153 \text{ g Hg} \cdot \dfrac{1 \text{ cm}^3}{13.546 \text{ g}} = 0.0113 \text{ cm}^3$

$0.0113 \text{ cm}^3 = \pi (\text{radius})^2 \left(16.75 \text{ mm} \cdot \dfrac{1 \text{ cm}}{10 \text{ mm}} \right)$

radius = 0.0463 cm

diameter = 2 × radius = 0.0927 cm

Chapter 2
Atoms and Elements

INSTRUCTOR'S NOTES

Although much of this chapter will be review for many students who have taken high school chemistry, the ideas included are so central to later study that class coverage will probably be necessary. Key topics are the structure of the atom and related information (atomic number, isotopes), the unit of a mole, and the periodic table. The final sections include a brief description of key elements organized around the periodic table. Two or three class periods will probably be necessary in order to address the essentials in this chapter.

SUGGESTED DEMONSTRATIONS

1. Properties of Elements

    - Take as many samples of elements as possible to your lecture on the elements and the periodic table.

    - The *Periodic Table Videodisc* is ideal for showing samples of elements, their reactions, and their uses.

    - See the series by Alton Banks in the *Journal of Chemical Education* titled "What's the Use?" This series describes a different element each month and gives references to the *Periodic Table Videodisc*.

    - Pinto, G. "Using Balls from Different Sports to Model the Variation of Atomic Sizes," *Journal of Chemical Education*, **1998**, *75*, 725.

2. Atomic Structure

    - Hohman, J. R. "Introduction of the Scientific Method and Atomic Theory to Liberal Arts Chemistry Students," *Journal of Chemical Education*, **1998**, *75*, 1578.

3. Chemical Periodicity

    - Like all the alkali metals, sodium reacts vigorously with halogens. When sodium metal is placed in a flask containing chlorine gas, sodium chloride is produced. During the reaction, a large quantity of heat and light is emitted. This reaction is shown on the *Redox Videodisc* and the *General ChemistryNow CD-ROM*.

4. The Mole Concept

    - To illustrate the mole, take 1 molar quantities of elements such as Mg, Al, C, Sn, Pb, Fe, and Cu to the classroom.

    - When doing examples in lecture, it is helpful to have a sample of the element available. For example, hold up a pre-weighed sample of magnesium wire and ask how many moles of metal it contains (and then ignite the wire to give a preview of the reaction chemistry described in Chapters 4 and 5.). Or, drop a pre-weighed piece of sodium metal into a dish of water on the overhead projector, and ask how many moles of sodium reacted.

SOLUTIONS TO STUDY QUESTIONS

2.1   Atoms contain the fundamental particles protons (+1 charge), neutrons (zero charge), and electrons (–1 charge). Protons and neutrons are in the nucleus of an atom. Electrons are the least massive of the three particles.

2.2   Rutherford was surprised to observe that some of the alpha particles were deflected at large angles and that a few of the alpha particles were deflected almost straight back. He concluded that all the positive charge and most of the mass of the atom is concentrated in a very small volume, the nucleus, and electrons occupy the rest of the space in the atom.

2.3   The discovery of radioactivity showed that atoms must be divisible; that is, atoms must be composed of even smaller, subatomic particles.

2.4   A mass spectrometer.

2.5   Exercise 2.1 provides the relative sizes of the nuclear and atomic diameters, with the nuclear radius on the order of 0.001 pm and the atomic radius approximately 100 pm. If the nuclear diameter is 6 cm, then the atomic diameter is 600,000 cm (or 6 km).

2.6   Each gold atom has a diameter of 2×145 pm = 290. pm

$$36 \text{ cm} \cdot \frac{1 \text{ m}}{100 \text{ cm}} \cdot \frac{10^{12} \text{ pm}}{1 \text{ m}} \cdot \frac{1 \text{ Au atom}}{290. \text{ pm}} = 1.2 \times 10^9 \text{ Au atoms}$$

2.7   Radon, Rn

2.8

	Symbol	Atomic number	Atomic weight	Group	Period	
Titanium	Ti	22	47.867	4B	4	Metal
Thallium	Tl	81	204.3833	3A	6	Metal

2.9   (a) Mass number = 12 + 15 = 27

        (b) Mass number = 22 + 26 = 48

        (c) Mass number = 30 + 32 = 62

2.10   (a) Mass number = 28 + 31 = 59

        (b) Mass number = 94 + 150 = 244

        (c) Mass number = 74 + 110 = 184

2.11   (a) $^{39}_{19}\text{K}$ (b) $^{84}_{36}\text{Kr}$ (c) $^{60}_{27}\text{Co}$

2.12   (a) $^{19}_{9}F$ (b) $^{52}_{24}Cr$ (c) $^{132}_{54}Xe$

2.13   electrons   protons   neutrons

	electrons	protons	neutrons
(a)	12	12	12
(b)	50	50	69
(c)	90	90	142

2.14   electrons   protons   neutrons

	electrons	protons	neutrons
(a)	6	6	7
(b)	29	29	34
(c)	83	83	122

2.15   Number of protons = number of electrons = 43; number of neutrons = 56

2.16   Number of protons = number of electrons = 95; number of neutrons = 146

2.17 $^{57}_{27}Co$ (30 neutrons), $^{58}_{27}Co$ (31 neutrons), and $^{60}_{27}Co$ (33 neutrons)

2.18 $^{19}_{9}X$, $^{20}_{9}X$, and $^{21}_{9}X$ are isotopes of X

2.19   The atomic weight of thallium is 204.3833. The fact that this weight is closer to 205 than 203 indicates that the 205 isotope is the more abundant.

2.20   Strontium has an atomic weight of 87.62 so ^{88}Sr is the most abundant.

2.21 $(^{6}Li$ mass $)$(% abundance) + $(^{7}Li$ mass)(% abundance) = atomic weight of Li

       (6.015121 u)(0.0750) + (7.016003 u)(0.9250) = 6.94 u

2.22 $(^{24}Mg$ mass)(% abundance) + $(^{25}Mg$ mass)(% abundance) + $(^{26}Mg$ mass)(% abundance)

          = atomic weight of Mg

       (23.985 u)(0.7899) + (24.986 u)(0.1000) + (25.983 u)(0.1101)

          = 24.31 u

2.23   (c) 50% Actual value is 51.84%

2.24   (d) 70% Actual value is 69.17%

2.25   Let x represent the abundance of ^{69}Ga and $(1-x)$ represent the abundance of ^{71}Ga.

       69.723 u = (x)(68.9257 u) + $(1-x)$(70.9249 u)

       x = 0.6012; ^{69}Ga abundance is 60.12%, ^{71}Ga abundance is 39.88%

2.26   Let x represent the abundance of ^{121}Sb and $(1-x)$ represent the abundance of ^{123}Sb.

121.760 u = $(x)(120.9038$ u$) + (1-x)(122.9042$ u$)$

$x = 0.5720$; ^{121}Sb abundance is 57.20%, ^{123}Sb abundance is 42.80%

2.27   (a) 2.5 mol Al $\cdot \dfrac{27.0 \text{ g Al}}{1 \text{ mol Al}} = 68$ g Al

(b) 1.25×10^{-3} mol Fe $\cdot \dfrac{55.85 \text{ g Fe}}{1 \text{ mol Fe}} = 0.0698$ g Fe

(c) 0.015 mol Ca $\cdot \dfrac{40.1 \text{ g Ca}}{1 \text{ mol Ca}} = 0.60$ g Ca

(d) 653 mol Ne $\cdot \dfrac{20.18 \text{ g Ne}}{1 \text{ mol Ne}} = 1.32 \times 10^{4}$ g Ne

2.28   (a) 4.24 mol Au $\cdot \dfrac{197.0 \text{ g Au}}{1 \text{ mol Au}} = 835$ g Au

(b) 15.6 mol He $\cdot \dfrac{4.003 \text{ g He}}{1 \text{ mol He}} = 62.4$ g He

(c) 0.063 mol Pt $\cdot \dfrac{195 \text{ g Pt}}{1 \text{ mol Pt}} = 12$ g Pt

(d) 3.63×10^{-4} mol Pu $\cdot \dfrac{244.7 \text{ g Pu}}{1 \text{ mol Pu}} = 0.0888$ g Pu

2.29   (a) 127.08 g Cu $\cdot \dfrac{1 \text{ mol Cu}}{63.546 \text{ g Cu}} = 1.9998$ mol Cu

(b) 0.012 g Li $\cdot \dfrac{1 \text{ mol Li}}{6.94 \text{ g Li}} = 1.7 \times 10^{-3}$ mol Li

(c) 5.0 mg Am $\cdot \dfrac{1 \text{ g}}{10^{3} \text{ mg}} \cdot \dfrac{1 \text{ mol Am}}{243 \text{ g Am}} = 2.1 \times 10^{-5}$ mol Am

(d) 6.75 g Al $\cdot \dfrac{1 \text{ mol Al}}{26.98 \text{ g Al}} = 0.250$ mol Al

2.30   (a) 16.0 g Na $\cdot \dfrac{1 \text{ mol Na}}{22.99 \text{ g Na}} = 0.696$ mol Na

(b) 0.876 g Sn $\cdot \dfrac{1 \text{ mol Sn}}{118.7 \text{ g Sn}} = 7.38 \times 10^{-3}$ mol Sn

(c) 0.0034 g Pt $\cdot \dfrac{1 \text{ mol Pt}}{195 \text{ g Pt}} = 1.7 \times 10^{-5}$ mol Pt

(d) 0.983 g Xe $\cdot \dfrac{1 \text{ mol Xe}}{131.3 \text{ g Xe}} = 7.49 \times 10^{-3}$ mol Xe

2.31   Helium has the smallest molar mass and will have the largest number of atoms. Iron has the largest molar mass and the smallest number of atoms.

$$1.0 \text{ g He} \cdot \frac{1 \text{ mol He}}{4.00 \text{ g He}} \cdot \frac{6.02 \times 10^{23} \text{ He atoms}}{1 \text{ mol He}} = 1.5 \times 10^{23} \text{ He atoms}$$

$$1.0 \text{ g Fe} \cdot \frac{1 \text{ mol Fe}}{55.8 \text{ g Fe}} \cdot \frac{6.02 \times 10^{23} \text{ Fe atoms}}{1 \text{ mol Fe}} = 1.1 \times 10^{22} \text{ Fe atoms}$$

2.32   A 1.0 mol sample of iron will have the largest mass because iron has the largest molar mass.

$$1.0 \text{ mol Fe} \cdot \frac{55.8 \text{ g Fe}}{1 \text{ mol Fe}} = 55.8 \text{ g Fe}$$

2.33 $$\frac{63.546 \text{ g Cu}}{1 \text{ mol Cu}} \cdot \frac{1 \text{ mol Cu}}{6.02214 \times 10^{23} \text{ atoms}} = 1.0552 \times 10^{-22} \text{ g/atom}$$

2.34 $$\frac{47.867 \text{ g Ti}}{1 \text{ mol Ti}} \cdot \frac{1 \text{ mol Ti}}{6.02214 \times 10^{23} \text{ atoms}} = 7.9485 \times 10^{-23} \text{ g/atom}$$

2.35   Nonmetals: N, Nitrogen; P, Phosphorus

Metalloids: As, Arsenic; Sb, Antimony

Metal: Bi, Bismuth

2.36   Metals: K, Potassium; Ca, Calcium; Sc, Scandium; Ti, Titanium; V, Vanadium; Cr, Chromium;
       Mn, Manganese; Fe, Iron; Co, Cobalt; Ni, Nickel; Cu, Copper; Zn, Zinc; Ga, Gallium

Metalloids: Ge, Germanium; As, Arsenic

Nonmetals: Se, Selenium; Br, Bromine; Kr, Krypton

2.37   Periods 2 and 3 have 8 elements, Periods 4 and 5 have 18 elements, and Period 6 has 32 elements.

2.38   There are 26 elements in the seventh period, the majority of them are called the Actinides, and many of them are man-made elements.

2.39   (a) C, Cl

(b) C, Cl, Cs, Ca

(c) Ce

(d) Cr, Co, Cd, Cu, Ce, Cf, Cm

(e) Cm, Cf

(f) Cl

2.40   There are many correct answers for parts (a), (b), and (d). Some possible answers are shown below.

(a) C, carbon   (c) Cl, chlorine

(b) Na, sodium   (d) Ne, neon

2.41   Metals: Na, Ni, Np

Nonmetals: N, Ne

2.42   (a) Bk

(b) Br

(c) B

(d) Ba

(e) Bi

2.43   (a) sodium, scandium, strontium, silver, samarium

(b) sodium, silicon, sulfur, selenium, strontium

(c) scandium, silver

2.44   (a) Silicon is a metalloid and phosphorus is a nonmetal.

(b) Silicon is a possible conductor of electricity, phosphorus is not.

(c) Both are solids at 25 °C.

2.45

Symbol	^{58}Ni	^{33}S	^{20}Ne	^{55}Mn
Number of protons	28	16	10	25
Number of neutrons	30	17	10	30
Number of electrons	28	16	10	25
Name of element	nickel	sulfur	neon	manganese

2.46

Symbol	^{65}Cu	^{86}Kr	^{195}Pt	^{82}Kr
Number of protons	29	36	78	36
Number of neutrons	36	50	117	46
Number of electrons	29	36	78	36
Name of element	copper	krypton	platinum	krypton

2.47   The atomic weight of potassium is 39.0983 u, so the lighter isotope, ^{39}K is more abundant than ^{41}K.

2.48   *Crossword Puzzle*

S	N
B	I

2.49   (a) Mg and Fe are the most abundant metals. (Very similar abundance values)

(b) H is the most abundant nonmetal.

(c) Si is the most abundant metalloid.

(d) Fe is the most abundant transition element.

(e) F, Cl, and Br are the halogens included and of these Cl is the most abundant.

2.50   Buckminsterfullerene is an allotrope of carbon. The other two allotropes are graphite and diamond.

2.51   (d) 3.43×10^{-27} mol S_8 is impossible. This amount is less than one molecule of S_8.

2.52   Si, silicon. Silicon is a dark grey solid at room temperature and is a semiconductor used in the manufacture of computer chips.

2.53   Some possible answers:

(a) Ba, Barium   (f) Mg, Magnesium

(b) Si, Silicon   (g) Kr, Krypton

(c) C, Carbon   (h) S, Sulfur

(d) S, Sulfur   (i) As, Arsenic

(e) I, Iodine

2.54   Some possible answers:

(a) Zn, Zinc   (e) Na, Sodium

(b) Zr, Zirconium   (f) Xe, Xenon

(c) Pb, Lead   (g) Se, Selenium, a nonmetal

(d) Se, Selenium   (h) As, Arsenic

2.55   (a) Cobalt, nickel, and copper have the highest densities. The densities of all three metals are approximately 9 g/cm^3.

(b) The element in the second period with the largest density is boron while the element in the third period with the largest density is aluminum. Both of these elements belong to group 3A.

(c) The elements with very low densities are gases. These include hydrogen, helium, nitrogen, oxygen, fluorine, neon, chlorine, argon and krypton.

2.56   Carbon has three allotropes. Graphite consists of flat sheets of carbon atoms, diamond has carbon atoms attached to four other others in a tetrahedron, and buckminsterfullerene is a 60-atom cage of carbon atoms. Oxygen has two allotropes. Diatomic oxygen consists of molecules containing two oxygen atoms and ozone consists of molecules containing three oxygen atoms.

2.57   (a)   One mole of Na has a mass of approximately 23 g while a mole of Si has a mass of 28 g. A 0.5 mol sample of Si therefore represents a greater mass than a 0.5 mol sample of Na.

(b)   A 0.5 mol sample of Na has a mass of approximately 12.5 g, so 0.50 mol Na represents more mass than 9.0 g of Na.

(c)   The molar mass of K is approximately 39 g/mol while that of Fe is approximately 56 g/mol. A single atom of Fe has a greater mass than an atom of K., so 10 atoms of Fe represents more mass.

2.58 $52 \text{ g Ga} \cdot \dfrac{1 \text{ mol Ga}}{69.7 \text{ g Ga}} \cdot \dfrac{6.02 \times 10^{23} \text{ atoms Ga}}{1 \text{ mol Ga}} = 4.5 \times 10^{23} \text{ atoms Ga}$

$9.5 \text{ g Al} \cdot \dfrac{1 \text{ mol Al}}{27.0 \text{ g Al}} \cdot \dfrac{6.02 \times 10^{23} \text{ atoms Al}}{1 \text{ mol Al}} = 2.1 \times 10^{23} \text{ atoms Al}$

$112 \text{ g As} \cdot \dfrac{1 \text{ mol As}}{74.92 \text{ g As}} \cdot \dfrac{6.022 \times 10^{23} \text{ atoms As}}{1 \text{ mol As}} = 9.00 \times 10^{23} \text{ atoms As}$

The element with the largest number of atoms is As.

2.59   Boron has the smallest molar mass and will have the largest number of atoms.

$15 \text{ g B} \cdot \dfrac{1 \text{ mol B}}{10.8 \text{ g B}} \cdot \dfrac{6.02 \times 10^{23} \text{ atoms B}}{1 \text{ mol B}} = 8.4 \times 10^{23} \text{ atoms B}$

2.60   The atomic weight of lithium is closer to 7 than to 6, so ^{7}Li is 92.5% abundant and ^{6}Li is 7.5% abundant.

2.61 $0.00789 \text{ g Kr} \cdot \dfrac{1 \text{ mol Kr}}{83.80 \text{ g Kr}} = 9.42 \times 10^{-5} \text{ mol Kr}$

$9.42 \times 10^{-5} \text{ mol Kr} \cdot \dfrac{6.022 \times 10^{23} \text{ atoms Kr}}{1 \text{ mol Kr}} = 5.67 \times 10^{19} \text{ atoms Kr}$

2.62 $15 \text{ mg} \cdot \dfrac{1 \text{ g}}{10^{3} \text{ mg}} \cdot \dfrac{1 \text{ mol Fe}}{55.85 \text{ g Fe}} = 2.7 \times 10^{-4} \text{ mol Fe}$

$2.7 \times 10^{-4} \text{ mol Fe} \cdot \dfrac{6.02 \times 10^{23} \text{ atoms Fe}}{1 \text{ mol Fe}} = 1.6 \times 10^{20} \text{ atoms Fe}$

2.63   (a) 3.79×10^{24} atoms Fe $\cdot \dfrac{1 \text{ mol Fe}}{6.022 \times 10^{23} \text{ atoms Fe}} \cdot \dfrac{55.85 \text{ g Fe}}{1 \text{ mol Fe}} = 351 \text{ g Fe}$

   (b) $19.921 \text{ mol H}_2 \cdot \dfrac{2.0158 \text{ g H}_2}{1 \text{ mol H}_2} = 40.157 \text{ g H}_2$

   (c) $8.576 \text{ mol C} \cdot \dfrac{12.011 \text{ g C}}{1 \text{ mol C}} = 103.0 \text{ g C}$

   (d) $7.4 \text{ mol Si} \cdot \dfrac{28.1 \text{ g Si}}{1 \text{ mol Si}} = 210 \text{ g Si}$

   (e) $9.221 \text{ mol Na} \cdot \dfrac{22.990 \text{ g Na}}{1 \text{ mol Na}} = 212.0 \text{ g Na}$

   (f) 4.07×10^{24} atoms Al $\cdot \dfrac{1 \text{ mol Al}}{6.022 \times 10^{23} \text{ atoms Al}} \cdot \dfrac{26.98 \text{ g Al}}{1 \text{ mol Al}} = 182 \text{ g Al}$

   (g) $9.2 \text{ mol Cl}_2 \cdot \dfrac{70.9 \text{ g Cl}_2}{1 \text{ mol Cl}_2} = 650 \text{ g Cl}_2$

   H_2 (b) < C (c) < Al (f) < Si (d) < Na (e) < Fe (a) < Cl_2 (g)

2.64   0.744 g phosphorus combined with (1.704 g – 0.744 g) = 0.960 g O

   $\dfrac{(0.744/4) \text{ g P}}{(0.960/10) \text{ g O}} = \dfrac{1.94 \text{ g P}}{1 \text{ g O}}$

   $16.000 \text{ u O} \cdot \dfrac{1.94 \text{ g P}}{1 \text{ g O}} = 31.0 \text{ u P}$

2.65   (a) Each oil drop carries a charge that is a multiple of the average charge on an electron, 1.59×10^{-19} C.

   (b)
Oil Drop	Number of electrons
1	1
2	7
3	6
4	10
5	4

   (c) The average charge on the electron from the data is 1.59×10^{-19} C.

   The average deviation is 0.01×10^{-19}

   $\dfrac{(1.59 \times 10^{-19} \text{ C} - 1.60 \times 10^{-19} \text{ C})}{1.60 \times 10^{-19} \text{ C}} \cdot 100\% = -0.6\%$

2.66   (a) Use current values to determine the atomic mass of oxygen if H = 1.0000 u

$$1.0000 \text{ u H} \cdot \frac{15.9994 \text{ u O}}{1.00794 \text{ u H}} = 15.874 \text{ u O}$$

The value of Avogadro's number is based on the atomic mass of carbon.

$$1.0000 \text{ u H} \cdot \frac{12.011 \text{ u C}}{1.00794 \text{ u H}} = 11.916 \text{ u C}$$

$$11.916 \text{ u C} \cdot \frac{6.02214199 \times 10^{23} \text{ particles}}{12.0000 \text{ u C}} = 5.9802 \times 10^{23} \text{ particles}$$

(b) $$16.0000 \text{ u O} \cdot \frac{1.00794 \text{ u H}}{15.9994 \text{ u O}} = 1.00798 \text{ u H}$$

$$16.0000 \text{ u O} \cdot \frac{12.011 \text{ u C}}{15.9994 \text{ u O}} = 12.011 \text{ u C}$$

$$12.011 \text{ u C} \cdot \frac{6.02214199 \times 10^{23} \text{ particles}}{12.0000 \text{ u C}} = 6.0279 \times 10^{23} \text{ particles}$$

2.67 $$68 \text{ atoms K} \cdot \frac{1 \text{ mol K}}{6.02 \times 10^{23} \text{ atoms K}} \cdot \frac{39.1 \text{ g K}}{1 \text{ mol K}} = 4.4 \times 10^{-21} \text{ g K}$$

$$32 \text{ atoms Na} \cdot \frac{1 \text{ mol Na}}{6.02 \times 10^{23} \text{ atoms Na}} \cdot \frac{23.0 \text{ g Na}}{1 \text{ mol Na}} = 1.2 \times 10^{-21} \text{ g Na}$$

$$\text{weight \% K} = \frac{4.4 \times 10^{-21} \text{ g K}}{(4.4 \times 10^{-21} \text{ g K} + 1.2 \times 10^{-21} \text{ g Na})} \cdot 100\% = 78\% \text{ K}$$

2.68   (^{136}X mass)(% abundance) + (^{138}X mass)(% abundance) + (^{140}X mass)(% abundance)

$$+ (^{142}\text{X mass})(\% \text{ abundance}) = \text{atomic weight of Mg}$$

(135.9090 u)(0.00193) + (137.9057 u)(0.00250) + (139.9053 u)(0.8848) + (141.9090 u)(0.1107)

= 140.1046 u The element is cerium.

2.69   The electrons do not trace a particular path around the nucleus but rather exist as a "cloud" (see Figure 2.1). The radius of a He atom is 128 pm. If the nucleus is only 10^{-5} times as large as the atom, then the nuclear radius is about 0.00128 pm. This drawing is not to scale!

2.70   iron metal   nitrogen gas

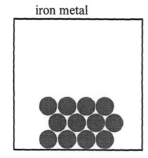 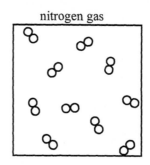

Iron consists of individual iron atoms that are packed together tightly in the solid phase. Nitrogen is a

diatomic gas and fills the container completely.

2.71   (b) The atomic weight of iron, (c) Avogadro's number, and (d) The density of iron are needed

$$1 \text{ cm}^3 \cdot \frac{7.87 \text{ g Fe}}{1 \text{ cm}^3} \cdot \frac{1 \text{ mol Fe}}{55.85 \text{ g Fe}} \cdot \frac{6.022 \times 10^{23} \text{ atoms Fe}}{1 \text{ mol Fe}} = 8.49 \times 10^{22} \text{ atoms Fe}$$

2.72   Element abundance generally decreases with increasing atomic number (with exceptions at Li–B and Sc–

Fe). Elements with an even atomic number appear to be slightly more abundant than those with an odd

atomic number.

2.73   Barium would be even more reactive than calcium, so a more vigorous evolution of hydrogen would occur

(it might even ignite). Mg, Ca, and Ba are in periods 3, 4, and 6, respectively. Reactivity increases on

going down a group in the periodic table.

2.74 $0.125 \text{ mol Na} \cdot \dfrac{22.99 \text{ g Na}}{1 \text{ mol Na}} \cdot \dfrac{1 \text{ cm}^3}{0.971 \text{ g Na}} = 2.96 \text{ cm}^3$

Edge = $\sqrt[3]{2.96 \text{ cm}^3}$ = 1.44 cm

2.75 $256 \text{ mol Li} \cdot \dfrac{6.941 \text{ g Li}}{1 \text{ mol Li}} \cdot \dfrac{1 \text{ cm}^3}{0.534 \text{ g Li}} = 3.33 \times 10^3 \text{ cm}^3$

Edge = $\sqrt[3]{3.33 \text{ '} 10^3 \text{ cm}^3}$ = 14.9 cm

2.76   Volume = $(0.015 \text{ cm})(15.3 \text{ cm}^3) = 0.23 \text{ cm}^3$

$0.23 \text{ cm}^3 \cdot \dfrac{7.19 \text{ g Cr}}{1 \text{ cm}^3} \cdot \dfrac{1 \text{ mol Cr}}{52.0 \text{ g Cr}} \cdot \dfrac{6.02 \times 10^{23} \text{ atoms Cr}}{1 \text{ mol Cr}} = 1.9 \times 10^{22} \text{ atoms Cr}$

2.77   Volume = $(\pi)(4.5 \text{ cm}/2)^2(12.00 \text{ cm}) = 190 \text{ cm}^3$

$190 \text{ cm}^3 \cdot \dfrac{0.971 \text{ g Na}}{1 \text{ cm}^3} \cdot \dfrac{1 \text{ mol Na}}{23.0 \text{ g Na}} \cdot \dfrac{6.02 \times 10^{23} \text{ atoms Na}}{1 \text{ mol Na}} = 4.9 \times 10^{24} \text{ atoms Na}$

2.78   (a) mass of nucleus = 1.06×10^{-22} g (electron mass is negligible)

nuclear radius = 4.8×10^{-6} nm $\cdot \dfrac{10^{-9} \text{ m}}{1 \text{ nm}} \cdot \dfrac{100 \text{ cm}}{1 \text{ m}} = 4.8 \times 10^{-13}$ cm

volume of nucleus = $(^{4}/_{3})(\pi)(4.8 \times 10^{-13} \text{ cm})^3 = 4.6 \times 10^{-37} \text{ cm}^3$

density of nucleus = $\dfrac{1.06 \times 10^{-22} \text{ g}}{4.6 \times 10^{-37} \text{ cm}^3} = 2.3 \times 10^{14}$ g/cm^3

(b) atomic radius = 0.125 nm $\cdot \dfrac{10^{-9} \text{ m}}{1 \text{ nm}} \cdot \dfrac{100 \text{ cm}}{1 \text{ m}} = 1.25 \times 10^{-8}$ cm

volume of Zn atom = $(^{4}/_{3})(\pi)(1.25 \times 10^{-8} \text{ cm})^3 = 8.18 \times 10^{-24} \text{ cm}^3$

volume of space occupied by electrons = $8.18 \times 10^{-24} \text{ cm}^3 - 4.6 \times 10^{-37} \text{ cm}^3$

$= 8.18 \times 10^{-24} \text{ cm}^3$

density of space occupied by electrons = $\dfrac{(30)(9.11 \times 10^{-28} \text{ g})}{8.18 \times 10^{-24} \text{ cm}^3} = 3.34 \times 10^{-3}$ g/cm^3

(c) The nucleus is much more dense than the space occupied by the electrons.

2.79   2.0000 g C $\cdot \dfrac{1 \text{ mol C}}{12.011 \text{ g C}} \cdot \dfrac{6.02214 \times 10^{23} \text{ atoms C}}{1 \text{ mol C}} = 1.0028 \times 10^{23}$ atoms C

The maximum mass of carbon that could have been on the balance is 2.0001 g, so the maximum number of atoms that could be present is also 1.0028×10^{23} atoms.

2.80   (a) Volume of cube = $(1.000 \text{ cm})^3 = 1.000 \text{ cm}^3$

1.000 cm^3 Pb $\cdot \dfrac{11.35 \text{ g Pb}}{1 \text{ cm}^3} \cdot \dfrac{1 \text{ mol Pb}}{207.2 \text{ g Pb}} \cdot \dfrac{6.0221 \times 10^{23} \text{ atoms Pb}}{1 \text{ mol Pb}} = 3.299 \times 10^{22}$ atoms Pb

(b) Volume of one lead atom = $\dfrac{(0.60)(1.000 \text{ cm}^3)}{3.299 \times 10^{22} \text{ atoms Pb}} = 1.819 \times 10^{-23} \text{ cm}^3$

$1.819 \times 10^{-23} \text{ cm}^3 = (^{4}/_{3})(\pi)(\text{Pb radius})^3$

Pb radius = 1.631×10^{-8} cm

2.81   See Screen 2.20 for one possible method.

Chapter 3
Molecules, Ions, and Their Compounds

INSTRUCTOR'S NOTES

This chapter deals with key aspects of describing matter on the molecular and ionic formula level, including representations of chemicals; formulas, names and properties; further work on the mole concept; the relationships between formulas and composition. Chapter 3 will probably require 3 lectures unless your students are well-versed in some of these topics.

Some points on which students have some problems or questions are:

(a) The rule of determining the charges on transition metal cations tells students that they can assume such ions usually have 2+ or 3+ charges (with 2+ charges especially prominent). They are often uneasy about being given this choice. We certainly emphasize that they will see other possibilities (and that even negative charges are possible but that they will not see them in the general chemistry course).

(b) Students have to be convinced that they have no choice but to learn the language of chemistry by memorizing the names and charges of polyatomic ions. They can be reminded that correct names and formulas are required to prevent serious consequences, such as the use of the wrong medicine which can have tragic results or the purchase of the wrong substance which leads to wasted resources.

(c) A very common problem students have is recognizing that $MgBr_2$, for example, is composed of Mg^{2+} and two Br^- ions. We have seen such combinations as Mg^{2+} and Br_2^{2-}.

SUGGESTED DEMONSTRATIONS

1. Elements That Form Molecules in Their Natural States
   - Use samples of H_2, O_2, N_2, and Br_2 to illustrate elements that are molecules.
2. Molecules and Allotropes
   - Show many molecular models in class, if possible, using the Molecular Modeling tool on the *General ChemistryNow CD-ROM*.
   - For the formation of polymeric sulfur, see the *General ChemistryNow CD-ROM*.
3. Formation of Compounds from Elements
   - Bring many samples of compounds to your lecture. Ignite H_2 in a balloon or burn Mg in O_2 to show how elements are turned into compounds. Also burn Mg in CO_2 to show CO_2 is made of C and that MgO can be made another way.
   - Use the *Periodic Table Videodisc* to illustrate the formation of compounds by elements reacting with O_2 and with acids and bases.
   - See the *General ChemistryNow CD-ROM* for the reaction between phosphorus and bromine.

4. Decomposition of a Compound into Its Elements
   - For the reaction between sugar and sulfuric acid see the *General ChemistryNow CD-ROM*.

5. Ionic Compounds
   - Bring a number of common, ionic compounds to class.
   - See the *General ChemistryNow CD-ROM* for molecular models of a sodium chloride unit cell, an extended lattice, and a space-filling unit cell.

6. Molar Quantities
   - Display molar quantities of NaCl, H_2O, sugar, and common ionic compounds. Especially show some hydrated salts to emphasize the inclusion of H_2O in their molar mass.
   - Display a teaspoon of water and ask how many moles, how many molecules, and how many total atoms are contained.
   - Display a piece of $CaCO_3$ and ask how many moles are contained in the piece and then how many total atoms.

7. Weight Percent of Elements
   - When talking about weight percent of elements, use NO_2 as an example and then make NO_2 from Cu and nitric acid.

8. Determine the Formula of a Hydrated Compound
   - Heat samples of hydrated $CoSO_4$ or $CuSO_4$ to illustrate analysis of hydrated compounds and the color change that can occur when water is released and evaporated.
   - For the discussion of analysis, heat a sample of $CoCl_2 \cdot 6\,H_2O$ in a crucible to illustrate how to determine the number of waters of hydration and also discuss the distinctive color change observed during this process.

SOLUTIONS TO STUDY QUESTIONS

3.1   The molecular formula of sulfuric acid is H_2SO_4. The structural formula is shown here. The O atoms are arranged around the sulfur at the corners of a tetrahedron. The hydrogen atoms are connected to two of the oxygen atoms. The molecule is not flat.

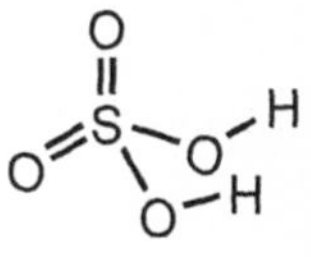

3.2   The formula of toluene is C_7H_8. The ring portion of the molecule is flat. The structure consists of a six-member ring of carbon atoms. Five of the carbon atoms in the ring are attached to an H atom, the sixth carbon is attached to a —CH_3 group.

3.3   The molecular formula of cisplatin is $Pt(NH_3)_2Cl_2$. The structural formula is.

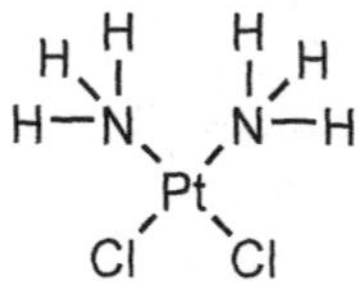

3.4   The H—C—O—H portion of the molecule lies in the plane of the paper. The other two H atoms attached to C are above and below the plane of the paper.

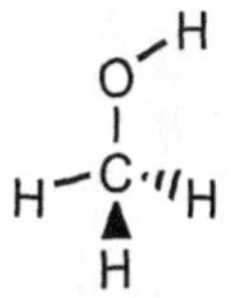

3.5   (a) Mg^{2+} (b) Zn^{2+} (c) Ni^{2+} (d) Ga^{3+}

3.6   (a) Se^{2-} (b) F^- (c) Fe^{2+}, Fe^{3+} (d) N^{3-}

3.7   (a) Ba^{2+} (e) S^{2-}
       (b) Ti^{4+} (f) ClO_4^-
       (c) PO_4^{3-} (g) Co^{2+}
       (d) HCO_3^- (h) SO_4^{2-}

3.8   (a) MnO_4^- (d) NH_4^+
       (b) NO_2^- (e) PO_4^{3-}
       (c) $H_2PO_4^-$ (f) SO_3^{2-}

3.9   Potassium loses 1 electron when it becomes a monatomic ion. Argon has the same number of electrons as the K^+ ion.

3.10   They both gain two electrons. O^{2-} has the same number of electrons as Ne and S^{2-} has the same number of electrons as Ar.

3.11 Ba^{2+}, Br^- $BaBr_2$

3.12 Co^{3+}, F^- CoF_3

3.13 (a) 2 K^+ ions, 1 S^{2-} ion   (d) 3 NH_4^+ ions, 1 PO_4^{3-} ion

      (b) 1 Co^{2+} ion, 1 SO_4^{2-} ion   (e) 1 Ca^{2+} ion, 2 ClO^- ions

      (c) 1 K^+ ion, 1 MnO_4^- ion

3.14 (a) 1 Mg^{2+} ion, 2 $CH_3CO_2^-$ ions   (d) 1 Ti^{4+} ion, 2 SO_4^{2-} ions

      (b) 1 Al^{3+} ion, 3 OH^- ions   (e) 1 K^+ ion, 1 $H_2PO_4^-$ ion

      (c) 1 Cu^{2+} ion, 1 CO_3^{2-} ion

3.15 Co^{2+}: CoO Co^{3+} Co_2O_3

3.16 (a) Pt^{2+}: $PtCl_2$ Pt^{4+}: $PtCl_4$

      (b) Pt^{2+}: PtS Pt^{4+}: PtS_2

3.17 (a) incorrect, $AlCl_3$ (c) correct

      (b) incorrect, KF   (d) correct

3.18 (a) incorrect, CaO   (c) incorrect, Fe_2O_3 or FeO

      (b) correct   (d) correct

3.19 (a) potassium sulfide   (c) ammonium phosphate

      (b) cobalt(II) sulfate   (d) calcium hypochlorite

3.20 (a) calcium acetate   (c) aluminum hydroxide

      (b) nickel(II) phosphate   (d) potassium dihydrogen phosphate

3.21 (a) $(NH_4)_2CO_3$ (d) $AlPO_4$

      (b) CaI_2 (e) $AgCH_3CO_2$

      (c) $CuBr_2$

3.22 (a) $Ca(HCO_3)_2$ (d) K_2HPO_4

      (b) $KMnO_4$ (e) Na_2SO_3

      (c) $Mg(ClO_4)_2$

3.23 Na_2CO_3 sodium carbonate   NaI   sodium iodide

      $BaCO_3$ barium carbonate BaI_2 barium iodide

3.24 $Mg_3(PO_4)_2$ magnesium phosphate $Mg(NO_3)_2$ magnesium nitrate

      $FePO_4$ iron(III) phosphate $Fe(NO_3)_3$ iron(III) nitrate

3.25   The force of attraction is stronger in NaF than in NaI because the distance between ion centers is smaller in NaF (235 pm) than in NaI (322 pm).

3.26   The attractive forces are stronger in CaO because the ion charges are greater (+2/–2 in CaO and +1/–1 in NaCl).

3.27   (a) nitrogen trifluoride   (c) boron triiodide

        (b) hydrogen iodide   (d) phosphorus pentafluoride

3.28   (a) dinitrogen pentaoxide   (c) oxygen difluoride

        (b) tetraphosphorus trisulfide   (d) xenon tetrafluoride

3.29   (a) SCl_2 (b) N_2O_5 (c) $SiCl_4$ (d) B_2O_3

3.30   (a) BrF_3 (d) P_2F_4

        (b) XeF_2 (e) C_4H_{10}

        (c) N_2H_4

3.31   (a) Fe_2O_3 159.69 g/mol

        (b) BCl_3 117.17 g/mol

        (c) $C_6H_8O_6$ 176.13 g/mol

3.32   (a) $Fe(C_6H_{11}O_7)_2$ 446.14 g/mol

        (b) $CH_3CH_2CH_2CH_2SH$ 90.19 g/mol

        (c) $C_{20}H_{24}N_2O_2$ 324.42 g/mol

3.33   (a) $Ni(NO_3)_2 \cdot 6\ H_2O$ 290.79 g/mol

        (b) $CuSO_4 \cdot 5\ H_2O$ 249.69 g/mol

3.34   (a) $H_2C_2O_4 \cdot 2\ H_2O$ 126.07 g/mol

        (b) $MgSO_4 \cdot 7\ H_2O$ 246.48 g/mol

3.35   (a) $0.0255\ \text{mol } C_3H_7OH \cdot \dfrac{60.10\ \text{g } C_3H_7OH}{1\ \text{mol } C_3H_7OH} = 1.53\ \text{g } C_3H_7OH$

        (b) $0.0255\ \text{mol } C_{11}H_{16}O_2 \cdot \dfrac{180.2\ \text{g } C_{11}H_{16}O_2}{1\ \text{mol } C_{11}H_{16}O_2} = 4.60\ \text{g } C_{11}H_{16}O_2$

        (c) $0.0255\ \text{mol } C_9H_8O_4 \cdot \dfrac{180.2\ \text{g } C_9H_8O_4}{1\ \text{mol } C_9H_8O_4} = 4.60\ \text{g } C_9H_8O_4$

3.36   (a) $0.123 \text{ mol } C_{14}H_{10}O_4 \cdot \dfrac{242.2 \text{ g } C_{14}H_{10}O_4}{1 \text{ mol } C_{14}H_{10}O_4} = 29.8 \text{ g } C_{14}H_{10}O_4$

        (b) $0.123 \text{ mol Pt(NH}_3)_2Cl_2 \cdot \dfrac{300.0 \text{ g Pt(NH}_3)_2Cl_2}{1 \text{ mol Pt(NH}_3)_2Cl_2} = 36.9 \text{ g Pt(NH}_3)_2Cl_2$

3.37 $2.50 \text{ kg } CH_3CN \cdot \dfrac{10^3 \text{ g}}{1 \text{ kg}} \cdot \dfrac{1 \text{ mol } CH_3CN}{41.05 \text{ g } CH_3CN} = 60.9 \text{ mol } CH_3CN$

3.38 $1260 \times 10^6 \text{ kg (CH}_3)_2CO \cdot \dfrac{10^3 \text{ g}}{1 \text{ kg}} \cdot \dfrac{1 \text{ mol (CH}_3)_2CO}{58.08 \text{ g (CH}_3)_2CO} = 2.17 \times 10^{10} \text{ mol (CH}_3)_2CO$

3.39 $1.00 \text{ kg } SO_3 \cdot \dfrac{10^3 \text{ g}}{1 \text{ kg}} \cdot \dfrac{1 \text{ mol } SO_3}{80.06 \text{ g } SO_3} = 12.5 \text{ mol } SO_3$

        $12.5 \text{ mol } SO_3 \cdot \dfrac{6.022 \times 10^{23} \text{ molecules}}{1 \text{ mol } SO_3} = 7.52 \times 10^{24} \text{ molecules } SO_3$

        $7.52 \times 10^{24} \text{ molecules } SO_3 \cdot \dfrac{1 \text{ S atom}}{1 \text{ } SO_3 \text{ molecule}} = 7.52 \times 10^{24} \text{ S atoms}$

        $7.52 \times 10^{24} \text{ molecules } SO_3 \cdot \dfrac{3 \text{ O atoms}}{1 \text{ } SO_3 \text{ molecule}} = 2.26 \times 10^{25} \text{ O atoms}$

3.40   (a) $324 \text{ mg } C_9H_8O_4 \cdot \dfrac{1 \text{ g}}{10^3 \text{ mg}} \cdot \dfrac{1 \text{ mol } C_9H_8O_4}{180.2 \text{ g } C_9H_8O_4} = 1.80 \times 10^{-3} \text{ mol } C_9H_8O_4$

        $1904 \text{ mg } NaHCO_3 \cdot \dfrac{1 \text{ g}}{10^3 \text{ mg}} \cdot \dfrac{1 \text{ mol } NaHCO_3}{84.007 \text{ g } NaHCO_3} = 0.02266 \text{ mol } NaHCO_3$

        $1000. \text{ mg } C_6H_8O_7 \cdot \dfrac{1 \text{ g}}{10^3 \text{ mg}} \cdot \dfrac{1 \text{ mol } C_6H_8O_7}{192.13 \text{ g } C_6H_8O_7} = 5.205 \times 10^{-3} \text{ mol } C_6H_8O_7$

        (b) $1.80 \times 10^{-3} \text{ mol } C_9H_8O_4 \cdot \dfrac{6.022 \times 10^{23} \text{ molecules}}{1 \text{ mol } C_9H_8O_4} = 1.08 \times 10^{21} \text{ molecules } C_9H_8O_4$

3.41   (a) $\dfrac{207.2 \text{ g Pb}}{239.3 \text{ g PbS}} \cdot 100\% = 86.59\% \text{ Pb}$ $\dfrac{32.07 \text{ g S}}{239.3 \text{ g PbS}} \cdot 100\% = 13.40\% \text{ S}$

        (b) $\dfrac{(3)(12.01) \text{ g C}}{44.096 \text{ g } C_3H_8} \cdot 100\% = 81.71\% \text{ C}$ $\dfrac{(8)(1.008) \text{ g H}}{44.096 \text{ g } C_3H_8} \cdot 100\% = 18.29\% \text{ H}$

        (c) $\dfrac{(10)(12.01) \text{ g C}}{150.21 \text{ g } C_{10}H_{14}O} \cdot 100\% = 79.95\% \text{ C}$ $\dfrac{(14)(1.008) \text{ g H}}{150.21 \text{ g } C_{10}H_{14}O} \cdot 100\% = 9.395\% \text{ H}$

        $\dfrac{16.00 \text{ g O}}{150.21 \text{ g } C_{10}H_{14}O} \cdot 100\% = 10.65\% \text{ O}$

3.42   (a) $\dfrac{(8)(12.01) \text{ g C}}{166.18 \text{ g } C_8H_{10}N_2O_2} \cdot 100\% = 57.82\% \text{ C}$ $\dfrac{(10)(1.008) \text{ g H}}{166.18 \text{ g } C_8H_{10}N_2O_2} \cdot 100\% = 6.066\% \text{ H}$

        $\dfrac{(2)(14.01) \text{ g N}}{166.18 \text{ g } C_8H_{10}N_2O_2} \cdot 100\% = 16.86\% \text{ N}$ $\dfrac{(2)(16.00) \text{ g O}}{166.18 \text{ g } C_8H_{10}N_2O_2} \cdot 100\% = 19.26\% \text{ O}$

(b) $\dfrac{(10)(12.01) \text{ g C}}{156.26 \text{ g C}_{10}\text{H}_{20}\text{O}} \cdot 100\% = 76.86\% \text{ C}$ $\dfrac{(20)(1.008) \text{ g H}}{156.26 \text{ g C}_{10}\text{H}_{20}\text{O}} \cdot 100\% = 12.90\% \text{ H}$

$\dfrac{16.00 \text{ g O}}{156.26 \text{ g C}_{10}\text{H}_{20}\text{O}} \cdot 100\% = 10.24\% \text{ O}$

(c) $\dfrac{58.93 \text{ g Co}}{237.93 \text{ g CoCl}_2 \cdot 6 \text{ H}_2\text{O}} \cdot 100\% = 24.77\% \text{ Co}$ $\dfrac{(2)(35.45) \text{ g Cl}}{237.93 \text{ g CoCl}_2 \cdot 6 \text{ H}_2\text{O}} \cdot 100\% = 29.80\% \text{ Cl}$

$\dfrac{(12)(1.008) \text{ g H}}{237.93 \text{ g CoCl}_2 \cdot 6 \text{ H}_2\text{O}} \cdot 100\% = 5.084\% \text{ H}$ $\dfrac{(6)(16.00) \text{ g O}}{237.93 \text{ g CoCl}_2 \cdot 6 \text{ H}_2\text{O}} \cdot 100\% = 40.35\% \text{ O}$

3.43 $\dfrac{207.2 \text{ g Pb}}{239.3 \text{ g PbS}} \cdot 100\% = 86.59\% \text{ Pb}$

$10.0 \text{ g PbS} \cdot \dfrac{86.59 \text{ g Pb}}{100.00 \text{ g PbS}} = 8.66 \text{ g Pb}$

3.44 $\dfrac{(2)(55.85) \text{ g Fe}}{159.70 \text{ g Fe}_2\text{O}_3} \cdot 100\% = 69.94\% \text{ Fe}$

$25.0 \text{ g Fe}_2\text{O}_3 \cdot \dfrac{69.94 \text{ g Fe}}{100.00 \text{ g Fe}_2\text{O}_3} = 17.5 \text{ g Fe}$

3.45 $\dfrac{63.55 \text{ g Cu}}{95.62 \text{ g CuS}} \cdot 100\% = 66.46\% \text{ Cu}$

$10.0 \text{ g Cu} \cdot \dfrac{100.00 \text{ g CuS}}{66.46 \text{ g Cu}} = 15.0 \text{ g CuS}$

3.46 $\dfrac{47.87 \text{ g Ti}}{157.72 \text{ g FeTiO}_3} \cdot 100\% = 30.35\% \text{ Ti}$

$750 \text{ g Ti} \cdot \dfrac{100.00 \text{ g FeTiO}_3}{30.35 \text{ g Ti}} = 2.4 \times 10^3 \text{ g FeTiO}_3$

3.47 Empirical formula mass = 59.04 g/mol $\dfrac{118.1 \text{ g/mol}}{59.04 \text{ g/mol}} = 2$

The molecular formula is $(\text{C}_2\text{H}_3\text{O}_2)_2$, or $\text{C}_4\text{H}_6\text{O}_4$

3.48 Empirical formula mass = 58.06 g/mol $\dfrac{116.1 \text{ g/mol}}{58.06 \text{ g/mol}} = 2$

The molecular formula is $(\text{C}_2\text{H}_4\text{NO})_2$, or $\text{C}_4\text{H}_8\text{N}_2\text{O}_2$

3.49

	Empirical formula	Molar mass (g/mol)	Molecular formula	
(a)	CH	26.0	26.0/13.0 = 2	C_2H_2
(b)	CHO	116.1	116.1/29.0 = 4	$\text{C}_4\text{H}_4\text{O}_4$
(c)	CH_2	112.2	$(\text{CH}_2)_8 =$	C_8H_{16}

3.50   Empirical formula   Molar mass (g/mol)   Molecular formula

(a) $C_2H_3O_3$ 150.1 $150.1/75.0 = 2$ $C_4H_6O_6$

(b) C_3H_8 44.1 $44.1/44.1 = 1$ C_3H_8

(c) B_5H_7 122.2 $(B_5H_7)_2 =$ $B_{10}H_{14}$

3.51   Assume 100.00 g of compound.

$$92.26 \text{ g C} \cdot \frac{1 \text{ mol C}}{12.011 \text{ g C}} = 7.681 \text{ mol C} \qquad 7.74 \text{ g H} \cdot \frac{1 \text{ mol H}}{1.008 \text{ g H}} = 7.68 \text{ mol H}$$

$$\frac{7.681 \text{ mol C}}{7.68 \text{ mol H}} = \frac{1 \text{ mol C}}{1 \text{ mol H}} \qquad \text{The empirical formula is CH}$$

$$\frac{26.02 \text{ g/mol}}{13.02 \text{ g/mol}} = 2 \qquad \text{The molecular formula is } C_2H_2$$

3.52   The compound is 88.5% B and 11.5% H. Assume 100.0 g of compound.

$$88.5 \text{ g B} \cdot \frac{1 \text{ mol B}}{10.81 \text{ g B}} = 8.19 \text{ mol B} \qquad 11.5 \text{ g H} \cdot \frac{1 \text{ mol H}}{1.008 \text{ g H}} = 11.4 \text{ mol H}$$

$$\frac{11.4 \text{ mol H}}{8.19 \text{ mol B}} = \frac{1.39 \text{ mol H}}{1 \text{ mol B}} = \frac{7/5 \text{ mol H}}{1 \text{ mol B}} = \frac{7 \text{ mol H}}{5 \text{ mol B}} \qquad \text{The empirical formula is } B_5H_7$$

3.53   The compound is 89.94% C and 10.06% H. Assume 100.00 g of compound.

$$89.94 \text{ g C} \cdot \frac{1 \text{ mol C}}{12.011 \text{ g C}} = 7.488 \text{ mol C} \qquad 10.06 \text{ g H} \cdot \frac{1 \text{ mol H}}{1.0079 \text{ g H}} = 9.981 \text{ mol H}$$

$$\frac{9.981 \text{ mol H}}{7.488 \text{ mol C}} = \frac{1.33 \text{ mol H}}{1 \text{ mol C}} = \frac{4/3 \text{ mol H}}{1 \text{ mol C}} = \frac{4 \text{ mol H}}{3 \text{ mol C}} \qquad \text{The empirical formula is } C_3H_4$$

$$\frac{120.2 \text{ g/mol}}{40.07 \text{ g/mol}} = 3 \qquad \text{The molecular formula is } C_9H_{12}$$

3.54   The compound is 36.84% N and 63.16% O. Assume 100.00 g of compound.

$$36.84 \text{ g N} \cdot \frac{1 \text{ mol N}}{14.007 \text{ g N}} = 2.630 \text{ mol N} \qquad 63.16 \text{ g O} \cdot \frac{1 \text{ mol O}}{15.999 \text{ g O}} = 3.948 \text{ mol O}$$

$$\frac{3.948 \text{ mol O}}{2.630 \text{ mol N}} = \frac{1.5 \text{ mol O}}{1 \text{ mol N}} = \frac{3 \text{ mol O}}{2 \text{ mol N}} \qquad \text{The empirical formula is } N_2O_3$$

3.55   Assume 100.00 g of compound.

$$63.15 \text{ g C} \cdot \frac{1 \text{ mol C}}{12.011 \text{ g C}} = 5.258 \text{ mol C} \qquad 5.30 \text{ g H} \cdot \frac{1 \text{ mol H}}{1.008 \text{ g H}} = 5.26 \text{ mol H}$$

$$31.55 \text{ g O} \cdot \frac{1 \text{ mol O}}{15.999 \text{ g O}} = 1.972 \text{ mol O}$$

$$\frac{5.258 \text{ mol C}}{1.972 \text{ mol O}} = \frac{2.667 \text{ mol C}}{1 \text{ mol O}} = \frac{8 \text{ mol C}}{3 \text{ mol O}} \qquad \frac{5.26 \text{ mol H}}{1.972 \text{ mol O}} = \frac{2.667 \text{ mol H}}{1 \text{ mol O}} = \frac{8 \text{ mol H}}{3 \text{ mol O}}$$

The empirical formula is $C_8H_8O_3$

The molar mass is equal to the empirical formula mass, so the molecular formula is also $C_8H_8O_3$

3.56   Assume 100.0 g of compound.

$74.0 \text{ g C} \cdot \dfrac{1 \text{ mol C}}{12.01 \text{ g C}} = 6.16 \text{ mol C}$ $8.65 \text{ g H} \cdot \dfrac{1 \text{ mol H}}{1.008 \text{ g H}} = 8.58 \text{ mol H}$

$17.35 \text{ g N} \cdot \dfrac{1 \text{ mol N}}{14.007 \text{ g N}} = 1.239 \text{ mol N}$

$\dfrac{6.16 \text{ mol C}}{1.239 \text{ mol N}} = \dfrac{5 \text{ mol C}}{1 \text{ mol N}}$ $\dfrac{8.58 \text{ mol H}}{1.239 \text{ mol N}} = \dfrac{7 \text{ mol H}}{1 \text{ mol N}}$ The empirical formula is C_5H_7N

$\dfrac{162 \text{ g/mol}}{81.1 \text{ g/mol}} = 2$ The molecular formula is $C_{10}H_{14}N_2$

3.57   1.687 g hydrated compound – 0.824 g $MgSO_4$ = 0.863 g H_2O

$0.863 \text{ g H}_2\text{O} \cdot \dfrac{1 \text{ mol H}_2\text{O}}{18.02 \text{ g H}_2\text{O}} = 0.0479 \text{ mol H}_2\text{O}$

$0.824 \text{ g MgSO}_4 \cdot \dfrac{1 \text{ mol MgSO}_4}{120.4 \text{ g MgSO}_4} = 0.00684 \text{ mol MgSO}_4$

$\dfrac{0.0479 \text{ mol H}_2\text{O}}{0.00684 \text{ mol MgSO}_4} = \dfrac{7.00 \text{ mol H}_2\text{O}}{1 \text{ mol MgSO}_4}$ There are 7 water molecules per formula unit of $MgSO_4$

3.58   4.74 g hydrated compound – 2.16 g H_2O = 2.58 g $KAl(SO_4)_2$

$2.16 \text{ g H}_2\text{O} \cdot \dfrac{1 \text{ mol H}_2\text{O}}{18.02 \text{ g H}_2\text{O}} = 0.120 \text{ mol H}_2\text{O}$

$2.58 \text{ g KAl(SO}_4)_2 \cdot \dfrac{1 \text{ mol KAl(SO}_4)_2}{258.2 \text{ g KAl(SO}_4)_2} = 0.00999 \text{ mol KAl(SO}_4)_2$

$\dfrac{0.120 \text{ mol H}_2\text{O}}{0.00999 \text{ mol KAl(SO}_4)_2} = \dfrac{12.0 \text{ mol H}_2\text{O}}{1 \text{ mol KAl(SO}_4)_2}$

There are 12 water molecules per formula unit of $KAl(SO_4)_2$; $x = 12$

3.59   0.678 g compound – 0.526 g Xe = 0.152 g F

$0.526 \text{ g Xe} \cdot \dfrac{1 \text{ mol Xe}}{131.3 \text{ g Xe}} = 0.00401 \text{ mol Xe}$ $0.152 \text{ g F} \cdot \dfrac{1 \text{ mol F}}{19.00 \text{ g F}} = 0.00800 \text{ mol F}$

$\dfrac{0.00800 \text{ mol F}}{0.00401 \text{ mol Xe}} = \dfrac{2 \text{ mol F}}{1 \text{ mol Xe}}$ The empirical formula is XeF_2

3.60   5.722 g compound – 1.256 g S = 4.466 g F

$1.256 \text{ g S} \cdot \dfrac{1 \text{ mol S}}{32.066 \text{ g S}} = 0.03917 \text{ mol S}$ $4.466 \text{ g F} \cdot \dfrac{1 \text{ mol F}}{18.998 \text{ g F}} = 0.2351 \text{ mol F}$

$\dfrac{0.2351 \text{ mol F}}{0.03917 \text{ mol S}} = \dfrac{6 \text{ mol F}}{1 \text{ mol S}}$ The empirical formula is SF_6; $x = 6$

3.61 $2.50 \text{ g Zn} \cdot \dfrac{1 \text{ mol Zn}}{65.39 \text{ g Zn}} = 0.0382 \text{ mol Zn}$ $9.70 \text{ g I} \cdot \dfrac{1 \text{ mol I}}{126.9 \text{ g I}} = 0.0764 \text{ mol I}$

$\dfrac{0.0764 \text{ mol I}}{0.0382 \text{ mol Zn}} = \dfrac{2 \text{ mol I}}{1 \text{ mol Zn}}$ The empirical formula is ZnI_2

3.62   3.69 g product $-$ 1.25 g Ge = 2.44 g Cl

$1.25 \text{ g Ge} \cdot \dfrac{1 \text{ mol Ge}}{72.61 \text{ g Ge}} = 0.0172 \text{ mol Ge}$ $2.44 \text{ g Cl} \cdot \dfrac{1 \text{ mol Cl}}{35.45 \text{ g Cl}} = 0.0688 \text{ mol Cl}$

$\dfrac{0.0688 \text{ mol Cl}}{0.0172 \text{ mol Ge}} = \dfrac{4 \text{ mol Cl}}{1 \text{ mol Ge}}$ The empirical formula is $GeCl_4$

3.63 $(NH_4)_2CO_3$ $(NH_4)_2SO_4$ $NiCO_3$ $NiSO_4$

3.64   (a) CH_3CO_2H (b) CH_3NH_2 (c) CH_2O

3.65   A strontium atom has 38 electrons. When an atom of strontium forms an ion, it loses two electrons, forming an ion having the same number of electrons as the noble gas krypton.

3.66 NH_4^+ ammonium ion   +1 charge

SO_4^{2-} sulfate ion -2 charge

Molar mass of ammonium sulfate = 132.14 g/mol

3.67   All five compounds contain three chlorine atoms. The compound with the lowest molar mass, (a) BCl_3, has the highest weight percent of chlorine.

$\dfrac{(3)(35.45) \text{ g Cl}}{117.16 \text{ g } BCl_3} \cdot 100\% = 90.77\% \text{ Cl}$

3.68   (a) $1.0 \text{ g } BeCl_2 \cdot \dfrac{1 \text{ mol } BeCl_2}{79.9 \text{ g } BeCl_2} \cdot \dfrac{3 \text{ mol atoms}}{1 \text{ mol } BeCl_2} \cdot \dfrac{6.02 \times 10^{23} \text{ atoms}}{1 \text{ mol atoms}} = 2.3 \times 10^{22} \text{ atoms}$

(b) $1.0 \text{ g } MgCl_2 \cdot \dfrac{1 \text{ mol } MgCl_2}{95.2 \text{ g } MgCl_2} \cdot \dfrac{3 \text{ mol atoms}}{1 \text{ mol } MgCl_2} \cdot \dfrac{6.02 \times 10^{23} \text{ atoms}}{1 \text{ mol atoms}} = 1.9 \times 10^{22} \text{ atoms}$

(c) $1.0 \text{ g } CaS \cdot \dfrac{1 \text{ mol } CaS}{72.1 \text{ g } CaS} \cdot \dfrac{2 \text{ mol atoms}}{1 \text{ mol } CaS} \cdot \dfrac{6.02 \times 10^{23} \text{ atoms}}{1 \text{ mol atoms}} = 1.7 \times 10^{22} \text{ atoms}$

(d) $1.0 \text{ g } SrCO_3 \cdot \dfrac{1 \text{ mol } SrCO_3}{148 \text{ g } SrCO_3} \cdot \dfrac{5 \text{ mol atoms}}{1 \text{ mol } SrCO_3} \cdot \dfrac{6.02 \times 10^{23} \text{ atoms}}{1 \text{ mol atoms}} = 2.0 \times 10^{22} \text{ atoms}$

(e) $1.0 \text{ g } BaSO_4 \cdot \dfrac{1 \text{ mol } BaSO_4}{233 \text{ g } BaSO_4} \cdot \dfrac{6 \text{ mol atoms}}{1 \text{ mol } BaSO_4} \cdot \dfrac{6.02 \times 10^{23} \text{ atoms}}{1 \text{ mol atoms}} = 1.6 \times 10^{22} \text{ atoms}$

The 1.0-g sample of (a) $BeCl_2$ has the largest number of atoms.

3.69   All five compounds contain one oxygen atom. The compound with the lowest molar mass, CO, has the highest weight percent of oxygen.

$\dfrac{16.00 \text{ g O}}{28.01 \text{ g CO}} \cdot 100\% = 57.12\% \text{ O}$

3.70   1 K^+ ion, 1 Al^{3+} ion, and 2 SO_4^{2-} ions

3.71   Borate ion BO_3^{3-} The borate ion is an anion.

3.72   An empirical formula gives the simplest possible ratio of atoms in a molecule. The molecular formula shows both the ratio of atoms and the total number of atoms in a molecule. The empirical formula of ethane is CH_3 and the molecular formula is C_2H_6.

3.73 3.0×10^{23} molecules represents 0.5 mol of adenine. The molar mass of adenine ($C_5H_5N_5$) is 135.13 g/mol, so 0.5 mol of adenine has a mass of 67.56 g. Forty grams of adenine therefore has less mass than 0.5 mol of adenine.

3.74   Molar mass of $BaCl_2$ = 208.23 g/mol   Molar mass of $SiCl_4$ = 169.90 g/mol

One mole of $BaCl_2$ has a greater mass, so 0.5 mol of $BaCl_2$ will have a greater mass than 0.5 mol of $SiCl_4$.

3.75 $0.05 \text{ mL } H_2O \cdot \dfrac{1 \text{ cm}^3}{1 \text{ mL}} \cdot \dfrac{1.00 \text{ g}}{1 \text{ cm}^3} \cdot \dfrac{1 \text{ mol } H_2O}{18.0 \text{ g}} \cdot \dfrac{6.02 \times 10^{23} \text{ molecules}}{1 \text{ mol}} = 2 \times 10^{21}$ molecules H_2O

3.76   (a) Molar mass = 305.42 g/mol

(b) 55 mg capsaicin $\cdot \dfrac{1 \text{ g}}{10^3 \text{ mg}} \cdot \dfrac{1 \text{ mol capsaicin}}{305.42 \text{ g}} = 1.8 \times 10^{-4}$ mol capsaicin

(c) $\dfrac{(18)(12.01) \text{ g C}}{305.42 \text{ g } C_{18}H_{27}NO_3} \cdot 100\% = 70.78\%$ C $\dfrac{(27)(1.008) \text{ g H}}{305.42 \text{ g } C_{18}H_{27}NO_3} \cdot 100\% = 8.911\%$ H

$\dfrac{14.01 \text{ g N}}{305.42 \text{ g } C_{18}H_{27}NO_3} \cdot 100\% = 4.587\%$ N $\dfrac{(3)(16.00) \text{ g O}}{305.42 \text{ g } C_{18}H_{27}NO_3} \cdot 100\% = 15.72\%$ O

(d) 55 mg capsaicin $\cdot \dfrac{70.78 \text{ mg C}}{100.00 \text{ mg } C_{18}H_{27}NO_3} = 39$ mg C

3.77   Molar mass = 245.77 g/mol

$$\frac{63.55 \text{ g Cu}}{245.77 \text{ g Cu(NH}_3)_4\text{SO}_4 \cdot \text{H}_2\text{O}} \cdot 100\% = 25.86\% \text{ Cu}$$

$$\frac{(4)(14.01) \text{ g N}}{245.77 \text{ g Cu(NH}_3)_4\text{SO}_4 \cdot \text{H}_2\text{O}} \cdot 100\% = 22.80\% \text{ N}$$

$$\frac{(14)(1.008) \text{ g H}}{245.77 \text{ g Cu(NH}_3)_4\text{SO}_4 \cdot \text{H}_2\text{O}} \cdot 100\% = 5.742\% \text{ H}$$

$$\frac{32.07 \text{ g S}}{245.77 \text{ g Cu(NH}_3)_4\text{SO}_4 \cdot \text{H}_2\text{O}} \cdot 100\% = 13.05\% \text{ S}$$

$$\frac{(5)(16.00) \text{ g O}}{245.77 \text{ g Cu(NH}_3)_4\text{SO}_4 \cdot \text{H}_2\text{O}} \cdot 100\% = 32.55\% \text{ O}$$

$$10.5 \text{ g Cu(NH}_3)\text{SO}_4 \cdot \text{H}_2\text{O} \cdot \frac{25.86 \text{ g Cu}}{100.00 \text{ g Cu(NH}_3)_4\text{SO}_4 \cdot \text{H}_2\text{O}} = 2.72 \text{ g Cu}$$

$$10.5 \text{ g Cu(NH}_3)_4\text{SO}_4 \cdot \text{H}_2\text{O} \cdot \frac{18.02 \text{ g H}_2\text{O}}{245.77 \text{ g Cu(NH}_3)_4\text{SO}_4 \cdot \text{H}_2\text{O}} = 0.770 \text{ g H}_2\text{O}$$

3.78   (a) Ethylene glycol $C_2H_6O_2$ Molar mass = 62.07 g/mol

$$\frac{(2)(12.01) \text{ g C}}{62.07 \text{ g C}_2\text{H}_6\text{O}_2} \cdot 100\% = 38.70\% \text{ C} \qquad \frac{(2)(16.00) \text{ g O}}{62.07 \text{ g C}_2\text{H}_6\text{O}_2} \cdot 100\% = 51.55\% \text{ O}$$

(b) Dihydroxyacetone $C_3H_6O_3$ Molar mass = 90.08 g/mol

$$\frac{(3)(12.01) \text{ g C}}{90.08 \text{ g C}_3\text{H}_6\text{O}_3} \cdot 100\% = 40.00\% \text{ C} \qquad \frac{(3)(16.00) \text{ g O}}{90.08 \text{ g C}_3\text{H}_6\text{O}_3} \cdot 100\% = 53.29\% \text{ O}$$

Dihydroxyacetone has a larger percentage of carbon and of oxygen.

3.79 $$\frac{1.5 \text{ mol H}}{1 \text{ mol C}} = \frac{3/2 \text{ mol H}}{1 \text{ mol C}} = \frac{3 \text{ mol H}}{2 \text{ mol C}} = \frac{6 \text{ mol H}}{4 \text{ mol C}}$$

$$\frac{1.25 \text{ mol O}}{1 \text{ mol C}} = \frac{5/4 \text{ mol O}}{1 \text{ mol C}} = \frac{5 \text{ mol O}}{4 \text{ mol C}} \qquad \text{The empirical formula is } C_4H_6O_5.$$

3.80 $$\frac{55.85 \text{ g Fe}}{151.92 \text{ g FeSO}_4} \cdot 100\% = 36.76\% \text{ Fe} \qquad \frac{55.85 \text{ g Fe}}{446.15 \text{ g Fe(C}_6\text{H}_{11}\text{O}_7)_2} \cdot 100\% = 12.52\% \text{ Fe}$$

The tablet containing $FeSO_4$ will deliver more atoms of iron.

3.81 $$0.109 \text{ g compound} \cdot \frac{38.82 \text{ g Fe}}{100.00 \text{ g compound}} \cdot \frac{1 \text{ mol Fe}}{55.85 \text{ g}} = 7.58 \times 10^{-4} \text{ mol Fe}$$

$$0.109 \text{ g compound} \cdot \frac{61.18 \text{ g C}_2\text{O}_4^{2-}}{100.00 \text{ g compound}} \cdot \frac{1 \text{ mol C}_2\text{O}_4^{2-}}{88.02 \text{ g}} = 7.58 \times 10^{-4} \text{ mol C}_2\text{O}_4^{2-}$$

$$\frac{7.58 \times 10^{-4} \text{ mol Fe}}{7.58 \times 10^{-4} \text{ mol C}_2\text{O}_4^{2-}} = \frac{1 \text{ mol Fe}}{1 \text{ mol C}_2\text{O}_4^{2-}} \qquad \text{The empirical formula is } FeC_2O_4$$

3.82   Assume 100.00 g of compound.

$$30.70 \text{ g Fe} \cdot \frac{1 \text{ mol Fe}}{55.845 \text{ g}} = 0.5497 \text{ mol Fe} \qquad\qquad 69.30 \text{ g CO} \cdot \frac{1 \text{ mol CO}}{28.010 \text{ g}} = 2.474 \text{ mol CO}$$

$$\frac{2.474 \text{ mol CO}}{0.5497 \text{ mol Fe}} = \frac{4.5 \text{ mol CO}}{1 \text{ mol Fe}} = \frac{9 \text{ mol CO}}{2 \text{ mol Fe}} \qquad\qquad \text{The empirical formula is } Fe_2(CO)_9$$

3.83   (a) $C_{10}H_{15}NO$ Molar mass = 165.23 g/mol

   (b) $\dfrac{(10)(12.01) \text{ g C}}{165.23 \text{ g } C_{10}H_{15}NO} \cdot 100\% = 72.69\% \text{ C}$

   (c) $0.125 \text{ g } C_{10}H_{15}NO \cdot \dfrac{1 \text{ mol } C_{10}H_{15}NO}{165.23 \text{ g}} = 7.57 \times 10^{-4} \text{ mol } C_{10}H_{15}NO$

   (d) $7.57 \times 10^{-4} \text{ mol } C_{10}H_{15}NO \cdot \dfrac{6.022 \times 10^{23} \text{ molecules}}{1 \text{ mol } C_{10}H_{15}NO} = 4.56 \times 10^{20} \text{ molecules}$

        $4.56 \times 10^{20} \text{ molecules} \cdot \dfrac{10 \text{ C atoms}}{1 \text{ molecule}} = 4.56 \times 10^{21} \text{ C atoms}$

3.84   (a) $C_7H_5NO_3S$

   (b) $125 \text{ mg } C_7H_5NO_3S \cdot \dfrac{1 \text{ g}}{10^3 \text{ mg}} \cdot \dfrac{1 \text{ mol } C_7H_5NO_3S}{183.19 \text{ g}} = 6.82 \times 10^{-4} \text{ mol } C_7H_5NO_3S$

   (c) $125 \text{ mg } C_7H_5NO_3S \cdot \dfrac{32.07 \text{ mg S}}{183.19 \text{ mg } C_7H_5NO_3S} = 21.9 \text{ mg S}$

3.85   Ionic compounds (metal + nonmetal)

   (c) Li_2S lithium sulfide

   (d) In_2O_3 indium oxide

   (g) CaF_2 calcium fluoride

3.86   (a)   chlorine trifluoride   (f)   oxygen difluoride

        (b)   nitrogen trichloride   (g)   potassium iodide, ionic

        (c)   strontium sulfate, ionic   (h)   aluminum sulfide, ionic

        (d)   calcium nitrate, ionic   (i)   phosphorus trichloride

        (e)   xenon tetrafluoride   (j)   potassium phosphate, ionic

3.87   (a) $NaOCl$, ionic   (f) $(NH_4)_2SO_3$, ionic

        (b) BI_3 (g) KH_2PO_4, ionic

        (c) $Al(ClO_4)_3$, ionic   (h) S_2Cl_2

        (d) $Ca(CH_3CO_2)_2$, ionic   (i) ClF_3

        (e) $KMnO_4$, ionic   (j) PF_3

3.88

Cation	Anion	Name	Formula
NH_4^+	Br^-	ammonium bromide	NH_4Br
Ba^{2+}	S^{2-}	barium sulfide	BaS
Fe^{2+}	Cl^-	iron(II) chloride	$FeCl_2$
Pb^{2+}	F^-	lead(II) fluoride	PbF_2
Al^{3+}	CO_3^{2-}	aluminum carbonate	$Al_2(CO_3)_3$
Fe^{3+}	O^{2-}	iron(III) oxide	Fe_2O_3

3.89

Cation	Anion	Name	Formula
Li^+	ClO_4^-	lithium perchlorate	$LiClO_4$
Al^{3+}	PO_4^{3-}	aluminum phosphate	$AlPO_4$
Li^+	Br^-	lithium bromide	$LiBr$
Ba^{2+}	NO_3^-	barium nitrate	$Ba(NO_3)_2$
Al^{3+}	O^{2-}	aluminum oxide	Al_2O_3
Fe^{3+}	CO_3^{2-}	iron(III) carbonate	$Fe_2(CO_3)_3$

3.90   Assume 100.0 g of compound.

$$14.6 \text{ g C} \cdot \frac{1 \text{ mol C}}{12.01 \text{ g C}} = 1.22 \text{ mol C} \qquad 39.0 \text{ g O} \cdot \frac{1 \text{ mol O}}{16.00 \text{ g O}} = 2.44 \text{ mol O}$$

$$46.3 \text{ g F} \cdot \frac{1 \text{ mol F}}{19.00 \text{ g F}} = 2.44 \text{ mol F}$$

$$\frac{2.44 \text{ mol O}}{1.22 \text{ mol C}} = \frac{2 \text{ mol O}}{1 \text{ mol C}} \qquad\qquad \frac{2.44 \text{ mol F}}{1.22 \text{ mol C}} = \frac{2 \text{ mol F}}{1 \text{ mol C}}$$

The empirical formula is CO_2F_2. The empirical formula mass is equal to the molar mass, so the molecular

formula is also CO_2F_2.

3.91   Assume 100.00 g of compound.

$93.71 \text{ g C} \cdot \dfrac{1 \text{ mol C}}{12.011 \text{ g C}} = 7.802 \text{ mol C}$ $6.29 \text{ g H} \cdot \dfrac{1 \text{ mol H}}{1.008 \text{ g H}} = 6.24 \text{ mol H}$

$\dfrac{7.802 \text{ mol C}}{6.24 \text{ mol H}} = \dfrac{1.25 \text{ mol C}}{1 \text{ mol H}} = \dfrac{5 \text{ mol C}}{4 \text{ mol H}}$ The empirical formula is C_5H_4

$\dfrac{128.16 \text{ g/mol}}{64.08 \text{ g/mol}} = 2$ The molecular formula is $(C_5H_4)_2$ or $C_{10}H_8$

3.92   Assume 100.00 g of compound.

$22.88 \text{ g C} \cdot \dfrac{1 \text{ mol C}}{12.011 \text{ g C}} = 1.905 \text{ mol C}$ $5.76 \text{ g H} \cdot \dfrac{1 \text{ mol H}}{1.008 \text{ g H}} = 5.71 \text{ mol H}$

$71.36 \text{ g As} \cdot \dfrac{1 \text{ mol As}}{74.922 \text{ g As}} = 0.9525 \text{ mol As}$

$\dfrac{1.905 \text{ mol C}}{0.9525 \text{ mol As}} = \dfrac{2 \text{ mol C}}{1 \text{ mol As}}$ $\dfrac{5.71 \text{ mol H}}{0.9525 \text{ mol As}} = \dfrac{6 \text{ mol H}}{1 \text{ mol As}}$

The empirical formula is C_2H_6As

$\dfrac{210 \text{ g/mol}}{105.0 \text{ g/mol}} = 2$ The molecular formula is $(C_2H_6As)_2$ or $C_4H_{12}As_2$

3.93   Assume 100.00 g of compound.

$58.77 \text{ g C} \cdot \dfrac{1 \text{ mol C}}{12.011 \text{ g C}} = 4.893 \text{ mol C}$ $13.81 \text{ g H} \cdot \dfrac{1 \text{ mol H}}{1.0079 \text{ g H}} = 13.70 \text{ mol H}$

$27.40 \text{ g N} \cdot \dfrac{1 \text{ mol N}}{14.007 \text{ g N}} = 1.956 \text{ mol N}$

$\dfrac{4.893 \text{ mol C}}{1.956 \text{ mol N}} = \dfrac{2.5 \text{ mol C}}{1 \text{ mol N}} = \dfrac{5 \text{ mol C}}{2 \text{ mol N}}$ $\dfrac{13.70 \text{ mol H}}{1.956 \text{ mol N}} = \dfrac{7 \text{ mol H}}{1 \text{ mol N}} = \dfrac{14 \text{ mol H}}{2 \text{ mol N}}$

The empirical formula is $C_5H_{14}N_2$. The empirical formula mass is equal to the molecular mass, so the molecular formula is also $C_5H_{14}N_2$.

3.94 $0.364 \text{ g Ni(CO)}_x - 0.125 \text{ g Ni} = 0.239 \text{ g CO}$

$0.239 \text{ g CO} \cdot \dfrac{1 \text{ mol CO}}{28.01 \text{ g CO}} = 0.00853 \text{ mol CO}$ $0.125 \text{ g Ni} \cdot \dfrac{1 \text{ mol Ni}}{58.69 \text{ g Ni}} = 0.00213 \text{ mol Ni}$

$\dfrac{0.00853 \text{ mol CO}}{0.00213 \text{ mol Ni}} = \dfrac{4 \text{ mol CO}}{1 \text{ mol Ni}}$ The compound formula is $NiCO_4$ ($x = 4$)

3.95   Assume 100.0 g of compound.

$$49.5 \text{ g C} \cdot \frac{1 \text{ mol C}}{12.01 \text{ g C}} = 4.12 \text{ mol C} \qquad 3.2 \text{ g H} \cdot \frac{1 \text{ mol H}}{1.01 \text{ g H}} = 3.2 \text{ mol H}$$

$$22.0 \text{ g O} \cdot \frac{1 \text{ mol O}}{16.00 \text{ g O}} = 1.38 \text{ mol O} \qquad 25.2 \text{ g Mn} \cdot \frac{1 \text{ mol Mn}}{54.94 \text{ g Mn}} = 0.459 \text{ mol Mn}$$

$$\frac{4.12 \text{ mol C}}{0.459 \text{ mol Mn}} = \frac{9 \text{ mol C}}{1 \text{ mol Mn}} \qquad \frac{3.2 \text{ mol H}}{0.459 \text{ mol Mn}} = \frac{7 \text{ mol H}}{1 \text{ mol Mn}}$$

$$\frac{1.38 \text{ mol O}}{0.459 \text{ mol Mn}} = \frac{3 \text{ mol O}}{1 \text{ mol Mn}}$$

The empirical formula is $C_9H_7MnO_3$.

3.96 $$\frac{(2)(30.97) \text{ g P}}{310.18 \text{ g Ca}_3(\text{PO}_4)_2} \cdot 100\% = 19.97\% \text{ P}$$

$$15.0 \text{ kg P} \cdot \frac{100.00 \text{ kg Ca}_3(\text{PO}_4)_2}{19.97 \text{ kg P}} = 75.1 \text{ kg Ca}_3(\text{PO}_4)_2$$

3.97 $$\frac{(2)(52.00) \text{ kg Cr}}{152.00 \text{ kg Cr}_2\text{O}_3} \cdot 100\% = 68.42\% \text{ Cr}$$

$$850 \text{ kg Cr} \cdot \frac{100.00 \text{ kg Cr}_2\text{O}_3}{68.42 \text{ kg Cr}} = 1200 \text{ kg Cr}_2\text{O}_3$$

3.98 $$\frac{(2)(121.8) \text{ g Sb}}{339.8 \text{ g Sb}_2\text{S}_3} \cdot 100\% = 71.69\% \text{ Sb}$$

$$1.00 \text{ kg ore} \cdot \frac{10^3 \text{ g}}{1 \text{ kg}} \cdot \frac{10.6 \text{ g Sb}}{100.0 \text{ g ore}} \cdot \frac{100.00 \text{ g Sb}_2\text{S}_3}{71.69 \text{ g Sb}} = 148 \text{ g Sb}_2\text{S}_3$$

3.99 $1.246 \text{ g I}_x\text{Cl}_y - 0.678 \text{ g I} = 0.568 \text{ g Cl}$

$$0.678 \text{ g I} \cdot \frac{1 \text{ mol I}}{126.9 \text{ g I}} = 0.00534 \text{ mol I} \qquad 0.568 \text{ g Cl} \cdot \frac{1 \text{ mol Cl}}{35.45 \text{ g Cl}} = 0.0160 \text{ mol Cl}$$

$$\frac{0.0160 \text{ mol Cl}}{0.00534 \text{ mol I}} = \frac{3 \text{ mol Cl}}{1 \text{ mol I}} \qquad \text{The empirical formula is ICl}_3$$

$$\frac{467 \text{ g/mol}}{233.3 \text{ g/mol}} = 2 \qquad \text{The molecular formula is I}_2\text{Cl}_6$$

3.100 $$2.04 \text{ g V} \cdot \frac{1 \text{ mol V}}{50.94 \text{ g V}} = 0.0400 \text{ mol V} \qquad 1.93 \text{ g S} \cdot \frac{1 \text{ mol S}}{32.07 \text{ g S}} = 0.0602 \text{ mol S}$$

$$\frac{0.0602 \text{ mol S}}{0.0400 \text{ mol V}} = \frac{1.5 \text{ mol S}}{1 \text{ mol V}} = \frac{3 \text{ mol S}}{2 \text{ mol V}} \qquad \text{The empirical formula is V}_2\text{S}_3$$

3.101 $$15.8 \text{ kg FeS}_2 \cdot \frac{55.85 \text{ kg Fe}}{119.99 \text{ kg FeS}_2} = 7.35 \text{ kg Fe}$$

3.102   (a) True. $0.500 \text{ mol } C_8H_{18} \cdot \dfrac{114.2 \text{ g } C_8H_{18}}{1 \text{ mol } C_8H_{18}} = 57.1 \text{ g } C_8H_{18}$

      (b) True. $\dfrac{(8)(12.01) \text{ g C}}{114.2 \text{ g } C_8H_{18}} \cdot 100\% = 84.1\% \text{ C}$

      (c) True.

      (d) False. $57.1 \text{ g } C_8H_{18} \cdot \dfrac{(18)(1.008) \text{ g H}}{114.2 \text{ g } C_8H_{18}} = 9.07 \text{ g H}$

3.103   (d) Na_2MoO_4

3.104 $\dfrac{74.75 \text{ g Cl}}{100.00 \text{ g MCl}_4} = \dfrac{(4)(35.453) \text{ g Cl}}{\text{molar mass MCl}_4}$ Molar mass $MCl_4 = 189.7 \text{ g}$

      Atomic weight M = $189.7 \text{ g MCl}_4 - (4)(35.453) \text{ g Cl} = 47.9 \text{ g}$ M is Ti, titanium

3.105 $2 \text{ tablets} \cdot \dfrac{300. \text{ mg}}{1 \text{ tablet}} \cdot \dfrac{1 \text{ g}}{10^3 \text{ mg}} \cdot \dfrac{1 \text{ mol } C_{21}H_{15}Bi_3O_{12}}{1086 \text{ g } C_{21}H_{15}Bi_3O_{12}} = 5.52 \times 10^{-4} \text{ mol } C_{21}H_{15}Bi_3O_{12}$

      $5.52 \times 10^{-4} \text{ mol } C_{21}H_{15}Bi_3O_{12} \cdot \dfrac{3 \text{ mol Bi}}{1 \text{ mol } C_{21}H_{15}Bi_3O_{12}} \cdot \dfrac{209.0 \text{ g Bi}}{1 \text{ mol Bi}} = 0.346 \text{ g Bi}$

3.106 $\dfrac{15.2 \text{ g O}}{100 \text{ g MO}_2} = \dfrac{(2)(16.00) \text{ g O}}{\text{molar mass MO}_2}$ Molar mass $MO_2 = 211 \text{ g}$

      Atomic weight M = $211 \text{ g MO}_2 - (2)(16.00) \text{ g O} = 179 \text{ g}$ M is Hf, hafnium

3.107   Molar mass of compound = $\dfrac{385 \text{ g}}{2.50 \text{ mol}} = 154 \text{ g/mol}$

      $154 \text{ g/mol} = (\text{molar mass of E}) + [4 \times (\text{molar mass of Cl})] = M_E + 4(35.45 \text{ g/mol})$

      $M_E = 12$, E is C (carbon).

3.108 $\dfrac{15.9 \text{ g}}{0.15 \text{ mol}} = 106 \text{ g/mol } A_2Z_3$ $\dfrac{9.3 \text{ g}}{0.15 \text{ mol}} = 62 \text{ g/mol } AZ_2$

      For AZ_2:   (atomic mass A) + (2)(atomic mass Z) = 62

      For A_2Z_3:   (2)(atomic mass A) + (3)(atomic mass Z) = 106

               (2)[62 − (2)(atomic mass Z)] + (3)(atomic mass Z) = 106

               atomic mass Z = 18 g/mol

               atomic mass A = 26 g/mol

3.109 $\dfrac{(3)(79.904) \text{ g Br}}{\text{molar mass Br}_3C_6H_3(C_8H_8)_x} \cdot 100\% = 10.46\% \text{ Br}$

      molar mass $Br_3C_6H_3(C_8H_8)_x = 2292 \text{ g/mol}$

      $2292 \text{ g/mol} = (3)(79.904) \text{ g Br} + (6)(12.011) \text{ g C} + (3)(1.0079) \text{ g H} + (x)(104.15) \text{ g } C_8H_8$

      $x = 19$

3.110 $\dfrac{55.85 \text{ g Fe}}{\text{molar mass hemoglobin}} \cdot 100\% = 0.335\% \text{ Fe}$

molar mass hemoglobin $= 1.67 \times 10^4$ g/mol

$\dfrac{(4)(55.85) \text{ g Fe}}{\text{molar mass hemoglobin}} \cdot 100\% = 0.335\% \text{ Fe}$

molar mass hemoglobin $= 6.67 \times 10^4$ g/mol

3.111   (a)   volume $= (0.0550 \text{ cm})(1.25 \text{ cm})^2 = 0.0859 \text{ cm}^3$ Ni

$0.0859 \text{ cm}^3 \text{ Ni} \cdot \dfrac{8.908 \text{ g Ni}}{1 \text{ cm}^3} = 0.765 \text{ g Ni}$

(b)   1.261 g compound $- 0.765$ g Ni $= 0.496$ g F

$0.765 \text{ g Ni} \cdot \dfrac{1 \text{ mol Ni}}{58.69 \text{ g Ni}} = 0.0130 \text{ mol Ni}$ $0.496 \text{ g F} \cdot \dfrac{1 \text{ mol F}}{19.00 \text{ g F}} = 0.0261 \text{ mol F}$

$\dfrac{0.0261 \text{ mol F}}{0.0130 \text{ mol Ni}} = \dfrac{2 \text{ mol F}}{1 \text{ mol Ni}}$ The empirical formula is NiF_2

(c) NiF_2, nickel(II) fluoride

3.112 Al^{3+} will be most strongly attracted to water because it has the largest positive charge (+3), and force of attraction is directly related to the magnitude of the ion charge.

3.113   Assume 100.0 g of sample.

$54.0 \text{ g C} \cdot \dfrac{1 \text{ mol C}}{12.01 \text{ g C}} = 4.50 \text{ mol C}$ $6.00 \text{ g H} \cdot \dfrac{1 \text{ mol H}}{1.008 \text{ g H}} = 5.95 \text{ mol H}$

$40.0 \text{ g O} \cdot \dfrac{1 \text{ mol O}}{16.00 \text{ g O}} = 2.50 \text{ mol O}$

$\dfrac{4.50 \text{ mol C}}{2.50 \text{ mol O}} = \dfrac{1.8 \text{ mol C}}{1 \text{ mol O}} = \dfrac{9 \text{ mol C}}{5 \text{ mol O}}$ $\dfrac{5.95 \text{ mol H}}{2.50 \text{ mol O}} = \dfrac{2.38 \text{ mol H}}{1 \text{ mol O}} = \dfrac{12 \text{ mol H}}{5 \text{ mol O}}$

Answer (d) $C_9H_{12}O_5$ is correct. The other students apparently did not correctly calculate the number of moles of material in 100.0 g or they improperly calculated the ratio of those moles in determining their empirical formula.

3.114 $0.832 \text{ g} - 0.739 \text{ g} = 0.093 \text{ g } H_2O$ $0.093 \text{ g } H_2O \cdot \dfrac{1 \text{ mol } H_2O}{18.02 \text{ g } H_2O} = 0.0052 \text{ mol } H_2O$

$0.739 \text{ g } CaCl_2 \cdot \dfrac{1 \text{ mol } CaCl_2}{111.0 \text{ g } CaCl_2} = 0.00666 \text{ mol } CaCl_2$

$\dfrac{0.0052 \text{ mol } H_2O}{0.00666 \text{ mol } CaCl_2} = \dfrac{0.78 \text{ mol } H_2O}{1 \text{ mol } CaCl_2}$

The students should (c) heat the crucible again and then reweigh it.

3.115   (a) $0.199 \text{ g U}_x\text{O}_y - 0.169 \text{ g U} = 0.030 \text{ g O}$

$$0.169 \text{ g U} \cdot \frac{1 \text{ mol U}}{238.0 \text{ g U}} = 7.10 \times 10^{-4} \text{ mol U}$$

$$0.030 \text{ g O} \cdot \frac{1 \text{ mol O}}{16.0 \text{ g O}} = 1.9 \times 10^{-3} \text{ mol O}$$

$$\frac{1.9 \times 10^{-3} \text{ mol O}}{7.10 \times 10^{-4} \text{ mol U}} = \frac{2.68 \text{ mol O}}{1 \text{ mol U}} = \frac{8 \text{ mol O}}{3 \text{ mol U}}$$

The empirical formula is U_3O_8, a mixture of uranium(IV) oxide and uranium(VI) oxide.

$$7.10 \times 10^{-4} \text{ mol U} \cdot \frac{1 \text{ mol U}_3\text{O}_8}{3 \text{ mol U}} = 2.37 \times 10^{-4} \text{ mol U}_3\text{O}_8$$

(b)   The atomic weight of U is 238.029 u, implying that the isotope ^{238}U is the most abundant.

(c) $0.865 \text{ g} - 0.679 \text{ g} = 0.186 \text{ g H}_2\text{O}$ lost upon heating

$$0.186 \text{ g H}_2\text{O} \cdot \frac{1 \text{ mol H}_2\text{O}}{18.02 \text{ g H}_2\text{O}} = 0.0103 \text{ mol H}_2\text{O}$$

$$0.679 \text{ g UO}_2(\text{NO}_3)_2 \cdot \frac{1 \text{ mol UO}_2(\text{NO}_3)_2}{394.0 \text{ g UO}_2(\text{NO}_3)_2} = 0.00172 \text{ mol UO}_2(\text{NO}_3)_2$$

$$\frac{0.0103 \text{ mol H}_2\text{O}}{0.00172 \text{ mol UO}_2(\text{NO}_3)_2} = \frac{6 \text{ mol H}_2\text{O}}{1 \text{ mol UO}_2(\text{NO}_3)_2}$$

The formula of the hydrated compound is $UO_2(NO_3)_2 \cdot 6 \, H_2O$

3.116   According to Coulomb's law, the force of attraction between oppositely charged ions increases with the ion charges and with decreasing ion-ion separation.

3.117   Step 1.   Use cube dimensions to calculate the volume of the cube.

Step 2.   Use cube volume and the density of alum (1.757 g/cm^3) to calculate the mass of alum.

Step 3.   Use mass of alum and the weight percent of aluminum in alum (5.69%) to calculate mass of Al.

Step 4.   Use mass of Al and the molar mass of Al to calculate moles of Al.

Step 5.   Use moles of Al and Avogadro's number to calculate number of Al atoms in the cube.

$$(3 \text{ cm})^3 \cdot \frac{1.757 \text{ g alum}}{1 \text{ cm}^3} \cdot \frac{5.69 \text{ g Al}}{100.00 \text{ g alum}} \cdot \frac{1 \text{ mol Al}}{26.98 \text{ g Al}} \cdot \frac{6.02 \times 10^{23} \text{ atoms Al}}{1 \text{ mol Al}} = 6 \times 10^{22} \text{ atoms Al}$$

3.118   When words are written with the red, hydrated compound, the words are not visible. However, when heated, the hydrated salt loses water to form anhydrous $CoCl_2$, which is deep blue, and the words are visible.

Chapter 4
Chemical Equations and Stoichiometry

INSTRUCTOR'S NOTES

In this chapter the mathematical concepts of chemical substances is expanded from the formulas in the last chapter to chemical equations.   This book always stresses the notion of the *stoichiometric factor* in chemical calculations. We constantly remind our students that everything funnels through this step because reactions occur in a ratio of the number of atoms or molecules of one substance to the number of atoms or molecules in another substance, such as 1 to 2 or 3 to 3. But, in the lab, we measure mass, not numbers of moles, so a conversion between these levels must be done.

Students often have difficulties with limiting reagent problems. For this reason we have incorporated a large number of solved examples in the text.   Correctly calculating the two ratios in Step 2 of the procedure is the key to using the method of this book.   The summary table given at the end of each example should help clarify the concept of a limiting reagent.

In percent yield problems some students reverse the identification of actual and theoretical.

Chemical analysis of mixtures and combustion analysis can also be troublesome. For the latter it may be useful to stress that the reason for producing CO_2 and H_2O is to "count" C and H atoms present in the original sample. Of course it is always a good idea to do as many examples as possible.

Chapter 4 requires approximately four lectures.

SUGGESTED DEMONSTRATIONS

1.   Illustrations of Chemical Reactions and Balancing Equations

- Burn sulfur in oxygen.
- Make NO_2 from a penny and concentrated HNO_3.
- Burn magnesium in air.
- Decompose H_2O_2.
- React various metals with HCl or H_2O.
- Wright, S. W. "A Method for Generating Oxygen from Consumer Chemicals," *Journal of Chemical Education* **2003**, *80*, 1158.
- Keiter, R. L.; Gamage, C. P. "Combustion of White Phosphorous," *Journal of Chemical Education* **2001**, *78*, 908.
- Senkbeil, E. G. "Combustion Demonstration Using Updated Flame Tornado," *Journal of Chemical Education* **2000**, *77*, 1449.

2. Stoichiometry

    • As an introduction to stoichiometry we have used the decomposition of ammonium nitrate:

$$NH_4NO_3(s) \rightarrow N_2O(g) + 2\ H_2O(g)$$

    This reaction is part of suggested demonstration found in Shakhashiri (Volume 1, page 51). The overall

    reaction is spectacular. However, one of the reaction products (ZnO) is irritating, so the reaction must be

    done in a very well ventilated room.

    • The reaction of Mg ribbon with O_2

$$2\ Mg(s) + O_2(g) \rightarrow 2\ MgO(s)$$

    is also useful as a demonstration reaction that can be tied to an example of a simple stoichiometry reaction.

    • A good classroom example for stoichiometry is the decomposition of H_2O_2:

$$2\ H_2O_2(\ell) \rightarrow 2\ H_2O(g) + O_2(g)$$

    We use it to power a small "rocket" made as in the following illustration.

THE HYDROGEN PEROXIDE ROCKET

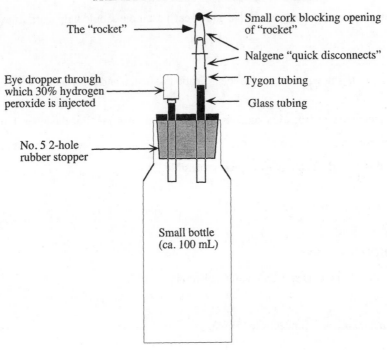

A small quantity of MnO_2 (1-2 g) is placed in the bottle as a catalyst. (We use a 100-mL bottle and find it

helps if the bottle is damp.) The top is placed in the bottle, and an eye dropper containing 30% H_2O_2 is

placed in the open hole of the 2-hole stopper. All of the H_2O_2 in the dropper is squirted into the bottle. The

decomposition reaction is rapid and exothermic, and the steam and O_2 generated provide the thrust for the

plastic "rocket." Under the right conditions the "rocket" will fly about 20-30 feet. (CAUTION: Wear

rubber gloves when handling the H_2O_2 and wash the residue down the drain with a large amount of water.)

The H_2O_2 rocket has proved to be a very useful lecture demonstration. Not only do the students enjoy it, but

it can be used to illustrate a redox reaction (Chapter 5), the concept of an exothermic reaction (Chapter 6),

and catalysis (Chapter 15).

3. Limiting Reactants

- One useful demonstration to use when discussing a limiting reagent situation is the production of H_2 from Ca in water.

$$Ca(s) + 2\ H_2O(\ell) \rightarrow Ca(OH)_2(s) + H_2(g)$$

This reaction is a good demonstration because both products are visible: bubbles of H_2 and solid $Ca(OH)_2$.

- Add a deficiency, a stoichiometric amount, and an excess of magnesium to three beakers of HCl on an overhead projector to demonstrate limiting reagents.

- Kashmar, R. J. "The Use of Cut-Out Molecular Models on the Overhead Projector to Illustrate Stoichiometry and Limiting Reagents," *Journal of Chemical Education*, **1997**, *74*, 791.

SOLUTIONS TO STUDY QUESTIONS

4.1 $C_5H_{12}(\ell) + 8\ O_2(g) \rightarrow 5\ CO_2(g) + 6\ H_2O(g)$

4.2 $N_2(g) + 3\ H_2(g) \rightarrow 2\ NH_3(g)$

4.3   (a) $4\ Cr(s) + 3\ O_2(g) \rightarrow 2\ Cr_2O_3(s)$

        (b) $Cu_2S(s) + O_2(g) \rightarrow 2\ Cu(s) + SO_2(g)$

        (c) $C_6H_5CH_3(\ell) + 9\ O_2(g) \rightarrow 4\ H_2O(\ell) + 7\ CO_2(g)$

4.4   (a) $2\ Cr(s) + 3\ Cl_2(g) \rightarrow 2\ CrCl_3(s)$

        (b) $SiO_2(s) + 2\ C(s) \rightarrow Si(s) + 2\ CO(g)$

        (c) $3\ Fe(s) + 4\ H_2O(g) \rightarrow Fe_3O_4(s) + 4\ H_2(g)$

4.5   (a) $Fe_2O_3(s) + 3\ Mg(s) \rightarrow 3\ MgO(s) + 2\ Fe(s)$

             iron(II) oxide, magnesium, magnesium oxide, iron

        (b) $AlCl_3(s) + 3\ NaOH(aq) \rightarrow Al(OH)_3(s) + 3\ NaCl(aq)$

             aluminum chloride, sodium hydroxide, aluminum hydroxide, sodium chloride

        (c) $2\ NaNO_3(s) + H_2SO_4(\ell) \rightarrow Na_2SO_4(s) + 2\ HNO_3(\ell)$

             sodium nitrate, hydrogen sulfate (sulfuric acid), sodium sulfate, hydrogen nitrate (nitric acid)

        (d) $NiCO_3(s) + 2\ HNO_3(aq) \rightarrow Ni(NO_3)_2(aq) + CO_2(g) + H_2O(\ell)$

             nickel(II) carbonate, hydrogen nitrate (nitric acid), nickel(II) nitrate, carbon dioxide, water

4.6   (a) $SF_4(g) + 2\ H_2O(\ell) \rightarrow SO_2(g) + 4\ HF(\ell)$

             sulfur tetrafluoride, water, sulfur dioxide, hydrogen fluoride

        (b) $4\ NH_3(aq) + 5\ O_2(g) \rightarrow 4\ NO(g) + 6\ H_2O(\ell)$

             ammonia, oxygen, nitrogen monoxide, water

        (c) $BF_3(g) + 3\ H_2O(\ell) \rightarrow 3\ HF(aq) + H_3BO_3(\ell)$

             boron trifluoride, water, hydrogen fluoride, hydrogen borate (boric acid)

4.7 $6.0\ \text{mol Al} \cdot \dfrac{3\ \text{mol O}_2}{4\ \text{mol Al}} = 4.5\ \text{mol O}_2$

        $6.0\ \text{mol Al} \cdot \dfrac{2\ \text{mol Al}_2\text{O}_3}{4\ \text{mol Al}} \cdot \dfrac{102\ \text{g}}{1\ \text{mol Al}_2\text{O}_3} = 310\ \text{g Al}_2\text{O}_3$

4.8 $0.750\ \text{g Al(OH)}_3 \cdot \dfrac{1\ \text{mol Al(OH)}_3}{78.00\ \text{g}} \cdot \dfrac{3\ \text{mol HCl}}{1\ \text{mol Al(OH)}_3} \cdot \dfrac{36.46\ \text{g}}{1\ \text{mol HCl}} = 1.05\ \text{g HCl}$

        $0.750\ \text{g Al(OH)}_3 \cdot \dfrac{1\ \text{mol Al(OH)}_3}{78.00\ \text{g}} \cdot \dfrac{3\ \text{mol H}_2\text{O}}{1\ \text{mol Al(OH)}_3} \cdot \dfrac{18.02\ \text{g}}{1\ \text{mol H}_2\text{O}} = 0.520\ \text{g H}_2\text{O}$

4.9 $2.56 \text{ g Al} \cdot \dfrac{1 \text{ mol Al}}{26.98 \text{ g}} \cdot \dfrac{3 \text{ mol Br}_2}{2 \text{ mol Al}} \cdot \dfrac{159.8 \text{ g}}{1 \text{ mol Br}_2} = 22.7 \text{ g Br}_2$

$2.56 \text{ g Al} + 22.7 \text{ g Br}_2 = 25.3 \text{ g Al}_2\text{Br}_6$

4.10   (a) $454 \text{ g Fe}_2\text{O}_3 \cdot \dfrac{1 \text{ mol Fe}_2\text{O}_3}{159.7 \text{ g}} \cdot \dfrac{2 \text{ mol Fe}}{1 \text{ mol Fe}_2\text{O}_3} \cdot \dfrac{55.85 \text{ g}}{1 \text{ mol Fe}} = 318 \text{ g Fe}$

       (b) $454 \text{ g Fe}_2\text{O}_3 \cdot \dfrac{1 \text{ mol Fe}_2\text{O}_3}{159.7 \text{ g}} \cdot \dfrac{3 \text{ mol CO}}{1 \text{ mol Fe}_2\text{O}_3} \cdot \dfrac{28.01 \text{ g}}{1 \text{ mol CO}} = 239 \text{ g CO}$

4.11   (a) $4 \text{ Fe(s)} + 3 \text{ O}_2\text{(g)} \rightarrow 2 \text{ Fe}_2\text{O}_3\text{(s)}$

       (b) $2.68 \text{ g Fe} \cdot \dfrac{1 \text{ mol Fe}}{55.85 \text{ g}} \cdot \dfrac{2 \text{ mol Fe}_2\text{O}_3}{4 \text{ mol Fe}} \cdot \dfrac{159.7 \text{ g}}{1 \text{ mol Fe}_2\text{O}_3} = 3.83 \text{ g Fe}_2\text{O}_3$

       (c) $3.83 \text{ g Fe}_2\text{O}_3 - 2.68 \text{ g Fe} = 1.15 \text{ g O}_2$

4.12   (a) CO_2, carbon dioxide, and H_2O, water

       (b) $CH_4\text{(g)} + 2 \text{ O}_2\text{(g)} \rightarrow CO_2\text{(g)} + 2 \text{ H}_2\text{O(g)}$

       (c) $25.5 \text{ g CH}_4 \cdot \dfrac{1 \text{ mol CH}_4}{16.04 \text{ g}} \cdot \dfrac{2 \text{ mol O}_2}{1 \text{ mol CH}_4} \cdot \dfrac{32.00 \text{ g}}{1 \text{ mol O}_2} = 102 \text{ g O}_2$

       (d) $25.5 \text{ g CH}_4 + 102 \text{ g O}_2 = 128 \text{ g reactants} = 128 \text{ g products}$

4.13   (a) $155 \text{ g SO}_2 \cdot \dfrac{1 \text{ mol SO}_2}{64.06 \text{ g}} \cdot \dfrac{2 \text{ mol CaCO}_3}{2 \text{ mol SO}_2} \cdot \dfrac{100.1 \text{ g}}{1 \text{ mol CaCO}_3} = 242 \text{ g CaCO}_3$

       (b) $155 \text{ g SO}_2 \cdot \dfrac{1 \text{ mol SO}_2}{64.06 \text{ g}} \cdot \dfrac{2 \text{ mol CaSO}_4}{2 \text{ mol SO}_2} \cdot \dfrac{136.1 \text{ g}}{1 \text{ mol CaSO}_4} = 329 \text{ g CaSO}_4$

4.14   (a) $BaCl_2\text{(aq)} + 2 \text{ AgNO}_3\text{(aq)} \rightarrow 2 \text{ AgCl(s)} + \text{Ba(NO}_3)_2\text{(aq)}$

       (b) $0.156 \text{ g BaCl}_2 \cdot \dfrac{1 \text{ mol BaCl}_2}{208.2 \text{ g}} \cdot \dfrac{2 \text{ mol AgNO}_3}{1 \text{ mol BaCl}_2} \cdot \dfrac{169.9 \text{ g}}{1 \text{ mol AgNO}_3} = 0.255 \text{ g AgNO}_3$

            $0.156 \text{ g BaCl}_2 \cdot \dfrac{1 \text{ mol BaCl}_2}{208.2 \text{ g}} \cdot \dfrac{2 \text{ mol AgCl}}{1 \text{ mol BaCl}_2} \cdot \dfrac{143.3 \text{ g}}{1 \text{ mol AgCl}} = 0.215 \text{ g AgCl}$

4.15 $2.5 \text{ mol PbS} \cdot \dfrac{3 \text{ mol O}_2}{2 \text{ mol PbS}} = 3.8 \text{ mol O}_2$

       $2.5 \text{ mol PbS} \cdot \dfrac{2 \text{ mol PbO}}{2 \text{ mol PbS}} = 2.5 \text{ mol PbO}$ $2.5 \text{ mol PbS} \cdot \dfrac{2 \text{ mol SO}_2}{2 \text{ mol PbS}} = 2.5 \text{ mol SO}_2$

Equation	2 PbS(s)	$+$ $3 \text{ O}_2\text{(g)}$	$\rightarrow$ 2 PbO(s)	$+$ $2 \text{ SO}_2\text{(g)}$
Initial amount (mol)	2.5	3.8	0	0
Change (mol)	−2.5	−3.8	+2.5	+2.5
Amount after reaction (mol)	0	0	2.5	2.5

4.16 $6.2 \text{ mol Fe}_2\text{O}_3 \cdot \dfrac{3 \text{ mol C}}{2 \text{ mol Fe}_2\text{O}_3} = 9.3 \text{ mol C}$

$6.2 \text{ mol Fe}_2\text{O}_3 \cdot \dfrac{4 \text{ mol Fe}}{2 \text{ mol Fe}_2\text{O}_3} = 12 \text{ mol Fe}$ $6.2 \text{ mol Fe}_2\text{O}_3 \cdot \dfrac{3 \text{ mol CO}_2}{2 \text{ mol Fe}_2\text{O}_3} = 9.3 \text{ mol CO}_2$

Equation	$2 \text{ Fe}_2\text{O}_3(s)$ +	$3 \text{ C}(s)$ →	$4 \text{ Fe}(s)$ +	$3 \text{ CO}_2(g)$
Initial amount (mol)	6.2	9.3	0	0
Change (mol)	–6.2	–9.3	+12	+9.3
Amount after reaction (mol)	0	0	12	9.3

4.17   (a) $4 \text{ Cr}(s) + 3 \text{ O}_2(g) \rightarrow 2 \text{ Cr}_2\text{O}_3(s)$

(b) $0.175 \text{ g Cr} \cdot \dfrac{1 \text{ mol Cr}}{52.00 \text{ g}} \cdot \dfrac{2 \text{ mol Cr}_2\text{O}_3}{4 \text{ mol Cr}} \cdot \dfrac{152.0 \text{ g}}{1 \text{ mol Cr}_2\text{O}_3} = 0.256 \text{ g Cr}_2\text{O}_3$

(c) $0.256 \text{ g Cr}_2\text{O}_3 - 0.175 \text{ g Cr} = 0.081 \text{ g O}_2$

Equation	$4 \text{ Cr}(s)$ +	$3 \text{ O}_2(g)$ →	$2 \text{ Cr}_2\text{O}_3(s)$
Initial amount (mol)	0.00337	0.00253	0
Change (mol)	–0.00337	–0.00253	+0.00168
Amount after reaction (mol)	0	0	0.00168

4.18   (a) CO_2, carbon dioxide, and H_2O, water

(b) $2 \text{ C}_2\text{H}_6(g) + 7 \text{ O}_2(g) \rightarrow 4 \text{ CO}_2(g) + 6 \text{ H}_2\text{O}(g)$

(c) $13.6 \text{ g C}_2\text{H}_6 \cdot \dfrac{1 \text{ mol C}_2\text{H}_6}{30.07 \text{ g}} \cdot \dfrac{7 \text{ mol O}_2}{2 \text{ mol C}_2\text{H}_6} \cdot \dfrac{32.00 \text{ g}}{1 \text{ mol O}_2} = 50.7 \text{ g O}_2$

(d) $13.6 \text{ g C}_2\text{H}_6 + 50.7 \text{ g O}_2 = 64.3 \text{ g reactants} = 64.3 \text{ g products}$

Equation	$2 \text{ C}_2\text{H}_6(g)$ +	$7 \text{ O}_2(g)$ →	$4 \text{ CO}_2(g)$ +	$6 \text{ H}_2\text{O}(g)$
Initial amount (mol)	0.452	1.58	0	0
Change (mol)	–0.452	–1.58	+0.904	+1.36
Amount after reaction (mol)	0	0	0.904	1.36

4.19 $15 \text{ g Na}_2\text{SO}_4 \cdot \dfrac{1 \text{ mol Na}_2\text{SO}_4}{142.0 \text{ g}} = 0.11 \text{ mol Na}_2\text{SO}_4$ $7.5 \text{ g C} \cdot \dfrac{1 \text{ mol C}}{12.0 \text{ g}} = 0.63 \text{ mol C}$

$\dfrac{0.63 \text{ mol C}}{0.11 \text{ mol Na}_2\text{SO}_4} = \dfrac{5.7 \text{ mol C}}{1 \text{ mol Na}_2\text{SO}_4} > \dfrac{4 \text{ mol C}}{1 \text{ mol Na}_2\text{SO}_4}$ Na_2SO_4 is the limiting reactant

$15 \text{ g Na}_2\text{SO}_4 \cdot \dfrac{1 \text{ mol Na}_2\text{SO}_4}{142.0 \text{ g}} \cdot \dfrac{1 \text{ mol Na}_2\text{S}}{1 \text{ mol Na}_2\text{SO}_4} \cdot \dfrac{78.0 \text{ g}}{1 \text{ mol Na}_2\text{S}} = 8.2 \text{ g Na}_2\text{S}$

Equation	$\text{Na}_2\text{SO}_4(aq)$	$+ \;\; 4\,\text{C}(s)$	$\rightarrow$	$\text{Na}_2\text{S}(aq)$	$+ \;\; 4\,\text{CO}(g)$
Initial amount (mol)	0.11	0.63		0	0
Change (mol)	−0.11	−0.44		+0.11	+0.11
Amount after reaction (mol)	0	0.19		0.11	0.44

4.20 $112 \text{ g CaO} \cdot \dfrac{1 \text{ mol CaO}}{56.08 \text{ g}} = 2.00 \text{ mol CaO}$ $224 \text{ g NH}_4\text{Cl} \cdot \dfrac{1 \text{ mol NH}_4\text{Cl}}{53.49 \text{ g}} = 4.19 \text{ mol NH}_4\text{Cl}$

$\dfrac{4.19 \text{ mol NH}_4\text{Cl}}{2.00 \text{ mol CaO}} = \dfrac{2.10 \text{ mol NH}_4\text{Cl}}{1 \text{ mol CaO}} > \dfrac{2 \text{ mol NH}_4\text{Cl}}{1 \text{ mol CaO}}$ CaO is the limiting reactant

$112 \text{ g CaO} \cdot \dfrac{1 \text{ mol CaO}}{56.08 \text{ g}} \cdot \dfrac{2 \text{ mol NH}_3}{1 \text{ mol CaO}} \cdot \dfrac{17.03 \text{ g}}{1 \text{ mol NH}_3} = 68.0 \text{ g NH}_3$

Equation	$\text{CaO}(s)$	$+ \; 2\,\text{NH}_4\text{Cl}(s)$	$\rightarrow$	$2\,\text{NH}_3(g)$	$+ \; \text{H}_2\text{O}(g)$	$+ \; \text{CaCl}_2(s)$
Initial amount (mol)	2.00	4.19		0	0	0
Change (mol)	−2.00	−4.00		+4.00	+2.00	+2.00
Amount after reaction (mol)	0	0.19		4.00	2.00	2.00

4.21 $\dfrac{35 \text{ mol F}_2}{1.6 \text{ mol S}_8} = \dfrac{22 \text{ mol F}_2}{1 \text{ mol S}_8}$ The required mole ratio is 24 mol F_2 to 1 mol S_8. Less F_2 is available

than required, so F_2 is the limiting reactant.

Equation	$\text{S}_8(s)$	$+ \; 24\,\text{F}_2(g)$	$\rightarrow$	$8\,\text{SF}_6(g)$
Initial amount (mol)	1.6	35		0
Change (mol)	−1.5	−35		+12
Amount after reaction (mol)	0.1	0		12

4.22 $32.0 \text{ g S}_8 \cdot \dfrac{1 \text{ mol S}_8}{256.5 \text{ g}} = 0.125 \text{ mol S}_8$ $71.0 \text{ g Cl}_2 \cdot \dfrac{1 \text{ mol Cl}_2}{70.91 \text{ g}} = 1.00 \text{ mol Cl}_2$

$\dfrac{1.00 \text{ mol Cl}_2}{0.125 \text{ mol S}_8} = \dfrac{8.00 \text{ mol Cl}_2}{1 \text{ mol S}_8} > \dfrac{4 \text{ mol Cl}_2}{1 \text{ mol S}_8}$ S_8 is the limiting reactant

Equation	$\text{S}_8(\ell)$	$+ \; 4\,\text{Cl}_2(g)$	$\rightarrow$	$4\,\text{S}_2\text{Cl}_2(\ell)$
Initial amount (mol)	0.125	1.00		0
Change (mol)	−0.125	−0.500		+0.500
Amount after reaction (mol)	0	0.50		0.500

4.23 (a) $995 \text{ g CH}_4 \cdot \dfrac{1 \text{ mol CH}_4}{16.04 \text{ g}} = 62.0 \text{ mol CH}_4$ $\qquad$ $2510 \text{ g H}_2\text{O} \cdot \dfrac{1 \text{ mol H}_2\text{O}}{18.02 \text{ g}} = 139 \text{ mol H}_2\text{O}$

$\dfrac{139 \text{ mol H}_2\text{O}}{62.0 \text{ mol CH}_4} = \dfrac{2.24 \text{ mol H}_2\text{O}}{1 \text{ mol CH}_4} > \dfrac{1 \text{ mol H}_2\text{O}}{1 \text{ mol CH}_4}$ $\qquad$ CH_4 is the limiting reactant

(b) $62.0 \text{ mol CH}_4 \cdot \dfrac{3 \text{ mol H}_2}{1 \text{ mol CH}_4} \cdot \dfrac{2.016 \text{ g}}{1 \text{ mol H}_2} = 375 \text{ g H}_2$

(c) CH_4 and H_2O react in a 1:1 mole ratio.

139 mol H_2O available − 62.0 mol H_2O used = 77 mol H_2O remains

$77 \text{ mol H}_2\text{O} \cdot \dfrac{18.0 \text{ g}}{1 \text{ mol H}_2\text{O}} = 1400 \text{ g H}_2\text{O}$

Equation	$CH_4(g) + H_2O(g) \rightarrow CO(g) + 3 \, H_2(g)$			
Initial amount (mol)	62.0	139	0	0
Change (mol)	−62.0	−62.0	+62.0	+186
Amount after reaction (mol)	0	77	62.0	186

4.24 (a) $2.70 \text{ g Al} \cdot \dfrac{1 \text{ mol Al}}{26.98 \text{ g}} = 0.100 \text{ mol Al}$ $\qquad$ $4.06 \text{ g Cl}_2 \cdot \dfrac{1 \text{ mol Cl}_2}{70.91 \text{ g}} = 0.0573 \text{ mol Cl}_2$

$\dfrac{0.100 \text{ mol Al}}{0.0573 \text{ mol Cl}_2} = \dfrac{1.75 \text{ mol Al}}{1 \text{ mol Cl}_2}$ $\qquad$ The required mole ratio is 2 mol Al to 3 mol Cl_2. More Al is

available than required, so Cl_2 is the limiting reactant.

(b) $0.0573 \text{ mol Cl}_2 \cdot \dfrac{2 \text{ mol AlCl}_3}{3 \text{ mol Cl}_2} \cdot \dfrac{133.3 \text{ g}}{1 \text{ mol AlCl}_3} = 5.09 \text{ g AlCl}_3$

(c) $0.0573 \text{ mol Cl}_2 \cdot \dfrac{2 \text{ mol Al}}{3 \text{ mol Cl}_2} \cdot \dfrac{26.98 \text{ g}}{1 \text{ mol Al}} = 1.03 \text{ g Al used}$

2.70 g Al available − 1.03 g Al used = 1.67 g Al remains

Equation	$2 \, Al(s) \quad + \quad 3 \, Cl_2(g) \quad \rightarrow \quad 2 \, AlCl_3(s)$		
Initial amount (mol)	0.100	0.0573	0
Change (mol)	−0.0382	−0.0573	+0.0382
Amount after reaction (mol)	0.062	0	0.0382

4.25 (a) $2 \, C_6H_{14}(\ell) + 19 \, O_2(g) \rightarrow 12 \, CO_2(g) + 14 \, H_2O(g)$

(b) $215 \text{ g C}_6\text{H}_{14} \cdot \dfrac{1 \text{ mol C}_6\text{H}_{14}}{86.18 \text{ g}} = 2.49 \text{ mol C}_6\text{H}_{14}$ $\qquad$ $215 \text{ g O}_2 \cdot \dfrac{1 \text{ mol O}_2}{32.00 \text{ g}} = 6.72 \text{ mol O}_2$

$\dfrac{6.72 \text{ mol O}_2}{2.49 \text{ mol C}_6\text{H}_{14}} = \dfrac{2.70 \text{ mol O}_2}{1 \text{ mol C}_6\text{H}_{14}} < \dfrac{19 \text{ mol O}_2}{2 \text{ mol C}_6\text{H}_{14}}$ $\qquad$ O_2 is the limiting reactant

$6.72 \text{ mol O}_2 \cdot \dfrac{12 \text{ mol CO}_2}{19 \text{ mol O}_2} \cdot \dfrac{44.01 \text{ g}}{1 \text{ mol CO}_2} = 187 \text{ g CO}_2$

$6.72 \text{ mol O}_2 \cdot \dfrac{14 \text{ mol H}_2\text{O}}{19 \text{ mol O}_2} \cdot \dfrac{18.02 \text{ g}}{1 \text{ mol H}_2\text{O}} = 89.2 \text{ g H}_2\text{O}$

(c) $6.72 \text{ mol O}_2 \cdot \dfrac{2 \text{ mol C}_6\text{H}_{14}}{19 \text{ mol O}_2} \cdot \dfrac{86.18 \text{ g}}{1 \text{ mol C}_6\text{H}_{14}} = 60.9 \text{ g C}_6\text{H}_{14}$ used

215 g C_6H_{14} available – 60.9 g C_6H_{14} used = 154 g C_6H_{14} remains

Equation	$2 \text{ C}_6\text{H}_{14}(\ell) + 19 \text{ O}_2(g) \rightarrow 12 \text{ CO}_2(g) + 14 \text{ H}_2\text{O}(g)$			
Initial amount (mol)	2.49	6.72	0	0
Change (mol)	–0.707	–6.72	+4.24	+4.95
Amount after reaction (mol)	1.78	0	4.24	4.95

4.26 $100. \text{ g C}_7\text{H}_6\text{O}_3 \cdot \dfrac{1 \text{ mol C}_7\text{H}_6\text{O}_3}{138.1 \text{ g}} \cdot \dfrac{1 \text{ mol C}_9\text{H}_8\text{O}_4}{1 \text{ mol C}_7\text{H}_6\text{O}_3} \cdot \dfrac{180.2 \text{ g}}{1 \text{ mol C}_9\text{H}_8\text{O}_4} = 130. \text{ g aspirin}$

$100. \text{ g C}_4\text{H}_6\text{O}_3 \cdot \dfrac{1 \text{ mol C}_4\text{H}_6\text{O}_3}{102.1 \text{ g}} \cdot \dfrac{1 \text{ mol C}_9\text{H}_8\text{O}_4}{1 \text{ mol C}_4\text{H}_6\text{O}_3} \cdot \dfrac{180.2 \text{ g}}{1 \text{ mol C}_9\text{H}_8\text{O}_4} = 176 \text{ g aspirin}$

The maximum amount that can be produced is 130. g aspirin.

Equation	$C_6H_4(OH)CO_2H \text{ (s)} + (CH_3CO)_2O(\ell) \rightarrow C_6H_4(OCOCH_3)CO_2H(s) + CH_3CO_2H(\ell)$			
Initial amount (mol)	0.724	0.979	0	0
Change (mol)	–0.724	–0.724	+0.724	+0.724
Amount after reaction (mol)	0	0.255	0.724	0.724

4.27 $\dfrac{332 \text{ g}}{407 \text{ g}} \cdot 100\% = 81.6\%$ yield

4.28 $\dfrac{16.3 \text{ g}}{68.0 \text{ g}} \cdot 100\% = 24.0\%$ yield

4.29   (a) $10.0 \text{ g CuSO}_4 \cdot \dfrac{1 \text{ mol CuSO}_4}{159.6 \text{ g}} \cdot \dfrac{1 \text{ mol Cu(NH}_3)_4\text{SO}_4}{1 \text{ mol CuSO}_4} \cdot \dfrac{227.7 \text{ g}}{1 \text{ mol Cu(NH}_3)_4\text{SO}_4} = 14.3 \text{ g Cu(NH}_3)_4\text{SO}_4$

(b) $\dfrac{12.6 \text{ g}}{14.3 \text{ g}} \cdot 100\% = 88.3\%$ yield

4.30   (a) $10.0 \text{ g CH}_3\text{SH} \cdot \dfrac{1 \text{ mol CH}_3\text{SH}}{48.11 \text{ g}} \cdot \dfrac{1 \text{ mol CH}_3\text{COSCH}_3}{2 \text{ mol CH}_3\text{SH}} \cdot \dfrac{90.15 \text{ g}}{1 \text{ mol CH}_3\text{COSCH}_3} = 9.37 \text{ g CH}_3\text{COSCH}_3$

(b) $\dfrac{8.65 \text{ g}}{9.37 \text{ g}} \cdot 100\% = 92.3\%$ yield

4.31   1.245 g mixture – 0.832 g after heating = 0.413 g H_2O lost

$0.413 \text{ g H}_2\text{O} \cdot \dfrac{1 \text{ mol H}_2\text{O}}{18.02 \text{ g}} \cdot \dfrac{1 \text{ mol CuSO}_4 \cdot 5 \text{ H}_2\text{O}}{5 \text{ mol H}_2\text{O}} \cdot \dfrac{249.7 \text{ g}}{1 \text{ mol CuSO}_4 \cdot 5 \text{ H}_2\text{O}} = 1.14 \text{ g CuSO}_4 \cdot 5 \text{ H}_2\text{O}$

$\dfrac{1.14 \text{ g CuSO}_4 \cdot 5 \text{ H}_2\text{O}}{1.245 \text{ g mixture}} \cdot 100\% = 91.9\% \text{ CuSO}_4 \cdot 5 \text{ H}_2\text{O}$

4.32   2.634 g mixture − 2.125 g after heating = 0.509 g H_2O lost

$$0.509 \text{ g } H_2O \cdot \frac{1 \text{ mol } H_2O}{18.02 \text{ g}} \cdot \frac{1 \text{ mol } CuCl_2 \cdot 2 H_2O}{2 \text{ mol } H_2O} \cdot \frac{170.5 \text{ g}}{1 \text{ mol } CuCl_2 \cdot 2 H_2O} = 2.41 \text{ g } CuCl_2 \cdot 2 H_2O$$

$$\frac{2.41 \text{ g } CuCl_2 \cdot 2 H_2O}{2.634 \text{ g mixture}} \cdot 100\% = 91.4\% \text{ } CuCl_2 \cdot 2 H_2O$$

4.33 $$0.558 \text{ g } CO_2 \cdot \frac{1 \text{ mol } CO_2}{44.01 \text{ g}} \cdot \frac{1 \text{ mol } CaCO_3}{1 \text{ mol } CO_2} \cdot \frac{100.1 \text{ g}}{1 \text{ mol } CaCO_3} = 1.27 \text{ g } CaCO_3$$

$$\frac{1.27 \text{ g}}{1.506 \text{ g}} \cdot 100\% = 84.3\% \text{ } CaCO_3$$

4.34 $$0.196 \text{ g } CO_2 \cdot \frac{1 \text{ mol } CO_2}{44.01 \text{ g}} \cdot \frac{2 \text{ mol } NaHCO_3}{1 \text{ mol } CO_2} \cdot \frac{84.01 \text{ g}}{1 \text{ mol } NaHCO_3} = 0.748 \text{ g } NaHCO_3$$

$$\frac{0.748 \text{ g}}{1.7184 \text{ g}} \cdot 100\% = 43.5\% \text{ } NaHCO_3$$

4.35 $$0.1964 \text{ g } TlI \cdot \frac{1 \text{ mol } TlI}{331.29 \text{ g}} \cdot \frac{1 \text{ mol } Tl_2SO_4}{2 \text{ mol } TlI} \cdot \frac{504.83 \text{ g}}{1 \text{ mol } Tl_2SO_4} = 0.1496 \text{ g } Tl_2SO_4$$

$$\frac{0.1496 \text{ g}}{10.20 \text{ g}} \cdot 100\% = 1.467\% \text{ } Tl_2SO_4$$

4.36 $$0.127 \text{ g } Al_2O_3 \cdot \frac{1 \text{ mol } Al_2O_3}{102.0 \text{ g}} \cdot \frac{2 \text{ mol } Al}{1 \text{ mol } Al_2O_3} \cdot \frac{26.98 \text{ g}}{1 \text{ mol } Al} = 0.0672 \text{ g } Al$$

$$\frac{0.0672 \text{ g}}{0.764 \text{ g}} \cdot 100\% = 8.79\% \text{ } Al$$

4.37 $$1.481 \text{ g } CO_2 \cdot \frac{1 \text{ mol } CO_2}{44.010 \text{ g}} \cdot \frac{1 \text{ mol } C}{1 \text{ mol } CO_2} = 0.03365 \text{ mol } C$$

$$0.303 \text{ g } H_2O \cdot \frac{1 \text{ mol } H_2O}{18.02 \text{ g}} \cdot \frac{2 \text{ mol } H}{1 \text{ mol } H_2O} = 0.0336 \text{ mol } H$$

$$\frac{0.03365 \text{ mol } C}{0.0336 \text{ mol } H} = \frac{1 \text{ mol } C}{1 \text{ mol } H} \qquad \text{The empirical formula is CH}$$

4.38 $$0.379 \text{ g } CO_2 \cdot \frac{1 \text{ mol } CO_2}{44.01 \text{ g}} \cdot \frac{1 \text{ mol } C}{1 \text{ mol } CO_2} = 0.00861 \text{ mol } C$$

$$0.1035 \text{ g } H_2O \cdot \frac{1 \text{ mol } H_2O}{18.015 \text{ g}} \cdot \frac{2 \text{ mol } H}{1 \text{ mol } H_2O} = 0.01149 \text{ mol } H$$

$$\frac{0.01149 \text{ mol } H}{0.00861 \text{ mol } C} = \frac{1.33 \text{ mol } H}{1 \text{ mol } C} = \frac{4/3 \text{ mol } H}{1 \text{ mol } C} = \frac{4 \text{ mol } H}{3 \text{ mol } C}$$

The empirical formula is C_3H_4

4.39   (a) $0.300 \text{ g CO}_2 \cdot \dfrac{1 \text{ mol CO}_2}{44.01 \text{ g}} \cdot \dfrac{1 \text{ mol C}}{1 \text{ mol CO}_2} = 0.00682 \text{ mol C}$

$0.123 \text{ g H}_2\text{O} \cdot \dfrac{1 \text{ mol H}_2\text{O}}{18.02 \text{ g}} \cdot \dfrac{2 \text{ mol H}}{1 \text{ mol H}_2\text{O}} = 0.0137 \text{ mol H}$

$\dfrac{0.0137 \text{ mol H}}{0.00682 \text{ mol C}} = \dfrac{2 \text{ mol H}}{1 \text{ mol C}}$

The empirical formula is CH_2

(b) $\dfrac{70.1 \text{ g/mol}}{14.0 \text{ g/mol}} = 5$ The molecular formula is $(CH_2)_5$ or C_5H_{10}

4.40   (a) $0.364 \text{ g CO}_2 \cdot \dfrac{1 \text{ mol CO}_2}{44.01 \text{ g}} \cdot \dfrac{1 \text{ mol C}}{1 \text{ mol CO}_2} = 0.00827 \text{ mol C}$

$0.0596 \text{ g H}_2\text{O} \cdot \dfrac{1 \text{ mol H}_2\text{O}}{18.02 \text{ g}} \cdot \dfrac{2 \text{ mol H}}{1 \text{ mol H}_2\text{O}} = 0.00661 \text{ mol H}$

$\dfrac{0.00827 \text{ mol C}}{0.00661 \text{ mol H}} = \dfrac{1.25 \text{ mol C}}{1 \text{ mol H}} = \dfrac{5/4 \text{ mol C}}{1 \text{ mol H}} = \dfrac{5 \text{ mol C}}{4 \text{ mol H}}$

The empirical formula is C_5H_4

(b) $\dfrac{128.2 \text{ g/mol}}{64.09 \text{ g/mol}} = 2$ The molecular formula is $(C_5H_4)_2$ or $C_{10}H_8$

4.41 $0.1356 \text{ g CO}_2 \cdot \dfrac{1 \text{ mol CO}_2}{44.010 \text{ g}} \cdot \dfrac{1 \text{ mol C}}{1 \text{ mol CO}_2} = 0.003081 \text{ mol C}$

$0.003081 \text{ mol C} \cdot \dfrac{12.011 \text{ g}}{1 \text{ mol C}} = 0.03701 \text{ g C}$

$0.0833 \text{ g H}_2\text{O} \cdot \dfrac{1 \text{ mol H}_2\text{O}}{18.02 \text{ g}} \cdot \dfrac{2 \text{ mol H}}{1 \text{ mol H}_2\text{O}} = 0.00925 \text{ mol H}$

$0.00925 \text{ mol H} \cdot \dfrac{1.008 \text{ g}}{1 \text{ mol H}} = 0.00932 \text{ g H}$

mass of O = sample mass − mass of C − mass of H

= 0.0956 g − 0.03701 g C − 0.00932 g H

= 0.0492 g O

$0.0492 \text{ g O} \cdot \dfrac{1 \text{ mol O}}{15.999 \text{ g}} = 0.00307 \text{ mol O}$

$\dfrac{0.003081 \text{ mol C}}{0.00307 \text{ mol O}} = \dfrac{1 \text{ mol C}}{1 \text{ mol O}}$ $\dfrac{0.00925 \text{ mol H}}{0.00307 \text{ mol O}} = \dfrac{3 \text{ mol H}}{1 \text{ mol O}}$

The empirical formula is CH_3O

$\dfrac{62.1 \text{ g/mol}}{31.0 \text{ g/mol}} = 2$ The molecular formula is $(CH_3O)_2$ or $C_2H_6O_2$

4.42 $0.3718 \text{ g CO}_2 \cdot \dfrac{1 \text{ mol CO}_2}{44.010 \text{ g}} \cdot \dfrac{1 \text{ mol C}}{1 \text{ mol CO}_2} = 0.008448 \text{ mol C}$

$0.008448 \text{ mol C} \cdot \dfrac{12.011 \text{ g}}{1 \text{ mol C}} = 0.1015 \text{ g C}$

$0.1522 \text{ g H}_2\text{O} \cdot \dfrac{1 \text{ mol H}_2\text{O}}{18.015 \text{ g}} \cdot \dfrac{2 \text{ mol H}}{1 \text{ mol H}_2\text{O}} = 0.01690 \text{ mol H}$

$0.01690 \text{ mol H} \cdot \dfrac{1.0079 \text{ g}}{1 \text{ mol H}} = 0.01703 \text{ g H}$

mass of O = sample mass – mass of C – mass of H

$= 0.1523 \text{ g} - 0.1015 \text{ g C} - 0.01703 \text{ g H}$

$= 0.0338 \text{ g O}$

$0.0338 \text{ g O} \cdot \dfrac{1 \text{ mol O}}{16.00 \text{ g}} = 0.00211 \text{ mol O}$

$\dfrac{0.008448 \text{ mol C}}{0.00211 \text{ mol O}} = \dfrac{4 \text{ mol C}}{1 \text{ mol O}}$ $\dfrac{0.01690 \text{ mol H}}{0.00211 \text{ mol O}} = \dfrac{8 \text{ mol H}}{1 \text{ mol O}}$

The empirical formula is C_4H_8O

The empirical formula mass is equal to the molar mass. The molecular formula is also C_4H_8O.

4.43 $0.0426 \text{ g NiO} \cdot \dfrac{1 \text{ mol NiO}}{74.69 \text{ g}} \cdot \dfrac{1 \text{ mol Ni}}{1 \text{ mol NiO}} = 5.70 \times 10^{-4} \text{ mol Ni}$

$0.100 \text{ g CO}_2 \cdot \dfrac{1 \text{ mol CO}_2}{44.01 \text{ g}} \cdot \dfrac{1 \text{ mol CO}}{1 \text{ mol CO}_2} = 2.27 \times 10^{-3} \text{ mol CO}$

$\dfrac{2.27 \times 10^{-3} \text{ mol CO}}{5.70 \times 10^{-4} \text{ mol Ni}} = \dfrac{4 \text{ mol CO}}{1 \text{ mol Ni}}$ The empirical formula is $Ni(CO)_4$

4.44 $0.799 \text{ g Fe}_2\text{O}_3 \cdot \dfrac{1 \text{ mol Fe}_2\text{O}_3}{159.7 \text{ g}} \cdot \dfrac{2 \text{ mol Fe}}{1 \text{ mol Fe}_2\text{O}_3} = 0.0100 \text{ mol Fe}$

$2.200 \text{ g CO}_2 \cdot \dfrac{1 \text{ mol CO}_2}{44.010 \text{ g}} \cdot \dfrac{1 \text{ mol CO}}{1 \text{ mol CO}_2} = 0.04999 \text{ mol CO}$

$\dfrac{0.04999 \text{ mol CO}}{0.0100 \text{ mol Fe}} = \dfrac{5 \text{ mol CO}}{1 \text{ mol Fe}}$ The empirical formula is $Fe(CO)_5$

4.45   (a) $CO_2(g) + 2 \text{ NH}_3(g) \rightarrow \text{NH}_2\text{CONH}_2(s) + H_2O(\ell)$

(b) $UO_2(s) + 4 \text{ HF(aq)} \rightarrow UF_4(s) + 2 \text{ H}_2\text{O}(\ell)$

$UF_4(s) + F_2(g) \rightarrow UF_6(s)$

(c) $TiO_2(s) + 2 \text{ Cl}_2(g) + 2 \text{ C(s)} \rightarrow \text{TiCl}_4(\ell) + 2 \text{ CO(g)}$

$TiCl_4(\ell) + 2 \text{ Mg(s)} \rightarrow \text{Ti(s)} + 2 \text{ MgCl}_2(s)$

4.46   (a) $Ca_3(PO_4)_2(s) + 2\ H_2SO_4(aq) \rightarrow Ca(H_2PO_4)_2(aq) + 2\ CaSO_4(s)$

        (b) $2\ NaBH_4(s) + H_2SO_4(aq) \rightarrow B_2H_6(g) + 2\ H_2(g) + Na_2SO_4(aq)$

        (c) $WO_3(s) + 3\ H_2(g) \rightarrow W(s) + 3\ H_2O(\ell)$

        (d) $(NH_4)_2Cr_2O_7(s) \rightarrow N_2(g) + 4\ H_2O(\ell) + Cr_2O_3(s)$

4.47   (a) CO_2, carbon dioxide, and H_2O, water

        (b) $2\ C_6H_6(\ell) + 15\ O_2(g) \rightarrow 12\ CO_2(g) + 6\ H_2O(\ell)$

        (c) $16.04\ g\ C_6H_6 \cdot \dfrac{1\ mol\ C_6H_6}{78.113\ g} \cdot \dfrac{15\ mol\ O_2}{2\ mol\ C_6H_6} \cdot \dfrac{31.999\ g}{1\ mol\ O_2} = 49.28\ g\ O_2$

        (d) $16.04\ g\ C_6H_6 + 49.28\ g\ O_2 = 65.32\ g$ products

4.48 $C(s) + O_2(g) \rightarrow CO_2(g)$

        If stoichiometric amounts are used, the mass of product (CO_2) is equal to the total mass of reactants:

        Mass $CO_2 = 10.0\ g + 26.6\ g = 36.6\ g\ CO_2$

4.49 $125\ mg\ acetoacetic\ acid \cdot \dfrac{1\ g}{10^3\ mg} \cdot \dfrac{1\ mol\ acetoacetic\ acid}{102.1\ g} \cdot \dfrac{1\ mol\ acetone}{1\ mol\ acetoacetic\ acid} \cdot \dfrac{58.08\ g}{1\ mol\ acetone}$

                                                                                    $= 0.0711\ g\ acetone$

4.50 $95\ mg\ urea \cdot \dfrac{1\ g}{10^3\ mg} \cdot \dfrac{1\ mol\ urea}{60.1\ g} \cdot \dfrac{1\ mol\ arginine}{1\ mol\ urea} \cdot \dfrac{174\ g}{1\ mol\ arginine} = 0.28\ g\ arginine$

        $95\ mg\ urea \cdot \dfrac{1\ g}{10^3\ mg} \cdot \dfrac{1\ mol\ urea}{60.1\ g} \cdot \dfrac{1\ mol\ ornithine}{1\ mol\ urea} \cdot \dfrac{132\ g}{1\ mol\ ornithine} = 0.21\ g\ ornithine$

4.51   (a) $2\ Fe(s) + 3\ Cl_2(g) \rightarrow 2\ FeCl_3(s)$

        (b) $10.0\ g\ Fe \cdot \dfrac{1\ mol\ Fe}{55.85\ g} \cdot \dfrac{3\ mol\ Cl_2}{2\ mol\ Fe} \cdot \dfrac{70.91\ g}{1\ mol\ Cl_2} = 19.0\ g\ Cl_2$

              $10.0\ g\ Fe \cdot \dfrac{1\ mol\ Fe}{55.85\ g} \cdot \dfrac{2\ mol\ FeCl_3}{2\ mol\ Fe} \cdot \dfrac{162.2\ g}{1\ mol\ FeCl_3} = 29.0\ g\ FeCl_3$

        (c) $\dfrac{18.5\ g}{29.0\ g} \cdot 100\% = 63.7\%$ yield

        (d)   10.0 g Fe requires 19.0 g Cl_2 for complete reaction, so chlorine is the limiting reactant if 10.0 g of each reac

              $10.0\ g\ Cl_2 \cdot \dfrac{1\ mol\ Cl_2}{70.91\ g} \cdot \dfrac{2\ mol\ FeCl_3}{3\ mol\ Cl_2} \cdot \dfrac{162.2\ g}{1\ mol\ FeCl_3} = 15.2\ g\ FeCl_3$

4.52   The total mass of the beakers and solutions after reaction is equal to the total mass before the reaction

        (99.3 g) because no gases were produced in the reaction.

4.53   (a) titanium(IV) chloride, water, titanium(IV) oxide, hydrogen chloride

      (b) $14.0 \text{ mL TiCl}_4 \cdot \dfrac{1.73 \text{ g}}{1 \text{ mL}} \cdot \dfrac{1 \text{ mol TiCl}_4}{189.7 \text{ g}} \cdot \dfrac{2 \text{ mol H}_2\text{O}}{1 \text{ mol TiCl}_4} \cdot \dfrac{18.02 \text{ g}}{1 \text{ mol H}_2\text{O}} = 4.60 \text{ g H}_2\text{O}$

      (c) $14.0 \text{ mL TiCl}_4 \cdot \dfrac{1.73 \text{ g}}{1 \text{ mL}} \cdot \dfrac{1 \text{ mol TiCl}_4}{189.7 \text{ g}} \cdot \dfrac{1 \text{ mol TiO}_2}{1 \text{ mol TiCl}_4} \cdot \dfrac{79.87 \text{ g}}{1 \text{ mol TiO}_2} = 10.2 \text{ g TiO}_2$

            $14.0 \text{ mL TiCl}_4 \cdot \dfrac{1.73 \text{ g}}{1 \text{ mL}} \cdot \dfrac{1 \text{ mol TiCl}_4}{189.7 \text{ g}} \cdot \dfrac{4 \text{ mol HCl}}{1 \text{ mol TiCl}_4} \cdot \dfrac{36.46 \text{ g}}{1 \text{ mol HCl}} = 18.6 \text{ g HCl}$

4.54   (a) According to the text (p. 145), O_2 is the limiting reactant.

          $750. \text{ g O}_2 \cdot \dfrac{1 \text{ mol O}_2}{32.00 \text{ g}} \cdot \dfrac{6 \text{ mol H}_2\text{O}}{5 \text{ mol O}_2} \cdot \dfrac{18.02 \text{ g}}{1 \text{ mol H}_2\text{O}} = 507 \text{ g H}_2\text{O}$

      (b) $750. \text{ g NH}_3 \cdot \dfrac{1 \text{ mol NH}_3}{17.03 \text{ g}} \cdot \dfrac{5 \text{ mol O}_2}{4 \text{ mol NH}_3} \cdot \dfrac{32.00 \text{ g}}{1 \text{ mol O}_2} = 1760 \text{ g O}_2$

4.55 $15.0 \text{ g NaNO}_3 \cdot \dfrac{1 \text{ mol NaNO}_3}{84.99 \text{ g}} \cdot \dfrac{1 \text{ mol NaN}_3}{1 \text{ mol NaNO}_3} \cdot \dfrac{65.01 \text{ g}}{1 \text{ mol NaN}_3} = 11.5 \text{ g NaN}_3$

      $15.0 \text{ g NaNH}_2 \cdot \dfrac{1 \text{ mol NaNH}_2}{39.01 \text{ g}} \cdot \dfrac{1 \text{ mol NaN}_3}{3 \text{ mol NaNH}_2} \cdot \dfrac{65.01 \text{ g}}{1 \text{ mol NaN}_3} = 8.33 \text{ g NaN}_3$

The maximum mass that can be produced is 8.33 g NaN_3.

4.56   (a) Sodium iodate, sodium hydrogen sulfite (or sodium bisulfite)

      (b) $1.00 \text{ kg I}_2 \cdot \dfrac{10^3 \text{ g}}{1 \text{ kg}} \cdot \dfrac{1 \text{ mol I}_2}{253.8 \text{ g}} \cdot \dfrac{2 \text{ mol NaIO}_3}{1 \text{ mol I}_2} \cdot \dfrac{197.9 \text{ g}}{1 \text{ mol NaIO}_3} = 1560 \text{ g NaIO}_3$

           $1.00 \text{ kg I}_2 \cdot \dfrac{10^3 \text{ g}}{1 \text{ kg}} \cdot \dfrac{1 \text{ mol I}_2}{253.8 \text{ g}} \cdot \dfrac{5 \text{ mol NaHSO}_3}{1 \text{ mol I}_2} \cdot \dfrac{104.1 \text{ g}}{1 \text{ mol NaHSO}_3} = 2050 \text{ g NaHSO}_3$

4.57   (a) $Cu_2S(s) + O_2(g) \rightarrow 2 \text{ Cu}(s) + SO_2(g)$

      (b) $500. \text{ g Cu}_2\text{S} \cdot \dfrac{1 \text{ mol Cu}_2\text{S}}{159.2 \text{ g}} \cdot \dfrac{2 \text{ mol Cu}}{1 \text{ mol Cu}_2\text{S}} \cdot \dfrac{63.55 \text{ g}}{1 \text{ mol Cu}} = 399 \text{ g Cu}$

4.58 $0.2070 \text{ g BaSO}_4 \cdot \dfrac{1 \text{ mol BaSO}_4}{233.39 \text{ g}} \cdot \dfrac{1 \text{ mol S}}{1 \text{ mol BaSO}_4} \cdot \dfrac{1 \text{ mol saccharin}}{1 \text{ mol S}} \cdot \dfrac{183.19 \text{ g}}{1 \text{ mol saccharin}} = 0.1625 \text{ g saccharin}$

$\dfrac{0.1625 \text{ g}}{0.2140 \text{ g}} \cdot 100\% = 75.92\% \text{ saccharin}$

4.59　　$0.422 \text{ g B}_2\text{O}_3 \cdot \dfrac{1 \text{ mol B}_2\text{O}_3}{69.62 \text{ g}} \cdot \dfrac{2 \text{ mol B}}{1 \text{ mol B}_2\text{O}_3} \cdot \dfrac{10.81 \text{ g}}{1 \text{ mol B}} = 0.131 \text{ g B}$

　　　　　$0.148 \text{ g B}_x\text{H}_y - 0.131 \text{ g B} = 0.017 \text{ g H}$

　　　　　$0.131 \text{ g B} \cdot \dfrac{1 \text{ mol B}}{10.81 \text{ g}} = 0.0121 \text{ mol B}$　　　　　$0.017 \text{ g H} \cdot \dfrac{1 \text{ mol H}}{1.01 \text{ g}} = 0.017 \text{ mol H}$

　　　　　$\dfrac{0.017 \text{ mol H}}{0.0121 \text{ mol B}} = \dfrac{1.4 \text{ mol H}}{1 \text{ mol B}} = \dfrac{7 \text{ mol H}}{5 \text{ mol B}}$　　　　The empirical formula is B_5H_7

4.60　　$11.64 \text{ g SiO}_2 \cdot \dfrac{1 \text{ mol SiO}_2}{60.084 \text{ g}} \cdot \dfrac{1 \text{ mol Si}}{1 \text{ mol SiO}_2} = 0.1937 \text{ mol Si}$

　　　　　$6.980 \text{ g H}_2\text{O} \cdot \dfrac{1 \text{ mol H}_2\text{O}}{18.015 \text{ g}} \cdot \dfrac{2 \text{ mol H}}{1 \text{ mol H}_2\text{O}} = 0.7749 \text{ mol H}$

　　　　　$\dfrac{0.7749 \text{ mol H}}{0.1937 \text{ mol Si}} = \dfrac{4 \text{ mol H}}{1 \text{ mol Si}}$　　　　The empirical formula is SiH_4

4.61　　$269 \text{ mg CO}_2 \cdot \dfrac{1 \text{ g}}{10^3 \text{ mg}} \cdot \dfrac{1 \text{ mol CO}_2}{44.01 \text{ g}} \cdot \dfrac{1 \text{ mol C}}{1 \text{ mol CO}_2} = 0.00611 \text{ mol C}$

　　　　　$0.00611 \text{ mol C} \cdot \dfrac{12.01 \text{ g}}{1 \text{ mol C}} = 0.0734 \text{ g C}$

　　　　　$110 \text{ mg H}_2\text{O} \cdot \dfrac{1 \text{ g}}{10^3 \text{ mg}} \cdot \dfrac{1 \text{ mol H}_2\text{O}}{18.0 \text{ g}} \cdot \dfrac{2 \text{ mol H}}{1 \text{ mol H}_2\text{O}} = 0.012 \text{ mol H}$

　　　　　$0.012 \text{ mol H} \cdot \dfrac{1.01 \text{ g}}{1 \text{ mol H}} = 0.012 \text{ g H}$

　　　　mass of O　　= sample mass – mass of C – mass of H

　　　　　　　　　= $(95.6 \text{ mg} \cdot \dfrac{1 \text{ g}}{10^3 \text{ mg}}) - 0.0734 \text{ g} - 0.012 \text{ g}$

　　　　　　　　　= 0.010 g O

　　　　　$0.010 \text{ g O} \cdot \dfrac{1 \text{ mol O}}{16.0 \text{ g}} = 0.00063 \text{ mol O}$

　　　　　$\dfrac{0.00611 \text{ mol C}}{0.00063 \text{ mol O}} = \dfrac{10 \text{ mol C}}{1 \text{ mol O}}$　　　　　$\dfrac{0.012 \text{ mol H}}{0.00063 \text{ mol O}} \approx \dfrac{20 \text{ mol H}}{1 \text{ mol O}}$

　　　　The empirical formula is $C_{10}H_{20}O$

4.62 $0.257 \text{ g CO}_2 \cdot \dfrac{1 \text{ mol CO}_2}{44.01 \text{ g}} \cdot \dfrac{1 \text{ mol C}}{1 \text{ mol CO}_2} = 0.00584 \text{ mol C}$

$0.00584 \text{ mol C} \cdot \dfrac{12.01 \text{ g}}{1 \text{ mol C}} = 0.0701 \text{ g C}$

$0.0350 \text{ g H}_2\text{O} \cdot \dfrac{1 \text{ mol H}_2\text{O}}{18.02 \text{ g}} \cdot \dfrac{2 \text{ mol H}}{1 \text{ mol H}_2\text{O}} = 0.00388 \text{ mol H}$

$0.00388 \text{ mol H} \cdot \dfrac{1.008 \text{ g}}{1 \text{ mol H}} = 0.00391 \text{ g H}$

mass of O = sample mass – mass of C – mass of H

$= 0.105 \text{ g} - 0.0701 - 0.00391$

$= 0.031 \text{ g O}$

$0.031 \text{ g O} \cdot \dfrac{1 \text{ mol O}}{16.0 \text{ g}} = 0.0019 \text{ mol O}$

$\dfrac{0.00584 \text{ mol C}}{0.0019 \text{ mol O}} = \dfrac{3 \text{ mol C}}{1 \text{ mol O}}$ $\dfrac{0.00388 \text{ mol H}}{0.0019 \text{ mol O}} = \dfrac{2 \text{ mol H}}{1 \text{ mol O}}$

The empirical formula is C_3H_2O

4.63   Answers taken from the Simulation on Screen 4.8:

(a) $FeCl_2 + Na_2S \rightarrow FeS + 2 NaCl$

(b) $FeCl_2$

(c) 27.7 g

(d) 15.4 g Na_2S

(e) 65 g

4.64 $3.00 \text{ kg Cu}_2\text{S} \cdot \dfrac{10^3 \text{ g}}{1 \text{ kg}} \cdot \dfrac{1 \text{ mol Cu}_2\text{S}}{159.2 \text{ g}} \cdot \dfrac{1 \text{ mol S}}{1 \text{ mol Cu}_2\text{S}} \cdot \dfrac{1 \text{ mol H}_2\text{SO}_4}{1 \text{ mol S}} \cdot \dfrac{98.08 \text{ g}}{1 \text{ mol H}_2\text{SO}_4} = 1850 \text{ g H}_2\text{SO}_4$

4.65 $0.376 \text{ g CO}_2 \cdot \dfrac{1 \text{ mol CO}_2}{44.01 \text{ g}} \cdot \dfrac{1 \text{ mol MCO}_3}{1 \text{ mol CO}_2} = 0.00854 \text{ mol MCO}_3$

$\dfrac{1.056 \text{ g}}{0.00854 \text{ mol}} = 124 \text{ g/mol}$

124 g/mol (MCO_3) – 60 g/mol (CO_3) = 64 g/mol   The metal is (b) copper, Cu

4.66 $M(s) + O_2 (g) \rightarrow MO_2(s)$

$(0.452 - 0.356) \text{ g O}_2 \cdot \dfrac{1 \text{ mol O}_2}{32.00 \text{ g}} \cdot \dfrac{1 \text{ mol M}}{1 \text{ mol O}_2} = 0.0030 \text{ mol M}$

$\dfrac{0.356 \text{ g}}{0.0030 \text{ mol}} = 120 \text{ g/mol}$ (119 g/mol with three significant figures)

The metal is probably Sn (118.67 g/mol)

4.67 $1.598 \text{ g TiO}_2 \cdot \dfrac{1 \text{ mol TiO}_2}{79.866 \text{ g}} \cdot \dfrac{1 \text{ mol Ti}}{1 \text{ mol TiO}_2} = 0.02001 \text{ mol Ti}$

$0.02001 \text{ mol Ti} \cdot \dfrac{47.867 \text{ g}}{1 \text{ mol Ti}} = 0.9577 \text{ g Ti}$

$1.438 \text{ g Ti}_x\text{O}_y - 0.9577 \text{ g Ti} = 0.480 \text{ g O}$

$0.480 \text{ g O} \cdot \dfrac{16.00 \text{ g}}{1 \text{ mol O}} = 0.0300 \text{ mol O}$

$\dfrac{0.0300 \text{ mol O}}{0.02001 \text{ mol Ti}} = \dfrac{3 \text{ mol O}}{2 \text{ mol Ti}}$ The empirical formula is Ti_2O_3

4.68 $0.301 \text{ g BaSO}_4 \cdot \dfrac{1 \text{ mol BaSO}_4}{233.4 \text{ g}} \cdot \dfrac{1 \text{ mol S}}{1 \text{ mol BaSO}_4} \cdot \dfrac{1 \text{ mol thioridazine}}{2 \text{ mol S}} \cdot \dfrac{370.6 \text{ g}}{1 \text{ mol thioridazine}} \cdot \dfrac{10^3 \text{ mg}}{1 \text{ g}}$

$= 239 \text{ mg thioridazine}$

$\dfrac{239 \text{ mg}}{12 \text{ tablets}} = 19.9 \text{ mg thioridazine per tablet}$

4.69 $0.1840 \text{ g AgCl} \cdot \dfrac{1 \text{ mol AgCl}}{143.32 \text{ g}} \cdot \dfrac{1 \text{ mol Cl}}{1 \text{ mol AgCl}} \cdot \dfrac{1 \text{ mol 2,4-D}}{2 \text{ mol Cl}} \cdot \dfrac{221.04 \text{ g}}{1 \text{ mol 2,4-D}} = 0.1419 \text{ g 2,4-D}$

$\dfrac{0.1419 \text{ g}}{1.236 \text{ g}} \cdot 100\% = 11.48\% \text{ 2,4-D}$

4.70 $234 \text{ kg KClO}_4 \cdot \dfrac{10^3 \text{ g}}{1 \text{ kg}} \cdot \dfrac{1 \text{ mol KClO}_4}{138.5 \text{ g}} \cdot \dfrac{4 \text{ mol KClO}_3}{3 \text{ mol KClO}_4} \cdot \dfrac{3 \text{ mol KClO}}{1 \text{ mol KClO}_3} \cdot \dfrac{1 \text{ mol Cl}_2}{1 \text{ mol KClO}} \cdot \dfrac{70.91 \text{ g}}{1 \text{ mol Cl}_2}$

$= 4.79 \times 10^5 \text{ g Cl}_2$

4.71   (a) $125 \text{ kg Zn} \cdot \dfrac{10^3 \text{ g}}{1 \text{ kg}} \cdot \dfrac{1 \text{ mol Zn}}{65.39 \text{ g}} \cdot \dfrac{1 \text{ mol ZnS}_2\text{O}_4}{1 \text{ mol Zn}} \cdot \dfrac{1 \text{ mol Na}_2\text{S}_2\text{O}_4}{1 \text{ mol ZnS}_2\text{O}_4} \cdot \dfrac{174.1 \text{ g}}{1 \text{ mol Na}_2\text{S}_2\text{O}_4}$

$= 3.33 \times 10^5 \text{ g Na}_2\text{S}_2\text{O}_4$

$500. \text{ kg SO}_2 \cdot \dfrac{10^3 \text{ g}}{1 \text{ kg}} \cdot \dfrac{1 \text{ mol SO}_2}{64.06 \text{ g}} \cdot \dfrac{1 \text{ mol ZnS}_2\text{O}_4}{2 \text{ mol SO}_2} \cdot \dfrac{1 \text{ mol Na}_2\text{S}_2\text{O}_4}{1 \text{ mol ZnS}_2\text{O}_4} \cdot \dfrac{174.1 \text{ g}}{1 \text{ mol Na}_2\text{S}_2\text{O}_4}$

$= 1.36 \times 10^6 \text{ g Na}_2\text{S}_2\text{O}_4$

The maximum mass produced is $3.33 \times 10^5 \text{ g Na}_2\text{S}_2\text{O}_4$ (333 kg).

(b) $333 \text{ kg Na}_2\text{S}_2\text{O}_4 \cdot \dfrac{100.0 \text{ kg commercial product}}{90.1 \text{ kg Na}_2\text{S}_2\text{O}_4} = 370. \text{ kg commercial product}$

4.72 $125 \text{ kg limestone} \cdot \dfrac{10^3 \text{ g}}{1 \text{ kg}} \cdot \dfrac{95.0 \text{ g CaCO}_3}{100.0 \text{ g limestone}} \cdot \dfrac{1 \text{ mol CaCO}_3}{100.1 \text{ g}} \cdot \dfrac{1 \text{ mol CaO}}{1 \text{ mol CaCO}_3} \cdot \dfrac{56.08 \text{ g}}{1 \text{ mol CaO}}$

$= 6.65 \times 10^4 \text{ g CaO}$ (66.5 kg)

4.73 $525 \text{ kg FeS}_2 \cdot \dfrac{10^3 \text{ g}}{1 \text{ kg}} \cdot \dfrac{1 \text{ mol FeS}_2}{120.0 \text{ g}} \cdot \dfrac{8 \text{ mol SO}_2}{4 \text{ mol FeS}_2} \cdot \dfrac{2 \text{ mol SO}_3}{2 \text{ mol SO}_2} \cdot \dfrac{1 \text{ mol H}_2\text{SO}_4}{1 \text{ mol SO}_3} \cdot \dfrac{98.08 \text{ g}}{1 \text{ mol H}_2\text{SO}_4}$

$= 8.58 \times 10^5 \text{ g H}_2\text{SO}_4$ (858 kg)

4.74 $8.63 \text{ g Ag} \cdot \dfrac{1 \text{ mol Ag}}{107.9 \text{ g}} \cdot \dfrac{1 \text{ mol Ag}_2\text{MoS}_4}{2 \text{ mol Ag}} \cdot \dfrac{439.9 \text{ g}}{1 \text{ mol Ag}_2\text{MoS}_4} = 17.6 \text{ g Ag}_2\text{MoS}_4$

        $3.36 \text{ g Mo} \cdot \dfrac{1 \text{ mol Mo}}{95.94 \text{ g}} \cdot \dfrac{1 \text{ mol Ag}_2\text{MoS}_4}{1 \text{ mol Mo}} \cdot \dfrac{439.9 \text{ g}}{1 \text{ mol Ag}_2\text{MoS}_4} = 15.4 \text{ g Ag}_2\text{MoS}_4$

        $4.81 \text{ g S} \cdot \dfrac{1 \text{ mol S}}{32.07 \text{ g}} \cdot \dfrac{1 \text{ mol Ag}_2\text{MoS}_4}{4 \text{ mol S}} \cdot \dfrac{439.9 \text{ g}}{1 \text{ mol Ag}_2\text{MoS}_4} = 16.5 \text{ g Ag}_2\text{MoS}_4$

The maximum mass that can be obtained is 15.4 g Ag_2MoS_4

4.75 $C_4H_8(g) + 6\ O_2(g) \rightarrow 4\ CO_2(g) + 4\ H_2O(g)$

        $2\ C_4H_{10}(g) + 13\ O_2(g) \rightarrow 8\ CO_2(g) + 10\ H_2O(g)$

The problem can be soved using either the mass of CO_2 or the mass of H_2O. Set up two equations with two unknowns.

$x \text{ g } C_4H_8 + y \text{ g } C_4H_{10} = 2.86 \text{ g}$

$8.80 \text{ g } CO_2 \cdot \dfrac{1 \text{ mol } CO_2}{44.01 \text{ g}} = \left(\dfrac{x \text{ g } C_4H_8}{56.11 \text{ g/mol}} \cdot \dfrac{4 \text{ mol } CO_2}{1 \text{ mol } C_4H_8} \right) + \left(\dfrac{y \text{ g } C_4H_{10}}{58.12 \text{ g/mol}} \cdot \dfrac{8 \text{ mol } CO_2}{2 \text{ mol } C_4H_8} \right)$

Substitute ($2.86 \text{ g} - x \text{ g } C_4H_8$) for y and solve.

$x = 1.27 \text{ g } C_4H_8$ $y = 2.86 \text{ g} - 1.27 \text{ g} = 1.59 \text{ g } C_4H_{10}$

$\dfrac{1.27 \text{ g } C_4H_8}{2.86 \text{ g mixture}} \cdot 100\% = 44.4\% \ C_4H_8$ $55.6\% \ C_4H_{10}$

4.76 $250 \text{ layers} \cdot \dfrac{0.60 \text{ nm}}{1 \text{ layer}} \cdot \dfrac{1 \text{ m}}{10^9 \text{ nm}} \cdot \dfrac{100 \text{ cm}}{1 \text{ m}} = 1.5 \times 10^5 \text{ cm thick}$

        $\text{volume} = (1.5 \times 10^5 \text{ cm})(3.00 \text{ m})(3.00 \text{ m})\left(\dfrac{100 \text{ cm}}{1 \text{ m}} \right)^2 = 1.4 \text{ cm}^3$

        $\text{mass} = 1.4 \text{ cm}^3 \cdot \dfrac{1.0 \text{ g}}{1 \text{ cm}^3} = 1.4 \text{ g } (CH_3)_2SiCl_2$

4.77 $0.682 \text{ g sample} - 0.467 \text{ g residue} = 0.215 \text{ g gas lost}$

Treating the gas lost as the compound H_2CO_3,

$0.215 \text{ g } H_2CO_3 \cdot \dfrac{1 \text{ mol } H_2CO_3}{62.03 \text{ g}} \cdot \dfrac{2 \text{ mol } NaHCO_3}{1 \text{ mol } H_2CO_3} \cdot \dfrac{84.01 \text{ g}}{1 \text{ mol } NaHCO_3} = 0.582 \text{ g } NaHCO_3$

$\dfrac{0.582 \text{ g}}{0.682 \text{ g}} \cdot 100\% = 85.4\% \ NaHCO_3$

4.78 $100.0 \text{ g impure ore} \cdot \dfrac{89.0 \text{ g CuS/Cu}_2\text{S mixture}}{100.0 \text{ g impure ore}} = 89.0 \text{ g CuS/Cu}_2\text{S mixture}$

$75.4 \text{ g impure Cu} \cdot \dfrac{89.5 \text{ g Cu}}{100.0 \text{ g impure Cu}} = 67.5 \text{ g Cu}$

$89.0 \text{ g mixture} = x \text{ g CuS} + y \text{ g Cu}_2\text{S}$

$67.5 \text{ g Cu} = (x \text{ g CuS})\left(\dfrac{63.55 \text{ g Cu}}{95.61 \text{ g CuS}}\right) + (y \text{ g Cu}_2\text{S})\left(\dfrac{127.09 \text{ g Cu}}{159.16 \text{ g Cu}_2\text{S}}\right)$

Substitute $(89.0 - x)$ for y and solve.

$y = 62.2 \text{ g Cu}_2\text{S} = 62.2\% \text{ Cu}_2\text{S}$

$x = 26.8 \text{ g CuS} = 26.8\% \text{ CuS}$

4.79   (a) $10.8 \text{ g product} - 2.0 \text{ g Fe} = 8.8 \text{ g Br}_2$

(b) $2.0 \text{ g Fe} \cdot \dfrac{1 \text{ mol Fe}}{55.8 \text{ g}} = 0.036 \text{ mol Fe}$ $8.8 \text{ g Br}_2 \cdot \dfrac{1 \text{ mol Br}_2}{160. \text{ g}} \cdot \dfrac{2 \text{ mol Br}}{1 \text{ mol Br}_2} = 0.11 \text{ mol Br}$

$\dfrac{0.11 \text{ mol Br}}{0.036 \text{ mol Fe}} = \dfrac{3 \text{ mol Br}}{1 \text{ mol Fe}}$

(c) $FeBr_3$

(d) $2 \text{ Fe(s)} + 3 \text{ Br}_2(\ell) \rightarrow 2 \text{ FeBr}_3\text{(s)}$

(e)   Iron(III) bromide

(f)   (i) When 1.00 g of Fe is added to the Br_2, Fe is the limiting reagent.

4.80   Panel (b) represents the outcome of the reaction. Cl_2 is the limiting reactant.

4.81   (a) $\dfrac{195.08 \text{ g Pt}}{300.05 \text{ g Pt(NH}_3)_2\text{Cl}_2} \cdot 100\% = 65.02 \% \text{ Pt}$ $\dfrac{(2)(14.01) \text{ g N}}{300.05 \text{ g Pt(NH}_3)_2\text{Cl}_2} \cdot 100\% = 9.338\% \text{ N}$

$\dfrac{(2)(35.45) \text{ g Cl}}{300.05 \text{ g Pt(NH}_3)_2\text{Cl}_2} \cdot 100\% = 23.63 \% \text{ Cl}$

(b) $16.0 \text{ g K}_2\text{PtCl}_4 \cdot \dfrac{1 \text{ mol K}_2\text{PtCl}_4}{415.1 \text{ g}} \cdot \dfrac{2 \text{ mol NH}_3}{1 \text{ mol K}_2\text{PtCl}_4} \cdot \dfrac{17.03 \text{ g}}{1 \text{ mol NH}_3} = 1.31 \text{ g NH}_3$

$16.0 \text{ g K}_2\text{PtCl}_4 \cdot \dfrac{1 \text{ mol K}_2\text{PtCl}_4}{415.1 \text{ g}} \cdot \dfrac{1 \text{ mol Pt(NH}_3)_2\text{Cl}_2}{1 \text{ mol K}_2\text{PtCl}_4} \cdot \dfrac{300.1 \text{ g}}{1 \text{ mol Pt(NH}_3)_2\text{Cl}_2} = 11.6 \text{ g Pt(NH}_3)\text{Cl}_2$

4.82 $2 \text{ Fe(s)} + 3 \text{ Cl}_2(g) \rightarrow 2 \text{ FeCl}_3(s)$

(a) $1.54 \text{ g} \cdot \dfrac{1 \text{ mol Fe}}{55.85 \text{ g}} \cdot \dfrac{3 \text{ mol Cl}_2}{2 \text{ mol Fe}} \cdot \dfrac{70.91 \text{ g}}{1 \text{ mol Cl}_2} = 2.93 \text{ g Cl}_2$

$1.54 \text{ g} \cdot \dfrac{1 \text{ mol Fe}}{55.85 \text{ g}} \cdot \dfrac{2 \text{ mol FeCl}_3}{2 \text{ mol Fe}} \cdot \dfrac{162.2 \text{ g}}{1 \text{ mol FeCl}_3} = 4.47 \text{ g FeCl}_3$

(b) $\text{FeCl}_3(aq) + 3 \text{ NaOH}(aq) \rightarrow \text{Fe(OH)}_3(s) + 3 \text{ NaCl}(aq)$

$2.0 \text{ g} \cdot \dfrac{1 \text{ mol FeCl}_3}{162.2 \text{ g}} \cdot \dfrac{1 \text{ mol Fe(OH)}_3}{1 \text{ mol FeCl}_3} \cdot \dfrac{106.9 \text{ g}}{1 \text{ mol Fe(OH)}_3} = 1.32 \text{ g Fe(OH)}_3$

$4.0 \text{ g} \cdot \dfrac{1 \text{ mol NaOH}}{40.00 \text{ g}} \cdot \dfrac{1 \text{ mol Fe(OH)}_3}{3 \text{ mol NaOH}} \cdot \dfrac{106.9 \text{ g}}{1 \text{ mol Fe(OH)}_3} = 3.56 \text{ g Fe(OH)}_3$

1.32 g Fe(OH)_3 is produced

4.83   See Screen 4.8 for an explanation and calculations that support these results.

4.84   Some aluminum remains in the beaker. Bromine was the limiting reactant.

Chapter 5
Reactions in Aqueous Solution

INSTRUCTOR'S NOTES

Chapter 5 is focused on chemical reactions in solution, including electrolytes, types of reactions, concentration, and solution stoichiometry. Chapter 5 has a heavy emphasis on chemistry at the molecular level. The images representing electrolytic behavior and chemical reactions at the molecular level are intended to help students make the transition to visualize molecules instead of chemical formulas. This chapter introduces pH as a way to describe the H^+ concentration in acidic and basic solutions.

We consider Chapter 5 an important early chapter in the book. We cover the material at this point in our course because our students use the concepts in the laboratory. However, *we emphasize that it is not crucial that this material be covered at this time in the course.* Some of the sections can be delayed, in particular, *it would be easy to cover the subject of redox reactions (Section 5.7) at some other point in the year,* such as when covering electrochemistry.

Chapter 5 introduces the properties of ionic compounds in aqueous solution and general guidelines to predict the aqueous solubility of simple ionic compounds. Although one can readily identify many exceptions to the guidelines in Figure 5.3, we do find them useful for students in a beginning course. We hope that the many photos of soluble and insoluble compounds in this chapter will help students remember some of these guidelines. Demos can also make this concept concrete for the students.

The section on net ionic equations (Section 5.2) can be a difficult one for students. We admit it does take time and effort to help the students come to grips with this concept. However, it is a useful one, since (1) many reactions are best seen in this fashion and (2) balancing reactions is made easier. Students can generally write balanced equations for exchange reactions, but they sometimes have a difficult time turning them into net ionic equations. Time and effort on everyone's part is needed here.

The introduction to acids and bases (Section 5.3) is somewhat brief at this stage, but it does enable one to use common acids and bases in examples and in the laboratory with the knowledge that students have some familiarity with them and with the pH scale.

Oxidation numbers have been introduced *only* as a way of telling if a redox reaction has occurred.

Chapter 5 requires approximately five lectures.

SUGGESTED DEMONSTRATIONS

1. Electrolytes

    - We always illustrate the conductivity, and the difference between strong and weak electrolytes, using an apparatus such as that in the Chapter Focus. We use solutions such as $CuSO_4$, Na_2CO_3, vinegar, and pure water. It is interesting to compare the behavior of these solutions with the conductivity of soda or juice.

    - Haworth, D. T.; Bartelt, M. R.; Kenney, M. J. "Solution Conductivity Apparatus," *Journal of Chemical Education* **1999**, *76*, 625.

    - Cortel, A. "Fast Ionic Migration of Copper Chromate," *Journal of Chemical Education* **2001**, *78*, 207.

2. Solubility of Ionic Compounds

    - It is very important to illustrate the solubility of salts. Our most recent demonstrations are outlined below. Throughout the demonstrations the solubility guidelines are projected onto the screen in the lecture room. *Note: Precipitation reactions **cannot** be illustrated on an overhead projector. The precipitate is seen only as a dark blob. However, even in a large lecture room, students can see the reaction if it is done in a large flask (1-2 L).*

      (a) A gram or so of KI is dissolved in a few hundred milliliters of water in one flask, and $Pb(NO_3)_2$ is dissolved in water in another flask. The students can clearly see the salts dissolve. On mixing the solutions, though, a bright yellow precipitate of PbI_2 appears, clearly demonstrating one of the exceptions to the general rule that halide salts are water-soluble.

      (b) A solution of $(NH_4)_2S$ is mixed with a solution of $Cd(NO_3)_2$ to show that metal sulfides (bright yellow CdS in this case) are generally not soluble.

      (c) $BaCl_2$ is dissolved in water while discussing halide solubility and mixed with a solution of $CuSO_4$ (which shows the usual solubility of sulfates). Precipitation of $BaSO_4$ on mixing the solutions then demonstrates the exceptions to the guideline regarding sulfates.

      (d) Our attempt at dissolving a piece of blackboard chalk fails, clearly showing that many carbonates are not soluble.

    - Other solubility demonstrations include:

      (a) Dissolve NaCl in water and then precipitate AgCl with $AgNO_3$.

      (b) Dissolve Na_2CO_3 and compare this with chalk.

      (c) Show a sample of fool's gold (iron pyrite) to illustrate the insolubility of metal sulfides.

      (d) Add NaOH to solutions of $Fe(NO_3)_3$ and $CuSO_4$ to get insoluble hydroxides.

      (e) deVos, W. "Using Large Glass Cylinders to Demonstrate Chemical Reactions," *Journal of Chemical Education* **1999**, *76*, 528.

      (f) Shakhashiri, B. Z. *Chemical Demonstrations: A Handbook for Teachers of Chemistry*; University of Wisconsin Press, 1983; Vol. 1, pp. 307-313.

3. Acid-Base Reaction

    - Although is it easy for students to see precipitation reactions done in large flasks, we find that acid-base reactions are difficult to demonstrate, since common ones are not spectacular. However, a suggested demonstration would be to dissolve a precipitate of $Ca(OH)_2$. At least the solid would be seen to dissolve on adding acid.

- Bring a pH meter to class to demonstrate the pH scale using common acids and bases.

4. Oxides

- Show samples of metal oxides, especially those of iron, aluminum, boron, lead, and magnesium. Show a sample of anodized aluminum or aluminum oxide sandpaper.

- Show samples of silica sand and quartz crystals.

- Take a sample of dry ice and discuss some of the chemistry of CO_2.

- React hot sulfur with pure O_2 (Shakhashiri, Vol. 2, pp. 184-189). This is especially effective in a very dark room. (Fill the bottle with pure O_2 before lecture and tightly stopper.)

- Make NO_2 from copper (a penny) and concentrated HNO_3. (Place a penny in about 15 mL of concentrated HNO_3 in a 2-L flask and stopper lightly with a rubber stopper. Although a little NO_2 comes out of the flask, in a large lecture room it is not noticeable.

5. Combustion Reaction

- A very simple demonstration of combustion reactions is the "plastic soda bottle rocket." Insert large nails on opposite sides of a plastic soda bottle near the bottom. Place a few milliliters of methanol in the bottle and shake to saturate the atmosphere in the bottle with alcohol. Place a cork in the top of the bottle (it will take some experimenting to see how firmly to seat the cork), and then touch one of the nails with a Tesla coil. The cork will fly out of the bottle with a loud bang.

- Fortman, J. J.; Rush, A. C.; Stamper, J. E. "Variations on the 'Whoosh' Bottle Alcohol Explosion Demonstration Including Safety Notes," *Journal of Chemical Education* **1999**, *76*, 1092.

6. Gas-Forming Reactions

- Derr, H. R.; Lewis, T.; Derr, B. J. "Gas Me Up, or, A Baking Powder Diver," *Journal of Chemical Education* **2000**, *77*, 171.

7. Oxidation-Reduction Chemistry

- After introducing the ideas of redox and the concept of oxidation numbers, we do a demonstration on the oxidation states of vanadium.

    Directions: Dissolve 1 g of ammonium vanadate in 200 mL of water. (Warm to dissolve completely.)

    (a) Add 3 M H_2SO_4 (20-50 mL), and the solution turns yellow owing to an acid-base reaction

    $$VO_3^- + 2\ H^+ \rightarrow VO_2^+ + H_2O$$

    (b) Add a handful of zinc chips. These reduce the V(V) to V(IV).

    $$2\ VO_2^+ + Zn + 4\ H^+ \rightarrow 2\ VO_2+\ (vanadyl,\ blue) + 2\ H_2O + Zn^{2+}$$

(c) The solution will slowly turn emerald green owing to another reduction step.

$$2 \, VO^{2+} \, (\text{blue}) + Zn + 4 \, H^+ \rightarrow 2 \, V^{3+} \, (\text{green}) + 2 \, H_2O + Zn^{2+}$$

(d) The solution will finally turn violet. We allow the reaction to continue throughout the lecture with a stopper on the flask. This excludes air well enough that the violet, aqueous vanadium(II) ion can form. (The vanadium(II) ion is readily oxidized by oxygen in air to V^{3+}. Therefore, to see the violet color air must be excluded.)

- Wellman, W. E.; Noble, M. E. "Greening the Blue Bottle," *Journal of Chemical Education* **2003**, *80*, 537.

- Volkovich, V. A.; Griffiths, T. R. "Catalytic Oxidation of Ammonia: A Sparkling Experiment," *Journal of Chemical Education* **2000**, *77*, 177.

- Elsworth, J. F. "Entertaining Chemistry—Two Colorful Reactions," *Journal of Chemical Education* **2000**, *77*, 484.

- Eliason, R.; Lee, E. J.; Wakefield, D.; Bergren, A. "Improvement of Sugar-Chlorate Rocket Demonstration," *Journal of Chemical Education* **2000**, *77*, 1580.

- Maya, H. D.; Neves, E. A. "A Further Demonstration of Sulfite-Induced Redox Cycling of Metal Ions Initiated by Shaking," *Journal of Chemical Education* **1999**, *76*, 930.

8. Solution Stoichiometry

- One of the biggest problems in teaching stoichiometry is to get the students to connect the words on paper with actual operations in the laboratory. To help in making this connection, we have included photos in the text of (a) the preparation of a solution starting with a solid compound (Figure 5.18), preparing a solution by dilution of a more concentrated one (Figure 5.19), and acid–base and redox titrations (Figure 5.23 and Example 5.16, respectively). We find it very helpful to demonstrate these processes in class as well.

SOLUTIONS TO STUDY QUESTIONS

5.1   Electrolytes are compounds whose aqueous solutions conduct electricity. Substances whose solutions are good electrical conductors are strong electrolytes (such as sodium chloride), poor electrical conductors are weak electrolytes (such as acetic acid).

5.2   Hydrochloric acid and nitric acid are strong electrolytes. Acetic acid is a weak electrolyte. Sodium hydroxide and potassium hydroxide are strong electrolytes. Calcium hydroxide is a weak electrolyte.

5.3   (a) $CuCl_2$

      (b) $AgNO_3$

      (c) K_2CO_3, KI, $KMnO_4$

5.4   (a) $Ba(NO_3)_2$

      (b) Na_2SO_4, $NaClO_4$, $NaCH_3CO_2$

      (c) KBr, Al_2Br_6

5.5   (a) K^+ and OH^- ions   (c) Li^+ and NO_3^- ions

      (b) K^+ and SO_4^{2-} ions   (d) NH_4^+ and SO_4^{2-} ions

5.6   (a) K^+ and I^- ions   (c) K^+ and HPO_4^{2-} ions

      (b) Mg^{2+} and $CH_3CO_2^-$ ions   (d) Na^+ and CN^- ions

5.7   (a) soluble; Na^+ and CO_3^{2-} ions   (c) insoluble

      (b) soluble; Cu^{2+} and SO_4^{2-} ions   (d) soluble; Ba^{2+} and Br^- ions

5.8   (a) soluble; Ni^{2+} and Cl^- ions   (c) soluble; Pb^{2+} and NO_3^- ions

      (b) soluble; Cr^{2+} and NO_3^- ions   (d) insoluble

5.9 $CdCl_2(aq) + 2\ NaOH(aq) \rightarrow Cd(OH)_2(s) + 2\ NaCl(aq)$

      $Cd^{2+}(aq) + 2\ OH^-(aq) \rightarrow Cd(OH)_2(s)$

5.10 $Ni(NO_3)_2(aq) + Na_2CO_3(aq) \rightarrow NiCO_3(s) + 2\ NaNO_3(aq)$

      $Ni^{2+}(aq) + CO_3^{2-}(aq) \rightarrow NiCO_3(s)$

5.11   (a) $NiCl_2(aq) + (NH_4)_2S(aq) \rightarrow NiS(s) + 2\ NH_4Cl(aq)$

           $Ni^{2+}(aq) + S^{2-}(aq) \rightarrow NiS(s)$

      (b) $3\ Mn(NO_3)_2(aq) + 2\ Na_3PO_4(aq) \rightarrow Mn_3(PO_4)_2(s) + 6\ NaNO_3(aq)$

           $3\ Mn^{2+}(aq) + 2\ PO_4^{3-}(aq) \rightarrow Mn_3(PO_4)_2(s)$

5.12   (a) $Pb(NO_3)_2(aq) + 2\ KBr(aq) \rightarrow PbBr_2(s) + 2\ KNO_3(aq)$

         $Pb^{2+}(aq) + 2\ Br^-(aq) \rightarrow PbBr_2(s)$

       (b) $Ca(NO_3)_2(aq) + 2\ KF(aq) \rightarrow CaF_2(s) + 2\ KNO_3(aq)$

         $Ca^{2+}(aq) + 2\ F^-(aq) \rightarrow CaF_2(s)$

       (c) $Ca(NO_3)_2(aq) + Na_2C_2O_4(aq) \rightarrow CaC_2O_4(s) + 2\ NaNO_3(aq)$

         $Ca^{2+}(aq) + C_2O_4{}^{2-}(aq) \rightarrow CaC_2O_4(s)$

5.13 $HNO_3(aq) \rightarrow H^+(aq) + NO_3{}^-(aq)$

5.14 $HClO_4(aq) \rightarrow H^+(aq) + ClO_4{}^-(aq)$

5.15 $H_2C_2O_4(aq) \rightarrow H^+(aq) + HC_2O_4{}^-(aq)$

       $HC_2O_4{}^-(aq) \rightarrow H^+(aq) + C_2O_4{}^{2-}(aq)$

5.16 $H_3PO_4(aq) \rightarrow H^+(aq) + H_2PO_4{}^-(aq)$

       $H_2PO_4{}^-(aq) \rightarrow H^+(aq) + HPO_4{}^{2-}(aq)$

       $HPO_4{}^{2-}(aq) \rightarrow H^+(aq) + PO_4{}^{3-}(aq)$

5.17 $MgO(s) + H_2O(\ell) \rightarrow Mg(OH)_2(s)$

5.18 $SO_3(g) + H_2O(\ell) \rightarrow H_2SO_4(aq)$

5.19   (a) $2\ CH_3CO_2H(aq) + Mg(OH)_2(s) \rightarrow Mg(CH_3CO_2)_2(aq) + 2\ H_2O(\ell)$

         acetic acid, magnesium hydroxide, magnesium acetate, water

       (b) $HClO_4(aq) + NH_3(aq) \rightarrow NH_4ClO_4(aq)$

         perchloric acid, ammonia, ammonium perchlorate

5.20   (a) $H_3PO_4(aq) + 3\ KOH(aq) \rightarrow K_3PO_4(aq) + 3\ H_2O(\ell)$

         phosphoric acid, potassium hydroxide, potassium phosphate, water

       (b) $H_2C_2O_4(aq) + Ca(OH)_2(s) \rightarrow CaC_2O_4(s) + 2\ H_2O(\ell)$

         oxalic acid, calcium hydroxide, calcium oxalate, water

5.21 $Ba(OH)_2(aq) + 2\ HNO_3(aq) \rightarrow Ba(NO_3)_2(aq) + 2\ H_2O(\ell)$

5.22 $2\ Al(OH)_3(s) + 3\ H_2SO_4(aq) \rightarrow Al_2(SO_4)_3(aq) + 6\ H_2O(\ell)$

5.23   (a) $(NH_4)_2CO_3(aq) + Cu(NO_3)_2 \rightarrow CuCO_3(s) + 2\ NH_4NO_3(aq)$

$CO_3^{2-}(aq) + Cu^{2+}(aq) \rightarrow CuCO_3(s)$

(b) $Pb(OH)_2(s) + 2\ HCl(aq) \rightarrow PbCl_2(s) + 2\ H_2O(\ell)$

$Pb(OH)_2(s) + 2\ H^+(aq) + 2\ Cl^-(aq) \rightarrow PbCl_2(s) + 2\ H_2O(\ell)$

(c) $BaCO_3(s) + 2\ HCl(aq) \rightarrow BaCl_2(aq) + H_2O(\ell) + CO_2(g)$

$BaCO_3(s) + 2\ H^+(aq) \rightarrow Ba^{2+}(aq) + H_2O(\ell) + CO_2(g)$

5.24   (a) $Zn(s) + 2\ HCl(aq) \rightarrow H_2(g) + ZnCl_2(aq)$

$Zn(s) + 2\ H^+(aq) \rightarrow H_2(g) + Zn^{2+}(aq)$

(b) $Mg(OH)_2(s) + 2\ HCl(aq) \rightarrow MgCl_2(aq) + 2\ H_2O(\ell)$

$Mg(OH)_2(s) + 2\ H^+(aq) \rightarrow Mg^{2+}(aq) + 2\ H_2O(\ell)$

(c) $2\ HNO_3(aq) + CaCO_3(s) \rightarrow Ca(NO_3)_2(aq) + H_2O(\ell) + CO_2(g)$

$2\ H^+(aq) + CaCO_3(s) \rightarrow Ca^{2+}(aq) + H_2O(\ell) + CO_2(g)$

5.25   (a) $AgNO_3(aq) + KI(aq) \rightarrow AgI(s) + KNO_3(aq)$

$Ag^+(aq) + I^-(aq) \rightarrow AgI(s)$

(b) $Ba(OH)_2(aq) + 2\ HNO_3(aq) \rightarrow Ba(NO_3)_2(aq) + 2\ H_2O(\ell)$

$OH^-(aq) + H^+(aq) \rightarrow H_2O(\ell)$

(c) $2\ Na_3PO_4(aq) + 3\ Ni(NO_3)_2(aq) \rightarrow Ni_3(PO_4)_2(s) + 6\ NaNO_3(aq)$

$2\ PO_4^{3-}(aq) + 3\ Ni^{2+}(aq) \rightarrow Ni_3(PO_4)_2(s)$

5.26   (a) $2\ NaOH(aq) + FeCl_2(aq) \rightarrow Fe(OH)_2(s) + 2\ NaCl(aq)$

$2\ OH^-(aq) + Fe^{2+}(aq) \rightarrow Fe(OH)_2(s)$

(b) $BaCl_2(aq) + Na_2CO_3(aq) \rightarrow BaCO_3(s) + 2\ NaCl(aq)$

$Ba^{2+}(aq) + CO_3^{2-}(aq) \rightarrow BaCO_3(s)$

5.27 $FeCO_3(s) + 2\ HNO_3(aq) \rightarrow Fe(NO_3)_2(aq) + CO_2(g) + H_2O(\ell)$

iron(II) carbonate, nitric acid, iron(II) nitrate, carbon dioxide, water

5.28 $MnCO_3(s) + 2\ HCl(aq) \rightarrow MnCl_2(aq) + CO_2(g) + H_2O(\ell)$

manganese(II) carbonate, hydrochloric acid, manganese(II) chloride, carbon dioxide, water

5.29   (a) $Ba(OH)_2(aq) + 2\ HCl(aq) \rightarrow BaCl_2(aq) + 2\ H_2O(\ell)$

acid-base reaction

(b) $2\ HNO_3(aq) + CoCO_3(s) \rightarrow Co(NO_3)_2(aq) + H_2O(\ell) + CO_2(g)$

gas-forming reaction

(c) $2\ Na_3PO_4(aq) + 3\ Cu(NO_3)_2(aq) \rightarrow Cu_3(PO_4)_2(s) + 6\ NaNO_3(aq)$

precipitation reaction

5.30   (a) $K_2CO_3(aq) + Cu(NO_3)_2(aq) \rightarrow CuCO_3(s) + 2\ KNO_3(aq)$

        precipitation reaction

        (b) $Pb(NO_3)_2(aq) + 2\ HCl(aq) \rightarrow PbCl_2(s) + 2\ HNO_3(aq)$

        precipitation reaction

        (c) $MgCO_3(s) + 2\ HCl(aq) \rightarrow MgCl_2(aq) + CO_2(g) + H_2O(\ell)$

        gas-forming reaction

5.31   (a) $MnCl_2(aq) + Na_2S(aq) \rightarrow MnS(s) + 2\ NaCl(aq)$

        precipitation reaction

        $Mn^{2+}(aq) + S^{2-}(aq) \rightarrow MnS(s)$

        (b) $K_2CO_3(aq) + ZnCl_2(aq) \rightarrow ZnCO_3(s) + 2\ KCl(aq)$

        precipitation reaction

        $CO_3^{2-}(aq) + Zn^{2+}(aq) \rightarrow ZnCO_3(s)$

5.32   (a) $Fe(OH)_3(s) + 3\ HNO_3(aq) \rightarrow Fe(NO_3)_3(aq) + 3\ H_2O(\ell)$

        Acid-base reaction

        $Fe(OH)_3(s) + 3\ H^+(aq) \rightarrow Fe^{3+}(aq) + 3\ H_2O(\ell)$

        (b) $FeCO_3(s) + 2\ HNO_3(aq) \rightarrow Fe(NO_3)_2(aq) + CO_2(g) + H_2O(\ell)$

        Gas-forming reaction

        $FeCO_3(s) + 2\ H^+(aq) \rightarrow Fe^{2+}(aq) + CO_2(g) + H_2O(\ell)$

5.33   (a) The formation of an insoluble compound, CuS

        (b) The formation of water, H_2O, in an acid-base reaction

5.34   Reaction (a) is a product-favored reaction.

5.35   (a) Br is +5 and O is –2   (d) Ca is +2 and H is –1

        (b) C is +3 and O is –2   (e) H is +1, Si is +4, and O is –2

        (c) F is –1   (f) H is +1, S is +6, and O is –2

5.36   (a) P is +5 and F is –1   (d) N is +5 and O is –2

        (b) H is +1, As is +5, and O is –2   (e) P is +5, O is –2, and Cl is –1

        (c) U is +4 and O is –2   (f) Xe is +6 and O is –2

5.37   (a) oxidation-reduction reaction

Oxidation number of Zn changes from 0 to +2, while that of N changes from +5 to +4

(b) acid-base reaction

(c) oxidation-reduction reaction

Oxidation number of Ca changes from 0 to +2, while that of H changes from +1 to 0

5.38   (a) precipitation reaction

(b) oxidation-reduction reaction

Oxidation number of Ca changes from 0 to +2, while that of O changes from 0 to –2

(c) oxidation-reduction reaction

Oxidation number of Fe changes from +2 to +3, while that of O changes from 0 to –2

5.39   (a) C_2H_4 is oxidized and is the reducing agent; O_2 is reduced and is the oxidizing agent

(b) Si is oxidized and is the reducing agent; Cl_2 is reduced and is the oxidizing agent

5.40   (a) $Cr_2O_7^{2-}$ is reduced and is the oxidizing agent; Sn^{2+} is oxidized and is the reducing agent.

(b) FeS is oxidized and is the reducing agent; NO_3^- is reduced and is the oxidizing agent.

5.41 $6.73 \text{ g Na}_2\text{CO}_3 \cdot \dfrac{1 \text{ mol Na}_2\text{CO}_3}{106.0 \text{ g}} = 0.0635 \text{ mol Na}_2\text{CO}_3$

$\dfrac{0.0635 \text{ mol Na}_2\text{CO}_3}{0.250 \text{ L}} = 0.254 \text{ M Na}_2\text{CO}_3$

$[\text{Na}^+] = 2 \times [\text{Na}_2\text{CO}_3] = 0.508 \text{ M Na}^+$ $[\text{CO}_3^{2-}] = [\text{Na}_2\text{CO}_3] = 0.254 \text{ M CO}_3^{2-}$

5.42 $2.335 \text{ g K}_2\text{Cr}_2\text{O}_7 \cdot \dfrac{1 \text{ mol K}_2\text{Cr}_2\text{O}_7}{294.18 \text{ g}} = 0.007937 \text{ mol K}_2\text{Cr}_2\text{O}_7$

$\dfrac{0.007937 \text{ mol K}_2\text{Cr}_2\text{O}_7}{0.500 \text{ L}} = 0.0159 \text{ M K}_2\text{Cr}_2\text{O}_7$

$[\text{K}^+] = 2 \times [\text{K}_2\text{Cr}_2\text{O}_7] = 0.0318 \text{ M}$ $[\text{Cr}_2\text{O}_7^{2-}] = [\text{K}_2\text{Cr}_2\text{O}_7] = 0.0159 \text{ M}$

5.43 $0.250 \text{ L} \cdot \dfrac{0.0125 \text{ mol KMnO}_4}{1 \text{ L}} \cdot \dfrac{158.0 \text{ g}}{1 \text{ mol KMnO}_4} = 0.494 \text{ g KMnO}_4$

5.44 $0.125 \text{ L} \cdot \dfrac{1.023 \times 10^{-3} \text{ mol Na}_3\text{PO}_4}{1 \text{ L}} \cdot \dfrac{163.9 \text{ g}}{1 \text{ mol Na}_3\text{PO}_4} = 0.0210 \text{ g Na}_3\text{PO}_4$

$[\text{Na}^+] = 3 \times [\text{Na}_3\text{PO}_4] = 3.069 \times 10^{-3} \text{ M}$ $[\text{PO}_4^{3-}] = [\text{Na}_3\text{PO}_4] = 1.023 \times 10^{-3} \text{ M}$

5.45 $25.0 \text{ g NaOH} \cdot \dfrac{1 \text{ mol NaOH}}{40.00 \text{ g}} \cdot \dfrac{1 \text{ L}}{0.123 \text{ mol NaOH}} \cdot \dfrac{10^3 \text{ mL}}{1 \text{ L}} = 5080 \text{ mL solution}$

5.46 $322 \text{ g KMnO}_4 \cdot \dfrac{1 \text{ mol KMnO}_4}{158.0 \text{ g}} \cdot \dfrac{1 \text{ L}}{2.06 \text{ mol KMnO}_4} = 0.989 \text{ L solution}$

5.47   (a) 0.50 M NH_4^+; 0.25 M SO_4^{2-}

      (b) 0.246 M Na^+; $0.123 \text{ M CO}_3^{2-}$

      (c) 0.056 M H^+; 0.056 M NO_3^-

5.48   (a) 0.12 M Ba^{2+}; 0.24 M Cl^-

      (b) 0.0125 M Cu^{2+}; $0.0125 \text{ M SO}_4^{2-}$

      (c) 1.000 M K^+; $0.500 \text{ M Cr}_2\text{O}_7^{2-}$

5.49 $500.0 \text{ mL} \cdot \dfrac{1 \text{ L}}{10^3 \text{ mL}} \cdot \dfrac{0.0200 \text{ mol Na}_2\text{CO}_3}{1 \text{ L}} \cdot \dfrac{105.99 \text{ g}}{1 \text{ mol Na}_2\text{CO}_3} = 1.06 \text{ g Na}_2\text{CO}_3$

Weigh out 1.06 g of Na_2CO_3 and place it in the 500.0 mL flask. Add a small amount of distilled water and mix until the solute dissolves. Add water until the meniscus of the solution rests at the calibrated mark on the neck of the volumetric flask. Cap the flask and swirl to ensure adequate mixing.

5.50 $0.250 \text{ L} \cdot \dfrac{0.15 \text{ mol H}_2\text{C}_2\text{O}_4}{1 \text{ L}} \cdot \dfrac{90.04 \text{ g}}{1 \text{ mol H}_2\text{C}_2\text{O}_4} = 3.4 \text{ g H}_2\text{C}_2\text{O}_4$

5.51 $c_d = c_c \cdot \dfrac{V_c}{V_d} = 1.50 \text{ M} \cdot \dfrac{25.0 \text{ mL}}{500. \text{ mL}} = 0.0750 \text{ M HCl}$

5.52 $c_d = c_c \cdot \dfrac{V_c}{V_d} = 0.0250 \text{ M} \cdot \dfrac{4.00 \text{ mL}}{10.0 \text{ mL}} = 0.0100 \text{ M CuSO}_4$

5.53   (a) $c_d = c_c \cdot \dfrac{V_c}{V_d} = 6.00 \text{ M} \cdot \dfrac{0.0208 \text{ L}}{1.00 \text{ L}} = 0.125 \text{ M H}_2\text{SO}_4$ Correct method

      (b) $c_d = c_c \cdot \dfrac{V_c}{V_d} = 3.00 \text{ M} \cdot \dfrac{0.0500 \text{ L}}{1.00 \text{ L}} = 0.150 \text{ M H}_2\text{SO}_4$

5.54   (a) $c_d = c_c \cdot \dfrac{V_c}{V_d} = 1.50 \text{ M} \cdot \dfrac{30.0 \text{ mL}}{300. \text{ mL}} = 0.150 \text{ M K}_2\text{Cr}_2\text{O}_7$

      (b) $c_d = c_c \cdot \dfrac{V_c}{V_d} = 0.600 \text{ M} \cdot \dfrac{250. \text{ mL}}{300. \text{ mL}} = 0.500 \text{ M K}_2\text{Cr}_2\text{O}_7$ Correct method

5.55 $[\text{H}^+] = 10^{-\text{pH}} = 10^{-3.40} = 4.0 \times 10^{-4} \text{ M}$ The solution is acidic (pH < 7)

5.56 $[\text{H}^+] = 10^{-\text{pH}} = 10^{-10.5} = 3 \times 10^{-11} \text{ M}$ The solution is basic (pH > 7)

5.57 $[\text{H}^+] = [\text{HNO}_3] = 0.0013 \text{ M}$

      $\text{pH} = -\log[\text{H}^+] = -\log(0.0013) = 2.89$

5.58 $[H^+] = [HClO_4] = 1.2 \times 10^{-4}$ M

$pH = -\log[H^+] = -\log(1.2 \times 10^{-4}) = 3.92$

5.59

	pH	$[H^+]$	
(a)	1.00	0.10 M	acidic
(b)	10.50	3.2×10^{-11} M	basic
(c)	4.89	1.3×10^{-5} M	acidic
(d)	7.64	2.3×10^{-8} M	basic

5.60

	pH	$[H^+]$	
(a)	9.17	6.7×10^{-10} M	basic
(b)	5.66	2.2×10^{-6} M	acidic
(c)	5.25	5.6×10^{-6} M	acidic
(d)	1.60	2.5×10^{-2} M	acidic

5.61 $2.50 \text{ g Ba(OH)}_2 \cdot \dfrac{1 \text{ mol Ba(OH)}_2}{171.3 \text{ g}} \cdot \dfrac{2 \text{ mol HNO}_3}{1 \text{ mol Ba(OH)}_2} \cdot \dfrac{1 \text{ L}}{0.109 \text{ mol HNO}_3} \cdot \dfrac{10^3 \text{ mL}}{1 \text{ L}} = 268 \text{ mL solution}$

5.62 $50.0 \text{ mL} \cdot \dfrac{1 \text{ L}}{10^3 \text{ mL}} \cdot \dfrac{0.125 \text{ mol HNO}_3}{1 \text{ L}} \cdot \dfrac{1 \text{ mol Na}_2\text{CO}_3}{2 \text{ mol HNO}_3} \cdot \dfrac{106.0 \text{ g}}{1 \text{ mol Na}_2\text{CO}_3} = 0.331 \text{ g Na}_2\text{CO}_3$

5.63 $15.0 \text{ L} \cdot \dfrac{0.35 \text{ mol NaCl}}{1 \text{ L}} \cdot \dfrac{2 \text{ mol NaOH}}{2 \text{ mol NaCl}} \cdot \dfrac{40.00 \text{ g}}{1 \text{ mol NaOH}} = 210 \text{ g NaOH}$

$15.0 \text{ L} \cdot \dfrac{0.35 \text{ mol NaCl}}{1 \text{ L}} \cdot \dfrac{1 \text{ mol Cl}_2}{2 \text{ mol NaCl}} \cdot \dfrac{70.91 \text{ g}}{1 \text{ mol Cl}_2} = 190 \text{ g Cl}_2$

5.64 $250. \text{ mL} \cdot \dfrac{1 \text{ L}}{10^3 \text{ mL}} \cdot \dfrac{0.146 \text{ mol H}_2\text{SO}_4}{1 \text{ L}} \cdot \dfrac{2 \text{ mol N}_2\text{H}_4}{1 \text{ mol H}_2\text{SO}_4} \cdot \dfrac{32.05 \text{ g}}{1 \text{ mol N}_2\text{H}_4} = 2.34 \text{ g N}_2\text{H}_4$

5.65 $0.225 \text{ g AgBr} \cdot \dfrac{1 \text{ mol AgBr}}{187.8 \text{ g}} \cdot \dfrac{2 \text{ mol Na}_2\text{S}_2\text{O}_3}{1 \text{ mol AgBr}} \cdot \dfrac{1 \text{ L}}{0.0138 \text{ mol Na}_2\text{S}_2\text{O}_3} \cdot \dfrac{10^3 \text{ mL}}{1 \text{ L}} = 174 \text{ mL solution}$

5.66 $2.05 \text{ g Al} \cdot \dfrac{1 \text{ mol Al}}{26.98 \text{ g}} \cdot \dfrac{2 \text{ mol KAl(OH)}_4}{2 \text{ mol Al}} \cdot \dfrac{134.1 \text{ g}}{1 \text{ mol KAl(OH)}_4} = 10.2 \text{ g KAl(OH)}_4$

$0.185 \text{ L} \cdot \dfrac{1.35 \text{ mol KOH}}{1 \text{ L}} \cdot \dfrac{2 \text{ mol KAl(OH)}_4}{2 \text{ mol KOH}} \cdot \dfrac{134.1 \text{ g}}{1 \text{ mol KAl(OH)}_4} = 33.5 \text{ g KAl(OH)}_4$

Al is the limiting reactant, so none will remain. The mass of KAl(OH)_4 produced in the reaction is 10.2 g.

5.67 $1.00 \text{ L} \cdot \dfrac{2.25 \text{ mol NaCl}}{1 \text{ L}} \cdot \dfrac{1 \text{ mol Pb(NO}_3)_2}{2 \text{ mol NaCl}} \cdot \dfrac{1 \text{ L}}{0.750 \text{ mol Pb(NO}_3)_2} \cdot \dfrac{10^3 \text{ mL}}{1 \text{ L}} = 1.50 \times 10^3 \text{ mL solution}$

5.68 $35.2 \text{ mL} \cdot \dfrac{1 \text{ L}}{10^3 \text{ mL}} \cdot \dfrac{0.546 \text{ mol NaOH}}{1 \text{ L}} \cdot \dfrac{1 \text{ mol H}_2\text{C}_2\text{O}_4}{2 \text{ mol NaOH}} \cdot \dfrac{1 \text{ L}}{0.125 \text{ mol H}_2\text{C}_2\text{O}_4} = 0.0769 \text{ L}$

5.69 $1.45 \text{ g NaOH} \cdot \dfrac{1 \text{ mol NaOH}}{40.00 \text{ g}} \cdot \dfrac{1 \text{ mol HCl}}{1 \text{ mol NaOH}} \cdot \dfrac{1 \text{ L}}{0.812 \text{ mol HCl}} \cdot \dfrac{10^3 \text{ mL}}{1 \text{ L}} = 44.6 \text{ mL}$

5.70 $2.152 \text{ g Na}_2\text{CO}_3 \cdot \dfrac{1 \text{ mol Na}_2\text{CO}_3}{105.99 \text{ g}} \cdot \dfrac{2 \text{ mol HCl}}{1 \text{ mol Na}_2\text{CO}_3} \cdot \dfrac{1 \text{ L}}{0.955 \text{ mol HCl}} \cdot \dfrac{10^3 \text{ mL}}{1 \text{ L}} = 42.5 \text{ mL}$

5.71 $2.150 \text{ g Na}_2\text{CO}_3 \cdot \dfrac{1 \text{ mol Na}_2\text{CO}_3}{105.99 \text{ g}} \cdot \dfrac{2 \text{ mol HCl}}{1 \text{ mol Na}_2\text{CO}_3} \cdot \dfrac{1}{0.03855 \text{ L}} = 1.052 \text{ M HCl}$

5.72 $0.902 \text{ g KHC}_8\text{H}_4\text{O}_4 \cdot \dfrac{1 \text{ mol KHC}_8\text{H}_4\text{O}_4}{204.22 \text{ g}} \cdot \dfrac{1 \text{ mol NaOH}}{1 \text{ mol KHC}_8\text{H}_4\text{O}_4} \cdot \dfrac{1}{0.02645 \text{ L}} = 0.167 \text{ M NaOH}$

5.73 $36.04 \text{ mL} \cdot \dfrac{1 \text{ L}}{10^3 \text{ mL}} \cdot \dfrac{0.509 \text{ mol NaOH}}{1 \text{ L}} \cdot \dfrac{1 \text{ mol H}_2\text{A}}{2 \text{ mol NaOH}} = 0.00917 \text{ mol H}_2\text{A}$

$\dfrac{0.954 \text{ g}}{0.00917 \text{ mol}} = 104 \text{ g/mol}$

5.74 $29.1 \text{ mL} \cdot \dfrac{1 \text{ L}}{10^3 \text{ mL}} \cdot \dfrac{0.513 \text{ mol NaOH}}{1 \text{ L}} = 0.0149 \text{ mol NaOH}$

$0.0149 \text{ mol NaOH} \cdot \dfrac{1 \text{ mol citric acid}}{3 \text{ mol NaOH}} = 0.00498 \text{ mol acid}$ $\dfrac{0.956 \text{ g}}{0.00498 \text{ mol}} = 192 \text{ g/mol}$

$0.0149 \text{ mol NaOH} \cdot \dfrac{1 \text{ mol tartaric acid}}{2 \text{ mol NaOH}} = 0.00746 \text{ mol acid}$ $\dfrac{0.956 \text{ g}}{0.00746 \text{ mol}} = 128 \text{ g/mol}$

The calculated molar mass matches that of citric acid (192 g/mol) but not that of tartaric acid (150. g/mol), so the unknown acid is citric acid.

5.75 $22.25 \text{ mL} \cdot \dfrac{1 \text{ L}}{10^3 \text{ mL}} \cdot \dfrac{0.0123 \text{ mol KMnO}_4}{1 \text{ L}} \cdot \dfrac{5 \text{ mol Fe}^{2+}}{1 \text{ mol KMnO}_4} \cdot \dfrac{55.85 \text{ g}}{1 \text{ mol Fe}^{2+}} = 0.0764 \text{ g Fe}$

$\dfrac{0.0764 \text{ g Fe}}{0.598 \text{ g sample}} \cdot 100\% = 12.8\% \text{ Fe}$

5.76 $27.85 \text{ mL} \cdot \dfrac{1 \text{ L}}{10^3 \text{ mL}} \cdot \dfrac{0.102 \text{ mol Br}_2}{1 \text{ L}} \cdot \dfrac{1 \text{ mol C}_6\text{H}_8\text{O}_6}{1 \text{ mol Br}_2} \cdot \dfrac{176.13 \text{ g}}{1 \text{ mol C}_6\text{H}_8\text{O}_6} = 0.500 \text{ g C}_6\text{H}_8\text{O}_6$

5.77   (a) One possible answer is NaBr

(b) One possible answer is $Cu(OH)_2$

(c) One possible answer is $CaCO_3$

(d) One possible answer is KNO_3

5.78   (a) One possible answer is $NaCH_3CO_2$

      (b) One possible answer is NiS

      (c) One possible answer is NaOH

      (d) One possible answer is $PbCl_2$

5.79 $Cu(NO_3)_2$ and $CuCl_2$ are soluble in water, $CuCO_3$ and $Cu_3(PO_4)_2$ are insoluble in water

5.80 NO_3^-, nitrate ion, and ClO_4^-, perchlorate ion

5.81   Nitrate ions are spectator ions in this acid-base reaction

$$2\,H^+(aq) + Mg(OH)_2(s) \rightarrow 2\,H_2O(\ell) + Mg^{2+}(aq)$$

5.82   (a) $CuS(s)$ copper(II) sulfide

$$Cu^{2+}(aq) + S^{2-}(aq) \rightarrow CuS(s)$$

      (b) $CaCO_3(s)$ calcium carbonate

$$Ca^{2+}(aq) + CO_3^{2-}(aq) \rightarrow CaCO_3(s)$$

      (c) $AgI(s)$ silver iodide

$$Ag^+(aq) + I^-(aq) \rightarrow AgI(s)$$

5.83   (a) Cl_2, chlorine, has been reduced and NaBr, sodium bromide, has been oxidized

      (b) Cl_2, chlorine, is the oxidizing agent and NaBr, sodium bromide, is the reducing agent

      (c) $125\ mL \cdot \dfrac{1\ L}{10^3\ mL} \cdot \dfrac{0.153\ mol\ NaBr}{1\ L} \cdot \dfrac{1\ mol\ Cl_2}{2\ mol\ NaBr} \cdot \dfrac{70.91\ g}{1\ mol\ Cl_2} = 0.678\ g\ Cl_2$

5.84   Oxidizing agents: HNO_3, Cl_2, O_2, $KMnO_4$ Reducing agent: Na

5.85 $1\ L \cdot \dfrac{0.1\ mol\ NaCl}{1\ L} \cdot \dfrac{58\ g}{1\ mol\ NaCl} = 6\ g\ NaCl$

      $1\ L \cdot \dfrac{0.06\ mol\ Na_2CO_3}{1\ L} \cdot \dfrac{106\ g}{1\ mol\ Na_2CO_3} = 6\ g\ Na_2CO_3$

Limited to one significant figure, the solutions contain the same amount of solute.

5.86   (a) reactant favored

      (b) product favored

5.87 $500.0\ mL \cdot \dfrac{1\ L}{10^3\ mL} \cdot \dfrac{0.20\ mol\ Na_2CO_3}{1\ L} \cdot \dfrac{106\ g}{1\ mol\ Na_2CO_3} = 11\ g\ Na_2CO_3$

Weigh out 11 g of Na_2CO_3 and place it in the 500.0 mL flask. Add a small amount of distilled water and mix until the solute dissolves. Add water until the meniscus of the solution rests at the calibrated mark on the neck of the volumetric flask. Cap the flask and swirl to ensure adequate mixing.

5.88 $250.\ mL\ \cdot\ \dfrac{1\ L}{10^3\ mL}\ \cdot\ \dfrac{0.500\ mol\ KCl}{1\ L}\ =0.125\ mol\ KCl$

Take one-fourth of the KCl, place it in the volumetric flask, and a small amount of distilled water and mix until the solute dissolves. Add water until the meniscus of the solution rests at the calibrated mark on the neck of the volumetric flask. Cap the flask and swirl to ensure adequate mixing.

5.89   In 0.015 M HCl, [H$^+$] = 0.015 M

In pH 1.2 solution, [H$^+$] = 10^{-pH} = $10^{-1.2}$ = 0.06 M

The pH 1.2 solution has a higher hydrogen ion concentration.

5.90 $H_2SO_4(aq) + 2\ KOH(aq) \rightarrow K_2SO_4(aq) + 2\ H_2O(\ell)$

$1.56\ g\ KOH\ \cdot\ \dfrac{1\ mol\ KOH}{56.11\ g}\ \cdot\ \dfrac{1\ mol\ H_2SO_4}{2\ mol\ KOH}\ \cdot\ \dfrac{1\ L}{0.054\ mol\ H_2SO_4}\ =0.257\ L\ (257\ mL)$

5.91   (a) $MgCO_3(s) + 2\ H^+(aq) \rightarrow CO_2(g) + Mg^{2+}(aq) + H_2O(\ell)$

Chloride ion, Cl$^-$, is the spectator ion in this reaction.

(b) gas-forming reaction

(c) [H$^+$] = 10^{-pH} = $10^{-1.56}$ = 0.028 M

$125\ mL\ \cdot\ \dfrac{1\ L}{10^3\ mL}\ \cdot\ \dfrac{0.028\ mol\ H^+}{1\ L}\ \cdot\ \dfrac{1\ mol\ MgCO_3}{2\ mol\ H^+}\ \cdot\ \dfrac{84.31\ g}{1\ mol\ MgCO_3}\ =0.15\ g\ MgCO_3$

5.92   (a) $(NH_4)_2S(aq) + Hg(NO_3)_2(aq) \rightarrow HgS(s) + 2\ NH_4NO_3(aq)$

(b) ammonium sulfide, mercury(II) nitrate, mercury(II) sulfide, ammonium nitrate

(c) precipitation reaction

5.93   (a) H_2O, NH_3, NH_4^+, and OH$^-$ (and a trace of H$^+$)

(b) H_2O, CH_3CO_2H, $CH_3CO_2^-$, and H$^+$ (and a trace of OH$^-$)

(c) H_2O, Na$^+$, and OH$^-$ (and a trace of H$^+$)

(d) H_2O, H$^+$, and Br$^-$ (and a trace of OH$^-$)

5.94 $H_3C_6H_5O_7(aq) + 3\ NaHCO_3(aq) \rightarrow 3\ H_2O(\ell) + 3\ CO_2(g) + Na_3C_6H_5O_7(aq)$

$0.100\ g\ H_3C_6H_5O_7\ \cdot\ \dfrac{1\ mol\ H_3C_6H_5O_7}{192.1\ g}\ \cdot\ \dfrac{3\ mol\ NaHCO_3}{1\ mol\ H_3C_6H_5O_7}\ \cdot\ \dfrac{84.01\ g}{1\ mol\ NaHCO_3}\ =0.131\ g$

5.95 $0.125\ L\ \cdot\ \dfrac{0.15\ mol\ CH_3CO_2H}{1\ L}\ \cdot\ \dfrac{1\ mol\ NaHCO_3}{1\ mol\ CH_3CO_2H}\ \cdot\ \dfrac{84.01\ g}{1\ mol\ NaHCO_3}\ =1.58\ g\ NaHCO_3$

15.0 g NaHCO$_3$ is available, so CH$_3$CO$_2$H is the limiting reactant

$0.125\ L\ \cdot\ \dfrac{0.15\ mol\ CH_3CO_2H}{1\ L}\ \cdot\ \dfrac{1\ mol\ NaCH_3CO_2}{1\ mol\ CH_3CO_2H}\ \cdot\ \dfrac{82.03\ g}{1\ mol\ NaCH_3CO_2}\ =1.54\ g\ NaCH_3CO_2$

5.96 $0.03351 \text{ L} \cdot \dfrac{0.0102 \text{ mol NaOH}}{1 \text{ L}} \cdot \dfrac{1 \text{ mol H}_3\text{C}_6\text{H}_5\text{O}_7}{3 \text{ mol NaOH}} \cdot \dfrac{192.13 \text{ g}}{1 \text{ mol H}_3\text{C}_6\text{H}_5\text{O}_7} = 0.219 \text{ g H}_3\text{C}_6\text{H}_5\text{O}_7$

5.97 $0.04021 \text{ L} \cdot \dfrac{0.246 \text{ mol I}_2}{1 \text{ L}} \cdot \dfrac{2 \text{ mol Na}_2\text{S}_2\text{O}_3}{1 \text{ mol I}_2} \cdot \dfrac{158.11 \text{ g}}{1 \text{ mol Na}_2\text{S}_2\text{O}_3} = 3.13 \text{ g Na}_2\text{S}_2\text{O}_3$

$\dfrac{3.13 \text{ g}}{3.232 \text{ g}} \cdot 100\% = 96.8\%$

5.98 $0.02958 \text{ L} \cdot \dfrac{0.550 \text{ mol NaOH}}{1 \text{ L}} \cdot \dfrac{1 \text{ mol H}_2\text{C}_2\text{O}_4}{2 \text{ mol NaOH}} \cdot \dfrac{90.035 \text{ g}}{1 \text{ mol H}_2\text{C}_2\text{O}_4} = 0.732 \text{ g H}_2\text{C}_2\text{O}_4$

$\dfrac{0.732 \text{ g}}{4.554 \text{ g}} \cdot 100\% = 16.1\%$

5.99   Some possible answers:

(a) Water soluble: $CuCl_2$, copper(II) chloride $Cu(NO_3)_2$, copper(II) nitrate

Water insoluble: $CuCO_3$, copper(II) carbonate   CuS, copper(II) sulfide

(b) Water soluble: $BaBr_2$, barium bromide $Ba(CH_3CO_2)_2$, barium acetate

Water insoluble: $BaSO_4$, barium sulfate $BaCrO_4$, barium chromate

5.100   (a) $K_2CO_3(aq) + 2 HClO_4(aq) \rightarrow 2 KClO_4(aq) + CO_2(g) + H_2O(\ell)$

gas-forming reaction

$CO_3^{2-}(aq) + 2 H^+(aq) \rightarrow CO_2(g) + H_2O(\ell)$

(b) $FeCl_2(aq) + (NH_4)_2S(aq) \rightarrow FeS(s) + 2 NH_4Cl(aq)$

precipitation reaction

$Fe^{2+}(aq) + S^{2-}(aq) \rightarrow FeS(s)$

(c) $Fe(NO_3)_2(aq) + Na_2CO_3(aq) \rightarrow FeCO_3(s) + 2 NaNO_3(aq)$

precipitation reaction

$Fe^{2+}(aq) + CO_3^{2-}(aq) \rightarrow FeCO_3(s)$

5.101   (a) $Pb(NO_3)_2(aq) + 2 KOH(aq) \rightarrow Pb(OH)_2(s) + 2 KNO_3(aq)$

$Pb^{2+}(aq) + 2 OH^-(aq) \rightarrow Pb(OH)_2(s)$

(b) $Cu(NO_3)_2(aq) + Na_2CO_3(aq) \rightarrow CuCO_3(s) + 2 NaNO_3(aq)$

$Cu^{2+}(aq) + CO_3^{2-}(aq) \rightarrow CuCO_3(s)$

5.102   (a) $pH = -\log[H^+] = -\log(0.105) = 0.979$

(b) $[H^+] = 10^{-pH} = 10^{-2.56} = 0.0028 \text{ M}$ The solution is acidic

(c) $[H^+] = 10^{-pH} = 10^{-9.67} = 2.1 \times 10^{-10} \text{ M}$ The solution is basic

(d) $c_d = c_c \cdot \dfrac{V_c}{V_d} = 2.56 \text{ M} \cdot \dfrac{10.0 \text{ mL}}{250. \text{ mL}} = 0.102 \text{ M}$

$pH = -\log[H^+] = -\log(0.102) = 0.990$

5.103   Net ionic equation: $H^+(aq) + HCO_3^-(aq) \rightarrow H_2O(\ell) + CO_2(g)$

$[H^+] = 10^{-pH} = 10^{-2.56} = 0.0028 \text{ M H}^+$

$0.125 \text{ L} \cdot \dfrac{0.0028 \text{ mol H}^+}{1 \text{ L}} \cdot \dfrac{1 \text{ mol NaHCO}_3}{1 \text{ mol H}^+} \cdot \dfrac{84.01 \text{ g}}{1 \text{ mol NaHCO}_3} = 0.029 \text{ g NaHCO}_3$

5.104 $0.500 \text{ L} \cdot \dfrac{2.50 \text{ mol HCl}}{1 \text{ L}} + 0.250 \text{ L} \cdot \dfrac{3.75 \text{ mol HCl}}{1 \text{ L}} = 2.19 \text{ mol HCl}$

$\dfrac{2.19 \text{ mol HCl}}{0.750 \text{ L}} = 2.92 \text{ M HCl}$

$pH = -\log[H^+] = -\log(2.92) = -0.465$

5.105 $HCl(aq) + NaOH(aq) \rightarrow NaCl(aq) + H_2O(\ell)$

$[H^+] = 10^{-1.92} = 0.012 \text{ M H}^+ = 0.012 \text{ M HCl}$ $0.250 \text{ L} \cdot \dfrac{0.012 \text{ mol}}{1 \text{ L}} = 0.0030 \text{ mol HCl}$

$0.250 \text{ L} \cdot \dfrac{0.0105 \text{ mol NaOH}}{1 \text{ L}} \cdot \dfrac{1 \text{ mol HCl}}{1 \text{ mol NaOH}} = 0.00263 \text{ mol HCl reacted}$

$0.0030 \text{ mol} - 0.00263 \text{ mol} \approx 0.0004 \text{ mol HCl remains}$

$pH = -\log\left(\dfrac{0.0004 \text{ mol}}{0.500 \text{ L}}\right) = 3.1$

5.106 $c_d = c_c \cdot \dfrac{V_c}{V_d} = 0.110 \text{ M} \cdot \dfrac{25.0 \text{ mL}}{100.0 \text{ mL}} = 0.0275 \text{ M}$

$0.0275 \text{ M} \cdot \dfrac{10.0 \text{ mL}}{250. \text{ mL}} = 0.00110 \text{ M Na}_2\text{CO}_3$

5.107 $0.200 \text{ L} \cdot \dfrac{50.0 \text{ g CH}_3\text{CO}_2\text{H}}{1 \text{ L vinegar}} \cdot \dfrac{1 \text{ mol CH}_3\text{CO}_2\text{H}}{60.05 \text{ g}} \cdot \dfrac{1 \text{ mol NaHCO}_3}{1 \text{ mol CH}_3\text{CO}_2\text{H}} \cdot \dfrac{84.01 \text{ g}}{1 \text{ mol NaHCO}_3} \cdot \dfrac{1 \text{ spoonful}}{3.8 \text{ g}}$

$= 3.7 \text{ spoonfuls of baking soda}$

Four spoonfuls of baking soda are required to consume the acetic acid.

5.108   (a)   Reactants: Na (+1), I (–1), H (+1), S (+6), O (–2), Mn (+4)

Products: Na (+1), S (+6), O (–2), Mn (+2), I (0), H (+1)

(b)   Oxidizing agent MnO_2, NaI is oxidized; Reducing agent NaI, MnO_2 is reduced

(c) $20.0 \text{ g NaI} \cdot \dfrac{1 \text{ mol NaI}}{149.9 \text{ g}} \cdot \dfrac{1 \text{ mol } I_2}{2 \text{ mol NaI}} \cdot \dfrac{253.8 \text{ g}}{1 \text{ mol } I_2} = 16.9 \text{ g } I_2$

$10.0 \text{ g MnO}_2 \cdot \dfrac{1 \text{ mol MnO}_2}{86.94 \text{ g}} \cdot \dfrac{1 \text{ mol } I_2}{1 \text{ mol MnO}_2} \cdot \dfrac{253.8 \text{ g}}{1 \text{ mol } I_2} = 29.2 \text{ g } I_2$

NaI is the limiting reactant; 16.9 g I_2 is produced

5.109 $0.250 \text{ L} \cdot \dfrac{0.125 \text{ mol HCl}}{1 \text{ L}} \cdot \dfrac{1 \text{ mol CaCO}_3}{2 \text{ mol HCl}} \cdot \dfrac{100.1 \text{ g}}{1 \text{ mol CaCO}_3} = 1.56 \text{ g CaCO}_3 \text{ required}$

2.56 g available – 1.56 g required = 1.00 g $CaCO_3$ remains

$0.250 \text{ L} \cdot \dfrac{0.125 \text{ mol HCl}}{1 \text{ L}} \cdot \dfrac{1 \text{ mol CaCl}_2}{2 \text{ mol HCl}} \cdot \dfrac{111.0 \text{ g}}{1 \text{ mol CaCl}_2} = 1.73 \text{ g CaCl}_2$

5.110 $0.03450 \text{ L} \cdot \dfrac{0.108 \text{ mol KMnO}_4}{1 \text{ L}} \cdot \dfrac{5 \text{ mol } C_2O_4^{2-}}{2 \text{ mol KMnO}_4} = 0.00932 \text{ mol } C_2O_4^{2-}$

Use mol $C_2O_4^{2-}$ to determine which formula is correct:

$0.00932 \text{ mol } C_2O_4^{2-} \cdot \dfrac{1 \text{ mol K[Fe(C}_2O_4)_2(H_2O)_2]}{2 \text{ mol } C_2O_4^{2-}} \cdot \dfrac{307.0 \text{ g}}{1 \text{ mol K[Fe(C}_2O_4)_2(H_2O)_2]} = 1.43 \text{ g compound}$

$0.00932 \text{ mol } C_2O_4^{2-} \cdot \dfrac{1 \text{ mol K}_3[Fe(C_2O_4)_3]}{3 \text{ mol } C_2O_4^{2-}} \cdot \dfrac{437.2 \text{ g}}{1 \text{ mol K}_3[Fe(C_2O_4)_3]} = 1.36 \text{ g compound}$

The correct formula is $K_3[Fe(C_2O_4)_3]$

5.111 $0.02363 \text{ L} \cdot \dfrac{1.500 \text{ mol HCl}}{1 \text{ L}} \cdot \dfrac{1 \text{ mol NH}_4^+}{1 \text{ mol HCl}} \cdot \dfrac{1 \text{ mol NH}_3}{1 \text{ mol NH}_4^+} = 0.03545 \text{ mol NH}_3$

$0.03545 \text{ mol NH}_3 \cdot \dfrac{17.030 \text{ g}}{1 \text{ mol NH}_3} = 0.6036 \text{ g NH}_3$

1.580 g compound – 0.6036 g NH_3 = 0.976 g $CrCl_3$

$0.976 \text{ g CrCl}_3 \cdot \dfrac{1 \text{ mol CrCl}_3}{158.4 \text{ g}} = 0.00616 \text{ mol CrCl}_3$ $x = \dfrac{0.03545 \text{ mol NH}_3}{0.00616 \text{ mol CrCl}_3} = 6$

5.112   (a) $(NH_4)_2PtCl_4(aq) + 2\ NH_3(aq) \rightarrow Pt(NH_3)_2Cl_2(aq) + 2\ NH_4Cl(aq)$

(b) $12.50\ g\ Pt(NH_3)_2Cl_2 \cdot \dfrac{1\ mol\ Pt(NH_3)_2Cl_2}{300.05\ g} \cdot \dfrac{1\ mol\ (NH_4)_2PtCl_4}{1\ mol\ Pt(NH_3)_2Cl_2} \cdot \dfrac{372.97\ g}{1\ mol\ (NH_4)_2PtCl_4}$

$$= 15.54\ g\ (NH_4)_2PtCl_4$$

$12.50\ g\ Pt(NH_3)_2Cl_2 \cdot \dfrac{1\ mol\ Pt(NH_3)_2Cl_2}{300.05\ g} \cdot \dfrac{2\ mol\ NH_3}{1\ mol\ Pt(NH_3)_2Cl_2} \cdot \dfrac{1\ L}{0.125\ mol\ NH_3} = 0.667\ L\ solution$

(c) $0.0370\ L \cdot \dfrac{0.475\ mol\ HCl}{1\ L} \cdot \dfrac{1\ mol\ C_5H_5N}{1\ mol\ HCl} = 0.0176\ mol\ C_5H_5N$ unused by titration

$1.50\ mL \cdot \dfrac{0.979\ g}{1\ mL} \cdot \dfrac{1\ mol\ C_5H_5N}{79.10\ g} = 0.0186\ mol\ C_5H_5N$ originally added

$0.0186\ mol - 0.0176\ mol = 0.0010\ mol\ C_5H_5N$ reacted with cisplatin

$0.150\ g\ Pt(NH_3)_2Cl_2 \cdot \dfrac{1\ mol\ Pt(NH_3)_2Cl_2}{300.0\ g} = 5.00 \times 10^{-4}\ mol\ Pt(NH_3)_2Cl_2$

$\dfrac{0.0010\ mol\ C_5H_5N}{5.00 \times 10^{-4}\ mol\ Pt(NH_3)_2Cl_2} = \dfrac{2\ mol\ C_5H_5N}{1\ mol\ Pt(NH_3)_2Cl_2}$

The compound formula is $Pt(NH_3)_2Cl_2(C_5H_5N)_2$

5.113 $1.0\ g \cdot \dfrac{1\ mol\ methylene\ blue}{320.\ g} \cdot \dfrac{1}{0.0500\ L} = 0.063\ M$ methylene blue

$V_d = \dfrac{c_c}{c_d} \cdot V_c = \dfrac{0.063\ M}{4.1 \times 10^{-8}\ M} \cdot 0.0500\ L = 7.6 \times 10^4\ L$

5.114 $0.0500\ L \cdot \dfrac{0.100\ mol\ HCl}{1\ L} = 0.00500\ mol\ HCl$ (total)

$0.0111\ L \cdot \dfrac{0.121\ mol\ NaOH}{1\ L} \cdot \dfrac{1\ mol\ HCl}{1\ mol\ NaOH} = 0.00134\ mol\ HCl$ (excess)

$0.00500\ mol\ HCl\ (total) - 0.00134\ mol\ HCl\ (excess) = 0.00366\ mol\ HCl$ (reacted with NH_3)

$0.00366\ mol\ HCl \cdot \dfrac{1\ mol\ NH_3}{1\ mol\ HCl} \cdot \dfrac{1\ mol\ (NH_4)_2SO_4}{2\ mol\ NH_3} \cdot \dfrac{132.1\ g}{1\ mol\ (NH_4)_2SO_4} = 0.242\ g\ (NH_4)_2SO_4$

$\dfrac{0.242\ g\ (NH_4)_2SO_4}{0.475\ g\ sample} \cdot 100\% = 50.8\%$

5.115   (a)   Reaction 1: Cu^{2+} is reduced and is the oxidizing agent; I^- is oxidized and is the reducing agent

Reaction 2: I_3^- is reduced and is the oxidizing agent; $S_2O_3^{2-}$ is oxidized and is the reducing agent

(b) $0.02632\ L \cdot \dfrac{0.101\ mol\ Na_2S_2O_3}{1\ L} \cdot \dfrac{1\ mol\ I_3^-}{2\ mol\ Na_2S_2O_3} = 0.00133\ mol\ I_3^-$

$0.00133\ mol\ I_3^- \cdot \dfrac{2\ mol\ Cu^{2+}}{1\ mol\ I_3^-} \cdot \dfrac{63.55\ g}{1\ mol\ Cu^{2+}} = 0.169\ g\ Cu$

$\dfrac{0.169\ g}{0.251\ g} \cdot 100\% = 67.3\%$

5.116 $0.125 \text{ L} \cdot \dfrac{2.55 \text{ mol HCl}}{1 \text{ L}} \cdot \dfrac{1 \text{ mol metal oxide}}{2 \text{ mol HCl}} = 0.159 \text{ mol metal oxide}$

Set up two equations with two unknowns.

$0.159 \text{ mol metal oxide} = (x \text{ g CaO} \cdot \dfrac{1 \text{ mol CaO}}{56.08 \text{ g}}) + (y \text{ g MgO} \cdot \dfrac{1 \text{ mol MgO}}{40.30 \text{ g}})$

$7.695 \text{ g metal oxide} = x \text{ g CaO} + y \text{ g MgO}$

Substitute $(7.695 \text{ g} - y \text{ g MgO})$ for x and solve.

$y = 3.17 \text{ g MgO}$

$x = 4.52 \text{ g CaO}$

$\dfrac{4.52 \text{ g CaO}}{7.695 \text{ g sample}} \cdot 100\% = 58.7\% \text{ CaO}$ $\dfrac{3.17 \text{ g MgO}}{7.695 \text{ g sample}} \cdot 100\% = 41.2\% \text{ MgO}$

5.117   (a) Au, gold, has been oxidized and is the reducing agent

O$_2$, oxygen, has been reduced and is the oxidizing agent

(b) $10^3 \text{ kg ore} \cdot \dfrac{10^3 \text{ g}}{1 \text{ kg}} \cdot \dfrac{0.019 \text{ g Au}}{100. \text{ g ore}} \cdot \dfrac{1 \text{ mol Au}}{197 \text{ g}} \cdot \dfrac{8 \text{ mol NaCN}}{4 \text{ mol Au}} \cdot \dfrac{1 \text{ L}}{0.075 \text{ mol NaCN}} = 26 \text{ L solution}$

5.118 $FeCl_3(aq) + 3 \text{ NaOH}(aq) \rightarrow Fe(OH)_3(s) + 3 \text{ NaCl}(aq)$

(a) $0.0250 \text{ L} \cdot \dfrac{0.234 \text{ mol FeCl}_3}{1 \text{ L}} \cdot \dfrac{1 \text{ mol Fe(OH)}_3}{1 \text{ mol FeCl}_3} \cdot \dfrac{106.9 \text{ g}}{1 \text{ mol Fe(OH)}_3} = 0.625 \text{ g Fe(OH)}_3$

$0.0425 \text{ L} \cdot \dfrac{0.453 \text{ mol NaOH}}{1 \text{ L}} \cdot \dfrac{1 \text{ mol Fe(OH)}_3}{3 \text{ mol NaOH}} \cdot \dfrac{106.9 \text{ g}}{1 \text{ mol Fe(OH)}_3} = 0.686 \text{ g Fe(OH)}_3$

NaOH is the excess reactant and 0.625 g Fe(OH)$_3$ precipitates

(b) $0.0250 \text{ L} \cdot \dfrac{0.234 \text{ mol FeCl}_3}{1 \text{ L}} \cdot \dfrac{3 \text{ mol NaOH}}{1 \text{ mol FeCl}_3} = 0.0176 \text{ mol NaOH required}$

$0.0425 \text{ L} \cdot \dfrac{0.453 \text{ mol NaOH}}{1 \text{ L}} - 0.0176 \text{ mol NaOH} = 0.0017 \text{ mol NaOH remains}$

$\dfrac{0.0017 \text{ mol}}{0.0675 \text{ L}} = 0.025 \text{ M NaOH}$

5.119   If both students base their calculations on the amount of HCl solution pipetted into the flask (20 mL), then the second student's result will be (e) the same as the first student's. However, if the HCl concentration is calculated using the diluted solution volume, student 1 will use a volume of 40 mL and student 2 will use a volume of 80 mL in the calculation. The second student's result will be (c) two times less than the first student's.

5.120   (a) $5 \text{ Fe}^{2+}(aq) + \text{MnO}_4^-(aq) + 8 \text{ H}^+(aq) \rightarrow 5 \text{ Fe}^{3+}(aq) + \text{Mn}^{2+}(aq) + 4 \text{ H}_2\text{O}(\ell)$

(b) MnO_4^- is the oxidizing agent and Fe^{2+} is the reducing agent

(c) Fe^{2+}

5.121   100 mL of 0.10 M HCl contains 0.010 mol of HCl. This requires 0.0050 mol of Zn or 3.27 g for complete reaction. Thus, in flask 2 the reaction just uses all of the Zn and produces 0.0050 mol H_2 gas. In flask 1, containing 7.00 g of Zn, some Zn remains after the HCl has been consumed; 0.005 mol H_2 gas is produced. In flask 3, there is insufficient Zn, so less hydrogen is produced.

5.122   One possible answer:

$BaCO_3(s) + 2\ HCl(aq) \rightarrow BaCl_2(aq) + H_2O(\ell) + CO_2(g)$

5.123   Possible answers:

(a) $BaCl_2(aq) + Na_2SO_4(aq) \rightarrow BaSO_4(s) + 2\ NaCl(aq)$

(b) $BaCO_3(s) + H_2SO_4(aq) \rightarrow BaSO_4(s) + H_2O(\ell) + CO_2(g)$

5.124   Possible answers:

(a) $Zn(OH)_2(s) + 2\ HCl(aq) \rightarrow ZnCl_2(aq) + 2\ H_2O(\ell)$

(b) $ZnCO_3(s) + 2\ HCl(aq) \rightarrow ZnCl_2(aq) + H_2O(\ell) + CO_2(g)$

(c) $Zn(s) + Cl_2(g) \rightarrow ZnCl_2(s)$

5.125 $\dfrac{0.033\ mol\ C_2H_5OH}{1\ L} \cdot \dfrac{46.1\ g}{1\ mol\ C_2H_5OH} \cdot \dfrac{10^3\ mg}{1\ g} \cdot \dfrac{1\ L}{10\ dL} = 150\ mg/dL$

The person is intoxicated and will be arrested.

Chapter 6
Principles of Reactivity: Energy and Chemical Reactions

INSTRUCTOR'S NOTES

The chapter begins coverage of energy considerations in chemistry. Although it may not immediately seem relevant to students, a few examples from their lives (food as an energy source) or future profession (warm-blooded animals for life science students; combustion in autos for engineering types) could help stimulate their interest.

Our experience is that students will have some difficulty with thermochemistry, primarily because they have problems with the concept of energy. Some demonstrations, described below, can help them.

Some concepts that are often confused include:

- Heat versus temperature (analogy of swimming pool water content versus depth).
- Calories versus joules, a distinction only in units, not in concept, though common usage of the former in food versus the latter in the classroom may imply a difference
- Sign conventions (see boxed explanation and summary tables)
- Heat gained and lost within the system in calorimetry experiments
- State functions versus non-state functions (analogy of altitude versus distance traveled)

This chapter need not be covered at this point in the course. However, we have used the notion of energy changes in our discussions of atomic properties and in the discussion of bond energies in the first chapter on bonding (Chapter 9). Also, if some students are only required to complete one semester of general chemistry for their particular major, they will still get an introduction to these concepts if this chapter is included in the order of the text.

This topic is normally covered in three to four lectures.

SUGGESTED DEMONSTRATIONS

1. Introduction to the Chapter
    - In spite of their experience, some students do not have a good "feeling" for heat and energy. Therefore, demonstrations are quite useful here. In particular, we open the lecture on heat transfer, thermometers, and heat capacity with the demonstration in Figure 6.7.
2. Product-Favored Reactions
    - See the *General ChemistryNow CD-ROM* for the Gummy Bear decomposition and the aluminum/bromine reaction.
    - Many product-favored reaction demonstrations were described in Chapter 5. For some excellent examples see Shakhashiri, B. Z. *Chemical Demonstrations: A Handbook for Teachers of Chemistry*; University of Wisconsin Press, 1983; Vol. 1.

3. Reactant-Favored Reactions

    - Bring mineral samples into lecture to demonstrate reactant-favored reactions.

4. Energy Conversion

    - See the *General ChemistryNow CD-ROM* for a screen showing examples of energy conversion.

    - See the *General ChemistryNow CD-ROM* for an animation of the law of energy conservation.

5. Heat Transfer

    - Heat a metal block in a Bunsen burner and plunge it into water to demonstrate heat transfer.

    - See the *General ChemistryNow CD-ROM* for an animation of heat transfer.

6. Exothermic Reactions

    - Keiter, R. L.; Gamage, C. P. "Combustion of White Phosphorous," *Journal of Chemical Education* **2001**, *78*, 908.

    - Campbell, D. J. "An Alcohol Rocket Car—A Variation on the 'Whoosh Bottle' Theme," *Journal of Chemical Education* **2001**, *78*, 910.

    - McAfee, L. V.; Jumper, C. F. "The Reusable Heat Pack," *Journal of Chemical Education* **1991**, *68*, 780.

    - Shakhashiri, B. Z. "The Nonburning Towel," *Chemical Demonstrations: A Handbook for Teachers of Chemistry*; University of Wisconsin Press, 1983; Vol. 1, pp. 13-14.

    - Shakhashiri, B. Z. "Reaction of Calcium Oxide and Water (Slaking of Lime)," *Chemical Demonstrations: A Handbook for Teachers of Chemistry*; University of Wisconsin Press, 1983; Vol. 1, pp. 19-20.

    - We often do the peroxide rocket again (Chapter 4 in this Manual) and blow up a hydrogen balloon.

7. Endothermic Reactions

    - Shakhashiri, B. Z. "Chemical Cold Pack," *Chemical Demonstrations: A Handbook for Teachers of Chemistry*; University of Wisconsin Press, 1983; Vol. 1, pp. 8-9.

    - Shakhashiri, B. Z. "Barium Hydroxide and Ammonium Salts," *Chemical Demonstrations: A Handbook for Teachers of Chemistry*; University of Wisconsin Press, 1983; Vol. 1, pp. 10-12.

    - The demonstration with the plastic bag and dry ice in Figure 6.13 is very effective and very easy to do.

8. Changes of State

    - Burgstahler, A. W.; Bricker, C. E. "Measuring the Heat of Sublimation of Dry Ice with a Polystyrene Foam Cup Calorimeter," *Journal of Chemical Education* **1991**, *68*, 332.

    - Vemulapalli, G. K. "A Discourse on the Drinking Bird," *Journal of Chemical Education* **1990**, *67*, 457.

    - Place some Dry Ice in a plastic bag and seal it (Figure 6.13). This process can also be used to demonstrate the First Law of Thermodynamics.

9. State Functions

    - Use a balloon to demonstrate state functions.

10. Calorimetry

    - When discussing calorimetry, we always take a laboratory calorimeter to the lecture so the students can see the various parts and get a better notion of how they work in practice.

SOLUTIONS TO STUDY QUESTIONS

6.1   Mechanical energy is used to move the lever, producing electrical and radiant energy

6.2   Mechanical energy, electrical energy, radiant energy

6.3 $1200 \text{ Cal} \cdot \dfrac{10^3 \text{ cal}}{1 \text{ Cal}} \cdot \dfrac{4.184 \text{ J}}{1 \text{ cal}} = 5.0 \times 10^6 \text{ J}$

6.4 $1670 \text{ kJ} \cdot \dfrac{10^3 \text{ J}}{1 \text{ kJ}} \cdot \dfrac{1 \text{ cal}}{4.184 \text{ J}} \cdot \dfrac{1 \text{ Cal}}{10^3 \text{ cal}} = 399 \text{ Cal}$

6.5 $170 \text{ kcal} \cdot \dfrac{10^3 \text{ cal}}{1 \text{ kcal}} \cdot \dfrac{4.184 \text{ J}}{1 \text{ cal}} \cdot \dfrac{1 \text{ kJ}}{10^3 \text{ J}} = 710 \text{ kJ}$

The food product with 170 kcal per serving has a greater energy content per serving.

6.6   A medium raw apple has an energy content of 72 kcal (301 kJ). A raw apricot has an energy content of 17 kcal (70 kJ).

6.7 $\dfrac{28.1 \text{ J}}{\text{mol} \cdot \text{K}} \cdot \dfrac{1 \text{ mol Hg}}{200.6 \text{ g}} = 0.140 \text{ J/g} \cdot \text{K}$

6.8 $\dfrac{1.74 \text{ J}}{\text{g} \cdot \text{K}} \cdot \dfrac{78.11 \text{ g}}{1 \text{ mol C}_6\text{H}_6} = 136 \text{ J/mol} \cdot \text{K}$

6.9 $q = (168 \text{ g})(0.385 \text{ J/g} \cdot \text{K})(298.8 \text{ K} - 261.0 \text{ K}) = 2440 \text{ J}$

6.10 $q = (50.00 \text{ mL} \cdot \dfrac{0.997 \text{ g}}{1 \text{ mL}})(4.184 \text{ J/g} \cdot \text{K})(301.90 \text{ K} - 298.67 \text{ K}) = 674 \text{ J}$

6.11 $2.25 \times 10^3 \text{ J} = (344 \text{ g})(0.449 \text{ J/g} \cdot \text{K})(T_f - 291.4 \text{ K})$

       $T_f = 306.0 \text{ K (32.8 °C)}$

6.12 $1.850 \times 10^3 \text{ J} = (500. \text{ g})(0.385 \text{ J/g} \cdot \text{K})(310. \text{ K} - T_i)$

       $T_i = 300. \text{ K (27 °C)}$

6.13 $q_{\text{metal}} + q_{\text{water}} = 0$

       $[(45.5 \text{ g})(0.385 \text{ J/g} \cdot \text{K})(T_f - 373.0 \text{ K})] + [(152 \text{ g})(4.184 \text{ J/g} \cdot \text{K})(T_f - 291.7 \text{ K})] = 0$

       $T_f = 294 \text{ K (21 °C)}$

6.14 $q_{\text{metal}} + q_{\text{water}} = 0$

       $[(182 \text{ g})(0.128 \text{ J/g} \cdot \text{K})(300.7 \text{ K} - T_i)] + [(22.1 \text{ g})(4.184 \text{ J/g} \cdot \text{K})(300.7 \text{ K} - 298.2 \text{ K})] = 0$

       $T_i = 311 \text{ K (37 °C)}$

6.15 $q_{\text{cool water}} + q_{\text{warm water}} = 0$

[(156 g)(4.184 J/g·K)(T$_f$ − 295 K)] + [(85.2 g)(4.184 J/g·K)(T$_f$ − 368 K)] = 0

T$_f$ = 321 K (48 °C)

6.16   The final temperature is greater than 22.5 °C, so the 65.1-g sample of water must be warmer than the 108-g sample.

$q_{\text{cool water}} + q_{\text{warm water}} = 0$

[(108 g)(4.184 J/g·K)(321.1 − 295.7 K)] + [(65.1 g)(4.184 J/g·K)(321.1 K − T$_i$)] = 0

T$_i$ = 363 K (90. °C)

6.17 $q_{\text{metal}} + q_{\text{water}} = 0$

[(13.8 g)(C_{Zn})(300.3 K − 372.0 K)] + [(45.0 g)(4.184 J/g·K)(300.3 K − 298.2 K)] = 0

C_{Zn} = 0.40 J/g·K

6.18 $q_{\text{metal}} + q_{\text{water}} = 0$

[(237 g)(C_{Mo})(288.5 K − 373.2 K)] + [(244 g)(4.184 J/g·K)(288.5 K − 283.2 K)] = 0

C_{Mo} = 0.27 J/g·K

6.19 1.0×10^3 mL H$_2$O · $\dfrac{1.00 \text{ g}}{1 \text{ mL}}$ · 333 J/g = 3.3×10^5 J

6.20   16 cubes · $\dfrac{62.0 \text{ g}}{1 \text{ cube}}$ · 333 J/g = 3.30×10^5 J

6.21   125 g · $\dfrac{1 \text{ mol C}_6\text{H}_6}{78.11 \text{ g}}$ · $\dfrac{30.8 \text{ kJ}}{1 \text{ mol C}_6\text{H}_6}$ = 49.3 kJ

6.22   92.5 g · $\dfrac{1 \text{ mol CH}_3\text{Cl}}{50.49 \text{ g}}$ · $\dfrac{21.40 \text{ kJ}}{1 \text{ mol CH}_3\text{Cl}}$ = 39.2 kJ

6.23   1.00 mL · $\dfrac{1 \text{ cm}^3}{1 \text{ mL}}$ · $\dfrac{13.6 \text{ g}}{1 \text{ cm}^3}$ = 13.6 g Hg

q_{total} = energy to cool liquid + energy to change phase from liquid to solid

$q_{\text{cool liquid}}$ = (13.6 g)(0.140 J/g·K)(234.4 K − 296.2 K) = −118 J

$q_{\text{phase change}}$ = −(13.6 g)(11.4 J/g) = −155 J

q_{total} = −118 J + (−155 J) = −273 J (273 J released to the surroundings)

6.24 q_{total} = energy to heat metal + energy to change phase from solid to liquid

$q_{\text{heat metal}}$ = (454 g)(0.227 J/g·K)(505.1 K − 298.2 K) = 2.13×10^4 J

$q_{\text{phase change}}$ = (454 g)(59.2 J/g) = 2.69×10^4 J

q_{total} = 2.13×10^4 J + 2.69×10^4 J = 4.82×10^4 J

6.25 q = energy to heat liquid + energy to change phase from liquid to vapor

$q_{\text{heat liquid}} = (1.00 \times 10^3 \text{ g})(2.44 \text{ J/g·K})(351.44 \text{ K} - 293.2 \text{ K}) = 1.42 \times 10^5 \text{ J}$

$q_{\text{phase change}} = (1.00 \times 10^3 \text{ g})(855 \text{ J/g}) = 8.55 \times 10^5 \text{ J}$

$q_{\text{total}} = 1.42 \times 10^5 \text{ J} + 8.55 \times 10^5 \text{ J} = 9.97 \times 10^5 \text{ J}$

6.26 $25.0 \text{ mL} \cdot \dfrac{0.80 \text{ g}}{1 \text{ mL}} = 20. \text{ g C}_6\text{H}_6$

q_{total} = energy to cool liquid + energy to change phase from liquid to solid

$q_{\text{cool liquid}} = (20. \text{ g})(1.74 \text{ J/g·K})(278.7 \text{ K} - 293.1 \text{ K}) = -5.0 \times 10^2 \text{ J}$

$q_{\text{phase change}} = -(20. \text{ g})(127 \text{ J/g}) = -2500 \text{ J}$

$q_{\text{total}} = -5.0 \times 10^2 \text{ J} + (-2500 \text{ J}) = -3.0 \times 10^3 \text{ J}$ (3.0×10^3 J released to the surroundings)

6.27   exothermic

$1.25 \text{ g NO} \cdot \dfrac{1 \text{ mol NO}}{30.01 \text{ g}} \cdot \dfrac{114.1 \text{ kJ}}{2 \text{ mol NO}} = 2.38 \text{ kJ heat evolved}$

6.28   endothermic

$10.0 \text{ g CaO} \cdot \dfrac{1 \text{ mol CaO}}{56.08 \text{ g}} \cdot \dfrac{464.8 \text{ kJ}}{1 \text{ mol CaO}} = 82.9 \text{ kJ heat required}$

6.29 $1.00 \times 10^3 \text{ mL} \cdot \dfrac{0.69 \text{ g}}{1 \text{ mL}} \cdot \dfrac{1 \text{ mol C}_8\text{H}_{18}}{114.2 \text{ g}} \cdot \dfrac{10,922 \text{ kJ}}{2 \text{ mol C}_8\text{H}_{18}} = 3.3 \times 10^4 \text{ kJ heat evolved}$

6.30 $1.00 \times 10^3 \text{ mL} \cdot \dfrac{1.044 \text{ g}}{1 \text{ mL}} \cdot \dfrac{1 \text{ mol CH}_3\text{CO}_2\text{H}}{60.05 \text{ g}} \cdot \dfrac{355.9 \text{ kJ}}{1 \text{ mol CH}_3\text{CO}_2\text{H}} = 6.19 \times 10^3 \text{ kJ heat evolved}$

6.31 $q_{\text{reaction}} + q_{\text{solution}} = 0$

$q_{\text{reaction}} + \left[(100.0 \text{ mL} + 50.0 \text{ mL}) \left(\dfrac{1.00 \text{ g}}{1 \text{ mL}} \right) \right](4.2 \text{ J/g·K})(297.43 \text{ K} - 295.65 \text{ K}) = 0$

$q_{\text{reaction}} = -1100 \text{ J}$

$0.1000 \text{ L} \cdot \dfrac{0.200 \text{ mol CsOH}}{1 \text{ L}} = 0.0200 \text{ mol CsOH}$

$\dfrac{-1100 \text{ J}}{0.0200 \text{ mol CsOH}} \cdot \dfrac{1 \text{ kJ}}{10^3 \text{ J}} = -56 \text{ kJ/mol CsOH}$

6.32 $q_{\text{reaction}} + q_{\text{solution}} = 0$

$q_{\text{reaction}} + [(125 \text{ mL} + 50.0 \text{ mL})\left(\dfrac{1.00 \text{ g}}{1 \text{ mL}}\right)](4.2 \text{ J/g·K})(297.55 \text{ K} - 294.65 \text{ K}) = 0$

$q_{\text{reaction}} = -2100 \text{ J}$

$0.125 \text{ L} \cdot \dfrac{0.250 \text{ mol CsOH}}{1 \text{ L}} = 0.0313 \text{ mol CsOH}$

$\dfrac{-2100 \text{ J}}{0.0313 \text{ mol CsOH}} \cdot \dfrac{1 \text{ kJ}}{10^3 \text{ J}} = -68 \text{ kJ/mol CsOH}$

6.33 $q_{\text{metal}} + q_{\text{water}} = 0$

$[(20.8 \text{ g})(C_{\text{Ti}})(297.5 \text{ K} - 372.7 \text{ K})] + [(75 \text{ g})(4.184 \text{ J/g·K})(297.5 \text{ K} - 294.9 \text{ K})] = 0$

$C_{\text{Ti}} = 0.52 \text{ J/g·K}$

6.34 $q_{\text{metal}} + q_{\text{water}} = 0$

$[(24.26 \text{ g})(C_{\text{Cr}})(298.8 \text{ K} - 371.5 \text{ K})] + [(82.3 \text{ g})(4.184 \text{ J/g·K})(298.8 \text{ K} - 296.5 \text{ K})] = 0$

$C_{\text{Cr}} = 0.45 \text{ J/g·K}$

6.35 $q_{\text{solution}} = (155.4 \text{ g})(4.2 \text{ J/g·K})(289.4 \text{ K} - 291.8 \text{ K}) = -1600 \text{ J}$

$5.44 \text{ g NH}_4\text{NO}_3 \cdot \dfrac{1 \text{ mol NH}_4\text{NO}_3}{80.04 \text{ g}} = 0.0680 \text{ mol NH}_4\text{NO}_3$

$q_{\text{dissolving}} = -q_{\text{solution}} = -\dfrac{-1600 \text{ J}}{0.0680 \text{ mol NH}_4\text{NO}_3} \cdot \dfrac{1 \text{ kJ}}{10^3 \text{ J}} = 23 \text{ kJ/mol NH}_4\text{NO}_3$

6.36   Assume $C_{\text{solution}} = 4.2 \text{ J/g·K}$

$q_{\text{solution}} = (140.2 \text{ g})(4.2 \text{ J/g·K})(302.0 \text{ K} - 293.4 \text{ K}) = 5100 \text{ J}$

$5.2 \text{ g H}_2\text{SO}_4 \cdot \dfrac{1 \text{ mol H}_2\text{SO}_4}{98.1 \text{ g}} = 0.053 \text{ mol H}_2\text{SO}_4$

$q_{\text{dissolving}} = -q_{\text{solution}} = -\dfrac{5100 \text{ J}}{0.053 \text{ mol H}_2\text{SO}_4} \cdot \dfrac{1 \text{ kJ}}{10^3 \text{ J}} = -96 \text{ kJ/mol H}_2\text{SO}_4$

6.37 $q = q_{\text{water}} + q_{\text{calorimeter}}$

$q = [(815 \text{ g})(4.184 \text{ J/g·K})(299.87 \text{ K} - 294.40 \text{ K})] + [(923 \text{ J/K})(299.87 \text{ K} - 294.40 \text{ K})]$

$q = 2.37 \times 10^4 \text{ J}$

$2.56 \text{ g S}_8 \cdot \dfrac{1 \text{ mol S}_8}{256.5 \text{ g}} \cdot \dfrac{8 \text{ mol SO}_2}{1 \text{ mol S}_8} = 0.0798 \text{ mol SO}_2$

$\dfrac{2.37 \times 10^4 \text{ J}}{0.0798 \text{ mol SO}_2} \cdot \dfrac{1 \text{ kJ}}{10^3 \text{ J}} = 297 \text{ kJ/mol SO}_2$

6.38 $q = q_{water} + q_{calorimeter}$

$q = [(775 \text{ g})(4.184 \text{ J/g·K})(300.53 \text{ K} - 298.15 \text{ K})] + [(893 \text{ J/K})((300.53 \text{ K} - 298.15 \text{ K})]$

$q = 9840 \text{ J}$

$0.300 \text{ g C} \cdot \dfrac{1 \text{ mol C}}{12.01 \text{ g}} = 0.0250 \text{ mol C}$

$\dfrac{9840 \text{ J}}{0.0250 \text{ mol C}} \cdot \dfrac{1 \text{ kJ}}{10^3 \text{ J}} = 394 \text{ kJ/mol C}$

6.39 $q = q_{water} + q_{calorimeter}$

$q = [(775 \text{ g})(4.184 \text{ J/g·K})(304.84 \text{ K} - 295.65 \text{ K})] + [(893 \text{ J/K})(304.84 \text{ K} - 295.65 \text{ K})]$

$q = 3.80 \times 10^4 \text{ J}$

$1.500 \text{ g C}_6\text{H}_5\text{CO}_2\text{H} \cdot \dfrac{1 \text{ mol C}_6\text{H}_5\text{CO}_2\text{H}}{122.12 \text{ g}} = 0.01228 \text{ mol C}_6\text{H}_5\text{CO}_2\text{H}$

$\dfrac{3.80 \times 10^4 \text{ J}}{0.01228 \text{ mol C}_6\text{H}_5\text{CO}_2\text{H}} \cdot \dfrac{1 \text{ kJ}}{10^3 \text{ J}} = 3090 \text{ kJ/mol C}_6\text{H}_5\text{CO}_2\text{H}$

6.40 $q = q_{water} + q_{calorimeter}$

$q = [(575 \text{ g})(4.184 \text{ J/g·K})(298.37 \text{ K} - 294.85 \text{ K})] + [(650 \text{ J/K})(298.37 \text{ K} - 294.85 \text{ K})]$

$q = 1.1 \times 10^4 \text{ J}$

$0.692 \text{ g C}_6\text{H}_{12}\text{O}_6 \cdot \dfrac{1 \text{ mol C}_6\text{H}_{12}\text{O}_6}{180.2 \text{ g}} = 0.00384 \text{ mol C}_6\text{H}_{12}\text{O}_6$

$\dfrac{1.1 \times 10^4 \text{ J}}{0.00384 \text{ mol C}_6\text{H}_{12}\text{O}_6} \cdot \dfrac{1 \text{ kJ}}{10^3 \text{ J}} = 2800 \text{ kJ/mol C}_6\text{H}_{12}\text{O}_6$

6.41 $q_{Ag} + q_{ice} = 0$

$[(50.0 \text{ g})(C_{Ag})(273.2 \text{ K} - 373.0 \text{ K})] + [(3.54 \text{ g})(333 \text{ J/g})] = 0$

$C_{Ag} = 0.236 \text{ J/g·K}$

6.42 $q_{Pt} + q_{ice} = 0$

$[(9.36 \text{ g})(C_{Pt})(273.2 \text{ K} - 371.8 \text{ K})] + [(0.37 \text{ g})(333 \text{ J/g})] = 0$

$C_{Pt} = 0.13 \text{ J/g·K}$

6.43   (a) $CH_4(g) + 2 \, O_2(g) \rightarrow CO_2(g) + 2 \, H_2O(g)$ $\Delta H° = -802.4 \text{ kJ}$

        $CO_2(g) + 2 \, H_2O(g) \rightarrow CH_3OH(g) + {}^3/_2 \, O_2(g)$ $\Delta H° = -(-676 \text{ kJ})$

        $CH_4(g) + {}^1/_2 \, O_2(g) \rightarrow CH_3OH(g)$ $\Delta H° = -126 \text{ kJ}$

(b)

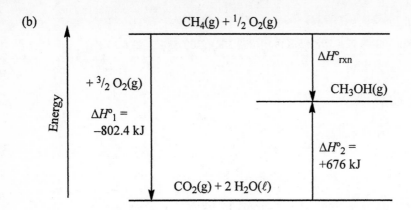

6.44   (a) $C_2H_4(g) + 3\ O_2(g) \rightarrow 2\ CO_2(g) + 2\ H_2O(\ell)$ $\Delta H^\circ = -1411.1$ kJ

$2\ CO_2(g) + 3\ H_2O(\ell) \rightarrow C_2H_5OH(\ell) + 3\ O_2(g)$ $\Delta H^\circ = -(-1367.5$ kJ$)$

$\overline{\hspace{4cm}}$

$C_2H_4(g) + H_2O(\ell) \rightarrow C_2H_5OH(\ell)$ $\Delta H^\circ = -43.6$ kJ

(b)

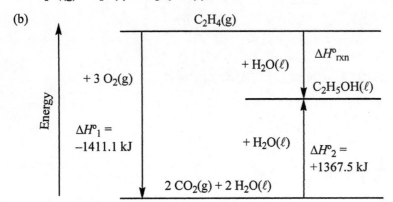

6.45 $^1/_2\ N_2(g) + {}^3/_2\ H_2(g) \rightarrow NH_3(g)$ $\Delta H^\circ = (-91.8$ kJ$)/2$

$NH_3(g) + {}^5/_4\ O_2(g) \rightarrow NO(g) + {}^3/_2\ H_2O(g)$ $\Delta H^\circ = (-906.2$ kJ$)/4$

$^3/_2\ H_2O(g) \rightarrow {}^3/_2\ H_2(g) + {}^3/_4\ O_2(g)$ $\Delta H^\circ = -(-241.8$ kJ$) \times {}^3/_2$

$\overline{\hspace{4cm}}$

$^1/_2\ N_2(g) + {}^1/_2\ O_2(g) \rightarrow NO(g)$ $\Delta H^\circ = 90.3$ kJ

6.46 $P_4(s) + 10\ Cl_2(g) \rightarrow 4\ PCl_5(s)$ $\Delta H^\circ = -1774.0$ kJ

$4\ PCl_5(s) \rightarrow 4\ PCl_3(\ell) + 4\ Cl_2(g)$ $\Delta H^\circ = -(-123.8$ kJ$) \times 4$

$\overline{\hspace{4cm}}$

$P_4(s) + 6\ Cl_2(g) \rightarrow 4\ PCl_3(\ell)$ $\Delta H^\circ = -1278.8$ kJ

$1.00 \text{ mol } PCl_3 \cdot \dfrac{-1278.8 \text{ kJ}}{4 \text{ mol } PCl_3} = -320. \text{ kJ/mol } PCl_3$

6.47 $C(s) + {}^1/_2\ O_2(g) + 2\ H_2(g) \rightarrow CH_3OH(\ell)$ $\Delta H_f^\circ = -238.4$ kJ

6.48 $Ca(s) + C(s) + {}^3/_2\ O_2(g) \rightarrow CaCO_3(s)$ $\Delta H_f^\circ = -1207.6$ kJ

6.49   (a) $2 \text{ Cr(s)} + {}^3/_2 \text{ O}_2\text{(g)} \rightarrow \text{Cr}_2\text{O}_3\text{(s)}$ $\qquad\qquad\qquad \Delta H_f^\circ = -1134.7 \text{ kJ}$

      (b) $2.4 \text{ g Cr} \cdot \dfrac{1 \text{ mol Cr}}{52.0 \text{ g}} \cdot \dfrac{1 \text{ mol Cr}_2\text{O}_3}{2 \text{ mol Cr}} \cdot \dfrac{-1134.7 \text{ kJ}}{1 \text{ mol Cr}_2\text{O}_3} = -26 \text{ kJ}$

6.50   (a) $\text{Mg(s)} + {}^1/_2 \text{ O}_2\text{(g)} \rightarrow \text{MgO(s)}$ $\qquad\qquad\qquad \Delta H_f^\circ = -601.24 \text{ kJ}$

      (b) $2.5 \text{ mol Mg} \cdot \dfrac{1 \text{ mol MgO}}{1 \text{ mol Mg}} \cdot \dfrac{-601.24 \text{ kJ}}{1 \text{ mol MgO}} = -1500 \text{ kJ}$

6.51   (a) $1.0 \text{ g P} \cdot \dfrac{1 \text{ mol P}}{31.0 \text{ g}} \cdot \dfrac{1 \text{ mol P}_4\text{O}_{10}}{4 \text{ mol P}} \cdot \dfrac{-2984.0 \text{ kJ}}{1 \text{ mol P}_4\text{O}_{10}} = -24 \text{ kJ}$

      (b) $0.20 \text{ mol NO} \cdot \dfrac{-90.29 \text{ kJ}}{1 \text{ mol NO}} = -18 \text{ kJ}$

      (c) $2.40 \text{ g NaCl} \cdot \dfrac{1 \text{ mol NaCl}}{58.44 \text{ g}} \cdot \dfrac{-411.12 \text{ kJ}}{1 \text{ mol NaCl}} = -16.9 \text{ kJ}$

      (d) $250 \text{ g Fe} \cdot \dfrac{1 \text{ mol Fe}}{55.8 \text{ g}} \cdot \dfrac{1 \text{ mol Fe}_2\text{O}_3}{2 \text{ mol Fe}} \cdot \dfrac{-824.2 \text{ kJ}}{1 \text{ mol Fe}_2\text{O}_3} = -1800 \text{ kJ}$

6.52   (a) $0.054 \text{ g S} \cdot \dfrac{1 \text{ mol S}}{32.1 \text{ g}} \cdot \dfrac{1 \text{ mol SO}_2}{1 \text{ mol S}} \cdot \dfrac{-296.84 \text{ kJ}}{1 \text{ mol SO}_2} = -0.50 \text{ kJ}$

      (b) $0.20 \text{ mol HgO} \cdot \dfrac{90.83 \text{ kJ}}{1 \text{ mol HgO}} = 18 \text{ kJ}$

      (c) $2.40 \text{ g NH}_3 \cdot \dfrac{1 \text{ mol NH}_3}{17.03 \text{ g}} \cdot \dfrac{-45.90 \text{ kJ}}{1 \text{ mol NH}_3} = -6.47 \text{ kJ}$

      (d) $1.05 \times 10^{-2} \text{ mol C} \cdot \dfrac{1 \text{ mol CO}_2}{1 \text{ mol C}} \cdot \dfrac{-393.509 \text{ kJ}}{1 \text{ mol CO}_2} = -4.13 \text{ kJ}$

6.53   (a) $\Delta H_f^\circ[\text{O}_2\text{(g)}] = 0 \text{ kJ/mol}$

         $\Delta H_{rxn}^\circ = 4 \, \Delta H_f^\circ[\text{NO(g)}] + 6 \, \Delta H_f^\circ[\text{H}_2\text{O(g)}] - 4 \, \Delta H_f^\circ[\text{NH}_3\text{(g)}]$

         $\Delta H_{rxn}^\circ = 4 \text{ mol } (90.29 \text{ kJ/mol}) + 6 \text{ mol } (-241.83 \text{ kJ/mol}) - 4 \text{ mol } (-45.90 \text{ kJ/mol})$

         $\Delta H_{rxn}^\circ = -906.22 \text{ kJ}$

      (b) $10.0 \text{ g NH}_3 \cdot \dfrac{1 \text{ mol NH}_3}{17.03 \text{ g}} \cdot \dfrac{-906.22 \text{ kJ}}{4 \text{ mol NH}_3} = -133 \text{ kJ}$ (133 kJ evolved)

6.54   (a) $\Delta H_{rxn}^\circ = \Delta H_f^\circ[\text{CaCO}_3\text{(s)}] + \Delta H_f^\circ[\text{H}_2\text{O(g)}] - (\Delta H_f^\circ[\text{Ca(OH)}_2\text{(s)}] + \Delta H_f^\circ[\text{CO}_2\text{(g)}])$

         $\Delta H_{rxn}^\circ = 1 \text{ mol } (-1207.6 \text{ kJ/mol}) + 1 \text{ mol } (-241.83 \text{ kJ/mol})$

                                     $- [1 \text{ mol } (-986.09 \text{ kJ/mol}) + 1 \text{ mol } (-393.509 \text{ kJ/mol})]$

         $\Delta H_{rxn}^\circ = -69.8 \text{ kJ}$

      (b) $1.00 \times 10^3 \text{ g Ca(OH)}_2 \cdot \dfrac{1 \text{ mol Ca(OH)}_2}{74.09 \text{ g}} \cdot \dfrac{-69.8 \text{ kJ}}{1 \text{ mol Ca(OH)}_2} = -942 \text{ kJ}$ (942 kJ evolved)

6.55   (a) $\Delta H_f^{\circ}[O_2(g)] = 0$ kJ/mol

$\Delta H^{\circ}_{rxn} = \Delta H_f^{\circ}[BaO(s)] - \Delta H_f^{\circ}[BaO_2(s)]$

$\Delta H^{\circ}_{rxn} = 1$ mol $(-553.5$ kJ/mol$) - 1$ mol $(-634.3$ kJ/mol$)$

$\Delta H^{\circ}_{rxn} = 80.8$ kJ   The reaction is endothermic

(b)

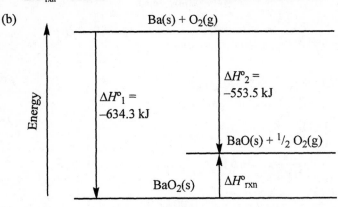

6.56   (a) $\Delta H_f^{\circ}[O_2(g)] = 0$ kJ/mol

$\Delta H^{\circ}_{rxn} = \Delta H_f^{\circ}[SO_3(g)] - \Delta H_f^{\circ}[SO_2(g)]$

$\Delta H^{\circ}_{rxn} = 1$ mol $(-395.77$ kJ/mol$) - 1$ mol $(-296.84$ kJ/mol$)$

$\Delta H^{\circ}_{rxn} = -98.93$ kJ   The reaction is exothermic

(b)

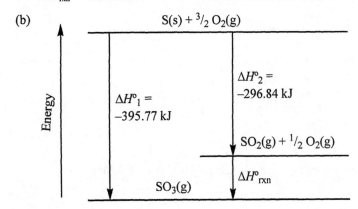

6.57 $\Delta H_f^{\circ}[O_2(g)] = 0$ kJ/mol

$\Delta H^{\circ}_{rxn} = 10\ \Delta H_f^{\circ}[CO_2(g)] + 4\ \Delta H_f^{\circ}[H_2O(\ell)] - \Delta H_f^{\circ}[C_{10}H_8(s)]$

-5156.1 kJ $= 10$ mol $(-393.509$ kJ/mol$) + 4$ mol $(-285.83$ kJ/mol$) - \Delta H_f^{\circ}[C_{10}H_8(s)]$

$\Delta H_f^{\circ}[C_{10}H_8(s)] = 77.7$ kJ/mol

6.58 $\Delta H_f^{\circ}[O_2(g)] = 0$ kJ/mol

$\Delta H^{\circ}_{rxn} = 8\ \Delta H_f^{\circ}[CO_2(g)] + 4\ \Delta H_f^{\circ}[H_2O(\ell)] - \Delta H_f^{\circ}[C_8H_8(\ell)]$

-4395.0 kJ $= 8$ mol $(-393.509$ kJ/mol$) + 4$ mol $(-285.83$ kJ/mol$) - \Delta H_f^{\circ}[C_8H_8(\ell)]$

$\Delta H_f^{\circ}[C_8H_8(\ell)] = 103.6$ kJ/mol

6.59   (a) Al(s) + $^3/_2$ Cl$_2$(g) → AlCl$_3$(s)   product-favored

$\Delta H^o{}_{rxn} = \Delta H_f^o[\text{AlCl}_3(s)] = -705.63$ kJ/mol

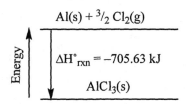

(b) HgO(s) → Hg(ℓ) + $^1/_2$ O$_2$(g)   reactant-favored

$\Delta H^o{}_{rxn} = -\Delta H_f^o[\text{HgO}(s)] = 90.83$ kJ/mol

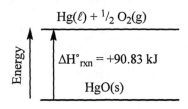

6.60   (a) O$_3$(g) → $^3/_2$ O$_2$(g)   product-favored

$\Delta H^o{}_{rxn} = -\Delta H_f^o[\text{O}_3(g)] = -142.67$ kJ/mol

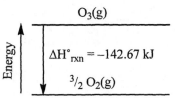

(b) MgCO$_3$(s) → MgO(s) + CO$_2$(g)   reactant-favored

$\Delta H^o{}_{rxn} = \Delta H_f^o[\text{MgO}(s)] + \Delta H_f^o[\text{CO}_2(g)] - \Delta H_f^o[\text{MgCO}_3(s)]$

$\Delta H^o{}_{rxn} = 1$ mol $(-601.24$ kJ/mol$) + 1$ mol $(-393.509$ kJ/mol$) - 1$ mol $(-1111.69$ kJ/mol$)$

$\Delta H^o{}_{rxn} = 116.94$ kJ

MgO(s) + CO$_2$(g)

Energy $\Delta H^\circ{}_{rxn} = 116.94$ kJ

MgCO$_3$(s)

6.61   (a) Exothermic: a process in which heat is transferred from a system to the surroundings

(the combustion of methane gives off heat)

Endothermic: a process in which heat is transferred from surroundings to the system

(ice melting absorbs heat)

(b) System: the object, or collection of objects, being studied (a chemical reaction taking place inside a calorimeter)

Surroundings: everything outside the system that can exchange energy with the system (the calorimeter and everything else outside the calorimeter)

(c) Specific heat capacity: the quantity of heat required to raise the temperature of 1 gram of a substance one kelvin (the specific heat capacity of water is 4.184 J/g·K)

(d) State function: a quantity that is characterized by changes that do not depend on which path is chosen in going from the initial state to the final state (enthalpy and internal energy)

(e) Standard state: the most stable form of a substance in the physical state that exists at a pressure of 1 bar and at a specified temperature (the standard state of carbon at 25 °C is graphite)

(f) Enthalpy change, ΔH: the difference between the final and initial heat content of a substance at constant pressure (the enthalpy change for melting ice at 0 °C is 6.00 kJ/mol)

(g) Standard enthalpy of formation: the enthalpy change for the formation of 1 mol of a compound directly from its component elements in their standard states (ΔH_f° for liquid H_2O is –285.83 kJ/mol)

6.62   (a) exothermic

(b) exothermic

(c) exothermic

(d) endothermic

6.63   (a) system: reaction between methane and oxygen

surroundings: the furnace and the rest of the universe

heat flows from system to surroundings

(b) system: water

surroundings: skin and the rest of the universe

heat flows from surroundings to the system

(c) system: water

surroundings: freezer and the rest of the universe

heat flows from system to surroundings

(d) system: reaction between aluminum and iron(III) oxide

surroundings: flask, laboratory bench, and the rest of the universe

heat flows from system to surroundings

6.64   (a), (c), and (d) are state functions

6.65 $\Delta E = q + w$ ΔE is the change in energy content, q is heat transferred to or from the system, and w is work transferred to or from the system

6.66   Standard state is the most stable form of a substance in the physical state that exists at a pressure of 1 bar and at a specified temperature. H_2O (liquid), NaCl (solid), Hg (liquid), CH_4 (gas)

6.67 ΔH_f° O(g) = 249.170 kJ/mol ΔH_f° O_2(g) = 0 kJ/mol ΔH_f° O_3(g) = 142.67 kJ/mol

The standard state of oxygen is O_2(g)

O_2(g) $\rightarrow$ 2 O(g) ΔH° = 2 mol (249.170 kJ/mol) – 0 kJ/mol = 498.34 kJ   (endothermic)

$^3/_2$ O_2(g) $\rightarrow$ O_3(g) ΔH° = 1 mol (142.67 kJ/mol) – 0 kJ/mol = 142.67 kJ

6.68   The final temperature is 31 °C.

q_{Al} + q_{water} = 0

[(10.0 g)(C_{Al})(304 K – 353 K)] + [(10.0 g)(4.184 J/g·K)(304 K – 293 K)] = 0

C_{Al} = 0.94 J/g·K

6.69 $SnBr_2$(s) + $TiCl_2$(s) $\rightarrow$ $SnCl_2$(s) + $TiBr_2$(s) ΔH° = –4.2 kJ

$TiCl_4$(ℓ) $\rightarrow$ $TiCl_2$(s) + Cl_2(g) ΔH° = +273 kJ

$SnCl_2$(s)+ Cl_2(g) $\rightarrow$ $SnCl_4$(ℓ) ΔH° = –195

$SnBr_2$(s) + $TiCl_4$(ℓ) $\rightarrow$ $TiBr_2$(s) + $SnCl_4$(ℓ) ΔH°_{net} = 74 kJ

6.70 q_{metal} + q_{water} = 0

[(27.3 g)(C_{Pb})(299.47 K – 372.05 K)] + [(15.0 g)(4.184 J/g·K)(299.47 K – 295.65 K)] = 0

C_{Pb} = 0.121 J/g·K

6.71 q_{water} = (50.0 g)(4.184 J/g·K)(–40 K) = –8400 J

$q_{ethanol}$ = (100. g)(2.46 J/g·K)(–40 K) = –9800 J   Ethanol gives up more heat

6.72 q_{Cu} + q_{water} = 0

[(192 g)(0.385 J/g·K)(T_f – 373.2 K)] + [(751 g)(4.184 J/g·K)(T_f – 277.2 K)] = 0

T_f = 279 K (6.2 °C)

6.73   187 J = (93.45 g)(C_{silver})(300.2 K – 291.7 K)

C_{silver} = 0.24 J/g·K

6.74   q = energy to melt ice + energy to heat liquid + energy to vaporize liquid

$q_{melt\ ice}$ = (60.1 g)(333 J/g) = 2.00×10^4 J

$q_{heat\ liquid}$ = (60.1 g)(4.184 J/g·K)(373.2 K – 273.2 K) = 2.51×10^4 J

$q_{vaporize\ liquid}$ = (60.1 g)(2260 J/g) = 1.36×10^5 J

q_{total} = 2.00×10^4 J + 2.51×10^4 J + 1.36×10^5 J = 1.8×10^5 J

6.75 $q_{water} + q_{ice} = 0$

$[(100.0 \text{ g})(4.184 \text{ J/g·K})(273.2 \text{ K} - 333.2 \text{ K})] + [(m_{ice\ melted})(333 \text{ J/g})] = 0$

$m_{ice\ melted} = 75.4 \text{ g}$

6.76   Assume the density of the tea is 1.00 g/mL and specific heat capacity is 4.184 J/g·K

$q_{tea} + q_{ice} = 0$

$[(5.00 \times 10^2 \text{ g})(4.184 \text{ J/g·K})(273.2 \text{ K} - 293.2 \text{ K})] + [(m_{ice\ melted})(333 \text{ J/g}) = 0$

$m_{ice\ melted} = 126 \text{ g}$

$(3 \times 45 \text{ g}) - 126 \text{ g} = 9 \text{ g ice remaining}$

6.77   Assume the density of the tea is 1.00 g/mL and specific heat capacity is 4.184 J/g·K

$q_{tea} + q_{melt\ ice} + q_{warm\ ice} = 0$

$[(5.00 \times 10^2 \text{ g})(4.184 \text{ J/g·K})(T_f - 293.2 \text{ K})] + [(90. \text{ g})(333 \text{ J/g})] + [(90. \text{ g})(4.184 \text{ J/g·K})(T_f - 273.2 \text{ K})] = 0$

$T_f = 278 \text{ K } (4.8 \text{ °C})$

6.78   Assume the density of the cola is 1.00 g/mL and specific heat capacity is 4.184 J/g·K

Energy required to cool cola to 0 °C:

$q_{cola} = (240 \text{ g})(4.184 \text{ J/g·K})(273.2 \text{ K} - 283.7 \text{ K}) = -1.1 \times 10^4 \text{ J}$

Energy supplied by melting one ice cube:

$q_{ice} = (45 \text{ g})(333 \text{ J/g}) = 1.5 \times 10^4 \text{ J}$

(a)   The temperature is 0 °C and some ice remains

$q_{cola} + q_{melt\ ice} = 0$

$-1.1 \times 10^4 \text{ J} + (m_{ice\ melted})(333 \text{ J/g}) = 0$

$m_{ice\ melted} = 32 \text{ g}$

$45 \text{ g} - 32 \text{ g} = 13 \text{ g ice remaining}$

6.79 $q_{solution} = (250. \text{ g} + 125 \text{ g})(4.2 \text{ J/g·K})(296.05 \text{ K} - 294.30 \text{ K})$

$q_{solution} = 2.8 \times 10^3 \text{ J}$

$q_{rxn} = -q_{solution} = -2.8 \times 10^3 \text{ J}$

Reactants are present in equimolar amounts

$0.250 \text{ L} \cdot \dfrac{0.16 \text{ mol AgNO}_3}{1 \text{ L}} \cdot \dfrac{1 \text{ mol AgCl}}{1 \text{ mol AgNO}_3} = 0.040 \text{ mol AgCl}$

$\dfrac{-2.8 \times 10^3 \text{ J}}{0.040 \text{ mol AgCl}} \cdot \dfrac{1 \text{ kJ}}{10^3 \text{ J}} = -69 \text{ kJ/mol AgCl}$

6.80 $q_{solution} = (200. \text{ g} + 200. \text{ g})(4.2 \text{ J/g·K})(2.44 \text{ K})$

$q_{solution} = 4.1 \times 10^3 \text{ J}$

$q_{rxn} = -q_{solution} = -4.1 \times 10^3 \text{ J}$

Reactants are present in equimolar amounts

$$0.200 \text{ L} \cdot \frac{0.75 \text{ mol Pb(NO}_3)_2}{1 \text{ L}} \cdot \frac{1 \text{ mol PbBr}_2}{1 \text{ mol Pb(NO}_3)_2} = 0.15 \text{ mol PbBr}_2$$

$$\frac{-4.1 \times 10^3 \text{ J}}{0.15 \text{ mol PbBr}_2} \cdot \frac{1 \text{ kJ}}{10^3 \text{ J}} = -27 \text{ kJ/mol PbBr}_2$$

6.81 $q = q_{water} + q_{calorimeter}$

$q = [(415 \text{ g})(4.184 \text{ J/g·K})(293.87 \text{ K} - 292.05 \text{ K})] + [(155 \text{ J/K})(293.87 \text{ K} - 292.05 \text{ K})]$

$q = 3.44 \times 10^3 \text{ J}$

$$7.647 \text{ g NH}_4\text{NO}_3 \cdot \frac{1 \text{ mol NH}_4\text{NO}_3}{80.043 \text{ g}} = 0.09554 \text{ mol NH}_4\text{NO}_3$$

$$\frac{3.44 \times 10^3 \text{ J}}{0.09554 \text{ mol}} \cdot \frac{1 \text{ kJ}}{10^3 \text{ J}} = 36.0 \text{ kJ/mol NH}_4\text{NO}_3 \text{ evolved}$$

6.82 $q = q_{water} + q_{calorimeter}$

$q = [(650 \text{ g})(4.184 \text{ J/g·K})(295.5 \text{ K} - 291.7 \text{ K})] + [(550 \text{ J/K})(295.5 \text{ K} - 291.7 \text{ K})]$

$q = 1.2 \times 10^4 \text{ J}$

$$4.20 \text{ g C}_2\text{H}_5\text{OH} \cdot \frac{1 \text{ mol C}_2\text{H}_5\text{OH}}{46.07 \text{ g}} = 0.0912 \text{ mol C}_2\text{H}_5\text{OH}$$

$$\frac{1.2 \times 10^4 \text{ J}}{0.0912 \text{ mol}} \cdot \frac{1 \text{ kJ}}{10^3 \text{ J}} = 140 \text{ kJ/mol C}_2\text{H}_5\text{OH}$$

$\Delta H_{combustion} = -q = -140 \text{ kJ/mol}$

6.83   (a) $2 \text{ B(s)} + {}^3/_2 \text{ O}_2\text{(g)} \rightarrow \text{B}_2\text{O}_3\text{(s)}$ $\Delta H°_{rxn} = (-2543.8 \text{ kJ})/2$

   $3 \text{ H}_2\text{(g)} + {}^3/_2 \text{ O}_2\text{(g)} \rightarrow 3 \text{ H}_2\text{O(g)}$ $\Delta H°_{rxn} = (-241.8 \text{ kJ}) \times 3$

   $\text{B}_2\text{O}_3\text{(s)} + 3 \text{ H}_2\text{O(g)} \rightarrow \text{B}_2\text{H}_6\text{(g)} + 3 \text{ O}_2\text{(g)}$ $\Delta H°_{rxn} = -(-2032.9 \text{ kJ})$

   _____

   $2 \text{ B(s)} + 3 \text{ H}_2\text{(g)} \rightarrow \text{B}_2\text{H}_6\text{(g)}$ $\Delta H°_{rxn} = 35.6 \text{ kJ}$

(b) $\Delta H_f° = 35.6 \text{ kJ/mol}$

(c)

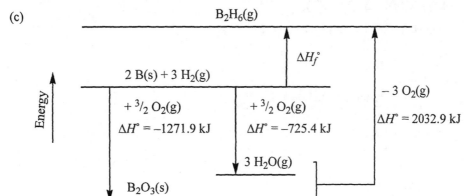

(d) reactant-favored

6.84   (a) $\Delta H^\circ_{rxn} = \Delta H_f^\circ[CH_3Cl(g)] + \Delta H_f^\circ[HCl(g)] - (\Delta H_f^\circ[CH_4(g)] + 2 \Delta H_f^\circ[Cl(g)])$

$\Delta H^\circ_{rxn} = 1 \text{ mol } (-83.68 \text{ kJ/mol}) + 1 \text{ mol } (-92.31 \text{ kJ/mol})$

$- [1 \text{ mol } (-74.87 \text{ kJ/mol}) + 2 \text{ mol } (121.3 \text{ kJ/mol})]$

$\Delta H^\circ_{rxn} = -343.7 \text{ kJ}$ product-favored

(b)

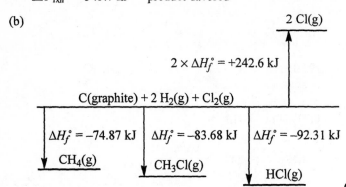

6.85 $\Delta H_f^\circ[Mg(s)] = \Delta H_f^\circ[H_2(g)] = 0 \text{ kJ/mol}$

$\Delta H^\circ_{rxn} = \Delta H_f^\circ[Mg(OH)_2(s)] - 2 \Delta H_f^\circ[H_2O(\ell)]$

$\Delta H^\circ_{rxn} = 1 \text{ mol } (-924.54 \text{ kJ/mol}) - 2 \text{ mol } (-285.83 \text{ kJ/mol})$

$\Delta H^\circ_{rxn} = -352.88 \text{ kJ} = -3.5288 \times 10^5 \text{ J}$

$q_{water} = (25 \text{ g})(4.184 \text{ J/g·K})(358 \text{ K} - 298 \text{ K}) = 6.3 \times 10^3 \text{ J}$

$6.3 \times 10^3 \text{ J} \cdot \dfrac{1 \text{ mol Mg}}{3.5288 \times 10^5 \text{ J}} \cdot \dfrac{24.3 \text{ g}}{1 \text{ mol Mg}} = 0.43 \text{ g Mg}$

6.86   (a) product-favored

(b) $\Delta H_f^\circ[O_2(g)] = \Delta H_f^\circ[N_2(g)] = 0 \text{ kJ/mol}$

$\Delta H^\circ_{rxn} = 2 \Delta H_f^\circ[H_2O(g)] - \Delta H_f^\circ[N_2H_4(\ell)]$

$-534.3 \text{ kJ} = 2 \text{ mol } (-241.83 \text{ kJ}) - \Delta H_f^\circ[N_2H_4(\ell)]$

$\Delta H_f^\circ[N_2H_4(\ell)] = 50.6 \text{ kJ/mol}$

6.87   (a) $\Delta H_f^\circ[C(s)] = \Delta H_f^\circ[H_2(g)] = 0 \text{ kJ/mol}$

$\Delta H^\circ_{rxn} = \Delta H_f^\circ[CO(g)] - \Delta H_f^\circ[H_2O(g)]$

$\Delta H^\circ_{rxn} = 1 \text{ mol } (-110.525 \text{ kJ/mol}) - 1 \text{ mol } (-241.83 \text{ kJ/mol})$

$\Delta H^\circ_{rxn} = 131.31 \text{ kJ}$

(b) reactant-favored

(c) $1000.0 \text{ kg} \cdot \dfrac{10^3 \text{ g}}{1 \text{ kg}} \cdot \dfrac{1 \text{ mol C}}{12.011 \text{ g}} \cdot \dfrac{131.31 \text{ kJ}}{1 \text{ mol C}} = 1.0932 \times 10^7 \text{ kJ}$

6.88   This problem was solved assuming $H_2O(\ell)$ is a product in the combustion reactions, but also could be correctly solved using $H_2O(g)$ as a product.

Propane: $C_3H_8(g) + 5 O_2(g) \rightarrow 3 CO_2(g) + 4 H_2O(\ell)$

$\Delta H_f^\circ[O_2(g)] = 0 \text{ kJ/mol}$

$\Delta H°_{rxn} = 3 \Delta H_f°[CO_2(g)] + 4 \Delta H_f°[H_2O(\ell)] - \Delta H_f°[C_3H_8(g)]$

$\Delta H°_{rxn} = 3 \text{ mol } (-393.509 \text{ kJ/mol}) + 4 \text{ mol } (-285.83 \text{ kJ/mol}) - 1 \text{ mol } (-104.7 \text{ kJ/mol})$

$\Delta H°_{rxn} = -2219.1 \text{ kJ}$

$$\frac{-2219.1 \text{ kJ}}{1 \text{ mol C}_3\text{H}_8} \cdot \frac{1 \text{ mol C}_3\text{H}_8}{44.096 \text{ g}} = -50.325 \text{ kJ/g}$$

Butane: $C_4H_{10}(g) + {}^{13}/_2 O_2(g) \rightarrow 4 CO_2(g) + 5 H_2O(\ell)$

$\Delta H_f°[O_2(g)] = 0 \text{ kJ/mol}$

$\Delta H°_{rxn} = 4 \Delta H_f°[CO_2(g)] + 5 \Delta H_f°[H_2O(\ell)] - \Delta H_f°[C_4H_{10}(g)]$

$\Delta H°_{rxn} = 4 \text{ mol } (-393.509 \text{ kJ/mol}) + 5 \text{ mol } (-285.83 \text{ kJ/mol}) - 1 \text{ mol } (-127.1 \text{ kJ/mol})$

$\Delta H°_{rxn} = -2876.1 \text{ kJ}$

$$\frac{-2876.1 \text{ kJ}}{1 \text{ mol C}_4\text{H}_{10}} \cdot \frac{1 \text{ mol C}_4\text{H}_{10}}{58.123 \text{ g}} = -49.482 \text{ kJ/g}$$

Gasoline: $C_8H_{18}(\ell) + {}^{25}/_2 O_2(g) \rightarrow 8 CO_2(g) + 9 H_2O(\ell)$

$\Delta H_f°[O_2(g)] = 0 \text{ kJ/mol}$

$\Delta H°_{rxn} = 8 \Delta H_f°[CO_2(g)] + 9 \Delta H_f°[H_2O(\ell)] - \Delta H_f°[C_8H_{18}(\ell)]$

$\Delta H°_{rxn} = 8 \text{ mol } (-393.509 \text{ kJ/mol}) + 9 \text{ mol } (-285.83 \text{ kJ/mol}) - 1 \text{ mol } (-259.2 \text{ kJ/mol})$

$\Delta H°_{rxn} = -5261.3 \text{ kJ}$

$$\frac{-5261.3 \text{ kJ}}{1 \text{ mol C}_8\text{H}_{18}} \cdot \frac{1 \text{ mol C}_8\text{H}_{18}}{114.230 \text{ g}} = -47.810 \text{ kJ/g}$$

Ethanol: $C_2H_5OH(\ell) + 3 O_2(g) \rightarrow 2 CO_2(g) + 3 H_2O(\ell)$

$\Delta H_f°[O_2(g)] = 0 \text{ kJ/mol}$

$\Delta H°_{rxn} = 2 \Delta H_f°[CO_2(g)] + 3 \Delta H_f°[H_2O(\ell)] - \Delta H_f°[C_2H_5OH(\ell)]$

$\Delta H°_{rxn} = 2 \text{ mol } (-393.509 \text{ kJ/mol}) + 3 \text{ mol } (-285.83 \text{ kJ/mol}) - 1 \text{ mol } (-277.0 \text{ kJ/mol})$

$\Delta H°_{rxn} = -1367.5 \text{ kJ}$

$$\frac{-1367.5 \text{ kJ}}{1 \text{ mol C}_2\text{H}_5\text{OH}} \cdot \frac{1 \text{ mol C}_2\text{H}_5\text{OH}}{46.069 \text{ g}} = -29.684 \text{ kJ/g}$$

The hydrocarbons give off more heat per gram than the ethanol. Of the hydrocarbons, the smaller ones give off more heat than the larger ones. More C—C and C—H bonds are broken in combustion per gram of fuel, meaning that more energy is released per gram in the smaller hydrocarbons.

6.89   Methanol: $2 CH_3OH(\ell) + 3 O_2(g) \rightarrow 2 CO_2(g) + 4 H_2O(\ell)$

$\Delta H_f°[O_2(g)] = 0 \text{ kJ/mol}$

$\Delta H°_{rxn} = 2 \Delta H_f°[CO_2(g)] + 4 \Delta H_f°[H_2O(\ell)] - 2 \Delta H_f°[CH_3OH(\ell)]$

$\Delta H°_{rxn} = 2 \text{ mol } (-393.509 \text{ kJ/mol}) + 4 \text{ mol } (-285.83 \text{ kJ/mol}) - 2 \text{ mol } (-238.4 \text{ kJ/mol})$

$\Delta H°_{rxn} = -1453.5 \text{ kJ}$

$$\frac{-1453.5 \text{ kJ}}{2 \text{ mol CH}_3\text{OH}} \cdot \frac{1 \text{ mol CH}_3\text{OH}}{32.042 \text{ g}} = -22.68 \text{ kJ/g}$$

Gasoline: $C_8H_{18}(\ell) + {}^{25}/_2\ O_2(g) \rightarrow 8\ CO_2(g) + 9\ H_2O(\ell)$

$\Delta H_f^{\circ}[O_2(g)] = 0$ kJ/mol

$\Delta H^{\circ}_{rxn} = 8\ \Delta H_f^{\circ}[CO_2(g)] + 9\ \Delta H_f^{\circ}[H_2O(\ell)] - \Delta H_f^{\circ}[C_8H_{18}(\ell)]$

$\Delta H^{\circ}_{rxn} = 8$ mol (-393.509 kJ/mol) $+ 9$ mol (-285.83 kJ/mol) $- 1$ mol (-259.2 kJ/mol)

$\Delta H^{\circ}_{rxn} = -5461.3$ kJ

$$\frac{-5461.3\ \text{kJ}}{1\ \text{mol}\ C_8H_{18}} \cdot \frac{1\ \text{mol}\ C_8H_{18}}{114.230\ \text{g}} = -47.810\ \text{kJ/g}$$

6.90 $\Delta H_f^{\circ}[O_2(g)] = \Delta H_f^{\circ}[N_2(g)] = 0$ kJ/mol

Hydrazine:

$\Delta H^{\circ}_{rxn} = 2\ \Delta H_f^{\circ}[H_2O(g)] - \Delta H_f^{\circ}[N_2H_4(\ell)]$

$\Delta H^{\circ}_{rxn} = 2$ mol (-241.83 kJ/mol) $- 1$ mol (50.6 kJ/mol)

$\Delta H^{\circ}_{rxn} = -534.3$ kJ

$$\frac{-534.3\ \text{kJ}}{1\ \text{mol}\ N_2H_4} \cdot \frac{1\ \text{mol}\ N_2H_4}{32.045\ \text{g}} = -16.67\ \text{kJ/g}\ N_2H_4$$

1,1-Dimethylhydrazine:

$\Delta H^{\circ}_{rxn} = 2\ \Delta H_f^{\circ}[CO_2(g)] + 4\ \Delta H_f^{\circ}[H_2O(g)] - \Delta H_f^{\circ}[N_2H_2(CH_3)_2(\ell)]$

$\Delta H^{\circ}_{rxn} = 2$ mol (-393.509 kJ/mol) $+ 4$ mol (-241.83 kJ/mol) $- 1$ mol (48.9 kJ/mol)

$\Delta H^{\circ}_{rxn} = -1803.2$ kJ

$$\frac{-1803.2\ \text{kJ}}{1\ \text{mol}\ N_2H_2(CH_3)_2} \cdot \frac{1\ \text{mol}\ N_2H_2(CH_3)_2}{60.099\ \text{g}} = -30.004\ \text{kJ/g}\ N_2H_2(CH_3)_2$$

1,1-Dimethylhydrazine gives more heat per gram when reacting with oxygen

6.91   (a) $Sr(s) + {}^1/_2\ O_2(g) \rightarrow SrO(s)$ $\Delta H_f^{\circ} = -592$ kJ

          $SrO(s) + CO_2(g) \rightarrow SrCO_3(s)$ $\Delta H^{\circ}_{rxn} = -234$ kJ

          $C(\text{graphite}) + O_2(g) \rightarrow CO_2(g)$ $\Delta H_f^{\circ} = -394$ kJ

          _____

          $Sr(s) + C(\text{graphite}) + {}^3/_2\ O_2(g) \rightarrow SrCO_3(s)$ $\Delta H^{\circ} = -1220.$ kJ

        (b)

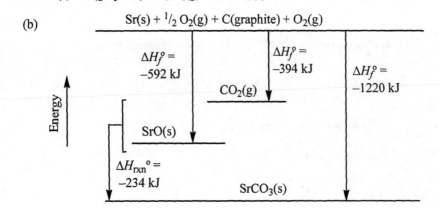

6.92   (a) $q_{soda} = (350\ g)(4.184\ J/g \cdot K)(310.\ K - 278\ K) = 4.7 \times 10^4\ J$

$q_{body} = -q_{soda} = -4.7 \times 10^4\ J$ (or $4.7 \times 10^4\ J$ expended by your body)

(b) $-4.7 \times 10^4\ J \cdot \dfrac{1\ cal}{4.184\ J} \cdot \dfrac{1\ Cal}{10^3\ cal} = -11\ Cal$ (or 11 Cal expended by your body)

net energy change = 1 Cal + (–11 Cal) = –10. Cal (or 10 Cal expended by your body)

(c) net energy change = 240 Cal + (–11 Cal) = 230 Cal (or 230 Cal absorbed by your body)

6.93   C(graphite) $+\,^1/_2\ H_2(g) + \,^3/_2\ Cl_2(g) \rightarrow CHCl_3(g)$ $\Delta H_f^o = -103.1\ kJ$

$CH_4(g) + 2\ O_2(g) \rightarrow 2\ H_2O(\ell) + CO_2(g)$ $\Delta H^o_{rxn} = -890.3\ kJ$

$^3/_2\ Cl_2(g) + \,^3/_2\ H_2(g) \rightarrow 3\ HCl(g)$ $\Delta H^o_{rxn} = -(+184.6\ kJ) \times\, ^3/_2$

$CO_2(g) \rightarrow C(graphite) + O_2(g)$ $\Delta H^o_{rxn} = -(-393.5\ kJ)$

$2\ H_2O(\ell) \rightarrow 2\ H_2(g) + O_2(g)$ $\Delta H^o_{rxn} = -(-285.8\ kJ) \times 2$

$CH_4(g) + 3\ Cl_2(g) \rightarrow 3\ HCl(g) + CHCl_3(g)$ $\Delta H^o_{rxn} = -305.2\ kJ$

6.94 $C(s) + H_2O(g) \rightarrow CO(g) + H_2(g)$

$\Delta H_f^o[C(s)] = \Delta H_f^o[H_2(g)] = 0\ kJ/mol$

$\Delta H^o_{rxn} = \Delta H_f^o[CO(g)] - \Delta H_f^o[H_2O(g)]$

$\Delta H^o_{rxn} = 1\ mol\ (-110.525\ kJ/mol) - 1\ mol\ (-241.83\ kJ/mol)$

$\Delta H^o_{rxn} = 131.31\ kJ$

$1.00\ kg \cdot \dfrac{10^3\ g}{1\ kg} \cdot \dfrac{1\ mol\ C}{12.011\ g} \cdot \dfrac{131.31\ kJ}{1\ mol\ C} = 1.09 \times 10^4\ kJ$

$C(s) + O_2(g) \rightarrow CO_2(g)$

$\Delta H^o_{rxn} = \Delta H_f^o[CO_2(g)] = -393.509\ kJ$

$1.09 \times 10^4\ kJ \cdot \dfrac{1\ mol\ C}{393.509\ kJ} \cdot \dfrac{12.011\ g}{1\ mol\ C} = 334\ g\ C$

6.95   Combustion of 1.00 kg carbon:

$C(s) + O_2(g) \rightarrow CO_2(g)$ $\Delta H°_{rxn} = \Delta H_f°[CO_2(g)] = -393.509$ kJ

$1.00 \text{ kg} \cdot \dfrac{10^3 \text{ g}}{1 \text{ kg}} \cdot \dfrac{1 \text{ mol C}}{12.011 \text{ g}} \cdot \dfrac{-393.509 \text{ kJ}}{1 \text{ mol C}} = -3.28 \times 10^4 \text{ kJ}$

Combustion of water gas obtained from 1.00 kg carbon:

$CO(g) + {}^1\!/_2\, O_2(g) \rightarrow CO_2(g)$

$\Delta H°_{rxn} = \Delta H_f°[CO_2(g)] - \Delta H_f°[CO(g)] = 1 \text{ mol }(-393.509 \text{ kJ/mol}) - 1 \text{ mol }(-110.525 \text{ kJ/mol})$

$\Delta H°_{rxn} = -282.984$ kJ

$1.00 \text{ kg} \cdot \dfrac{10^3 \text{ g}}{1 \text{ kg}} \cdot \dfrac{1 \text{ mol C}}{12.01 \text{ g}} \cdot \dfrac{1 \text{ mol CO}}{1 \text{ mol C}} \dfrac{-282.984 \text{ kJ}}{1 \text{ mol CO}} = -2.36 \times 10^4 \text{ kJ}$

$H_2(g) + {}^1\!/_2\, O_2(g) \rightarrow H_2O(g)$

$\Delta H°_{rxn} = \Delta H_f°[H_2O(g)] = -241.83$ kJ

$1.00 \text{ kg} \cdot \dfrac{10^3 \text{ g}}{1 \text{ kg}} \cdot \dfrac{1 \text{ mol C}}{12.01 \text{ g}} \cdot \dfrac{1 \text{ mol H}_2}{1 \text{ mol C}} \dfrac{-241.83 \text{ kJ}}{1 \text{ mol H}_2O} = -2.01 \times 10^4 \text{ kJ}$

$-2.36 \times 10^4 \text{ kJ} + -2.01 \times 10^4 \text{ kJ} = -4.37 \times 10^4 \text{ kJ}$

The combustion of water gas produces more energy (but some carbon must be burned to provide the heat for the water gas reaction in the first place).

6.96   (a)

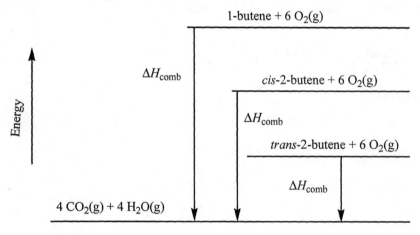

(b) $C_4H_8(g) + 6\, O_2(g) \rightarrow 4\, CO_2(g) + 4\, H_2O(g)$

$\Delta H_{combustion} = 4\, \Delta H_f°[CO_2(g)] + 4\, \Delta H_f°[H_2O(g)] - \Delta H_f°[C_4H_8(g)]$

cis-2-butene

$-2687.5 \text{ kJ} = 4 \text{ mol }(-393.509 \text{ kJ/mol}) + 4 \text{ mol }(-241.83 \text{ kJ/mol}) - \Delta H_f°[C_4H_8(g)]$

$\Delta H_f°[C_4H_8(g)] = 146.1$ kJ/mol

trans-2-butene

$-2684.2 \text{ kJ} = 4 \text{ mol }(-393.509 \text{ kJ/mol}) + 4 \text{ mol }(-241.83 \text{ kJ/mol}) - \Delta H_f°[C_4H_8(g)]$

$\Delta H_f°[C_4H_8(g)] = 142.8$ kJ/mol

1-butene

-2696.7 kJ $= 4$ mol $(-393.509$ kJ/mol$) + 4$ mol $(-241.83$ kJ/mol$) - \Delta H_f^\circ[C_4H_8(g)]$

$\Delta H_f^\circ[C_4H_8(g)] = 155.3$ kJ/mol

(c)

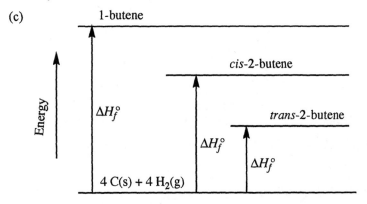

(d) $\Delta H_f^\circ[trans\text{-}2\text{-butene}] - \Delta H_f^\circ[cis\text{-}2\text{-butene}] = 142.8$ kJ $- 146.1$ kJ $= -3.3$ kJ/mol

6.97   Yes, the first law is a version of the general principle of conservation of energy applied specifically to the system. See Section 6.4.

6.98   People who make perpetual motion machines claim they produce more energy than is supplied to the machines. According to the law of conservation of energy, this is impossible.

6.99   (a) product-favored   (b) reactant-favored

6.100   Thermodynamics is the study of the transformation of energy. Kinetics is the study of rates of chemical reactions. Sand is not thermodynamically favored to turn into elemental Si and O_2.

6.101   (a) The temperature of the colder object increases, and its particles move faster. The temperature of the warmer object decreases, and its particles move slower.

(b) The two objects have the same temperature.

6.102   Radiant and electrical energy in the solar panel; chemical and electrical energy in the fuel cell; mechanical energy to move the car

6.103   Reaction 1: $Ca(s) + \frac{1}{2} O_2(g) \rightarrow CaO(s)$ $\Delta H(1)$

Reaction 2: $S_8(s) + 12 O_2(g) \rightarrow 8 SO_3(g)$ $\Delta H(2)$

Reaction 3: $CaO(s) + SO_3(g) \rightarrow CaSO_4(s)$ $\Delta H(3)$

Combine reactions to produce desired overall reaction:

$Ca(s) + \frac{1}{2} O_2(g) \rightarrow CaO(s)$ $\Delta H(1)$

$\frac{1}{8} S_8(s) + \frac{3}{2} O_2(g) \rightarrow SO_3(g)$ $\frac{1}{8} \times \Delta H(2)$

$CaO(s) + SO_3(g) \rightarrow CaSO_4(s)$ $\Delta H(3)$

$Ca(s) + \frac{1}{8} S_8(s) + 2 O_2(g) \rightarrow CaSO_4(s)$ $\Delta H = \Delta H(1) + [\frac{1}{8} \times \Delta H(2)] + \Delta H(3)$

The enthalpy values for reactions 1, 2, and 3 could be determined experimentally using calorimetry.

For Reaction 3: $CaO(s) + SO_3(g) \rightarrow CaSO_4(s)$

$\Delta H^{\circ}_{rxn} = \Delta H_f^{\circ}[CaSO_4(s)] - (\Delta H_f^{\circ}[CaO(s)] + \Delta H_f^{\circ}[SO_3(g)])$

$-402.7 \text{ kJ} = \Delta H_f^{\circ}[CaSO_4(s)] - [1 \text{ mol } (-635.09 \text{ kJ/mol}) + 1 \text{ mol } (-395.77 \text{ kJ/mol})]$

$\Delta H_f^{\circ}[CaSO_4(s)] = -1433.6 \text{ kJ/mol}$

6.104   There is a rough non-linear correspondence, which shows that the specific heat increases with decreasing atomic weight. Using the relationship $C_{metal} \propto 1/\text{atomic weight}$, or $C_{metal} \times \text{atomic weight} = \text{constant} \approx 26$, $C_{Pt} \approx 26/195 \approx 0.130 \text{ J/g·K}$. This is in good agreement with the literature value (0.133 J/g·K).

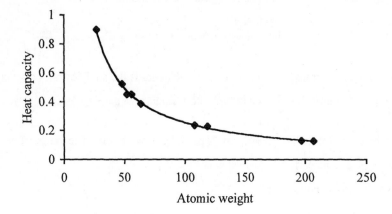

6.105   Al: $\dfrac{0.897\ J}{g \cdot K} \cdot \dfrac{26.98\ g}{1\ mol\ Al} = 24.2\ J/mol \cdot K$

Fe: $\dfrac{0.449\ J}{g \cdot K} \cdot \dfrac{55.85\ g}{1\ mol\ Fe} = 25.1\ J/mol \cdot K$

Cu: $\dfrac{0.385\ J}{g \cdot K} \cdot \dfrac{63.55\ g}{1\ mol\ Cu} = 24.5\ J/mol \cdot K$

Au: $\dfrac{0.129\ J}{g \cdot K} \cdot \dfrac{197.0\ g}{1\ mol\ Au} = 25.4\ J/mol \cdot K$

The molar heat capacity values for the four metals are quite similar, with an average of 24.8 J/mol·K.

Ag: $\dfrac{24.8\ J}{mol \cdot K} \cdot \dfrac{1\ mol\ Ag}{107.9\ g\ Au} = 0.230\ J/g \cdot K$ (close to the correct value of 0.236 J/g·K)

6.106   To extract heat from the inside of the refrigerator, work has to be done. That work (by the condenser and motor) releases heat to the environment (your room). So while the temporary relief of cool air from the inside of the refrigerator is pleasant, the motor has to do work—and heats your room.

6.107 $275\ m^2 \cdot 2.50\ m \cdot \dfrac{1\ L}{10^{-3}\ m^3} \cdot \dfrac{1.22\ g}{1\ L} \cdot \dfrac{1\ mol\ air}{28.9\ g} = 2.90 \times 10^4\ mol\ air$

$q_{air} = (2.90 \times 10^4\ mol)(29.1\ J/mol \cdot K)(295.2\ K - 288.2\ K) = 5.9 \times 10^6\ J = 5.9 \times 10^3\ kJ$

$CH_4(g) + 2\ O_2(g) \rightarrow CO_2(g) + 2\ H_2O(g)$

$\Delta H^{\circ}_{comb} = \Delta H_f^{\circ}[CO_2(g)] + 2\ \Delta H_f^{\circ}[H_2O(g)] - \Delta H_f^{\circ}[CH_4(g)]$

$\Delta H^{\circ}_{comb} = 1\ mol\ (-393.509\ kJ/mol) + 2\ mol\ (-241.83\ kJ/mol) - 1\ mol\ (-74.87\ kJ/mol)$

$\Delta H^{\circ}_{comb} = -802.30\ kJ$

$5.9 \times 10^3\ kJ \cdot \dfrac{1\ mol\ CH_4}{802.30\ kJ} \cdot \dfrac{16.04\ g}{1\ mol\ CH_4} = 120\ g\ CH_4$

6.108   (a) $CaBr_2(s) + H_2O(g) \rightarrow CaO(s) + 2\ HBr(g)$

$Hg(\ell) + 2\ HBr(g) \rightarrow HgBr_2(s) + H_2(g)$

$HgBr_2(s) + CaO(s) \rightarrow HgO(s) + CaBr_2(s)$

$HgO(s) \rightarrow Hg(\ell) + {}^1/_2\ O_2(g)$

___

$H_2O(g) \rightarrow H_2(g) + {}^1/_2\ O_2(g)$

(b) $1000.\ kg \cdot \dfrac{10^3\ g}{1\ kg} \cdot \dfrac{1\ mol\ H_2O}{18.015\ g} \cdot \dfrac{1\ mol\ H_2}{1\ mol\ H_2O} \cdot \dfrac{2.0158\ g}{1\ mol\ H_2} = 1.119 \times 10^5\ g\ (111.9\ kg)$

(c) Step 1:

$$\Delta H°_{rxn} = \Delta H_f°[CaO(s)] + 2\ \Delta H_f°[HBr(g)] - (\Delta H_f°[CaBr_2(s)] + \Delta H_f°[H_2O(g)])$$

$$\Delta H°_{rxn} = 1\ mol\ (-635.09\ kJ/mol) + 2\ mol\ (-36.29\ kJ/mol)$$

$$- [1\ mol\ (-683.2\ kJ/mol) + 1\ mol\ (-241.83\ kJ/mol)]$$

$$\Delta H°_{rxn} = 217.4\ kJ \qquad\qquad reactant\text{-}favored$$

Step 2:

$$\Delta H°_{rxn} = \Delta H_f°[HgBr_2(s)] - 2\ \Delta H_f°[HBr(g)]$$

$$\Delta H°_{rxn} = 1\ mol\ (-169.5\ kJ/mol) - 2\ mol\ (-36.29\ kJ/mol)$$

$$\Delta H°_{rxn} = -96.9\ kJ \qquad\qquad product\text{-}favored$$

Step 3:

$$\Delta H°_{rxn} = \Delta H_f°[HgO(s)] + \Delta H_f°[CaBr_2(s)] - (\Delta H_f°[HgBr_2(s)] + \Delta H_f°[CaO(s)])$$

$$\Delta H°_{rxn} = 1\ mol\ (-90.83\ kJ/mol) + 1\ mol\ (-683.2\ kJ/mol)$$

$$- [1\ mol\ (-169.5\ kJ/mol) + 1\ mol\ (-635.09\ kJ/mol)]$$

$$\Delta H°_{rxn} = 30.6\ kJ \qquad\qquad reactant\text{-}favored$$

Step 4:

$$\Delta H°_{rxn} = -\Delta H_f°[HgO(s)]$$

$$\Delta H°_{rxn} = 90.83\ kJ \qquad\qquad reactant\text{-}favored$$

(d) The commercial feasibility of this process is limited by the three reactant-favored steps.

6.109 $1\ mile^2 \cdot 1\ inch \cdot \left(\dfrac{1\ km}{0.62137\ mile}\right)^2 \left(\dfrac{10^3\ m}{1\ km}\right)^2 \left(\dfrac{10^2\ cm}{1\ m}\right)^2 \cdot \dfrac{2.54\ cm}{1\ inch} \cdot \dfrac{1.0\ g}{1\ cm^3} = 6.6 \times 10^{10}\ g\ H_2O$

$q = 6.6 \times 10^{10}\ g\ \cdot \dfrac{1\ mol\ H_2O}{18.0\ g} \cdot \dfrac{44.0\ kJ}{1\ mol\ H_2O} = 1.6 \times 10^{11}\ kJ$ released to surroundings

Equivalent to $1.6 \times 10^{11}\ kJ \cdot \dfrac{1\ ton\ dynamite}{4.2 \times 10^6\ kJ} = 3.8 \times 10^4$ tons of dynamite exploding

6.110   See Screen 6.19 for the answer to this problem.

Chapter 7
Atomic Structure

INSTRUCTOR'S NOTES

This chapter and the next one (Chapter 8) are aimed at giving students a firm foundation for understanding of the key theories of chemistry. Therefore, we devote a total of about 9 lectures to these chapters, with much of that time devoted to electron configurations—particularly of ions—and to periodic properties.

Challenges for teaching this material include:

- Pre-existing misconceptions (orbits versus orbitals)
- Non-intuitive aspects of quantum mechanics (wave nature of particles, quantized energy).
- The concept of quantum numbers which may have no precedent for students
- An image representing a probability (orbital) rather than a definitive physical entity

A careful study of the figures should help in their understanding of these ideas.

Students should be urged to master both the new concepts and the mathematical relationships among them. It may be hard for them to appreciate the significance of the quantum model, but they will soon see consequences of this world in periodic properties, bonding, polarity and later in spectroscopy.

SUGGESTED DEMONSTRATIONS

1. Line Spectra
   - One place where our students have some difficulty is in understanding the ideas of "line spectra." This subject is not so important when discussed in terms of the Bohr model as it is in understanding the general idea of the absorption and emission of energy by atoms or molecules. To help students understand line spectra, we give each of them a small diffraction grating. (Large sheets from a scientific supply house are cut into small pieces, and each piece is mounted in cardboard and held with a staple.) Using these gratings, students can view the spectra of light from discharge tubes in the classroom.
   - Hughes, E. Jr.; George, A. "Suitable Light Sources and Spectroscopes for Student Observation of Emission Spectra in Lecture Halls," *Journal of Chemical Education*, **1984**, *61*, 908.

2. Properties of Waves
   - If you have access to a laser pointer, the Optical Transform Kit available from the Institute for Chemical Education (Department of Chemistry, University of Wisconsin, 1101 University Avenue, Madison, WI 53706) can be used to project diffraction patterns on the wall of a lecture room.

3. Atomic Orbitals
   - To illustrate the shapes of atomic orbitals, we use a set of wooden orbital models. These are currently obtainable from Klinger Educational Products Corp., 112-9 14th Road, College Point, New York, 11356.

SOLUTIONS TO STUDY QUESTIONS

7.1   (a) microwaves

      (b) red light

      (c) infrared light

7.2   (a) red, orange, yellow

      (b) blue

      (c) blue

7.3   (a) green

      (b) $595 \text{ nm} \cdot \dfrac{10^{-9} \text{ m}}{1 \text{ nm}} = 5.95 \times 10^{-7} \text{ m}$ $\qquad v = \dfrac{c}{\lambda} = \dfrac{2.998 \times 10^8 \text{ m} \cdot \text{s}^{-1}}{5.95 \times 10^{-7} \text{ m}} = 5.04 \times 10^{14} \text{ s}^{-1}$

7.4   (a) $\lambda = \dfrac{c}{v} = \dfrac{2.998 \times 10^8 \text{ m} \cdot \text{s}^{-1}}{1150 \times 10^3 \text{ s}^{-1}} = 261 \text{ m}$ $\qquad 225 \text{ m} \cdot \dfrac{1 \text{ wavelength}}{261 \text{ m}} = 0.863 \text{ wavelengths}$

      (b) $\lambda = \dfrac{c}{v} = \dfrac{2.998 \times 10^8 \text{ m} \cdot \text{s}^{-1}}{98.1 \times 10^6 \text{ s}^{-1}} = 3.06 \text{ m}$ $\qquad 225 \text{ m} \cdot \dfrac{1 \text{ wavelength}}{3.06 \text{ m}} = 73.6 \text{ wavelengths}$

7.5 $5.0 \times 10^2 \text{ nm} \cdot \dfrac{10^{-9} \text{ m}}{1 \text{ nm}} = 5.0 \times 10^{-7} \text{ m}$

    $E = \dfrac{hc}{\lambda} = \dfrac{(6.626 \times 10^{-34} \text{ J} \cdot \text{s})(2.998 \times 10^8 \text{ m} \cdot \text{s}^{-1})}{5.0 \times 10^{-7} \text{ m}} = 4.0 \times 10^{-19} \text{ J/photon}$

    $4.0 \times 10^{-19} \text{ J/photon} \cdot \dfrac{6.02 \times 10^{23} \text{ photons}}{1 \text{ mol}} = 2.4 \times 10^5 \text{ J/mol photons}$

7.6 $410 \text{ nm} \cdot \dfrac{10^{-9} \text{ m}}{1 \text{ nm}} = 4.1 \times 10^{-7} \text{ m}$ $\qquad v = \dfrac{c}{\lambda} = \dfrac{2.998 \times 10^8 \text{ m} \cdot \text{s}^{-1}}{4.1 \times 10^{-7} \text{ m}} = 7.3 \times 10^{14} \text{ s}^{-1}$

    $E = hv = (6.626 \times 10^{-34} \text{ J} \cdot \text{s})(7.3 \times 10^{14} \text{ s}^{-1}) = 4.8 \times 10^{-19} \text{ J/photon}$

    $4.8 \times 10^{-19} \text{ J/photon} \cdot \dfrac{6.02 \times 10^{23} \text{ photons}}{1 \text{ mol}} = 2.9 \times 10^5 \text{ J/mol photons}$

According to the text, red light has an energy of 1.75×10^5 J/mol

$\dfrac{2.9 \times 10^5 \text{ J}}{1.75 \times 10^5 \text{ J}} = 1.7$

Violet light is 1.7 times more energetic than red light.

7.7 $396.15 \text{ nm} \cdot \dfrac{10^{-9} \text{ m}}{1 \text{ nm}} = 3.9615 \times 10^{-7} \text{ m}$

$\nu = \dfrac{c}{\lambda} = \dfrac{2.99792 \times 10^{8} \text{ m} \cdot \text{s}^{-1}}{3.9615 \times 10^{-7} \text{ m}} = 7.5676 \times 10^{14} \text{ s}^{-1}$

$E = h\nu = (6.62607 \times 10^{-34} \text{ J·s})(7.5676 \times 10^{14} \text{ s}^{-1}) = 5.0144 \times 10^{-19} \text{ J/photon}$

$5.0144 \times 10^{-19} \text{ J/photon} \cdot \dfrac{6.02214 \times 10^{23} \text{ photons}}{1.00 \text{ mol}} = 3.02 \times 10^{5} \text{ J/mol photons}$

7.8   285.2 nm is in the ultraviolet region, 383.8 nm is just at the edge of the visible region, and 518.4 nm is in the visible region. The most energetic line has the shortest wavelength, 285.2 nm.

$285.2 \text{ nm} \cdot \dfrac{10^{-9} \text{ m}}{1 \text{ nm}} = 2.852 \times 10^{-7} \text{ m}$

$E = \dfrac{hc}{\lambda} = \dfrac{(6.6261 \times 10^{-34} \text{ J·s})(2.9979 \times 10^{8} \text{ m} \cdot \text{s}^{-1})}{2.852 \times 10^{-7} \text{ m}} \cdot \dfrac{6.0221 \times 10^{23} \text{ photons}}{1 \text{ mol}} = 4.194 \times 10^{5} \text{ J/mol}$

7.9   (d) FM radiowaves   (c) microwaves   (a) yellow light   (b) X-rays

—increasing energy per photon→

7.10   (a) radar   (b) microwaves   (d) red light   (e) ultraviolet radiation   (c) γ-rays

—increasing energy per photon→

7.11 $2.0 \times 10^{2} \text{ kJ/mol} \cdot \dfrac{1 \text{ mol}}{6.02 \times 10^{23} \text{ photons}} \cdot \dfrac{10^{3} \text{ J}}{1 \text{ kJ}} = 3.3 \times 10^{-19} \text{ J/photon}$

$\lambda = \dfrac{hc}{E} = \dfrac{(6.626 \times 10^{-34} \text{ J·s})(2.998 \times 10^{8} \text{ m} \cdot \text{s}^{-1})}{3.3 \times 10^{-19} \text{ J}} = 6.0 \times 10^{-7} \text{ m (visible region)}$

7.12 $540 \text{ nm} \cdot \dfrac{10^{-9} \text{ m}}{1 \text{ nm}} = 5.4 \times 10^{-7} \text{ m}$

$E = \dfrac{hc}{\lambda} = \dfrac{(6.626 \times 10^{-34} \text{ J·s})(2.998 \times 10^{8} \text{ m} \cdot \text{s}^{-1})}{5.4 \times 10^{-7} \text{ m}} = 3.7 \times 10^{-19} \text{ J/photon}$

This radiation does not have enough energy to activate the switch. This is also true for radiation with wavelengths greater than 540 nm.

7.13   (a) The most energetic line has the shortest wavelength, 253.652 nm.

(b) $253.652 \text{ nm} \cdot \dfrac{10^{-9} \text{ m}}{1 \text{ nm}} = 2.53652 \times 10^{-7} \text{ m}$

$\nu = \dfrac{c}{\lambda} = \dfrac{2.997925 \times 10^{8} \text{ m} \cdot \text{s}^{-1}}{2.53652 \times 10^{-7} \text{ m}} = 1.18190 \times 10^{15} \text{ s}^{-1}$

$E = h\nu = (6.626069 \times 10^{-34} \text{ J·s})(1.18190 \times 10^{15} \text{ s}^{-1}) = 7.83135 \times 10^{-19} \text{ J/photon}$

(c) The 404.656 nm line is violet, while the 435.833 nm line is blue.

7.14   (a) The infrared region

(b) None of the lines mentioned are in the spectrum shown in Figure 7.9. None of the lines listed are in the visible region.

(c) The most energetic line has the shortest wavelength, 837.761 nm.

(d) $865.438 \text{ nm} \cdot \dfrac{10^{-9} \text{ m}}{1 \text{ nm}} = 8.65438 \times 10^{-7} \text{ m}$

$\nu = \dfrac{c}{\lambda} = \dfrac{2.997925 \times 10^8 \text{ m} \cdot \text{s}^{-1}}{8.65438 \times 10^{-7} \text{ m}} = 3.46406 \times 10^{14} \text{ s}^{-1}$

$E = h\nu = (6.626069 \times 10^{-34} \text{ J} \cdot \text{s})(3.46406 \times 10^{14} \text{ s}^{-1}) = 2.29531 \times 10^{-19} \text{ J/photon}$

7.15   Violet; $n_{initial} = 6$ and $n_{final} = 2$

7.16 $\lambda = 91.2 \text{ nm } (9.12 \times 10^{-8} \text{ m})$

$\nu = \dfrac{c}{\lambda} = \dfrac{2.998 \times 10^8 \text{ m} \cdot \text{s}^{-1}}{9.12 \times 10^{-8} \text{ m}} = 3.29 \times 10^{15} \text{ s}^{-1}$

$n_{initial} = \infty$ and $n_{final} = 1$

7.17   (a) From $n = 5$ to $n = 4, 3, 2,$ or 1 $= 4$ lines

From $n = 4$ to $n = 3, 2,$ or 1 $= 3$ lines

From $n = 3$ to $n = 2$ or 1 $= 2$ lines

From $n = 2$ to $n = 1$ $= 1$ line

Total $= 10$ lines possible

(b) Highest frequency (highest energy) $n = 5$ to $n = 1$

(c) Longest wavelength (lowest energy) $n = 5$ to $n = 4$

7.18   (a) From $n = 4$ to $n = 3, 2,$ or 1 $= 3$ lines

From $n = 3$ to $n = 2$ or 1 $= 2$ lines

From $n = 2$ to $n = 1$ $= 1$ line

Total $= 6$ lines possible

(b) Lowest energy $n = 4$ to $n = 3$

(c) Shortest wavelength (highest energy) $n = 4$ to $n = 1$

7.19   (a) $n = 3$ to $n = 2$

(b) $n = 4$ to $n = 1$

The energy levels are progressively closer at higher levels, so the energy difference from $n = 4$ to $n = 1$ is greater than from $n = 5$ to $n = 2$.

7.20   (a) $n = 2$ to $n = 4$ and (d) $n = 3$ to $n = 5$

7.21 $\Delta E = -Rhc\left(\dfrac{1}{n^2_{\text{final}}} - \dfrac{1}{n^2_{\text{initial}}}\right) = -1312 \text{ kJ/mol}\left(\dfrac{1}{1^2} - \dfrac{1}{3^2}\right) = -1166 \text{ kJ/mol}$

$1166 \text{ kJ/mol} \cdot \dfrac{1 \text{ mol}}{6.0221 \times 10^{23} \text{ photons}} \cdot \dfrac{10^3 \text{ J}}{1 \text{ kJ}} = 1.936 \times 10^{-18} \text{ J/photon}$

$\nu = \dfrac{E}{h} = \dfrac{1.936 \times 10^{-18} \text{ J}}{6.6261 \times 10^{-34} \text{ J} \cdot \text{s}} = 2.922 \times 10^{15} \text{ s}^{-1}$

$\lambda = \dfrac{c}{\nu} = \dfrac{2.9979 \times 10^8 \text{ m} \cdot \text{s}^{-1}}{2.922 \times 10^{15} \text{ s}^{-1}} = 1.026 \times 10^{-7} \text{ m (ultraviolet region)}$

7.22 $\Delta E = -Rhc\left(\dfrac{1}{n^2_{\text{final}}} - \dfrac{1}{n^2_{\text{initial}}}\right) = -1312 \text{ kJ/mol}\left(\dfrac{1}{3^2} - \dfrac{1}{4^2}\right) = -63.78 \text{ kJ/mol}$

$63.78 \text{ kJ/mol} \cdot \dfrac{1 \text{ mol}}{6.0221 \times 10^{23} \text{ photons}} \cdot \dfrac{10^3 \text{ J}}{1 \text{ kJ}} = 1.059 \times 10^{-19} \text{ J/photon}$

$\nu = \dfrac{E}{h} = \dfrac{1.059 \times 10^{-19} \text{ J}}{6.6261 \times 10^{-34} \text{ J} \cdot \text{s}} = 1.598 \times 10^{14} \text{ s}^{-1}$

$\lambda = \dfrac{c}{\nu} = \dfrac{2.9979 \times 10^8 \text{ m} \cdot \text{s}^{-1}}{1.598 \times 10^{14} \text{ s}^{-1}} = 1.876 \times 10^{-6} \text{ m (infrared region)}$

7.23 $\dfrac{2.5 \times 10^8 \text{ cm}}{1 \text{ s}} \cdot \dfrac{1 \text{ m}}{10^2 \text{ cm}} = 2.5 \times 10^6 \text{ m/s}$

$\lambda = \dfrac{h}{mv} = \dfrac{6.626 \times 10^{-34} \text{ J} \cdot \text{s}}{(9.109 \times 10^{-31} \text{ kg})(2.5 \times 10^6 \text{ m} \cdot \text{s}^{-1})} = 2.9 \times 10^{-10} \text{ m}$

7.24 $\lambda = \dfrac{h}{mv} = \dfrac{6.626 \times 10^{-34} \text{ J} \cdot \text{s}}{(9.11 \times 10^{-31} \text{ kg})(1.3 \times 10^8 \text{ m} \cdot \text{s}^{-1})} = 5.6 \times 10^{-12} \text{ m}$

7.25 $1.0 \times 10^2 \text{ g} \cdot \dfrac{1 \text{ kg}}{10^3 \text{ g}} = 0.10 \text{ kg}$ $\lambda = \dfrac{h}{mv} = \dfrac{6.626 \times 10^{-34} \text{ J} \cdot \text{s}}{(0.10 \text{ kg})(30 \text{ m} \cdot \text{s}^{-1})} = 2.2 \times 10^{-34} \text{ m}$

$5.6 \times 10^{-3} \text{ nm} \cdot \dfrac{1 \text{ m}}{10^9 \text{ nm}} = 5.6 \times 10^{-12} \text{ m}$

$v = \dfrac{h}{m\lambda} = \dfrac{6.626 \times 10^{-34} \text{ J} \cdot \text{s}}{(0.10 \text{ kg})(5.6 \times 10^{-12} \text{ m})} = 1.2 \times 10^{-21} \text{ m} \cdot \text{s}^{-1}$

7.26 $\dfrac{7.00 \times 10^2 \text{ mile}}{1 \text{ hour}} \cdot \dfrac{1 \text{ km}}{0.6214 \text{ mile}} \cdot \dfrac{10^3 \text{ m}}{1 \text{ km}} \cdot \dfrac{1 \text{ hour}}{3600 \text{ s}} = 313 \text{ m} \cdot \text{s}^{-1}$

$\lambda = \dfrac{h}{mv} = \dfrac{6.626 \times 10^{-34} \text{ J} \cdot \text{s}}{(1.50 \times 10^{-3} \text{ kg})(313 \text{ m} \cdot \text{s}^{-1})} = 1.41 \times 10^{-33} \text{ m}$

7.27   (a) ℓ can be 0, 1, 2, 3

(b) m_ℓ can be 0, ±1, ±2

(c) $n = 4, \ell = 0, m_\ell = 0$

(d) $n = 4, \ell = 3, m_\ell = 0, \pm1, \pm2, \pm3$

7.28   (a) The orbital type is *d*. It is a 4*d* orbital.

        (b) When $n = 5$, $\ell = 0, 1, 2, 3$, and 4

            $\ell = 0$ 1 *s* orbital

            $\ell = 1$ 3 *p* orbitals

            $\ell = 2$ 5 *d* orbitals

            $\ell = 3$ 7 *f* orbitals

            $\ell = 4$ 9 *g* orbitals

            There are a total of 5^2 or 25 orbitals in the $n = 5$ electron shell.

        (c) In an *f* subshell there are 7 orbitals. $m_\ell = 0, \pm1, \pm2$, and ±3

7.29

n	ℓ	m_ℓ
4	1	−1
4	1	0
4	1	1

7.30

n	ℓ	m_ℓ
5	2	−2
5	2	−1
5	2	0
5	2	1
5	2	2

7.31   When $n = 4$, there are four subshells, 4*s*, 4*p*, 4*d*, and 4*f*

7.32   When $n = 5$, there are five subshells, 5*s*, 5*p*, 5*d*, 5*f*, and 5*g*

7.33   (a) When $n = 2$, the maximum value of ℓ is 1

        (b) When $\ell = 0$, m_ℓ can only have a value of 0

        (c) When $\ell = 0$, m_ℓ can only have a value of 0

7.34   (b) and (c) are valid sets of quantum numbers

        (a) incorrect; when $n = 3$, the maximum value of ℓ is 2

        (d) incorrect; when $\ell = 3$, m_ℓ can only have values of 0, ±1, ±2, or ±3

7.35   (a) none; when $\ell = 0$, m_ℓ can only have a value of 0

        (b) 3 orbitals

        (c) 11 orbitals

        (d) 1 orbital

7.36   (a) 7 orbitals

(b) 25 orbitals

(c) None; ℓ cannot have a value equal to n

(d) 1 orbital

7.37 $2d$ and $3f$ cannot exist. They do not follow the $\ell = 0, 1, 2, ..., n - 1$ rule

7.38 $2f$ and $1p$ are incorrect designations. They do not follow the $\ell = 0, 1, 2, ..., n - 1$ rule

7.39

		n	ℓ	m_ℓ
(a) $2p$		2	1	-1
		2	1	0
		2	1	1
(b) $3d$		3	2	-2
		3	2	-1
		3	2	0
		3	2	1
		3	2	2
(c) $4f$		4	3	-3
		4	3	-2
		4	3	-1
		4	3	0
		4	3	1
		4	3	2
		4	3	3

7.40

		n	ℓ	m_ℓ
(a) $5f$		5	3	-3
		5	3	-2
		5	3	-1
		5	3	0
		5	3	1
		5	3	2
		5	3	3

(b) 4d	4	2	–2
	4	2	–1
	4	2	0
	4	2	1
	4	2	2
(c) 2s	2	0	0

7.41   (d) 4d

7.42   (d) s orbital

7.43   The value of ℓ indicates the number of nodal surfaces

(a) 2s: $\ell = 0$, zero nodal surfaces

(b) 5d: $\ell = 2$, two nodal surfaces

(c) 5f: $\ell = 3$, three nodal surfaces

7.44   The value of ℓ indicates the number of nodal surfaces

(a) 4f: $\ell = 3$, three nodal surfaces

(b) 2p: $\ell = 1$, one nodal surface

(c) 6s: $\ell = 0$, zero nodal surfaces

7.45   (a) correct

(b) Incorrect; the intensity of a light beam is independent of frequency and is related to the number of photons of light with a certain energy.

(c) correct

7.46   The Lyman series is found in the ultraviolet region and the Balmer series is in the visible region.

7.47   s   0 nodal surface

p   1 nodal surface

d   2 nodal surfaces

f   3 nodal surfaces

7.48

orbital	maximum number in a given shell
s	1
p	3
d	5
f	7

7.49 ℓ value   orbital type

            3   f

            0   s

            1   p

            2   d

7.50 s orbital p_x orbital

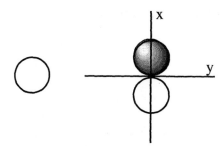

7.51   orbital type   number of orbitals in a given subshell   number of nodal surfaces

            s 1   0

            p 3   1

            d 5   2

            f 7   3

7.52 $\Delta E = -Rhc\left(\dfrac{1}{n^2_{\text{final}}} - \dfrac{1}{n^2_{\text{initial}}}\right) = -1312 \text{ kJ/mol}\left(\dfrac{1}{5^2} - \dfrac{1}{6^2}\right) = -16.04 \text{ kJ/mol}$

$16.04 \text{ kJ/mol} \cdot \dfrac{1 \text{ mol}}{6.0221 \times 10^{23} \text{ photons}} \cdot \dfrac{10^3 \text{ J}}{1 \text{ kJ}} = 2.663 \times 10^{-20} \text{ J/photon}$

$\nu = \dfrac{E}{h} = \dfrac{2.663 \times 10^{-20} \text{ J}}{6.6261 \times 10^{-34} \text{ J} \cdot \text{s}} = 4.019 \times 10^{13} \text{ s}^{-1}$

$\lambda = \dfrac{c}{\nu} = \dfrac{2.9979 \times 10^8 \text{ m} \cdot \text{s}^{-1}}{4.019 \times 10^{13} \text{ s}^{-1}} = 7.460 \times 10^{-6} \text{ m}$

7.53   (a) green light

        (b) Shorter wavelength corresponds to higher energy. Green light has a wavelength of 500 nm and red

             light has a wavelength of 680 nm.

        (c) green light

7.54 $375 \text{ nm} \cdot \dfrac{10^{-9} \text{ m}}{1 \text{ nm}} = 3.75 \times 10^{-7} \text{ m}$

$E = \dfrac{hc}{\lambda} = \dfrac{(6.626 \times 10^{-34} \text{ J} \cdot \text{s})(2.998 \times 10^8 \text{ m} \cdot \text{s}^{-1})}{3.75 \times 10^{-7} \text{ m}} \cdot \dfrac{6.022 \times 10^{23} \text{ photons}}{1.00 \text{ mol}} \cdot \dfrac{1 \text{ kJ}}{10^3 \text{ J}} = 319 \text{ kJ/mol}$

7.55   (a) $\lambda = \dfrac{c}{v} = \dfrac{2.998 \times 10^8 \text{ m} \cdot \text{s}^{-1}}{850 \times 10^6 \text{ s}^{-1}} = 0.35$ m

     (b) $E = h\nu = (6.626 \times 10^{-34} \text{ J}\cdot\text{s})(850 \times 10^6 \text{ s}^{-1}) \cdot \dfrac{6.02 \times 10^{23} \text{ photons}}{1.00 \text{ mol}} = 0.34$ J/mol

     (c) $E = \dfrac{hc}{\lambda} = \dfrac{(6.626 \times 10^{-34} \text{ J}\cdot\text{s})(2.998 \times 10^8 \text{ m}\cdot\text{s}^{-1})}{4.2 \times 10^{-7} \text{ m}} \cdot \dfrac{6.02 \times 10^{23} \text{ photons}}{1.00 \text{ mol}} = 2.8 \times 10^5$ J/mol

     $\dfrac{2.8 \times 10^5 \text{ J/mol}}{0.34 \text{ J/mol}} = 84{,}000$

     (d) Blue light is 84,000 times more energetic than the radiation sent from cell phones.

7.56 $E = \dfrac{hc}{\lambda} = \dfrac{(6.626 \times 10^{-34} \text{ J}\cdot\text{s})(2.998 \times 10^8 \text{ m}\cdot\text{s}^{-1})}{4.7 \times 10^{-7} \text{ m}} = 4.2 \times 10^{-19}$ J/photon

     $\dfrac{2.50 \times 10^{-14} \text{ J}}{4.2 \times 10^{-19} \text{ J/photon}} = 5.9 \times 10^4$ photons

7.57   He: $\Delta E = -Z^2 Rhc \left(\dfrac{1}{n_{\text{final}}^2} - \dfrac{1}{n_{\text{initial}}^2} \right) = -(2^2)(1312 \text{ kJ/mol}) \left(\dfrac{1}{\infty^2} - \dfrac{1}{1^2} \right) = 5248$ kJ/mol

     H: $\Delta E = -Z^2 Rhc \left(\dfrac{1}{n_{\text{final}}^2} - \dfrac{1}{n_{\text{initial}}^2} \right) = -(1^2)(1312 \text{ kJ/mol}) \left(\dfrac{1}{\infty^2} - \dfrac{1}{1^2} \right) = 1312$ kJ/mol

7.58   (i)   (b) $n = 7$ to $n = 6$

     (ii) (a) $n = 7$ to $n = 1$

     (iii) (a) $n = 7$ to $n = 1$

7.59 $1s, 2s = 2p, 3s = 3p = 3d, 4s$

7.60   (a) 3   (d) 5   (g) 25

     (b) 3   (e) 5   (h) 1

     (c) 1   (f) 7

7.61 $1.173 \times 10^6 \text{ eV} \cdot \dfrac{9.6485 \times 10^4 \text{ J/mol}}{1 \text{ eV}} \cdot \dfrac{1 \text{ mol}}{6.0221 \times 10^{23} \text{ photons}} = 1.879 \times 10^{-13}$ J/photon

     $\nu = \dfrac{E}{h} = \dfrac{1.879 \times 10^{-13} \text{ J}}{6.6261 \times 10^{-34} \text{ J}\cdot\text{s}} = 2.836 \times 10^{20} \text{ s}^{-1}$

     $\lambda = \dfrac{c}{v} = \dfrac{2.9979 \times 10^8 \text{ m}\cdot\text{s}^{-1}}{2.836 \times 10^{20} \text{ s}^{-1}} = 1.057 \times 10^{-12}$ m

7.62 $q_{eye} = (11 \text{ g})(4.0 \text{ J/g·K})(3.0 \text{ K}) = 130 \text{ J}$

$$E = \frac{hc}{\lambda} = \frac{(6.626 \times 10^{-34} \text{ J·s})(2.998 \times 10^8 \text{ m·s}^{-1})}{0.12 \text{ m}} = 1.7 \times 10^{-24} \text{ J/photon}$$

$$\frac{130 \text{ J}}{1.7 \times 10^{-24} \text{ J/photon}} = 8.0 \times 10^{25} \text{ photons}$$

7.63 $7.8 \times 10^7 \text{ km} \cdot \dfrac{10^3 \text{ m}}{1 \text{ km}} \cdot \dfrac{1 \text{ s}}{2.998 \times 10^8 \text{ m}} = 260 \text{ seconds (4.3 minutes)}$

7.64   (a) The most energetic line has the shortest wavelength, 357.9 nm

(b) blue-indigo

7.65   (a) size and energy

(b) ℓ

(c) more

(d) 7

(e) 1

(f) d, s, p

(g) 0, 1, 2, 3, 4

(h) 16

7.66   (a) size and energy; shape

(b) 0, 1, 2

(c) f

(d) 4; 2; –2

(e)
letter	p	d
ℓ value	1	2
nodal planes	1	2

(f) f

(g) $2d, 3f$

(h) $n = 2, \ell = 1, m_\ell = 2$ is not valid

(i) (i)   3

(ii) 9

(iii) none

(iv) 1

7.67   An electron orbiting the nucleus could occupy only certain orbits or energy levels in which it is stable. An electron in an atom will remain in its lowest energy level unless disturbed.

7.68   Bohr's circular orbit model contradicts the laws of classical physics, and Bohr had to artificially introduce the concept of quantization to explain how these electron orbits could be stable.

7.69   (c) Electrons moving from a given level to one of lower n results in the emission of energy, which is observed as light.

7.70   The square of the wave function is the probability of finding the electron within a given region of space, also known as the electron density. This region of space where an electron of a given energy is most probably located is its orbital. The units for $4\pi r^2\psi$ are 1/distance.

7.71   The electron behaves simultaneously as a wave and a particle. The modern view of atomic structure is based on the wave properties of the electron, and describes regions around an atom's nucleus in which there is the highest probability of finding a given electron.

7.72   (b), (e) – (j)

7.73   (a) and (b)

7.74 $N = 1, L = 1, M = -1, 0, +1$ 3 orbitals

$N = 2, L = 2, M = -1, 0, +1$ 3 orbitals

$N = 3, L = 3, M = -1, 0, +1$ 3 orbitals

A total of 9 orbitals in the first three electron shells

7.75   A photon with wavelength of 93.8 nm has enough energy to promote an electron from $n = 1$ to $n = 6$.

From $n = 6$ to $n = 5, 4, 3, 2,$ or 1	= 5 lines
From $n = 5$ to $n = 4, 3, 2,$ or 1	= 4 lines
From $n = 4$ to $n = 3, 2,$ or 1	= 3 lines
From $n = 3$ to $n = 2$ or 1	= 2 lines
From $n = 2$ to $n = 1$	= 1 line
Total	= 15 lines possible

The wavelengths for emissions with $n_{final} = 1, 2,$ and 3 are shown in Figure 7.12.

$n = 6$ to $n = 5$:

$$\Delta E = -Rhc\left(\frac{1}{n_{final}^2} - \frac{1}{n_{initial}^2}\right) = -1312 \text{ kJ/mol}\left(\frac{1}{5^2} - \frac{1}{6^2}\right) = -16.04 \text{ kJ/mol}$$

$$16.04 \text{ kJ/mol} \cdot \frac{1 \text{ mol}}{6.0221 \times 10^{23} \text{ photons}} \cdot \frac{10^3 \text{ J}}{1 \text{ kJ}} = 2.663 \times 10^{-20} \text{ J/photon}$$

$$\lambda = \frac{hc}{E} = \frac{(6.6261 \times 10^{-34} \text{ J} \cdot \text{s})(2.9979 \times 10^8 \text{ m} \cdot \text{s}^{-1})}{2.663 \times 10^{-20} \text{ J/photon}} = 7.460 \times 10^{-6} \text{ m } (7460. \text{ nm})$$

$n = 6$ to $n = 4$:

$$\Delta E = -Rhc\left(\frac{1}{n_{final}^2} - \frac{1}{n_{initial}^2}\right) = -1312 \text{ kJ/mol}\left(\frac{1}{4^2} - \frac{1}{6^2}\right) = -45.56 \text{ kJ/mol}$$

$$45.56 \text{ kJ/mol} \cdot \frac{1 \text{ mol}}{6.0221 \times 10^{23} \text{ photons}} \cdot \frac{10^3 \text{ J}}{1 \text{ kJ}} = 7.565 \times 10^{-20} \text{ J/photon}$$

$$\lambda = \frac{hc}{E} = \frac{(6.6261 \times 10^{-34} \text{ J} \cdot \text{s})(2.9979 \times 10^8 \text{ m} \cdot \text{s}^{-1})}{7.565 \times 10^{-20} \text{ J/photon}} = 2.626 \times 10^{-6} \text{ m } (2626 \text{ nm})$$

$n = 5$ to $n = 4$:

$$\Delta E = -Rhc\left(\frac{1}{n_{final}^2} - \frac{1}{n_{initial}^2}\right) = -1312 \text{ kJ/mol}\left(\frac{1}{4^2} - \frac{1}{5^2}\right) = -29.52 \text{ kJ/mol}$$

$$29.52 \text{ kJ/mol} \cdot \frac{1 \text{ mol}}{6.0221 \times 10^{23} \text{ photons}} \cdot \frac{10^3 \text{ J}}{1 \text{ kJ}} = 4.902 \times 10^{-20} \text{ J/photon}$$

$$\lambda = \frac{hc}{E} = \frac{(6.6261 \times 10^{-34} \text{ J} \cdot \text{s})(2.9979 \times 10^8 \text{ m} \cdot \text{s}^{-1})}{4.902 \times 10^{-20} \text{ J/photon}} = 4.052 \times 10^{-6} \text{ m } (4052 \text{ nm})$$

7.76   (a) Group VII B, period 5

(b) $n = 5, \ell = 0, m_\ell = 0$

(c) $0.141 \times 10^6 \text{ eV} \cdot \frac{9.6485 \times 10^4 \text{ J/mol}}{1 \text{ eV}} \cdot \frac{1 \text{ mol}}{6.0221 \times 10^{23} \text{ photons}} = 2.26 \times 10^{-14} \text{ J/photon}$

$$\nu = \frac{E}{h} = \frac{2.26 \times 10^{-14} \text{ J}}{6.626 \times 10^{-34} \text{ J} \cdot \text{s}} = 3.41 \times 10^{19} \text{ s}^{-1}$$

$$\lambda = \frac{c}{\nu} = \frac{2.998 \times 10^8 \text{ m} \cdot \text{s}^{-1}}{3.41 \times 10^{19} \text{ s}^{-1}} = 8.79 \times 10^{-12} \text{ m}$$

(d) (i) $HTcO_4(aq) + NaOH(aq) \rightarrow NaTcO_4(aq) + H_2O(\ell)$

(ii) $4.5 \times 10^{-3} \text{ g} \cdot \frac{1 \text{ mol Tc}}{97.9 \text{ g}} \cdot \frac{1 \text{ mol NaTcO}_4}{1 \text{ mol Tc}} \cdot \frac{185 \text{ g}}{1 \text{ mol NaTcO}_4} = 8.5 \times 10^{-3} \text{ g NaTcO}_4$

$4.5 \times 10^{-3} \text{ g} \cdot \frac{1 \text{ mol Tc}}{97.9 \text{ g}} \cdot \frac{1 \text{ mol HTcO}_4}{1 \text{ mol Tc}} \cdot \frac{1 \text{ mol NaOH}}{1 \text{ mol HTcO}_4} \cdot \frac{40.0 \text{ g}}{1 \text{ mol NaOH}} = 1.8 \times 10^{-3} \text{ g NaOH}$

7.77   According to de Broglie's equation, $\lambda = \dfrac{h}{mv}$, any moving particle has an associated wavelength.

However, a heavy particle such as a golf ball has an incredibly small wavelength that cannot be measured with any instrument now available.

7.78   The light is emitted from atoms or ions in excited states as they decay from an excited electronic state to a lower energy state. In the "neon" light, the electric current provides the energy needed to excite the gaseous atoms. In the flame, the ions in the salt are excited by the thermal energy of the flame.

7.79   The pickle glows because the materials in the pickle are being excited by the addition of the energy (electric current). The pickle has been soaked in brine (NaCl), so the electrons in the sodium atom are excited and release energy as they return to lower energy states, providing yellow light. The same kind of light is visible in many street lamps.

7.80   Three emission lines are emitted. The photon excites an electron from $n = 1$ to $n = 4$. Six possible emissions are possible:

$n = 4$ to $n = 3$	$\lambda = 1875$ nm
$n = 4$ to $n = 2$	$\lambda = 486.1$ nm
$n = 4$ to $n = 1$	$\lambda = 97.3$ nm
$n = 3$ to $n = 2$	$\lambda = 656.3$ nm
$n = 3$ to $n = 1$	$\lambda = 102.6$ nm
$n = 2$ to $n = 1$	$\lambda = 121.6$ nm

Chapter 8
Atomic Electron Configurations and Chemical Periodicity

INSTRUCTOR'S NOTES

As noted in the previous chapter, about 9 lectures are devoted to the material in Chapters 7 & 8.

Students have experience with magnetism so the early inclusion of this topic in the chapter should provide them with something familiar to relate to the new information which they are learning. Continuing the study of magnetism through the application of the well-known MRI technique should provide some motivation to comprehend the theory behind it.

Challenges for teaching this material include:

- Nodes in probability ("How does the electron get to the other side of the nucleus?")
- Subshell filling order (Figure 8.5)
- Exceptions to the usual filling order of electrons in the transition metals
- Electron configurations of transition metal ions
- The indistinctness of atomic size
- Exceptions to periodic properties.

Note: The definition of electron affinity used is the energy involved when an atom in the gas phase acquires an electron. Some texts use a different definition. Therefore, for example, the electron affinity for F is –328 kJ/mol. In class, we emphasize that the affinity for an addition electron beyond the number in the neutral atom increases (becomes more negative) moving across a period.

SUGGESTED DEMONSTRATIONS

1. Electron Configurations
   - Garofalo, A. "Housing Electrons: Relating Quantum Numbers, Energy Levels, and Electron Configurations," *Journal of Chemical Education*, **1997**, *74*, 709.
2. Paramagnetism of Oxygen
   - Shakhashiri, B. Z. "Preparation and Properties of Liquid Oxygen," *Chemical Demonstrations: A Handbook for Teachers of Chemistry*; University of Wisconsin Press, 1985; Vol. 2, pp. 147-152.
   - Shimada, H.; Yasuoda, T.; Mitsuzawa, S. "Observation of the Paramagnetic Property of Oxygen by Simple Method," *Journal of Chemical Education* **1990**, *67*, 63.
   - See the *General ChemistryNow CD-ROM* for a demonstration of paramagnetic liquid oxygen.
3. Periodic Properties of the Elements
   - The *Periodic Table Videodisc* and the *Periodic Table Live!* CD-ROM from *JCE: Software* are most valuable with this chapter. See the information in the Preface to this *Manual* and the following article:

Kotz, J. *Journal of Chemical Education* **1989**, *66*, 750. The *Periodic Table Videodisc* and the *Periodic Table Live!* CD-ROM can be used to illustrate periodic trends in reactions. The videodisc is an image data base that contains images of the elements reacting with air, water, acids, and a base. In addition, it has information on the uses of the elements. We use it, for example, to illustrate the trend in reactivity of the alkali and alkaline earth metals with air and water. In addition, we carry out the reactions of some of the alkali and alkaline earth metals with water in petri dishes on the overhead projector.

SOLUTIONS TO STUDY QUESTIONS

8.1   P $1s^2 2s^2 2p^6 3s^2 3p^3$

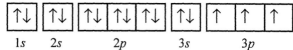

Phosphorus is in Group 5A and has five electrons in its outer shell.

Cl $1s^2 2s^2 2p^6 3s^2 3p^5$

Chlorine is in Group 7A and has seven electrons in its outer shell.

8.2   Mg $1s^2 2s^2 2p^6 3s^2$

Magnesium is in group 2A and has two electrons in its outer shell.

Ar $1s^2 2s^2 2p^6 3s^2 3p^6$

Argon is in group 8A and has eight electrons in its outer shell.

8.3   Cr $1s^2 2s^2 2p^6 3s^2 3p^6 3d^5 4s^1$

Fe $1s^2 2s^2 2p^6 3s^2 3p^6 3d^6 4s^2$

8.4   V $1s^2 2s^2 2p^6 3s^2 3p^6 3d^3 4s^2$

8.5   (a)   As $[Ar]3d^{10}4s^2 4p^3$

(b)   Kr $[Ar]3d^{10}4s^2 4p^6$

8.6   (a)   Sr $[Kr]5s^2$

(b)   Zr $[Kr]4d^2 5s^2$

(c)   Rh $[Kr]4d^7 5s^2$ (actual configuration $[Kr]4d^8 5s^1$)

(d)   Sn $[Kr]4d^{10}5s^2 5p^2$

8.7   (a)   Ta $[Xe]4f^{14}5d^3 6s^2$

(b)   Pt $[Xe]4f^{14}5d^8 6s^2$ (actual configuration $[Xe]4f^{14}5d^9 6s^1$)

8.8   (a)   Sm $[Xe]4f^5 5d^1 6s^2$ (actual configuration $[Xe]4f^6 6s^2$)

(b)   Yb $[Xe]4f^{13}5d^1 6s^2$ (actual configuration $[Xe]4f^{14}6s^2$)

8.9   Am $[Rn]5f^7 7s^2$

8.10   (a) Pu $[Rn]5f^56d^17s^2$ (actual configuration $[Rn]5f^67s^2$)

      (b) Cm $[Rn]5f^76d^17s^2$

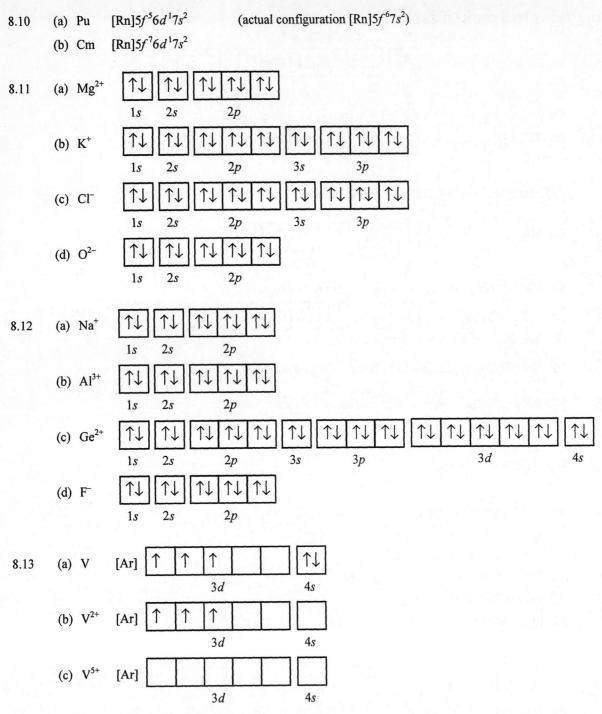

The V^{2+} ion is paramagnetic with three unpaired electrons

8.14   (a) Ti   [Ar]

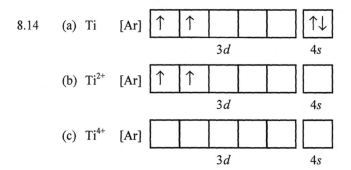

(c) Ti^{4+} [Ar]

The Ti^{2+} ion is paramagnetic with two unpaired electrons.

8.15   (a) Mn   [Ar]

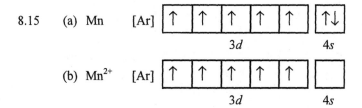

(c) Yes, the +2 ion is paramagnetic.

(d) The ion has five unpaired electrons.

8.16   Ni^{2+} [Ar]   Paramagnetic

Ni^{3+} [Ar]   Paramagnetic

8.17   (a) m_s can only have values of $\pm^1/_2$ $m_s = +^1/_2$

(b) when $\ell = 1$, m_ℓ can only have values of $0, \pm1$ $m_\ell = 0$

(c) the maximum value of ℓ is $(n-1)$ $\ell = 2$

8.18   (a) the maximum value of ℓ is $(n-1)$ $\ell = 1$

(b) m_s can only have values of $\pm^1/_2$ $m_s = +^1/_2$

(c) when $\ell = 1$, m_ℓ can only have values of $0, \pm1$ $m_\ell = 0$

8.19   (a) 14 electrons

(b) 2 electrons

(c) none; the maximum value of ℓ is $(n-1)$

8.20   (a) 18 electrons

(b) 10 electrons

(c) 1 electron

(d) none; when $\ell = 0$, m_ℓ can only have a value of 0

8.21   Mg   [Ne]   [↑↓]
               3s

$n = 3, \ell = 0, m_\ell = 0, m_s = +^1/_2$

$n = 3, \ell = 0, m_\ell = 0, m_s = -^1/_2$

8.22   P   [Ne]   [↑↓] [↑] [↑] [↑]
              3s   3p

$n = 3, \ell = 0, m_\ell = 0, m_s = +^1/_2$

$n = 3, \ell = 0, m_\ell = 0, m_s = -^1/_2$

$n = 3, \ell = 1, m_\ell = -1, m_s = +^1/_2$

$n = 3, \ell = 1, m_\ell = 0, m_s = +^1/_2$

$n = 3, \ell = 1, m_\ell = +1, m_s = +^1/_2$

8.23   Ga   [Ar]   [↑↓] [↑↓] [↑↓] [↑↓] [↑↓]   [↑↓]   [↑] [ ] [ ]
                               3d   4s   4p

$n = 4, \ell = 1, m_\ell = 0, m_s = +^1/_2$

8.24   [↑] [↑] [ ] [ ] [ ]   [↑↓]
              3d   4s

$n = 3, \ell = 2, m_\ell = 2, m_s = +^1/_2$

$n = 3, \ell = 2, m_\ell = 1, m_s = +^1/_2$

$n = 4, \ell = 0, m_\ell = 0, m_s = +^1/_2$

$n = 4, \ell = 0, m_\ell = 0, m_s = -^1/_2$

8.25   C < B < Al < Na < K

8.26   P < Ge < Ca < Sr < Rb

8.27   (a) $Cl^- > Cl$ (b) Al > O   (c) In > I

8.28   (a) Cs > Rb   (b) $O^{2-} > O$ (c) As > Br

8.29   (c) Li < Si < C < Ne

8.30   K < Li < C < N

8.31   (a) Na   (b) O   (c) Na < Mg < P < O

8.32   (a) Al   (b) Al

       (c) C (based on periodic trends)

            Si (according to experimental data)

       (d) Al < B < C

8.33   (a) S < O < F   The trend is to increase to the right and decrease down the periodic table.

       (b) O   The trend is to decrease down the periodic table.

       (c) Cl   The trend is to be more negative to the right and less negative down the periodic

            table

       (d) O^{2-} Ions are larger than neutral atoms. O^{2-} and F^- are isoelectronic, but the O^{2-} ion

            has only 8 protons in its nucleus to attract the 10 electrons whereas the F^- ion

            has 9.

8.34   (a) F < O < S   The trend is to increase to the left and down the periodic table.

       (b) Based on a knowledge of first-order periodic trends, we would predict that S should have the largest

            IE of the group P, Si, S, and Se. However, recall that the O atom IE is smaller than that of N, so it is

            not surprising that the same effect carries over into the third period. That is, the order of ionization

            energies is Si < Se < S < P.

       (c) $F^- < O^{2-} < N^{3-}$ These ions are isoelectronic and size increases as the number of protons in the

            nucleus available to attract the electrons decreases.

       (d) Cs < Ba < Sr The trend is to increase to the right and decrease down the periodic table.

8.35   (a) (b) is diamagnetic, (c) is paramagnetic, and (a) is ferromagnetic

       (b) Solid (a) is most strongly attracted to a magnetic field; solid (b) is least strongly attracted.

8.36   Rf $[Rn]5f^{14}6d^27s^2$

8.37   U   [Rn]

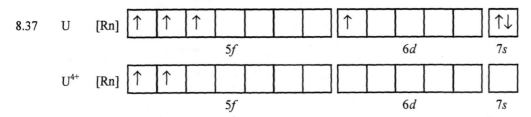

Both uranium and the uranium(IV) ion are paramagnetic.

8.38   (a) Ce   [Xe]

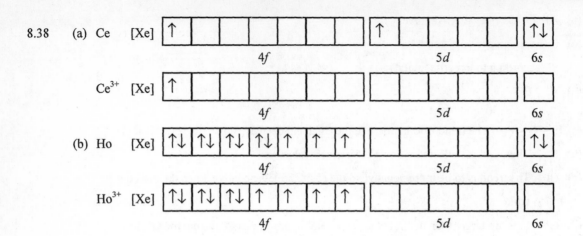

8.39   (a) atomic number = (2 + 8 + 8 + 2) = 20

(b) total number of s electrons = (2 + 2 + 2 + 2) = 8

(c) total number of p electrons = (6 + 6) = 12

(d) total number of d electrons = 0

(e) The element is Ca, calcium, a metal

8.40   Mt   [Rn]$5f^{14}6d^77s^2$ Co, Rh, Ir

8.41   (b) the maximum value of ℓ is $(n-1)$

8.42 $n = 4$, $\ell = 1$, $m_\ell = -1$, $m_s = +\frac{1}{2}$

$n = 4$, $\ell = 1$, $m_\ell = -1$, $m_s = -\frac{1}{2}$

$n = 4$, $\ell = 1$, $m_\ell = 0$, $m_s = +\frac{1}{2}$

$n = 4$, $\ell = 1$, $m_\ell = 0$, $m_s = -\frac{1}{2}$

$n = 4$, $\ell = 1$, $m_\ell = +1$, $m_s = +\frac{1}{2}$

$n = 4$, $\ell = 1$, $m_\ell = +1$, $m_s = -\frac{1}{2}$

8.43   (a) Nd [Xe]$4f^46s^2$

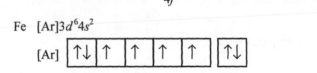

Fe [Ar]$3d^64s^2$

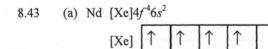

B   [He]$2s^22p^1$

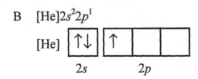

(b) All three elements are paramagnetic.

(c) Nd³⁺ [Xe]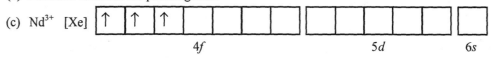

                              4f   5d   6s

paramagnetic

Fe³⁺ [Ar]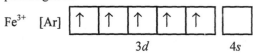

                     3d   4s

paramagnetic

8.44   (a) P, phosphorus

        (b) Be, beryllium

        (c) N, nitrogen

        (d) Tc, technetium

        (e) Cl, chlorine

        (f) Zn, zinc

8.45   K < Ca < Si < P

8.46 $Cl^- < Cl < Ca^{2+}$

    Ca^{2+} and Cl^- are isoelectronic. Ca^{2+} has a larger IE than Cl^- because the calcium ion has a 2+ charge and removing another electron from that ion would take more energy. Removing an electron from the chloride ion would require less energy than the removal of an electron from the Cl atom due to electron repulsion forces.

8.47   (a) metal

        (b) B

        (c) B

        (d) A

8.48   (a) alkaline earth metal

        (b) nonmetal (halogen)

        (c) B

        (d) B

8.49 In^{4+} Indium has three outer shell electrons, so it is unlikely to form a 4+ ion

        Fe^{6+} Ions with charges greater than +3 or +4 are unlikely to form

        Sn^{5+} Tin has four outer shell electrons, so it is unlikely to form a 5+ ion

8.50 $S^{2-} > Cl^- > K^+ > Ca^{2+}$

8.51   (a) Se

       (b) Br^-

       (c) Na

       (d) N

       (e) N^{3-}

8.52   (a) $Ca^{2+} < K^+ < Cl^-$

       (b) $Cl^- < K^+ < Ca^{2+}$

       (c) $Cl^- < K^+ < Ca^{2+}$

8.53   (a) Na

       (b) C

       (c) Na < Al < B < C

8.54   Tc and Rh

8.55   (a) Co, cobalt

       (b) paramagnetic (three unpaired electrons)

       (c) The 3+ ion would be formed by the loss of both $4s$ electrons and one d electron leaving four unpaired
           electrons

8.56   (a) V, vanadium

       (b) Group 5B, Period 4

       (c) Transition element

       (d) Paramagnetic, three unpaired electrons

       (e) $n = 3, \ell = 2, m_\ell = -2, m_s = +\frac{1}{2}$

           $n = 3, \ell = 2, m_\ell = -1, m_s = +\frac{1}{2}$

           $n = 3, \ell = 2, m_\ell = 0, m_s = +\frac{1}{2}$

           $n = 4, \ell = 0, m_\ell = 0, m_s = +\frac{1}{2}$

           $n = 4, \ell = 0, m_\ell = 0, m_s = -\frac{1}{2}$

       (f) V^{2+} $[Ar]3d^3$ The two $4s$ electrons are removed and the resulting ion is paramagnetic

8.57   For Li^+, there is one less electron to be attracted by the same nuclear charge, but the outer electrons are in
       the $n = 1$ shell, closer to the nucleus. For F^-, there is one additional electron in the $2p$ orbital. This adds
       additional electron–electron repulsions while the nuclear charge remains the same.

8.58   K^{2+} Potassium has one outer shell electron, so it is unlikely to form a 2+ ion

Al^{4+} Aluminum has three outer shell electrons, so it is unlikely to form a 4+ ion

F^{2-} Fluorine has seven outer shell electrons, so adding one electron forms an anion with the same number of electrons as the nearest noble gas. Adding a second electron would increase electron–electron repulsions and require a great amount of energy.

8.59   K(g)   →   K$^+$(g)

$1s^22s^22p^63s^23p^64s^1$ $1s^22s^22p^63s^23p^6$

K$^+$(g)   →   K^{2+}(g)

$1s^22s^22p^63s^23p^6$ $1s^22s^22p^63s^23p^5$

The first ionization is for the removal of an electron from the outermost valence shell of electrons. The second electron, however, is removed from the $3p$ subshell. This subshell is significantly lower in energy than the $4s$ subshell and considerably more energy is required to remove this second electron.

8.60   For s- and p-block elements, first ionization energy generally decreases down a group because the electron removed is increasingly farther from the nucleus, thus reducing the nucleus-electron attractive force.

8.61   (a)   In going from one element to the next across a period, the effective nuclear charge increases slightly and the attraction between the nucleus and electrons increases.

(b)   The slight decrease in atomic radius of the transition metals is a result of increased repulsions of $(n–1)d$ electrons for ns electrons. This repulsion reduces the effects of the increasing nuclear charge across a period.

8.62   Li, lithium Of the four elements shown, only Li is in Group 1A. The loss of the first electron results in an ion with a filled outer shell. Removal of a second electron (from a filled electron shell) would require a much larger amount of energy.

8.63   There are many arguments for an Mg/O compound being composed of Mg^{2+} and O^{2-} ions. A few are:

(1)   The groups characteristically form ions with noble gas configurations; Group 2A loses two electrons and Group 6A gains two electrons.

(2)   Look at other ionic compounds from the same groups; MgS and CaO.

(3)   Calculate and compare ΔH_f° values for the two compounds Mg$^+$/O$^-$ and Mg^{2+}/O^{2-}. The Mg^{2+}/O^{2-} combination is more favorable thermodynamically.

Some possible experiments:

(1)   Determine the first and second ionization energy values for Mg and the first and second electron affinity values for O.

(2)   Determine the melting point of MgO and compare it to the +1/–1 compound NaF (990 °C) and the +2/–2 compound CaO (2580 °C).

8.64   Ca is smaller than K, so we would expect the first IE of Ca to be greater than that of K. Once K has lost one electron, it has a noble gas (Ar) configuration. Removal of a second electron (from a filled electron shell) requires much additional energy. Ca, on the other hand, can lose a "second" electron to obtain a noble gas configuration with a much smaller amount of energy (smaller IE).

8.65   (a)   The effective nuclear charge increases, causing the valence orbital energies to become more negative on   moving across the period.

        (b)   As the valence orbital energies become more negative, it is increasingly difficult to remove an electron from the atom, and the IE increases. Toward the end of the period, the orbital energies have become so negative that removing an electron requires significant energy. Instead, the effective nuclear charge has reached the point that it is energetically more favorable for the atom to gain an electron.

        (c)   The valence orbital energies are in the order:

        Li (–530.7 kJ) < Be (–897.3 kJ) > B (–800.8 kJ) < C (–1032 kJ)

        This means it is more difficult to remove an electron from Be than from either Li or B. The energy is more negative for C than for B, so it is more difficult to remove an electron from C than from B.

8.66   Generally the increasing effective nuclear charge across a period causes ionization energy to also increase. For sulfur, however, two of its four $2p$ electrons are paired in the same orbital. The greater repulsion experienced by these electrons makes it easier to remove one of them, and the ionization energy of sulfur is lower than expected.

8.67   Atomic radius decreases from potassium to vanadium. Because the mass of these elements increases from K to V as the radius decreases, the density is expected to increase.

8.68   The fifth and sixth period transition metals have similar atomic radii. The sixth period transition metals have a higher mass resulting in higher density for the sixth period transition metals.

8.69   (a)   Element 113 $[Rn]5f^{14}6d^{10}7s^27p^1$

        Element 115 $[Rn]5f^{14}6d^{10}7s^27p^3$

        (b)   Element 113: Group 3A, B, Al, Ga, In, Tl

        Element 115: Group 5A, N, P, As, Sb, Bi

        (c)   Argon, Ar

8.70   To form CaF_3, calcium would have to form a 3+ cation. Since calcium (in Group 2A) normally forms 2+ cations (with noble gas configuration), the formation of the 3+ cation is highly unlikely.

8.71   (a)   S

↑↓	↑↓	↑↓	↑↓	↑↓	↑↓	↑↓	↑	↑

        $1s$ $2s$ $2p$ $3s$ $3p$

(b) $n = 3$, $\ell = 1$, $m_\ell = 1$, $m_s = -{}^1/_2$

(c)   smallest ionization energy: S   smallest radius: O

(d) $S < S^{2-}$

(e) $675 \text{ g SOCl}_2 \cdot \dfrac{1 \text{ mol SOCl}_2}{119.0 \text{ g}} \cdot \dfrac{1 \text{ mol SCl}_2}{1 \text{ mol SOCl}_2} \cdot \dfrac{103.0 \text{ g}}{1 \text{ mol SCl}_2} = 584 \text{ g SCl}_2$

(f) $10.0 \text{ g SO}_3 \cdot \dfrac{1 \text{ mol SO}_3}{80.06 \text{ g}} \cdot \dfrac{1 \text{ mol SOCl}_2}{1 \text{ mol SO}_3} \cdot \dfrac{119.0 \text{ g}}{1 \text{ mol SOCl}_2} = 14.9 \text{ g SOCl}_2$

$10.0 \text{ g SCl}_2 \cdot \dfrac{1 \text{ mol SCl}_2}{103.0 \text{ g}} \cdot \dfrac{1 \text{ mol SOCl}_2}{1 \text{ mol SCl}_2} \cdot \dfrac{119.0 \text{ g}}{1 \text{ mol SOCl}_2} = 11.6 \text{ g SOCl}_2$

The theoretical yield of $SOCl_2$ is 11.6 g

(g) $\Delta H^{\circ}_{rxn} = \Delta H^{\circ}_f[SO_2(g)] + \Delta H^{\circ}_f[SOCl_2(g)] - (\Delta H^{\circ}_f[SO_3(g)] + \Delta H^{\circ}_f[SCl_2(g)])$

$-96.0 \text{ kJ} = 1 \text{ mol } (-296.84 \text{ kJ/mol}) + 1 \text{ mol } (-212.5 \text{ kJ/mol})$

$- [1 \text{ mol } (-395.77 \text{ kJ/mol}) + \Delta H^{\circ}_f[SCl_2(g)]]$

$\Delta H^{\circ}_f[SCl_2(g)] = -17.6 \text{ kJ/mol}$

8.72   (a)   The reducing agent is Na. The low ionization energy of sodium plays a major role in making it a good reducing agent.

(b)   The oxidizing agent is Cl_2. Among other properties, the element has a high electron affinity.

(c) Na_2Cl would have a Cl^{2-} ion. Adding a second electron to Cl^- means placing an electron in a higher energy electron shell. Conversely, $NaCl_2$ would have a Na^{2+} ion. Here one would have to remove the second electron from the atom's core.

8.73

Atom distance	Calculated (pm)	Measured (pm)
B—F	154	130
P—F	186	178
C—H	114	109
C—O	143	150

Chapter 9
Bonding and Molecular Structure: Fundamental Concepts

INSTRUCTOR'S NOTES

We pay particular attention to the following topics:

- drawing electron dot structures for main group elements

- resonance structures for simple molecules

- bond properties (order, length, energy, polarity)

- VSEPR theory

- molecular polarity.

Students sometimes want to skip the steps in determining a Lewis structure and try to divine the answer from just looking at the formula. The very different structures of SO_2 and CO_2 even though their formulas are both AB_2 should provide a good warning of the danger of this practice.

Resonance might well seem very strange for students who are used to definitive and simple answers. This topic and formal charge will be very important for those students who will be continuing their studies in organic chemistry. The distinction among the terms ionic charge, oxidation number and formal charge will need to be carefully delineated to avoid confusion.

With regard to VSEPR theory, we use the term "electron-pair geometry" to designate the positions of the stereochemically active pairs. We find our students then differentiate between the geometry of the electron pairs (electron-pair geometry) and the positions of the atoms in the molecule or ion (molecular geometry). However, there is still some problem getting students to see that, while the electron-pair geometry determines the positions of the atoms, the word description given the molecular geometry reflects only the atom positions. Model kits (e.g., Darling Models) can be very helpful in comprehending the various shapes that are discussed.

This chapter includes a very wide range of examples for each of the main subjects so a comprehensive coverage of the topics is possible.   About five to six lectures are needed.

SUGGESTED DEMONSTRATIONS

1.   Electron-Pair and Molecular Geometry

- The most useful demonstrations here are models of electron-pair and molecular geometries. We find it useful to illustrate the former with balloons as indicated in Figure 9.7. Purchase a bag of round "party balloons" at a stationery or drug store. After blowing them up, tie them together in pairs; additionally, make at least one set of three tied together. All of the models in Figure 9.7 can be assembled easily in class as you discuss various geometries. The students are always impressed that these are the natural geometries assumed.

- Molecular models of ionic and covalent compounds can be found on the *General ChemistryNow CD-ROM*

- Large scale molecular models are very useful. Styrofoam orbital models can be purchased from Aldrich Chemical Company. Smaller models can be purchased from Allyn and Bacon, Inc.

- Parker, J. "VSEPR Theory Demo," *Journal of Chemical Education*, **1997**, *74*, *776*.

SOLUTIONS TO STUDY QUESTIONS

9.1   (a) O   Group 6A   6 valence electrons

        (b) B   Group 3A   3 valence electrons

        (c) Na   Group 1A   1 valence electron

        (d) Mg   Group 2A   2 valence electrons

        (e) F   Group 7A   7 valence electrons

        (f) S   Group 6A   6 valence electrons

9.2   (a) C   Group 4A   4 valence electrons

        (b) Cl   Group 7A   7 valence electrons

        (c) Ne   Group 8A   8 valence electrons

        (d) Si   Group 4A   4 valence electrons

        (e) Se   Group 6A   6 valence electrons

        (f) Al   Group 3A   3 valence electrons

9.3   Group 3A   3 bonds

        Group 4A   4 bonds

        Group 5A   3 bonds

        Group 6A   2 bonds

        Group 7A   1 bond

9.4   P, Cl, Se, and Sn can accommodate more than four valence electron pairs.

9.5   Most negative: MgS

        Least negative: KI

9.6   MgCl (Mg typically forms Mg^{2+} ions)

        BaF_3 (Ba typically forms Ba^{2+} ions)

        CsKr (Kr is not likely to form a Kr^- ion)

9.7   RbI < LiI < LiF < CaO

9.8 $Li(s) \rightarrow Li(g)$ $\Delta H_f^\circ = +159.37$ kJ/mol

        $Li(g) \rightarrow Li^+(g) + e^-$ IE $= +520.$ kJ/mol

        $^1/_2\ F_2(g) \rightarrow F(g)$ $\Delta H_f^\circ = +78.99$ kJ/mol

        $F(g) + e^- \rightarrow F^-(g)$ EA $= -328.0$ kJ/mol

        $Li^+(g) + F^-(g) \rightarrow LiF(s)$ $\Delta H_{lattice} = -1037$ kJ/mol

        _____

        $Li(s) + {}^1/_2\ F_2(g) \rightarrow LiF(s)$ $\Delta H_f^\circ = -607$ kJ/mol

9.9   As the ion-ion distance decreases, the force of attraction between the ions increases. This should make the lattice more stable, and more energy should be required to melt the compound.

9.10   (a) NaCl   (b) MgO   (c) MgS

9.11   (a)   (c)

        (b)   (d)

9.12   (a)   (c)

        (b)   (d)

9.13   (a)   (c)

        (b)   (d)

9.14   (a)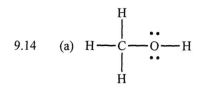

(c)

(b)

9.15   (a) O=S—O ⟷ O—S=O

(b) [O=N—O]⁻ ⟷ [O—N=O]⁻

(c) [S≡C—N]⁻ ⟷ [S=C=N]⁻ ⟷ [S—C≡N]⁻

9.16   (a) [O=N—O]⁻ ⟷ [O—N—O]⁻ ⟷ [O—N=O]⁻

(b) O=N—O—H ⟷ O—N—O—H ⟷ O—N=O—H

(c) N≡N—O ⟷ N=N=O ⟷ N—N≡O

9.17   (a) F—Br—F

(c) F—Xe—F

(b) [I—I—I]⁻

(d) [F—Xe—F]⁺

9.18   (a)

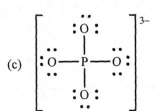

(c) $\left[\ddot{B}r - I - \ddot{B}r \right]^{-}$

(b) $\ddot{F} - I - \ddot{F}$ (with F above)

(d) $\left[\ddot{F} - Br - \ddot{F} \right]^{+}$

9.19   (a) $H - N - \ddot{C}l$ (with H above)

electron pair geometry, tetrahedral

molecular geometry, trigonal pyramidal

(b) $\ddot{C}l - O - \ddot{C}l$

electron pair geometry, tetrahedral

molecular geometry, bent

(c) $\left[\ddot{S} = C = \ddot{N} \right]^{-}$

electron pair geometry, linear

molecular geometry, linear

(d) $H - \ddot{O} - \ddot{F}$

electron pair geometry, tetrahedral

molecular geometry, bent

9.20   (a) $\left[\ddot{F} - \ddot{C}l - \ddot{F} \right]^{+}$

electron-pair geometry, tetrahedral

molecular geometry, bent

(b) $\left[\ddot{C}l - Sn - \ddot{C}l \right]^{-}$ (with Cl above)

electron-pair geometry, tetrahedral

molecular geometry, trigonal pyramidal

(c) $\left[\ddot{O} - P - \ddot{O} \right]^{3-}$ (with O above and O below)

electron-pair geometry, tetrahedral

molecular geometry, tetrahedral

(d) $\ddot{S} = C = \ddot{S}$

electron-pair geometry, linear

molecular geometry, linear

9.21   (a) $\ddot{O} = C = \ddot{O}$

electron-pair geometry, linear

molecular geometry, linear

(c) $\ddot{O} = \ddot{O} - \ddot{O}$

electron-pair geometry, trigonal planar

molecular geometry, bent

(b) $\left[\overset{..}{\underset{..}{O}} = \overset{..}{N} - \overset{..}{\underset{..}{O}} \colon \right]^{-}$

electron-pair geometry, trigonal planar

molecular geometry, bent

(d) $\left[\colon\overset{..}{\underset{..}{O}} - \overset{..}{\underset{..}{Cl}} - \overset{..}{\underset{..}{O}}\colon \right]^{-}$

electron-pair geometry, tetrahedral

molecular geometry, bent

Ozone (c) and nitrite ion (b) are isoelectronic (18 electrons) and have identical electron-pair and molecular geometries.

9.22   (a) $\left[\colon\overset{..}{\underset{..}{O}} - \overset{\overset{\colon O\colon}{\|}}{C} - \overset{..}{\underset{..}{O}}\colon \right]^{2-}$

electron-pair geometry, trigonal planar

molecular geometry, trigonal planar

(b) $\left[\colon\overset{..}{\underset{..}{O}} - \overset{\overset{\colon O\colon}{\|}}{N} - \overset{..}{\underset{..}{O}}\colon \right]^{-}$

electron-pair geometry, trigonal planar

molecular geometry, trigonal planar

(c) $\left[\colon\overset{..}{\underset{..}{O}} - \overset{\overset{\colon\overset{..}{O}\colon}{|}}{S} - \overset{..}{\underset{..}{O}} \right]^{2-}$

electron-pair geometry, tetrahedral

molecular geometry, trigonal pyramidal

(d) $\left[\colon\overset{..}{\underset{..}{O}} - \overset{\overset{\colon\overset{..}{O}\colon}{|}}{Cl} - \overset{..}{\underset{..}{O}}\colon \right]^{-}$

electron-pair geometry, tetrahedral

molecular geometry, trigonal pyramidal

Ions (a) and (b) are isoelectronic (24 valence electrons) and have identical electron-pair and molecular geometries. Molecules (c) and (d) are also isoelectronic (26 valence electrons) and have identical electron-pair and molecular geometries.

9.23   (a) $\left[\colon\overset{..}{\underset{..}{F}} - \overset{..}{\underset{..}{Cl}} - \overset{..}{\underset{..}{F}}\colon \right]^{-}$

electron-pair geometry, trigonal bipyramid

molecular geometry, linear

(b) $\colon\overset{..}{\underset{..}{F}} - \overset{\overset{\colon\overset{..}{F}\colon}{|}}{\underset{..}{Cl}} - \overset{..}{\underset{..}{F}}\colon$

electron-pair geometry = trigonal bipyramid

molecular geometry, T-shaped

(c) $\left[\colon\overset{..}{\underset{..}{F}} - \overset{\overset{\colon\overset{..}{F}\colon}{|}}{\underset{\underset{\colon\overset{..}{F}\colon}{|}}{Cl}} - \overset{..}{\underset{..}{F}}\colon \right]^{-}$

electron-pair geometry, octahedral

molecular geometry, square planar

(d) $\overset{\colon\overset{..}{F}\colon}{\underset{\colon\overset{..}{F}}{\underset{\colon\overset{..}{F}\colon}{Cl}}}$

electron-pair geometry, octahedral

molecular geometry, square pyramidal

9.24   (a)

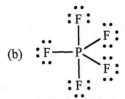

electron-pair geometry, octahedral

molecular geometry, octahedral

(c)

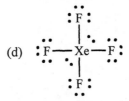

electron-pair geometry, trigonal bipyramid

molecular geometry, seesaw

(b)

electron-pair geometry, trigonal bipyramid

molecular geometry, trigonal bipyramid

(d)

electron-pair geometry, octahedral

molecular geometry, square planar

9.25   (a) O—S—O = 120°

(b) F—B—F = 120°

(c) Cl—C—Cl = 120°

(d) H—C—H = 109°   C—C≡N = 180°

9.26   (a) Cl—S—Cl = 109°

(b) N—N—O = 180°

(c) angle 1 = 120°; angle 2 = 120°; angle 3 = 109°

9.27   angle 1 = 120°; angle 2 = 109°; angle 3 = 120°; angle 4 = 109°; angle 5 = 109°

The —CH₂—CH(NH₂)—CO₂H chain cannot be linear because the first two carbon atoms have bond angles of 109° (with their connecting atoms) and the third carbon has a 120° bond angle with the C and O on either side.

9.28   angle 1 = 109°; angle 2 = 120°; angle 3 = 120°

9.29   (a)

$H = 1 - 0 - \frac{1}{2}(2) = 0$

$N = 5 - 2 - \frac{1}{2}(6) = 0$

(c)

$H = 1 - 0 - \frac{1}{2}(2) = 0$

$B = 3 - 0 - \frac{1}{2}(8) = -1$

(b)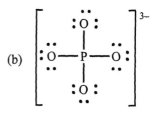

$$O = 6 - 6 - \frac{1}{2}(2) = -1$$
$$P = 5 - 0 - \frac{1}{2}(8) = 1$$

(d) H — N — O — H (with H above N)

$$H = 1 - 0 - \frac{1}{2}(2) = 0$$
$$N = 5 - 2 - \frac{1}{2}(6) = 0$$
$$O = 6 - 4 - \frac{1}{2}(4) = 0$$

9.30   (a) S ═══ C ═══ O

$$S = 6 - 4 - \frac{1}{2}(4) = 0$$
$$C = 4 - 0 - \frac{1}{2}(8) = 0$$
$$O = 6 - 4 - \frac{1}{2}(4) = 0$$

(c) O ═══ O — O

$$O = 6 - 4 - \frac{1}{2}(4) = 0$$
$$O = 6 - 2 - \frac{1}{2}(6) = 1$$
$$O = 6 - 6 - \frac{1}{2}(2) = -1$$

(b) [H — C — O]⁻ (with O double-bonded above C)

$$H = 1 - 0 - \frac{1}{2}(2) = 0$$
$$C = 4 - 0 - \frac{1}{2}(8) = 0$$
$$O = 6 - 4 - \frac{1}{2}(4) = 0$$
$$O = 6 - 6 - \frac{1}{2}(2) = -1$$

(d) H — C — O — H (with O double-bonded above C)

$$H = 1 - 0 - \frac{1}{2}(2) = 0$$
$$C = 4 - 0 - \frac{1}{2}(8) = 0$$
$$O = 6 - 4 - \frac{1}{2}(4) = 0$$
$$O = 6 - 4 - \frac{1}{2}(4) = 0$$
$$H = 1 - 0 - \frac{1}{2}(2) = 0$$

9.31   (a) [O ═══ N ═══ O]⁺

$$O = 6 - 4 - \frac{1}{2}(4) = 0$$
$$N = 5 - 0 - \frac{1}{2}(8) = 1$$

(c) F — N — F (with F above N)

$$F = 7 - 6 - \frac{1}{2}(2) = 0$$
$$N = 5 - 2 - \frac{1}{2}(6) = 0$$

(b) [O ═══ N — O]⁻

$$O = 6 - 4 - \frac{1}{2}(4) = 0$$
$$N = 5 - 2 - \frac{1}{2}(6) = 0$$
$$O = 6 - 6 - \frac{1}{2}(2) = -1$$

(d) H — O — N — O (with O double-bonded above N)

$$H = 1 - 0 - \frac{1}{2}(2) = 0$$
$$O = 6 - 4 - \frac{1}{2}(4) = 0$$
$$N = 5 - 0 - \frac{1}{2}(8) = 1$$
$$O = 6 - 4 - \frac{1}{2}(4) = 0$$
$$O = 6 - 6 - \frac{1}{2}(2) = -1$$

9.32   (a)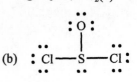

(c)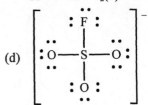

$O = 6 - 6 - \frac{1}{2}(2) = -1$

$S = 6 - 2 - \frac{1}{2}(6) = 1$

$O = 6 - 4 - \frac{1}{2}(4) = 0$

$O = 6 - 6 - \frac{1}{2}(2) = -1$

$S = 6 - 0 - \frac{1}{2}(8) = 2$

$Cl = 7 - 6 - \frac{1}{2}(2) = 0$

(b)

(d)

$Cl = 7 - 6 - \frac{1}{2}(2) = 0$

$S = 6 - 2 - \frac{1}{2}(6) = 1$

$O = 6 - 6 - \frac{1}{2}(2) = -1$

$O = 6 - 6 - \frac{1}{2}(2) = -1$

$S = 6 - 0 - \frac{1}{2}(8) = 2$

$F = 7 - 6 - \frac{1}{2}(2) = 0$

9.33   Arrow points toward the negative end of the bond dipole

(a) C—O

$\longrightarrow$

(c) B—O

$\longrightarrow$

(b) P—Cl

$\longrightarrow$

(d) B—F

$\longrightarrow$

9.34 | Bond | Atom more negatively charged |
|---|---|
| (a) C—N | N |
| (b) C—H | C |
| (c) C—Br | Br |
| (d) S—O | O |

9.35   (a) The C—H and C=O bonds are polar; the C—C and C=C bonds are nonpolar

(b) The C=O bond is the most polar bond; the O atom is the more negative atom

9.36   (a) All of the bonds in urea are polar.

(b) The C=O bond is the most polar bond; the O atom is the negative end of the dipole.

9.37   (a)   The formal charge on O is −1 and on H it is 0. This conforms with the relative electronegativities. The bond is polar with O the negative end.

(b)   Even though the formal charge on B is 1 and on H is 0, H is slightly more electronegative. The four H atoms therefore likely bear the −1 charge of the ion. The B—H bonds are polar with the H atom the negative end.

(c)   The C—H and CO bonds are polar. The negative charge lies on the O atoms.

9.38   (a)   Even though the formal charge on O is 1 and on H is 0, H is less electronegative. The three H atoms therefore likely bear the +1 charge of the ion. The O—H bonds are polar with the H atom the positive end.

(b)   Even though the formal charge on N is 1 and on H is 0, H is less electronegative. The four H atoms therefore likely bear the +1 charge of the ion. The N—H bonds are polar with the H atom the positive end.

(c)   The formal charge on N is +1 and on O it is 0. This conforms with the relative electronegativities. The bonds are polar with N the positive end.

(d)   The formal charge on N is +1 and on F it is 0. This conforms with the relative electronegativities. The bonds are polar with N the positive end.

9.39   (a) $:N{\equiv}N-\overset{..}{\underset{..}{O}}:$ ⟷ $\overset{..}{\underset{..}{N}}{=}N{=}\overset{..}{\underset{..}{O}}$ ⟷ $:\overset{..}{\underset{..}{N}}-N{\equiv}O:$

(b) $N = 5 - 2 - \frac{1}{2}(6) = 0$

$N = 5 - 0 - \frac{1}{2}(8) = 1$

$O = 6 - 6 - \frac{1}{2}(2) = -1$

$N = 5 - 4 - \frac{1}{2}(4) = -1$

$N = 5 - 0 - \frac{1}{2}(8) = 1$

$O = 6 - 4 - \frac{1}{2}(4) = 0$

$N = 5 - 6 - \frac{1}{2}(2) = -2$

$N = 5 - 0 - \frac{1}{2}(8) = 1$

$O = 6 - 2 - \frac{1}{2}(6) = 1$

(c)   The first resonance structure is most reasonable (the most electronegative element, oxygen, has a negative formal charge).

9.40   (a)   Yes, both ions contain 24 valence electrons

(b) CO_3^{2-} has three reasonable resonance structures and BO_3^{2-} has four

(c)

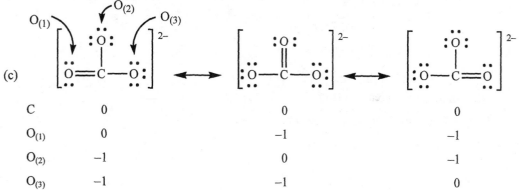

C	0	0	0
$O_{(1)}$	0	−1	−1
$O_{(2)}$	−1	0	−1
$O_{(3)}$	−1	−1	0

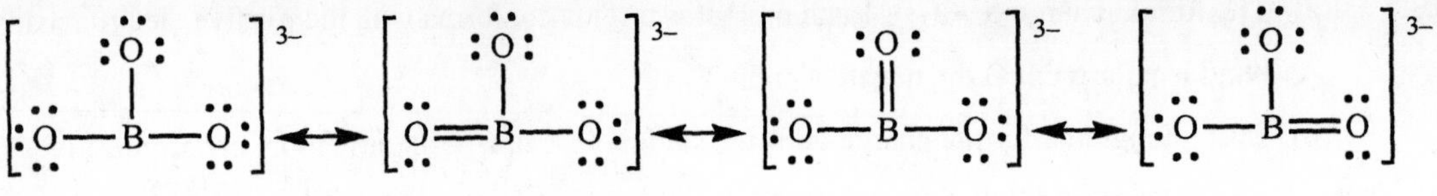

B	0	–1	–1	–1
$O_{(1)}$	–1	0	–1	–1
$O_{(2)}$	–1	–1	0	–1
$O_{(3)}$	–1	–1	–1	0

(d) The H^+ ion would attach to the oxygen atom

9.41

$O = 6 - 4 - \frac{1}{2}(4) = 0$ $O = 6 - 6 - \frac{1}{2}(2) = -1$

$N = 5 - 2 - \frac{1}{2}(6) = 0$ $N = 5 - 2 - \frac{1}{2}(6) = 0$

$O = 6 - 6 - \frac{1}{2}(2) = -1$ $O = 6 - 4 - \frac{1}{2}(4) = 0$

The H^+ ion would attach to the oxygen

9.42

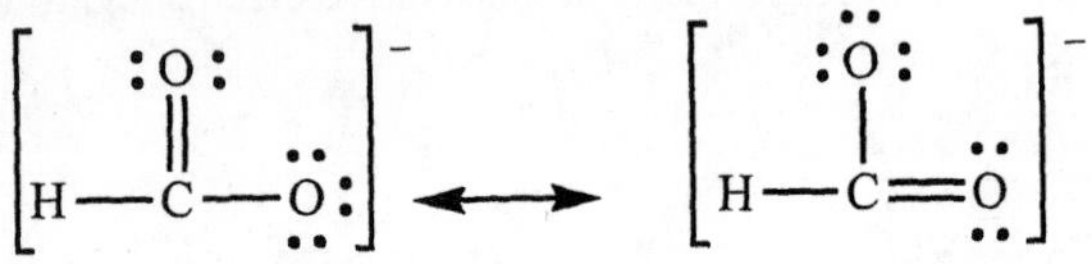

$H = 2 - 0 - \frac{1}{2}(2) = 0$ $H = 2 - 0 - \frac{1}{2}(2) = 0$

$C = 4 - 0 - \frac{1}{2}(8) = 0$ $C = 4 - 0 - \frac{1}{2}(8) = 0$

$O = 6 - 4 - \frac{1}{2}(4) = 0$ $O = 6 - 6 - \frac{1}{2}(2) = -1$

$O = 6 - 6 - \frac{1}{2}(2) = -1$ $O = 6 - 4 - \frac{1}{2}(4) = 0$

The H^+ ion would attach to the oxygen

9.43

Molecule	$\Delta\chi$ for bond
H_2O	O—H = 3.5 – 2.1 = 1.4
NH_3	N—H = 3.0 – 2.1 = 0.9
CO_2	O—C = 3.5 – 2.5 = 1.0
ClF	F—Cl = 4.0 – 3.0 = 1.0
CCl_4	Cl—C = 3.0 – 2.5 = 0.5

(i)   The bonds are most polar in H_2O.

(ii) CO_2 and CCl_4 are nonpolar molecules.

(iii) The F atom in ClF is more negatively charged.

9.44   Molecule $\Delta\chi$ for bond

        CH_4 C—H = 2.5 – 2.1 = 0.4

        NH_2Cl N—Cl = 3.0 – 3.0 = 0

                              N—H = 3.0 – 2.1 = 0.9

        BF_3 F—B = 4.0 – 2.0 = 2.0

        CS_2 C—S = 2.5 – 2.5 = 0

(i)   The B—F bonds in BF_3 are the most polar.

(ii) CH_4, BF_3, and CS_2 are nonpolar molecules.

9.45   Molecule $\Delta\chi$ for bond   molecular geometry   molecular polarity

        $BeCl_2$ Cl—Be = 3.0 – 1.5 = 1.5   linear   nonpolar

        HBF_2 H—B = 2.1 – 2.0 = 0.1

                    F—B = 4.0 – 2.0 = 2.0   trigonal planar   polar

F atoms negative end of dipole; H positive end of dipole

        CH_3Cl Cl—C = 3.0 – 2.5 = 0.5

                    C—H = 2.5 – 2.1 = 0.4   tetrahedral   polar

Cl negative end of dipole; H atoms positive end of dipole

        SO_3 S—O = 2.5 – 3.5 = 1.0   trigonal planar   nonpolar

9.46   Molecule $\Delta\chi$ for bond   molecular geometry   molecular polarity

        CO   C—O = 2.5 – 3.5 = 1.0   linear   polar

        BCl_3 B—Cl = 2.0 – 3.0 = 1.0   trigonal planar   nonpolar

        CF_4 C—F = 2.5 – 4.0 = 1.5   tetrahedral   nonpolar

        PCl_3 P—Cl = 2.1 – 3.0 = 0.9   trigonal pyramidal   polar

        GeH_4 Ge—H = 1.9 – 2.1 = 0.2   tetrahedral   nonpolar

BCl_3, CF_4, and GeH_4 are nonpolar molecules; CF_4 has the most polar bonds.

9.47   (a) H_2CO two carbon-hydrogen single bonds   bond order = 1

                              one carbon-oxygen double bond   bond order = 2

      (b) SO_3^{2-} three sulfur-oxygen single bonds   bond order = 1

      (c) NO_2^+ two nitrogen-oxygen double bonds   bond order = 2

      (d) NOCl   (assume atoms are connected N—O—Cl)

                              one nitrogen-oxygen double bond   bond order = 2

                              one oxygen-chlorine single bond   bond order = 1

9.48   (a) CN⁻   one carbon-nitrogen triple bond   bond order = 3

        (b) CH_3CN three carbon-hydrogen single bonds   bond order = 1

                      one carbon-carbon single bond   bond order = 1

                      one carbon-nitrogen triple bond   bond order = 3

        (c) SO_3 two sulfur-oxygen single bonds   bond order = 1

                      one sulfur-oxygen double bond   bond order = 2

                      with resonance structures, overall bond order = 1.33

        (d) $CH_3CH=CH_2$ six carbon-hydrogen single bonds   bond order = 1

                      one carbon-carbon single bond   bond order = 1

                      one carbon-carbon double bond   bond order = 2

9.49   (a) B—Cl   (c) P—O

        (b) C—O   (d) C=O

9.50   (a) Si—O   (c) C—F

        (b) C—O   (d) C≡N

9.51 NO_2^+ two NO double bonds   NO bond order = 2

        NO_2^- one NO single bond, one NO double bond

               two resonance structures   NO bond order = $^3/_2$

        NO_3^- two NO single bonds, one NO triple bond

               three resonance structures   NO bond order = $^4/_3$

        NO_3^- has the longest NO bonds (lowest bond order)

        NO_2^+ has the shortest NO bonds (highest bond order)

9.52 HCO_2^- one CO single bond, one CO double bond

               two resonance structures   CO bond order = $^3/_2$

        CH_3OH one CO single bond   CO bond order = 1

        CO_3^{2-} two CO single bonds, one CO double bond

               three resonance structures   CO bond order = $^4/_3$

        CH_3OH has the longest CO bond (lowest bond order)

        HCO_2^- has the shortest CO bonds (highest bond order)

9.53   The carbon-oxygen bond in formaldehyde is a double bond with a bond order of 2. The carbon-oxygen bond in carbon monoxide is a triple bond with a bond order of 3. Carbon monoxide has the shorter CO bond and the stronger CO bond.

9.54   The nitrogen-nitrogen bond in hydrazine is a single bond with a bond order of 1. The nitrogen-nitrogen

bond in N_2O has a bond order greater than one, so it has the shorter and stronger nitrogen-nitrogen bond.

9.55   One C=C double bond and one H—H single bond are broken in the reaction

One C—C single bond and two C—H single bonds are formed in the reaction

$\Delta H^\circ_{rxn} = (1 \text{ mol} \cdot D_{C=C} + 1 \text{ mol} \cdot D_{H-H}) - (1 \text{ mol} \cdot D_{C-C} + 2 \text{ mol} \cdot D_{C-H})$

$\Delta H^\circ_{rxn} = 1 \text{ mol } (610 \text{ kJ/mol}) + 1 \text{ mol } (436 \text{ kJ/mol}) - [1 \text{ mol } (346 \text{ kJ/mol}) + 2 \text{ mol } (413 \text{ kJ/mol})]$

$\Delta H^\circ_{rxn} = -126 \text{ kJ}$

9.56   One C≡O triple bond and one Cl—Cl single bond are broken in the reaction

One C=O double bond and two C—Cl single bonds are formed in the reaction

$\Delta H^\circ_{rxn} = (1 \text{ mol} \cdot D_{C\equiv O} + 1 \text{ mol} \cdot D_{Cl-Cl}) - (1 \text{ mol} \cdot D_{C=O} + 2 \text{ mol} \cdot D_{C-Cl})$

$\Delta H^\circ_{rxn} = 1 \text{ mol } (1046 \text{ kJ/mol}) + 1 \text{ mol } (242 \text{ kJ/mol}) - [1 \text{ mol } (745 \text{ kJ/mol}) + 2 \text{ mol } (339 \text{ kJ/mol})]$

$\Delta H^\circ_{rxn} = -135 \text{ kJ}$

9.57 $\Delta H^\circ_{rxn} = (2 \text{ mol} \cdot D_{O-F} + 2 \text{ mol} \cdot D_{O-H}) - (1 \text{ mol} \cdot D_{O=O} + 2 \text{ mol} \cdot D_{H-F})$

$-318 \text{ kJ} = 2 \text{ mol} \cdot D_{O-F} + 2 \text{ mol } (463 \text{ kJ/mol}) - [1 \text{ mol } (498 \text{ kJ/mol}) + 2 \text{ mol } (565 \text{ kJ/mol})]$

$D_{O-F} = 192 \text{ kJ/mol}$

9.58 $\Delta H^\circ_{rxn} = 2 \text{ mol} \cdot D_{OO \text{ in ozone}} - 2 \text{ mol} \cdot D_{O=O}$

$-394 \text{ kJ} = 2 \text{ mol} \cdot D_{OO \text{ in ozone}} - 2 \text{ mol } (498 \text{ kJ/mol})$

$D_{OO \text{ in ozone}} = 301 \text{ kJ/mol}$

$D_{O-O} = 146 \text{ kJ}$

$D_{O=O} = 498 \text{ kJ}$

The estimate of the oxygen-oxygen bond energy in ozone is between the values for the single and double

oxygen-oxygen bond energies. The bond order in ozone is 1.5, which is between the bond order values for

a single bond (bond order = 1) and a double bond (bond order = 2). Therefore, the oxygen-oxygen bond

energy in ozone does correlate with its bond order.

9.59   Li   1 valence electron

Ti   4 valence electrons

Zn   2 valence electrons

Si   4 valence electrons

Cl   7 valence electrons

9.60   •K + :F̈• → [K⁺   :F̈: ⁻]   The bonding in KF is ionic.

9.61   Ionic: KI and MgS   Covalent: CS_2 and P_4O_{10}

9.62   Lattice energy is the energy of formation of one mole of a solid crystalline ionic compound when ions in the gas phase combine. The lithium ion is smaller than the cesium ion, so the LiF lattice energy should be more negative than the CsF lattice energy.

9.63 $CaCl_4$ is not likely to exist. Calcium has two outer shell electrons so it is unlikely to form a Ca^{4+} ion. Removal of two more electrons from Ca^{2+} (with a filled electron shell) would require a large amount of energy.

9.64

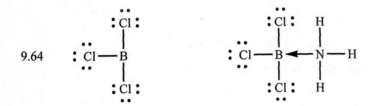

9.65 SeF_4, BrF_4^-, XeF_4

9.66 NH_3 and SO_3 follow the octet rule

NO_2 and O_2^- are odd-electron molecules/ions

9.67   Acetylene has two C—H bonds with a bond order of 1 and a CC triple bond with a bond order of 3. Phosgene has two C—Cl single bonds with a bond order of 1 and a CO double bond with a bond order of 2.

9.68

bond order = (3 pairs linking CO)/(2 CO links) = $^3/_2$

9.69 NO_3^-

bond order = (4 pairs linking NO)/(3 NO links) = $^4/_3$

9.70   C—F < C—O < C—N < C—C < C—B

9.71   Bond energy values needed: O=O, O—H, and H—H

$\Delta H°_{rxn} = 1\ mol \cdot D_{O=O} + 2\ mol \cdot D_{H-H} - 4\ mol \cdot D_{O-H}$

$\Delta H°_{rxn} = 1\ mol\ (498\ kJ/mol) + 2\ mol\ (436\ kJ/mol) - 4\ mol\ (463\ kJ/mol)$

$\Delta H°_{rxn} = -482\ kJ$

9.72   The electroneutrality principle states that the electrons in a molecule are distributed in such a way that the charges on the atoms are as close to zero as possible and that when a negative charge occurs it should be placed on the most electronegative atom. Similarly, a positive charge should be on the least electronegative atom.

9.73   (a)   :O≡C—O: ⟷ O=C=O ⟷ :O—C≡O:

(b)   [:N≡N—N:]⁻ ⟷ [N=N=N]⁻ ⟷ [:N—N≡N:]⁻

(c)   [:C≡N—O:]⁻ ⟷ [C=N=O]⁻ ⟷ [:C—N≡O:]⁻

All three have 16 valence electrons and are linear

9.74 SO_2 is a polar molecule and has a dipole moment.

9.75   The N—O bonds in NO_2^- have a bond order of 1.5 while in NO_2^+ the bond order is 2. The shorter bonds (110 pm) are the N—O bonds with the higher bond order (2) while the N—O bonds with a bond order of 1.5 are longer (124 pm).

9.76 NO_2^- has a smaller bond angle (about 120°) than NO_2^+ (180°). The former has a trigonal-planar electron pair geometry, whereas the latter is linear.

9.77 ClF_2^+ [:F—Cl—F:]⁺ ClF_2^- [:F—Cl—F:]⁻

F—Cl—F = 109°   F—Cl—F = 180°

ClF_2^- has a greater bond angle because there is an additional lone pair of electrons around the central atom.

9.78   [:C≡N:]⁻

The negative (formal) charge resides on C, so the H^+ should attach to that atom and form HCN.

9.79   [:O—S—O:]²⁻ with :O: above S   The H^+ will attach to the oxygen atom of SO_3^{2-}

9.80   Two N—O single bonds are broken and one O=O double bond is formed in the reaction

$\Delta H^\circ_{rxn} = 2 \text{ mol} \cdot D_{N-O} - 1 \text{ mol} \cdot D_{O=O}$

$\Delta H^\circ_{rxn} = 2 \text{ mol } (201 \text{ kJ/mol}) - 1 \text{ mol } (498 \text{ kJ/mol})$

$\Delta H^\circ_{rxn} = -96 \text{ kJ}$

9.81   (a)   Two O—H bonds do not change during the reaction.

$\Delta H^\circ_{rxn} = (6 \text{ mol} \cdot D_{C-H} + 2 \text{ mol} \cdot D_{C-O} + 3 \text{ mol} \cdot D_{O=O}) - (4 \text{ mol} \cdot D_{C=O} + 6 \text{ mol} \cdot D_{O-H})$

$\Delta H^\circ_{rxn} = 6 \text{ mol } (413 \text{ kJ/mol}) + 2 \text{ mol } (358 \text{ kJ/mol}) + 3 \text{ mol } (498 \text{ kJ/mol})$

$- [4 \text{ mol } (732 \text{ kJ/mol}) + 6 \text{ mol } (463 \text{ kJ/mol})]$

$\Delta H^\circ_{rxn} = -1018 \text{ kJ for the combustion of 2 mol } CH_3OH$

$\Delta H^\circ_{rxn} = -509 \text{ kJ/mol } CH_3OH$

(b) $\Delta H_f^\circ[O_2(g)] = 0 \text{ kJ/mol}$

$\Delta H^\circ_{rxn} = 2 \, \Delta H_f^\circ[CO_2(g)] + 4 \, \Delta H_f^\circ[H_2O(g)] - 2 \, \Delta H_f^\circ[CH_3OH(g)]$

$\Delta H^\circ_{rxn} = 2 \text{ mol } (-393.509 \text{ kJ/mol}) + 4 \text{ mol } (-241.83 \text{ kJ/mol}) - 2 \text{ mol } (-201.0 \text{ kJ/mol})$

$\Delta H^\circ_{rxn} = -1352.3 \text{ kJ for the combustion of 2 mol } CH_3OH$

$\Delta H^\circ_{rxn} = -676.2 \text{ kJ/mol } CH_3OH$

9.82   (a)   angle 1 = 120°; angle 2 = 180°; angle 3 = 120°

(b)   The C=C bond is shorter than the C—C bond

(c)   The C=C bond is stronger than the C—C bond

(d)   The C≡N bond is the most polar; $\Delta\chi = 3.0 - 2.5 = 0.5$

9.83   (a)

(b)   −1   1   −1   −2   1   0   −3   1   1

The first resonance structure is most reasonable because the negative formal charge is on the most

electronegative atom.

(c)   Carbon, the least electronegative element in the ion, has a negative formal charge. In addition, all

three resonance structures have an unfavorable charge distribution.

9.84   (a)   angle 1 = 120°; angle 2 = 109°, angle 3 = 120°

(b)   The C=O bond is the shortest carbon-oxygen bond in the molecule.

(c)   The O—H bond is the most polar; $\Delta\chi = 3.5 - 2.1 = 1.4$

9.85   (a)   The three lone pairs of XeF_2 occupy the equatorial positions. There the angles between lone pairs are

120°, so there is less lone pair/lone pair repulsion with this arrangement.

(b)   The two lone pairs on the Cl atom occupy the equatorial positions. The reasoning is the same as for

XeF_2.

9.86

The electron-pair geometry is trigonal planar, the molecular geometry is trigonal planar, and all bond angles are approximately 120°.

9.87 (a) angle 1 = 109°; angle 2 = 120°; angle 3 = 109°; angle 4 = 109°; angle 5 = 109°

(b) The O—H bond is the most polar bond.

9.88 (a)

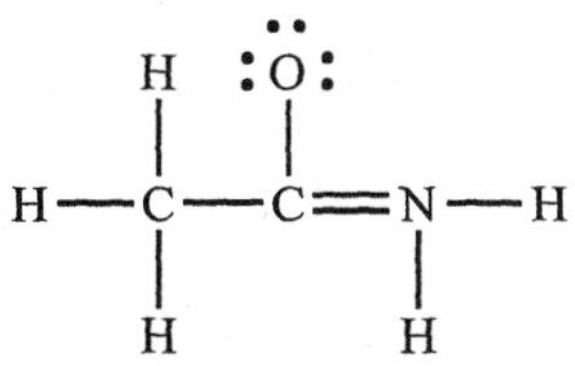

In this resonance structure there is a +1 formal charge on N whereas the other resonance structure has 0 formal charge on both O and N.

(b) The 120° bond angle suggest that his resonance structure may contribute to the resonance hybrid.

9.89 Four N—H bonds do not change during the reaction

$\Delta H^{\circ}_{rxn} = (2\ mol \cdot D_{C-N} + 1\ mol \cdot D_{C=O}) - (1\ mol \cdot D_{N-N} + 1\ mol \cdot D_{C\equiv})$

$\Delta H^{\circ}_{rxn} = 2\ mol\ (305\ kJ/mol) + 1\ mol\ (745\ kJ/mol) - [1\ mol\ (163\ kJ/mol) + 1\ mol\ (1046\ kJ/mol)]$

$\Delta H^{\circ}_{rxn} = 146\ kJ$

9.90 (a) S: $6 - 4 - \frac{1}{2}(4) = 0$ O: $6 - 4 - \frac{1}{2}(4) = 0$

(b) angle 1 = 109°; angle 2 = 109°; angle 3 = 120°

(c) The C=C bonds are shorter than the C—C bonds

(d) The C–O bond is most polar

(e) The molecule is polar

(f) The four C atoms are planar and trigonal, so the ring as a whole is planar.

9.91 (a) Two C—H bonds and one O=O bond are broken and two O—C bonds and two H—O bonds are formed in tl

$\Delta H^{\circ}_{rxn} = (2\ mol \cdot D_{C-H} + 1\ mol \cdot D_{O=O}) - (2\ mol \cdot D_{O-C} + 2\ mol \cdot D_{H-O})$

$\Delta H^{\circ}_{rxn} = 2\ mol\ (413\ kJ/mol) + 1\ mol\ (498\ kJ/mol) - [2\ mol\ (358\ kJ/mol) + 2\ mol\ (463\ kJ/mol)]$

$\Delta H^{\circ}_{rxn} = -318\ kJ$ exothermic

(b) Acetone is polar

(c) The O—H hydrogen atoms are the most positive in dihydroxyacetone

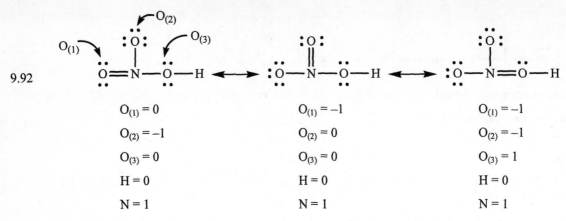

9.92

$$O_{(1)} = 0 \qquad\qquad O_{(1)} = -1 \qquad\qquad O_{(1)} = -1$$
$$O_{(2)} = -1 \qquad\qquad O_{(2)} = 0 \qquad\qquad O_{(2)} = -1$$
$$O_{(3)} = 0 \qquad\qquad O_{(3)} = 0 \qquad\qquad O_{(3)} = 1$$
$$H = 0 \qquad\qquad H = 0 \qquad\qquad H = 0$$
$$N = 1 \qquad\qquad N = 1 \qquad\qquad N = 1$$

The third resonance structure is the least important since it has a positive formal charge on one of the oxygen atoms.

9.93   (a) The C=C bond is stronger than the C—C bond

(b) The C—C bond is longer

(c) Ethylene is nonpolar; acrolein is polar

(d) Four C—H bonds and one C=C bond do not change during the reaction

$$\Delta H^{\circ}_{rxn} = 1\ mol \cdot D_{C\equiv} \ - (1\ mol \cdot D_{C-C} + 1\ mol \cdot D_{C=O})$$

$$\Delta H^{\circ}_{rxn} = 1\ mol\ (1046\ kJ/mol) - [1\ mol\ (346\ kJ/mol) + 1\ mol\ (745\ kJ/mol)]$$

$$\Delta H^{\circ}_{rxn} = -45\ kJ \quad\ \ exothermic$$

9.94   (a)

$$H\!-\!\!\underset{\displaystyle\underset{H}{|}}{\overset{\displaystyle\overset{H}{|}}{O}}\!-\!\!\underset{\displaystyle\underset{H}{|}}{C}\!-\!\!\overset{\displaystyle\overset{:O:}{\|}}{C}\!-\!H$$

H—O—C = 109°; O—C—H = 109°; O—C—C = 109°; H—C—C = 109°;

C—C=O = 120°; C—C—H = 120°; O=C—H = 120°

(b) $H\!-\!C\!\equiv\!C\!-\!C\!\equiv\!N\!:$

9.95   Two C—H bonds do not change during the reaction

$$\Delta H^{\circ}_{rxn} = (1\ mol \cdot D_{C=C} + 1\ mol \cdot D_{Cl-Cl}) - (1\ mol \cdot D_{C\equiv C} + 2\ mol \cdot D_{C-Cl})$$

$$\Delta H^{\circ}_{rxn} = 1\ mol\ (835\ kJ/mol) + 1\ mol\ (242\ kJ/mol) - [1\ mol\ (610\ kJ/mol) + 2\ mol\ (339\ kJ/mol)]$$

$$\Delta H^{\circ}_{rxn} = -211\ kJ$$

9.96   Lewis structure   electron-pair geometry   molecular geometry

(a) :F—B—F: trigonal planar   trigonal planar
     (with F on top)

(b) :F—C—F: tetrahedral   tetrahedral
     (with F on top and bottom)

(c) :F—P—F: tetrahedral   trigonal pyramid
     (with F on top)

(d) :F—O—F: tetrahedral   bent

(e) H—F: linear   linear

None of the molecules have the same molecular geometry. Molecules (b), (c), and (d) have identical electron-pair geometries.

9.97   (a) angle 1 = 109°; angle 2 = 120°; angle 3 = 120°; angle 4 = 109°; angle 5 = 109°

        (b) The O—H bonds are most polar

9.98   Bond dissociation energy is the enthalpy change for breaking a bond in a molecule with the reactants and products on the gas phase. The process of breaking bonds is always endothermic; the value always has a positive sign.

9.99   Four electron pairs form a pyramidal molecule if one of the electron pairs is a lone electron pair. A bent molecule is obtained if two electron pairs are lone electron pairs. In either case, the bond angle is approximately 109°.

9.100   In water there are four electron pairs around the O atom. The electron-pair geometry is the geometry adopted by these four pairs. The molecular geometry is the geometry described by the atoms of the molecule. In water the electron-pair geometry is tetrahedral, whereas the molecular geometry is bent.

9.101   (a) BrO and OH are odd-electron molecules

(b) Reaction 1:

$\Delta H^\circ_{rxn} = 1 \text{ mol} \cdot D_{Br-Br} = 193 \text{ kJ}$

Reaction 2:

$\Delta H^\circ_{rxn} = 1 \text{ mol} \cdot D_{O=O} - (2 \text{ mol} \cdot D_{Br-O})$

$\Delta H^\circ_{rxn} = 1 \text{ mol } (498 \text{ kJ/mol}) - 2 \text{ mol } (201 \text{ kJ/mol})$

$\Delta H^\circ_{rxn} = 96 \text{ kJ}$

Reaction 3:

No bonds change during the reaction.

$\Delta H^\circ_{rxn} = 0 \text{ kJ}$

(c) $^1/_2 \text{ H}_2(g) + {}^1/_2 \text{ O}_2(g) + {}^1/_2 \text{ Br}_2(\ell) \rightarrow \text{HOBr}(g)$

$\Delta H^\circ_{rxn} = ({}^1/_2 \text{ mol} \cdot D_{H-H} + {}^1/_2 \text{ mol} \cdot D_{O=O} + {}^1/_2 \text{ mol} \cdot D_{Br-Br}) - (1 \text{ mol} \cdot D_{H-O} + 1 \text{ mol} \cdot D_{Br-O})$

$\Delta H^\circ_{rxn} = {}^1/_2 \text{ mol } (436 \text{ kJ/mol}) + {}^1/_2 \text{ mol } (498 \text{ kJ/mol}) + {}^1/_2 \text{ mol } (193 \text{ kJ/mol})$

$- [1 \text{ mol } (463 \text{ kJ/mol}) + 1 \text{ mol } (201 \text{ kJ/mol})]$

$\Delta H^\circ_{rxn} = -101 \text{ kJ}$

(d) The reactions in part (b) are endothermic and the reaction in (c) is exothermic.

9.102   (a)

(b)

The bond angles around N are approximately 109°. All other angles are 120°

(c) The C=C bond is stronger than the C—C bond.

(d) The molecule is polar.

(e) $28 \text{ g chips} \cdot \dfrac{1.7 \text{ mg acrylamide}}{10^3 \text{ g chips}} \cdot \dfrac{1 \text{ g}}{10^3 \text{ mg}} \cdot \dfrac{1 \text{ mol acrylamide}}{71.1 \text{ g}} = 6.7 \times 10^{-7} \text{ mol acrylamide}$

9.103   Lattice energy depends directly on ion charges and inversely on the distance between ions. The sizes of the Cl^-, Br^-, and I^- ions fall in a relatively narrow range (181, 196, and 220 pm, respectively), and the ion sizes change by only 15–24 pm from one ion to the next. Therefore, their lattice energies are expected to decrease in a narrow range. The F^- ion (133 pm), however, is only 74% as large as the Cl^- ion, so the lattice energy of NaF is much more negative.

9.104   The data collected from the models on the CD-ROM, show that carbon-carbon bonds are generally shorter as the bond order increases.

Name	Bond Distance (Å)	Bond Order
Ethane	1.540	1
Butane	1.540	1
Ethylene	1.352	2
Acetylene	1.226	3
Benzene	1.397	1.5

9.105   (a) BF_3 is not a polar molecule. HBF_2 and H_2BF are polar molecules

(b) $BeCl_2$ is not a polar molecule. BeClBr is a polar molecule.

9.106   (a)

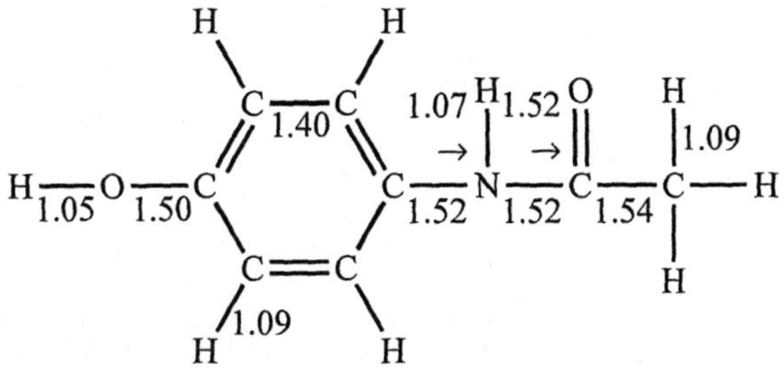

Bond angles in the ring and around the OH, NH and C=O groups are 120°. Bond angles around the CH_3 group are 109°.

(b) 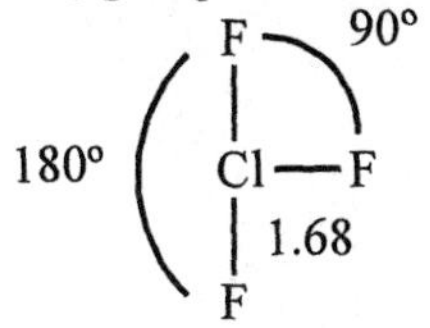 180°

(c)

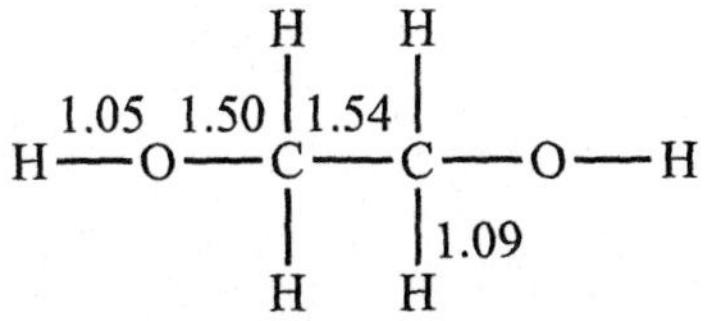

All bond angles are 109°.

Chapter 10
Bonding and Molecular Structure:
Orbital Hybridization and Molecular Orbitals

INSTRUCTOR'S NOTES

This chapter is a natural complement to the previous chapter's introduction to bonding and related subjects.

The emphasis in this chapter is on valence bond theory, with only about one and a half lectures on molecular orbital theory. Although MO theory is not always included in general chemistry, its wide application in organic chemistry argues for at least minimally addressing the topic.

The consistent answers for molecular geometry which arise from VSEPR and valence bond theory is a good point to make.

The following computer programs are helpful when teaching this material.

- ChemDraw, produced by CambridgeSoft Corporation
- There are many molecular modeling programs that can be used to build molecular models and hybrid and molecular orbitals. There are some molecular orbitals on the *General ChemistryNow CD-ROM* that can be viewed using the Molecular Modeling tool on the CD-ROM.

About three or four lectures are scheduled for this chapter.

SUGGESTED DEMONSTRATIONS

1. Orbital Overlap
   - For an overhead demonstration of orbital overlap, see Rothchild, R. "Efficiency of Orbital Overlap: Visual Demonstration," *Journal of Chemical Education,* **1981,** *58,* 757.
2. Hybrid Orbitals
   - In these lectures it is most useful to show models of molecules with the hybrid orbitals in place. Suitable models can be obtained from Aldrich Chemical Company.
   - Emerson, D. W. "A Colorful Demonstration to Simulate Orbital Hybridization," *Journal of Chemical Education,* **1988,** *65,* 454.
   - Samoshin, V. V. "Orbital Models Made of Plastic Soda Bottles," *Journal of Chemical Education,* **1998,** *75,* 985.
3. Molecular Orbital Theory
   - Shakhashiri, B. Z.; Dirreen, G. E.; Williams, L. G.; Smith, S. R. "Paramagnetism and Color of Liquid Oxygen: A Lecture Demonstration," *Journal of Chemical Education* **1980,** *57,* 373.
   - Saban, G. H.; Moran, T. F. "A Simple Demonstration of O₂ Paramagnetism. A Macroscopically Observable

Difference Between VB and MO Approaches to Bonding Theory," *Journal of Chemical Education* **1973**, *50*, 217.

- See the *General ChemistryNow CD-ROM* for a demonstration of the paramagnetism of liquid oxygen.

SOLUTIONS TO STUDY QUESTIONS

10.1

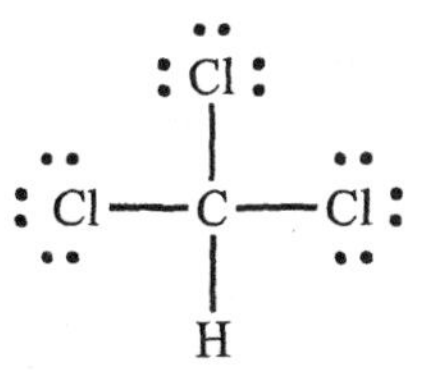

The electron-pair and molecular geometries are tetrahedral. The C atom is sp^3 hybridized. Three of these hybrid orbitals each overlap with a chlorine $3p$ orbital to form three C—Cl sigma bonds. One hybrid orbital overlaps with a hydrogen $1s$ orbital to from a C—H sigma bond.

10.2

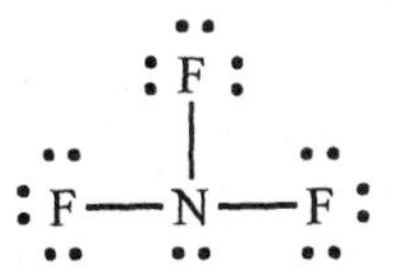

The electron pair geometry is tetrahedral and the molecular geometry is trigonal pyramidal. The N atom is sp^3 hybridized. Three of these hybrid orbitals each overlap a fluorine $2p$ orbital to form three N—F sigma bonds.

10.3 (a) $\underline{B}Br_3$ sp^2 (c) $\underline{C}H_2Cl_2$ sp^3

        (b) $\underline{C}O_2$ sp (d) $\underline{C}O_3^{2-}$ sp^2

10.4 (a) $\underline{C}Se_2$ sp (c) $\underline{C}H_2O$ sp^2

        (b) $\underline{S}O_2$ sp^2 (d) $\underline{N}H_4^+$ $\cdot sp^3$

10.5 (a) C: sp^3 O: sp^3

        (b) From left to right: sp^3, sp^2, sp^2

        (c) N: sp^3 $\underline{C}H_2$: sp^3 $\underline{C}O_2H$: sp^2

10.6   underlined atom   hybrid orbital set

        (a)   N   both N atoms are sp^3 hybridized

               C sp^2

        (b)   C of CH_3 sp^3

               C of C=C and C=O   both C atoms are sp^2 hybridized

        (c)   C of C=C sp^2

               C of C≡N sp

10.7

	electron-pair geometry	molecular geometry	hybridization
(a)	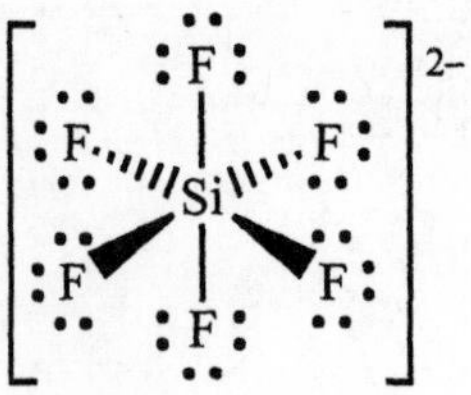 octahedral	octahedral	sp^3d^2
(b)	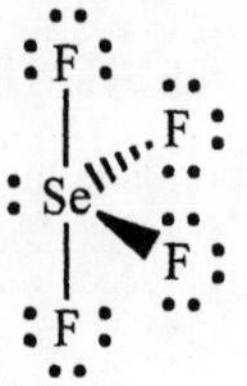 trigonal bipyramidal	see-saw	sp^3d
(c)	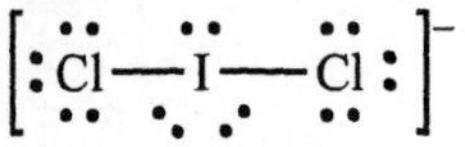 trigonal bipyramidal	linear	sp^3d
(d)	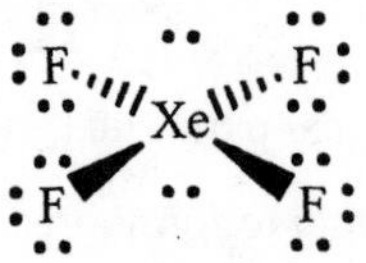 octahedral	square planar	sp^3d^2

10.8

	electron-pair geometry	molecular geometry	hybridization
(a)	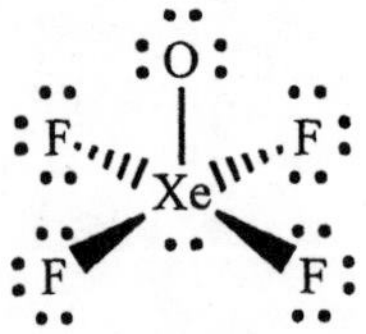 octahedral	square pyramid	sp^3d^2
(b)	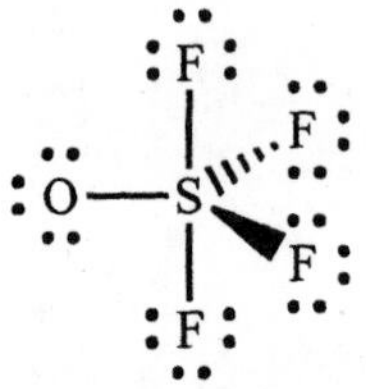 trigonal bipyramidal	see-saw	sp^3d
(c)	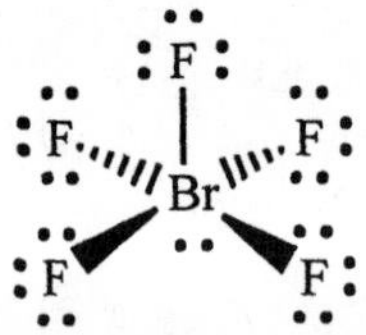 octahedral	square pyramid	sp^3d^2
(d)	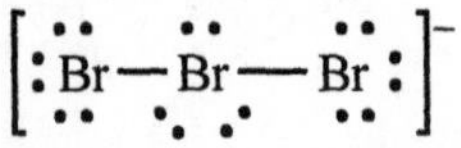 trigonal bipyramidal	linear	sp^3d

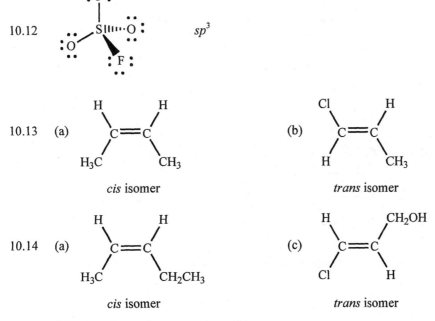

10.9

tetrahedral

sp^3

tetrahedral

sp^3

10.10

tetrahedral

sp^3

tetrahedral

sp^3

10.11   The C atom is sp^2 hybridized. Two of the sp^2 hybrid orbitals are used to form C—Cl σ bonds. The third is used to form the C—O σ bond. The p orbital not used in the C atom hybrid orbitals is used to form the CO π bond.

10.12 sp^3

10.13   (a)   (b)

cis isomer   *trans* isomer

10.14   (a)   (c)

cis isomer   *trans* isomer

(b) *cis* and *trans* isomers not possible

10.15 H_2^+: $(\sigma_{1s})^1$ Bond order = $^1/_2(1 - 0) = ^1/_2$ weaker H—H bond

H_2: $(\sigma_{1s})^2$ Bond order = $^1/_2(2 - 0) = 1$ stronger H—H bond

10.16 Li_2^+: $(\sigma_{1s})^2(\sigma^*_{1s})^2(\sigma_{2s})^1(\sigma^*_{2s})^0$ Bond order $= {}^1/_2(3-2) = {}^1/_2$

Li_2^- $(\sigma_{1s})^2(\sigma^*_{1s})^2(\sigma_{2s})^2(\sigma^*_{2s})^1$ Bond order $= {}^1/_2(4-3) = {}^1/_2$

Li_2 $(\sigma_{1s})^2(\sigma^*_{1s})^2(\sigma_{2s})^2(\sigma^*_{2s})^0$ Bond order $= {}^1/_2(4-2) = 1$

The bond order of Li_2 is greater than that of either of its ions.

10.17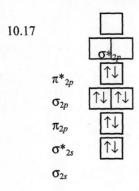

The C_2^{2-} ion has a bond order of ${}^1/_2(8-2) = 3$ (one σ bond and two π bonds). The C_2 molecule has two fewer electrons and a bond order of ${}^1/_2(6-2) = 2$. The C_2^{2-} ion is diamagnetic.

10.18 O_2:   [core electrons]$(\sigma_{2s})^2(\sigma^*_{2s})^2(\pi_{2p})^4(\sigma_{2p})^2(\pi^*_{2p})^2$

O_2^-:   [core electrons]$(\sigma_{2s})^2(\sigma^*_{2s})^2(\pi_{2p})^4(\sigma_{2p})^2(\pi^*_{2p})^3$

O_2^{2-}:   [core electrons]$(\sigma_{2s})^2(\sigma^*_{2s})^2(\pi_{2p})^4(\sigma_{2p})^2(\pi^*_{2p})^4$

Property	O_2	O_2^-	O_2^{2-}
(a) magnetic character	paramagnetic	paramagnetic	diamagnetic
(b) net number of σ bonds	1	1	1
net number of π bonds	1	$^1/_2$	0
(c) bond order	2	1.5	1
(d) bond length	short	medium	long

10.19   (a) [core electrons]$(\sigma_{2s})^2(\sigma^*_{2s})^2(\pi_{2p})^4(\sigma_{2p})^2$

(b) The HOMO is σ_{2p}

(c) diamagnetic

(d) Bond order $= {}^1/_2(8-2) = 3$ One σ bond and two π bonds

10.20   (a) The NO^+ ion has an even number of valence electrons (10 electrons) and so is predicted to be diamagnetic.

(b) NO^+: [core electrons]$(\sigma_{2s})^2(\sigma^*_{2s})^2(\pi_{2p})^4(\sigma_{2p})^2$ The HOMO is σ_{2p}

(c) Bond order $= {}^1/_2(8-2) = 3$

(d) The bond order of NO is 2.5, whereas that of NO^+ is 3. Therefore, NO^+ has a stronger bond than NO.

10.21

$$\begin{bmatrix} :\overset{\displaystyle\cdot\cdot}{\underset{}{F}}: \\ | \\ :\overset{\cdot\cdot}{\underset{\cdot\cdot}{F}}-Al-\overset{\cdot\cdot}{\underset{\cdot\cdot}{F}}: \\ | \\ :\overset{}{\underset{\displaystyle\cdot\cdot}{F}}: \end{bmatrix}^{-}$$

The electron-pair and molecular geometries are tetrahedral. The Al atom is sp^3 hybridized. Each of these orbitals overlaps a fluorine $2p$ orbital to form four Al—F sigma bonds.

10.22

$$\overset{\displaystyle :\overset{\cdot\cdot}{F}:}{\underset{}{}}$$
$$| $$
$$:\overset{\cdot\cdot}{\underset{\cdot\cdot}{F}}-\overset{}{\underset{\displaystyle\cdot\;\cdot}{Cl}}-\overset{\cdot\cdot}{\underset{\cdot\cdot}{F}}:$$

The electron-pair geometry is trigonal bipyramidal, and the molecular geometry is T-shaped. The Cl atom is sp^3d hybridized. Three of these hybrid orbitals each overlap a fluorine $2p$ orbital to form three Cl—F sigma bonds.

10.23   (a) SO_2 120° sp^2

        (b) SO_3 120° sp^2

        (c) SO_3^{2-} 109° sp^3

        (d) SO_4^{2-} 109° sp^3

SO_2 and SO_3 have the same bond angle and the S atom in each uses the same hybrid orbitals. SO_3^{2-} and SO_4^{2-} have the same bond angle and the S atom in each uses the same hybrid orbitals.

10.24

$$\begin{bmatrix} :\overset{\cdot\cdot}{\underset{\cdot\cdot}{F}}-\overset{\cdot\cdot}{\underset{\cdot\cdot}{Cl}}-\overset{\cdot\cdot}{\underset{\cdot\cdot}{F}}: \end{bmatrix}^{+} \qquad \begin{bmatrix} :\overset{\cdot\cdot}{\underset{\cdot\cdot}{F}}-\overset{}{\underset{\displaystyle\cdot\;\cdot}{Cl}}-\overset{\cdot\cdot}{\underset{\cdot\cdot}{F}}: \end{bmatrix}^{-}$$

electron-pair geometry	tetrahedral	trigonal bipyramidal
molecular geometry	bent	linear
Cl atom hybridization	sp^3	sp^3d

10.25

$$\begin{bmatrix} \overset{\cdot\cdot}{\underset{\cdot\cdot}{O}}=\overset{\cdot\cdot}{N}-\overset{\cdot\cdot}{\underset{\cdot\cdot}{O}}: \end{bmatrix}^{-} \longleftrightarrow \begin{bmatrix} :\overset{\cdot\cdot}{\underset{\cdot\cdot}{O}}-\overset{\cdot\cdot}{N}=\overset{\cdot\cdot}{\underset{\cdot\cdot}{O}} \end{bmatrix}^{-}$$

electron-pair geometry: trigonal planar

molecular geometry: bent

O—N—O bond angle = 120°

Average bond order = $^3/_2$

N atom hybridization: sp^2

10.26

$$\left[\begin{array}{c} :\ddot{O}: \\ \| \\ \ddot{O}=N-\ddot{O}: \end{array}\right]^{-} \longleftrightarrow \left[\begin{array}{c} :O: \\ \| \\ :\ddot{O}-N-\ddot{O}: \end{array}\right]^{-} \longleftrightarrow \left[\begin{array}{c} :\ddot{O}: \\ \| \\ :\ddot{O}-N=\ddot{O} \end{array}\right]^{-}$$

The N atom hybridization is the same in each structure (sp^2). The three sp^2 hybrid orbitals are used to form N—O σ bonds. The p orbital not used in the N atom hybrid orbitals is used to form the NO π bond.

10.27 $:N\equiv N-\ddot{O}: \longleftrightarrow \ddot{N}=N=\ddot{O} \longleftrightarrow :\ddot{N}-N\equiv O:$

In each structure the central N atom is sp hybridized. The other N atom hybridization changes from sp to sp^2 to sp^3. The two sp hybrid orbitals on the central N atom are used to form N—N and N—O σ bonds. The two p orbitals not used in the N atom hybridization are used to form NN and NO π bonds.

10.28

	O—C—O bond angle	CO bond order	C atom hybridization
CO_2	180°	2	sp
CO_3^{2-}	120°	$^4/_3$	sp^2

10.29   (a) All three molecules have the same molecular formula, C_2H_4O. They are isomers.

(b) Both carbon atoms in ethylene oxide are sp^3 hybridized. The CH_3 carbon in acetaldehyde is sp^3 hybridized and the C=O carbon is sp^2 hybridized. Both carbon atoms in vinyl alcohol are sp^2 hybridized.

(c)

	H—C—H angle
ethylene oxide	109°
acetaldehyde	109°
vinyl alcohol	120°

(d) All three molecules are polar.

(e) Vinyl alcohol has the strongest carbon-carbon bond, and acetaldehyde has the strongest carbon-oxygen bond.

10.30   (a) carbon 1: sp^2 carbon 2: sp^2

(b) angle A = 120°; angle B = 120°; angle C = 120°

(c) No, *cis-trans* isomerism is not possible

10.31   (a) CH_3 carbon atom: sp^3

C=N carbon atom: sp^2

N atom: sp^2

(b) C—N—O angle = 120°

10.32   (a)   angle A = 120°; angle B = 109°; angle C = 109°; angle D = 120°

        (b)   carbon 1: sp^2; carbon 2: sp^2; carbon 3: sp^3

10.33   (a)   C(1) = sp^2; O(2) = sp^3; N(3) = sp^3; C(4) = sp^3; P(5) = sp^3

        (b)   angle A = 120°; angle B = 109°; angle C = 109°; angle D = 109°

        (c)   The P—O and O—H bonds are most polar ($\Delta\chi = 1.4$)

10.34   (a)   1 π bond and 11 σ bonds.

        (b)   C(1) = sp^3, C(2) = sp^2, O(3) = sp^3

        (c)   The C=O bond is the shortest and strongest CO bond.

        (d)   angle A = 109°, angle B = 109°, angle C = 120°

10.35   (a)   The geometry about the boron atom is trigonal planar in BF_3, tetrahedral in H_3N—BF_3.

        (b)   Boron is sp^2 hybridized in BF_3, sp^3 hybridized in H_3N—BF_3.

        (c)   Yes

10.36   (a)   The angles around N and S are approximately 109°.

        (b)   The hybridization of the N atom does not change (sp^3 in NH_2^- and H_2N—SO_3^-). The S atom hybridization changes from sp^2 in SO_3 to sp^3 in H_2N—SO_3^-.

10.37   (a)   The C=O bond is the most polar bond in the molecule.

        (b)   There are 18 σ bonds and 5 π bonds in the molecule.

        (c)   The *trans* isomer is shown. The *cis* isomer is

        (d)   All carbon atoms in the molecule are sp^2 hybridized.

        (e)   All three angles are 120°.

10.38

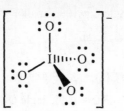

electron-pair geometry	tetrahedral	trigonal bipyramidal
molecular geometry	tetrahedral	trigonal bipyramidal
hybridization of I atom	sp^3	sp^3d

10.39   (a) sp^3d in SbF_5, sp^3d^2 in SbF_6^-

(b) $\left[H\!-\!\overset{\cdot\cdot}{\underset{\cdot\cdot}{F}}\!-\!H \right]^+$ The geometry of H_2F^+ is bent, and the F atom is sp^3 hybridized.

10.40

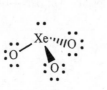

Electron-pair geometry	tetrahedral	tetrahedral
Molecular geometry	trigonal pyramidal	tetrahedral
Xe	sp^3 hybridized	sp^3 hybridized

10.41   (a) $\left[:\overset{\cdot\cdot}{O}\!-\!\overset{\cdot\cdot}{O}: \right]^-$ bond order = 1

(b) [core electrons]$(\sigma_{2s})^2(\sigma^*_{2s})^2(\pi_{2p})^4(\sigma_{2p})^2(\pi^*_{2p})^4$ bond order = $^1/_2(8-6) = 1$

(c) Yes, the two bonding theories lead to the same magnetic character (diamagnetic) and bond order.

10.42 N_2 [core electrons]$(\sigma_{2s})^2(\sigma^*_{2s})^2(\pi_{2p})^4(\sigma_{2p})^2$

N_2^+ [core electrons]$(\sigma_{2s})^2(\sigma^*_{2s})^2(\pi_{2p})^4(\sigma_{2p})^1$

N_2^- [core electrons]$(\sigma_{2s})^2(\sigma^*_{2s})^2(\pi_{2p})^4(\sigma_{2p})^2(\pi^*_{2p})^1$

	N_2	N_2^+	N_2^-
(a)	diamagnetic	paramagnetic	paramagnetic
(b)	2 π bonds	2 π bonds	1 $^1/_2$ π bonds
(c) bond order	3	2 $^1/_2$	2 $^1/_2$

(d) $N_2 < N_2^+ \approx N_2^-$

—increasing bond length→

(e) $N_2^+ \approx N_2^- < N_2$

—increasing bond strength→

10.43 B_2 and O_2 are diamagnetic, Li_2, B_2, and F_2 have a bond order of 1, C_2 and O_2 have a bond order of 2, and N_2 has the highest bond order, 3.

10.44 | Molecule or ion | Magnetic behavior | HOMO |
|---|---|---|
| (a) NO | paramagnetic | π^* |
| (b) OF^- | diamagnetic | π^* |
| (c) O_2^{2-} | diamagnetic | π^* |
| (d) Ne_2^+ | paramagnetic | σ^*_{2p} |
| (e) CN | paramagnetic | σ_{2p} |

10.45   CN   [core electrons]$(\sigma_{2s})^2(\sigma^*_{2s})^2(\pi_{2p})^4(\sigma_{2p})^1$

(a) The HOMO is σ_{2p}

(b) Bond order $= \frac{1}{2}(7-2) = 2\,\frac{1}{2}$

(c) One-half net σ bond and two net π bonds

(d) paramagnetic

10.46   (a) C_6 ring carbon atoms: sp^2; side chain carbon atoms: sp^3; N atom: sp^3

(b) angle A = 120°; angle B = 109°; angle C = 109°

(c) 23 σ bonds and 3 π bonds

(d) The molecule is polar

(e) The H^+ ion attaches to the most electronegative atom in the molecule, N

10.47   (a) All of the C atoms are sp^3 hybridized

(b) C—O—H angle = 109°

(c) The molecule is polar

(d) The six-member ring is non-planar. The ring could only be planar if the carbon atoms were sp^2 hybridized as in benzene.

10.48

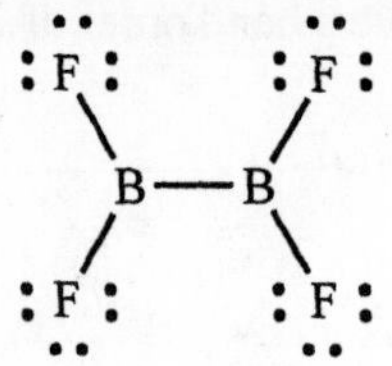

B is sp^2 hybridized, F—B—B = 120°

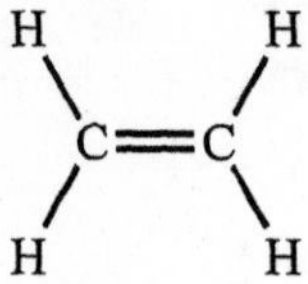

C is sp^2 hybridized, H—C—C = 120°

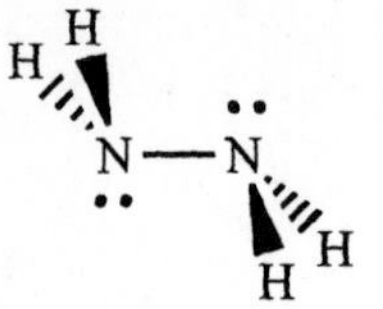

N is sp^3 hybridized, H—N—N = 109°

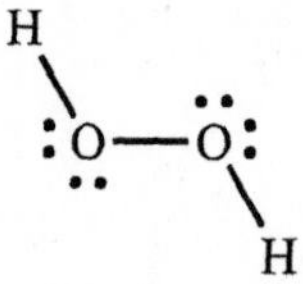

O is sp^3 hybridized, H—O—O = 109°

10.49   (a) The keto and enol forms are not resonance structures because both electron pairs and atoms have been rearr

(b) The terminal —CH$_3$ carbon atoms are sp^3 hybridized and the three central carbon atoms are sp^2 hybridized i

(c) Enol form: —CH$_3$ carbon atoms   tetrahedral

central three carbon atoms   trigonal planar

Keto form: —CH$_3$ carbon atoms   tetrahedral

central —CH$_2$— carbon atom   tetrahedral

C=O carbon atoms   trigonal planar

Only the center carbon atom changes geometry, from trigonal planar to tetrahedral

(d)

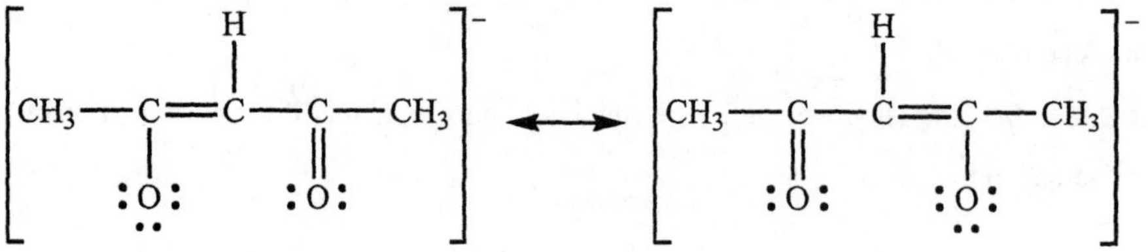

(e) Possible for the enol form

10.50   (a) Even though the atoms are sp^3 hybridized, the bond angles in the three-member ring must be 60°.

(b) sp^3

(c) Because the angles are significantly less than the expected value of 109°, the ring structure is strained and relatively easy to break. (The molecule is reactive.)

10.51   The maximum number of hybrid orbitals that a carbon atom can form is four and the minimum number that can be formed is two. Carbon has only four valence orbitals, one s and three p, so it cannot form more than four hybrid orbitals.

10.52   (a) CF_4 is isoelectronic with BF_4^- (32 valence electrons)

(b) SiF_4 (32 valence electrons) and SF_4 (34 valence electrons) are not isoelectronic

(c) BF_4^-: sp^3 SiF_4: sp^3 SF_4: sp^3d

10.53   (a)   C atom: sp^2; N atom: sp^3

(b)   Another resonance structure (showing only the peptide linkage and the formal charges on O and N) is

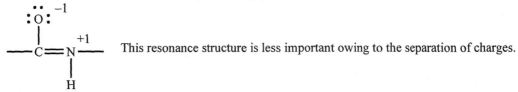

This resonance structure is less important owing to the separation of charges.

(c)   The fact that the amide link is planar indicates that the resonance structure shown above has some importance.

10.54   The higher the bond order, the shorter the bond length and the larger the bond energy. Acetylene has a carbon-carbon triple bond (bond order = 3), so it has the shortest and strongest carbon-carbon bond. Ethane has a carbon-carbon single bond (bond order = 1), so it has the longest and weakest carbon-carbon bond.

10.55   Molecular orbital theory correctly predicts the electronic structures for odd-electron molecules and other molecules such as O_2 that do not follow the electron-pairing assumptions of the Lewis dot structure approach.

10.56   Valence bond theory uses resonance to explain the bond order of 1.5 in O_3. Molecular orbital theory uses three π molecular orbitals (bonding, nonbonding, and antibonding) combined with sigma bonding and antibonding molecular orbitals to explain the bond order.

10.57   (a)   The number of hybrid orbitals is always equal to the number of atomic orbitals used.

(b)   No. All hybrid orbital sets involve an s orbital.

(c)   The energy of the hybrid orbital set is the weighted average of the energy of the combining atomic orbitals.

(d)   The shapes are identical. They are oriented in different directions in space.

(e)   As in (d), these hybrid orbitals have the same shape, but they are oriented in different planes.

10.58   (a)   The attractive forces must be greater than the repulsive forces if a covalent bond is to form.

(b)   When the atoms are widely separated, attractive and repulsive forces are minimized. As they approach each other, attractive forces increase until the energy reaches a minimum. As they approach still more closely, repulsive forces are maximized.

(c)   Unlike fluorine, neon does not have any orbitals with a single, unpaired electron.

10.59   (a) and (b) See the explanations on the Screen 10.7 "A Closer Look" sidebar.

(c) C(1) sp^3; C(2) sp^2; C(3) sp^2

10.60   (a) The molecule with the double bond requires a great deal more energy because the π bond must be broken in order for the ends of the molecule to rotate relative to each other.

(b) The CH_3 group can rotate freely with respect to the rest of the molecule.

(c) No. The carbon-carbon double bonds in the molecule prevent the CH_2 fragments from rotating.

Chapter 11
Carbon: More Than Just Another Element

INSTRUCTOR'S NOTES

The major theme of this chapter is the structure and reactivity of organic compounds. In presenting chemical reactivity, we introduce only a very few reaction types and then encourage the student to see how these could be put together to synthesize more complex organic compounds. As one can see from this chapter, we also believe it is important to use models when teaching the subject. Students will need to be trained to see molecular structures in three dimensions.

Students often learn a bit about organic chemistry in high school so this return to the subject can be a desirable thing for them. The numerous applications to the life sciences should stimulate the interest of the many students who aspire to careers in those fields.

Given the wide range of topics and the level of detail in the chapter it will probably be a good idea to clearly state your expectations for the students. This can be done by assigning a judicious selection of Study Questions.

Many of the figures in this Manual were prepared using *ChemDraw* from CambridgeSoft Corporation. Most of the molecular models in this chapter are included in the Molecular Modeling Database on the *General ChemistryNow CD-ROM*.

SUGGESTED DEMONSTRATIONS

1. Organic Demonstrations
    *   Burke, J. T. "An Acid Hydrocarbon: A Chemical Paradox," *Journal of Chemical Education* **2004**, *81*, 65.
    *   Bertolini, T. M. "Visualizing Bent Bonds in Cyclopropane," *Journal of Chemical Education* **2004**, *81*, 818.
    *   Silversmith, E. F. "Organic Lecture Demonstrations," *Journal of Chemical Education* **1988**, *65*, 70.
    *   Bronice, R. "Saturated and Unsaturated Fats: An Organic Chemistry Demonstration," *Journal of Chemical Education* **1985**, *62*, 320.

2. Polymers
    *   There is a section on polymer demonstrations in Shakhashiri, B. Z. *Chemical Demonstrations: A Handbook for Teachers of Chemistry*; University of Wisconsin Press, 1983; Vol. 1.
    *   Kolb, K. E.; Kolb, D. K. "Method for Separating or Identifying Plastics," *Journal of Chemical Education* **1991**, *68*, 348.
    *   Cross-linked polyvinyl alcohol (Figure 11.15) is a student favorite. About 40 grams of PVA are dissolved by heating in a liter of water. (Leave several hours for this process.) Solid sodium borate is stirred into a small quantity of this solution until cross-linking occurs to give the slimy material. To make the demonstration even more graphic, the slime can be colored with food coloring.

- Nylon-66 is quite simple to synthesize (Figure 11.18). With care our students once were able to pull a continuous filament that stretched from the front of a large lecture room to the back.

- Sperling, L. H. "On the Cross-Linked Structure of Rubber," *Journal of Chemical Education* **1982**, *59*, 651.

3. Nomenclature

- Crute, T. D. "Classroom Nomenclature Games—BINGO," *Journal of Chemical Education* **2000**, *77*, 481.

SOLUTIONS TO STUDY QUESTIONS

11.1   Heptane

11.2 $C_{12}H_{26}$

11.3   (c) $C_{14}H_{30}$ is an alkane

    (b) C_5H_{10} could be a cycloalkane

11.4   2,2,4-trimethylpentane

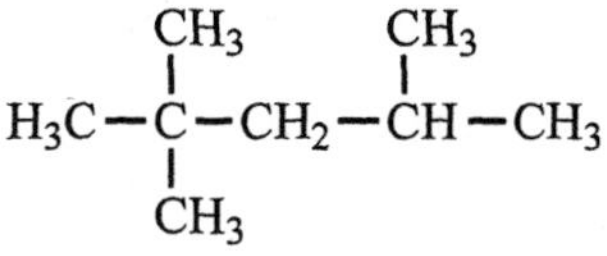

$$H_3C-\underset{\underset{CH_3}{|}}{\overset{\overset{CH_3}{|}}{C}}-CH_2-\underset{\overset{CH_3}{|}}{CH}-CH_3$$

    Two other possible isomers:

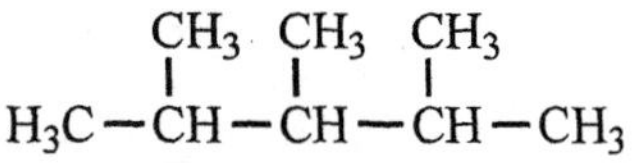

$$H_3C-\underset{\overset{CH_3}{|}}{CH}-\underset{\overset{CH_3}{|}}{CH}-\underset{\overset{CH_3}{|}}{CH}-CH_3 \qquad 2,3,4\text{-trimethylpentane}$$

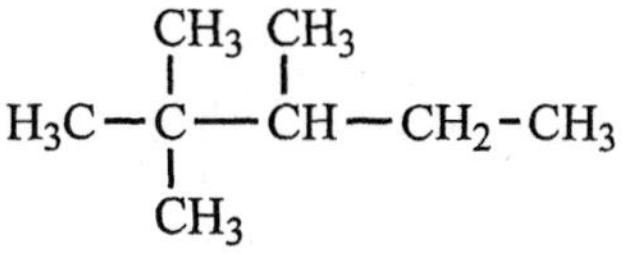

$$H_3C-\underset{\underset{CH_3}{|}}{\overset{\overset{CH_3}{|}}{C}}-\underset{\overset{CH_3}{|}}{CH}-CH_2\text{-}CH_3 \qquad 2,2,3\text{-trimethylpentane}$$

11.5   2,3-dimethylbutane

11.6   2,5-dimethylheptane

    One possible isomer:

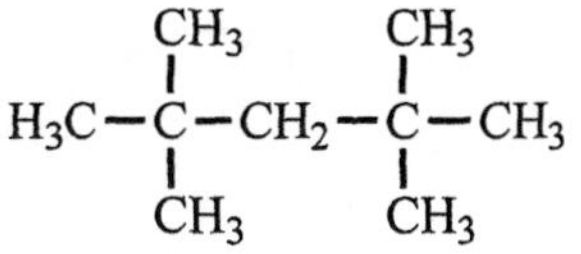

$$H_3C-\underset{\underset{CH_3}{|}}{\overset{\overset{CH_3}{|}}{C}}-CH_2-\underset{\underset{CH_3}{|}}{\overset{\overset{CH_3}{|}}{C}}-CH_3 \qquad 2,2,4,4\text{-tetramethylpentane}$$

11.7   (a) $H_3C-\underset{\overset{CH_3}{|}}{\overset{\overset{CH_3}{|}}{CH}}-CH-CH_2-CH_2-CH_3$

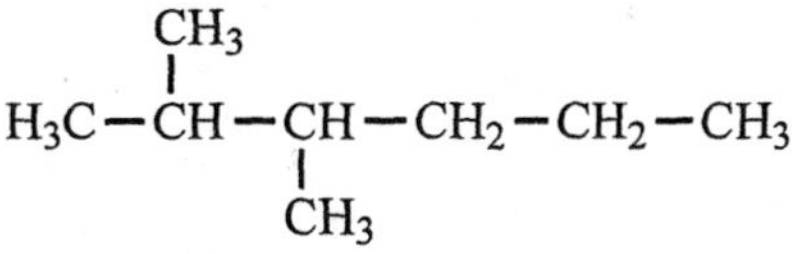

    (b) $H_3C-\underset{\overset{CH_3}{|}}{\overset{\overset{CH_3}{|}}{CH}}-CH-CH_2-CH_2-CH_2-CH_2-CH_3$

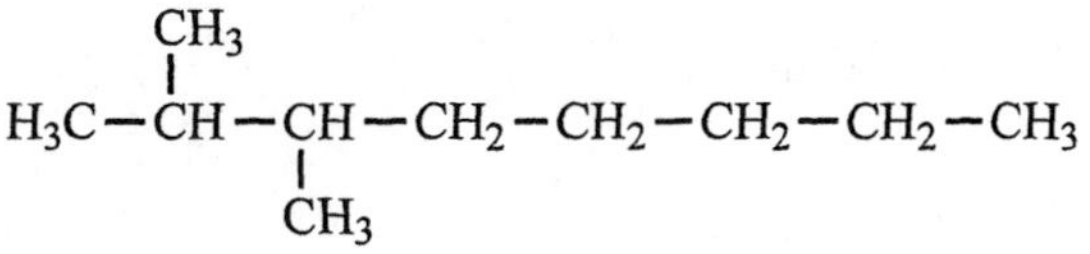

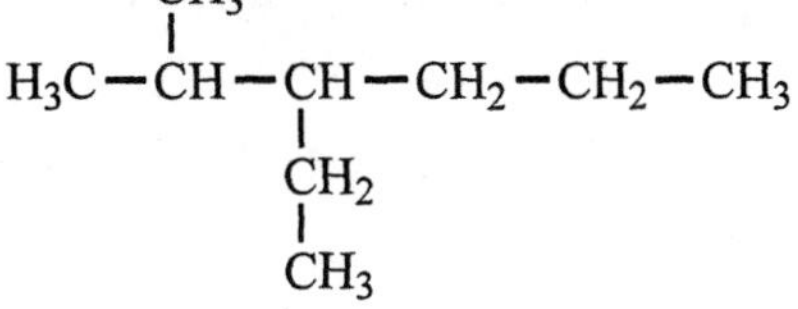

    (c) $H_3C-CH_2\text{-}\underset{\underset{\underset{CH_3}{|}}{CH_2}}{\overset{}{CH}}-CH_2-CH_2-CH_2-CH_3$

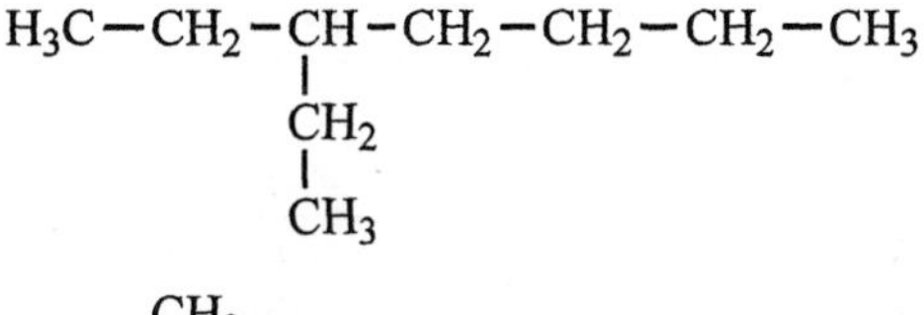

    (d) $H_3C-\underset{\underset{\underset{CH_3}{|}}{CH_2}}{\overset{\overset{CH_3}{|}}{CH}}-CH-CH_2-CH_2-CH_3$

11.8

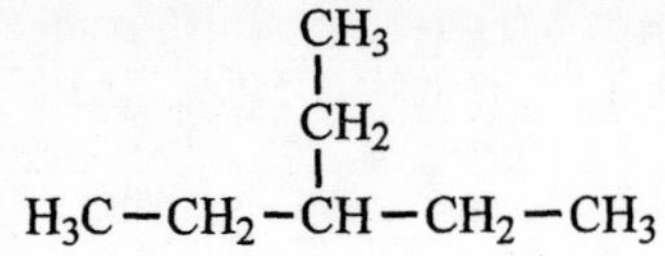

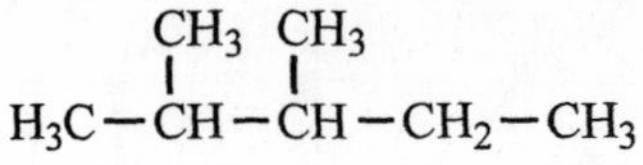

$$CH_3$$
$$|$$
$$CH_2$$
$$|$$
$$H_3C-CH_2-CH-CH_2-CH_3$$

$$CH_3 \quad CH_3$$
$$| \qquad |$$
$$H_3C-CH-CH-CH_2-CH_3$$

11.9

$$CH_3$$
$$|$$
$$H_3C-CH-CH_2-CH_2-CH_2-CH_2-CH_3$$ 2-methylheptane   not chiral

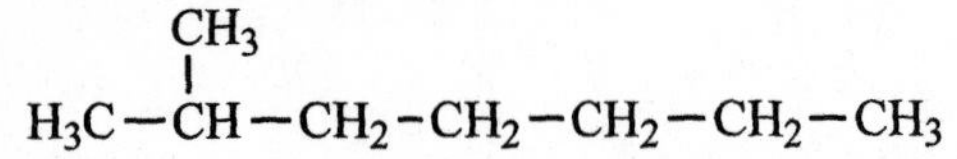

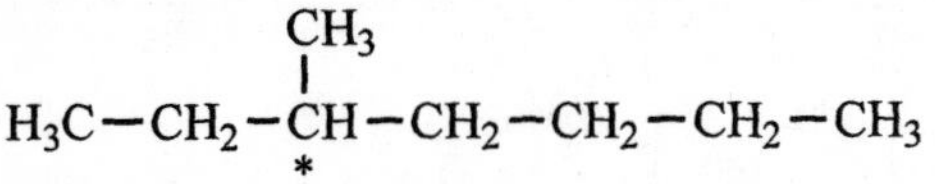

$$CH_3$$
$$|$$
$$H_3C-CH_2-CH-CH_2-CH_2-CH_2-CH_3$$ 3-methylheptane   chiral carbon (*)
$$*$$

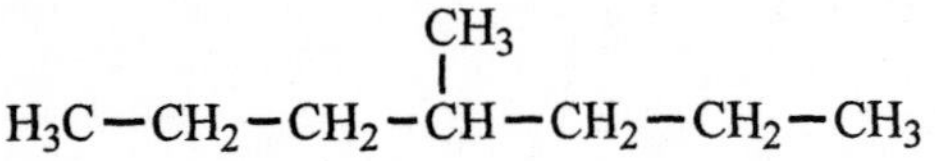

$$CH_3$$
$$|$$
$$H_3C-CH_2-CH_2-CH-CH_2-CH_2-CH_3$$ 4-methylheptane   not chiral

11.10

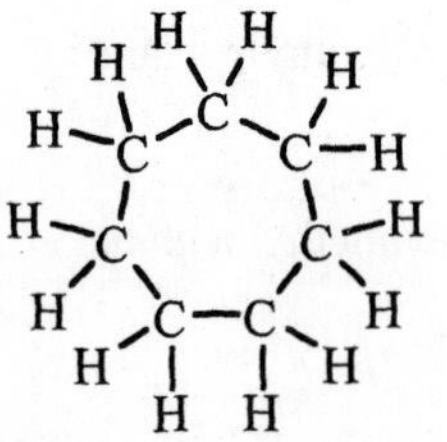

The ring is not planar. The geometry around each carbon atom is tetrahedral.

11.11

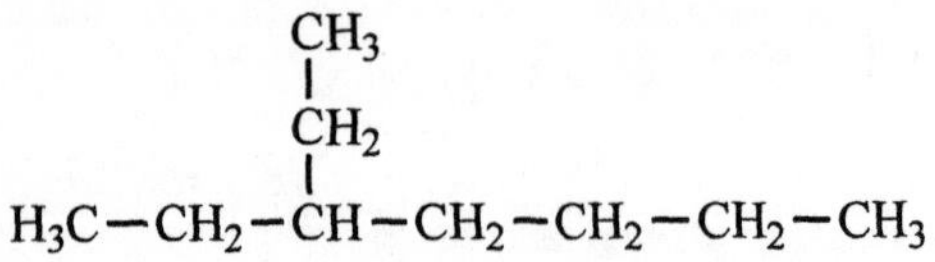

$$CH_3$$
$$|$$
$$CH_2$$
$$|$$
$$H_3C-CH_2-CH-CH_2-CH_2-CH_2-CH_3$$ 3-ethylheptane   not chiral

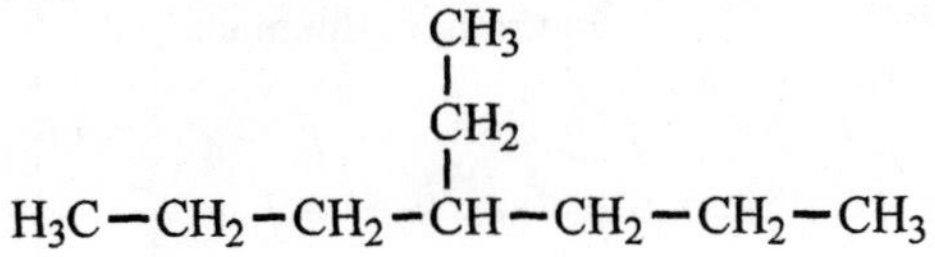

$$CH_3$$
$$|$$
$$CH_2$$
$$|$$
$$H_3C-CH_2-CH_2-CH-CH_2-CH_2-CH_3$$ 4-ethylheptane   not chiral

11.12

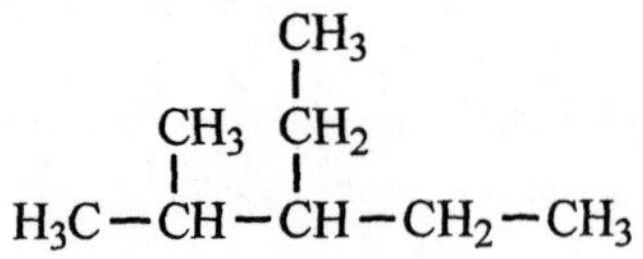

$$CH_3$$
$$|$$
$$CH_3 \quad CH_2$$
$$| \qquad |$$
$$H_3C-CH-CH-CH_2-CH_3$$ 3-ethyl-2-methylpentane

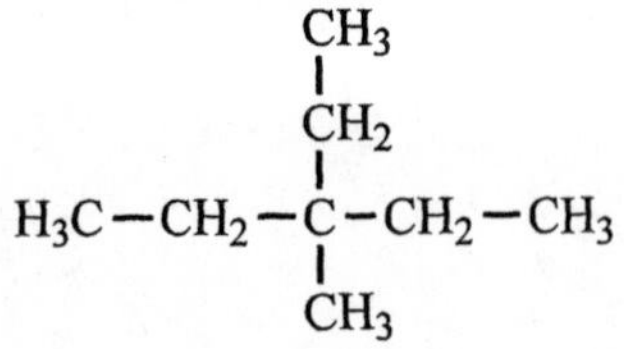

$$CH_3$$
$$|$$
$$CH_2$$
$$|$$
$$H_3C-CH_2-C-CH_2-CH_3$$ 3-ethyl-3-methylpentane
$$|$$
$$CH_3$$

11.13 C_4H_{10}, butane   Colorless gas at room temperature, only slightly soluble in water, more soluble in nonpolar solvents

$C_{12}H_{26}$, dodecane   Colorless liquid at room temperature, insoluble in water, soluble in nonpolar solvents

11.14   (a) $CH_4(g) + 4\ Cl_2(g) \rightarrow CCl_4(\ell) + 4\ HCl(g)$

(b) $C_6H_{12}(\ell) + 9\ O_2(g) \rightarrow 6\ CO_2(g) + 6\ H_2O(g)$

11.15

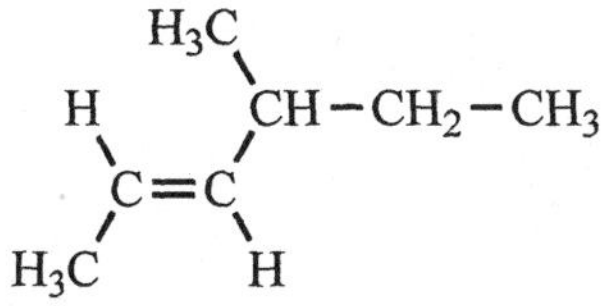

trans-4-methyl-2-hexene 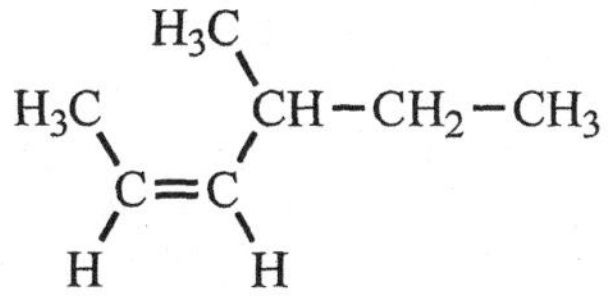   cis-4-methyl-2-hexene

11.16   In order to have *cis* and *trans* isomers, the alkene must have different atoms or groups on the carbons that

are double bonded:

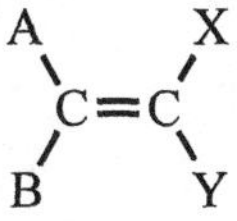

That is, A ≠ B and X ≠ Y. Alkynes do not have *cis* and *trans* isomerism

because the *sp* hybridization of the carbon atoms produces a linear molecule. Alkanes do not have *cis* and

tran isomerism because free rotation occurs around carbon-carbon single bonds.

11.17   (a)

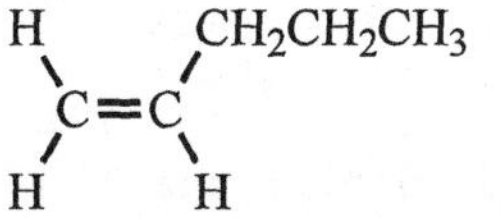

1-pentene   3-methyl-1-butene

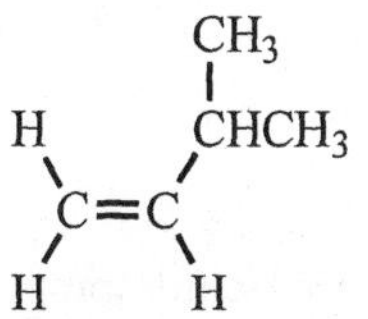

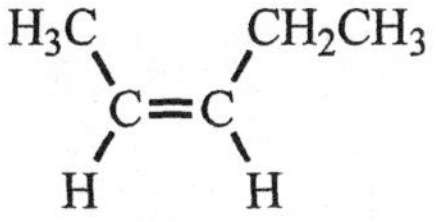

cis-2-pentene   *trans*-2-pentene

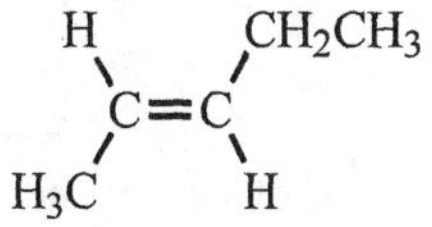

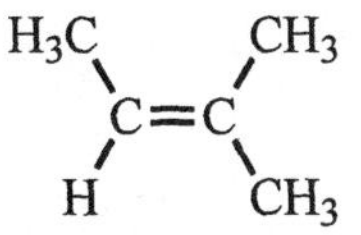

2-methyl-2-butene   2-methyl-1-butene

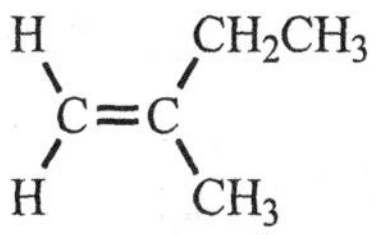

(b)

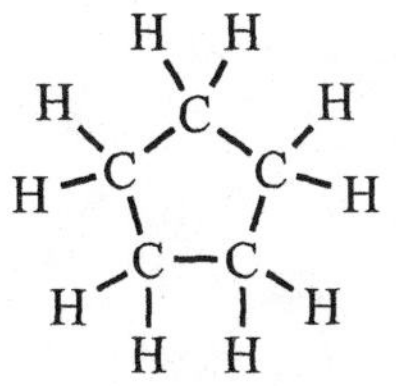

cyclopentane

11.18

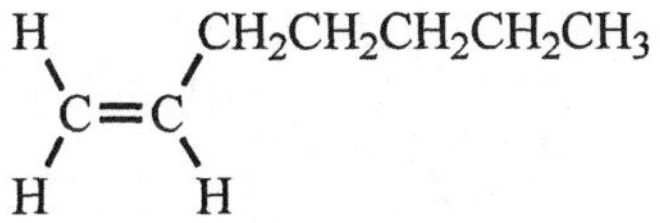

1-heptene

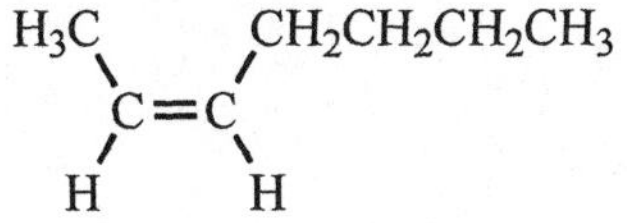

cis-2-heptene   *trans*-2-heptene

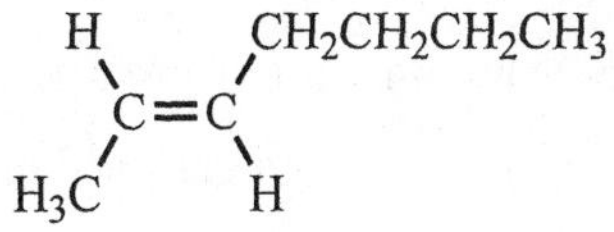

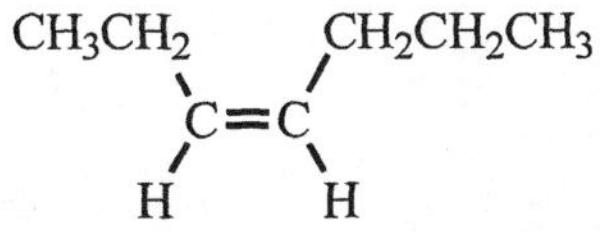

cis-3-heptene   *trans*-3-heptene

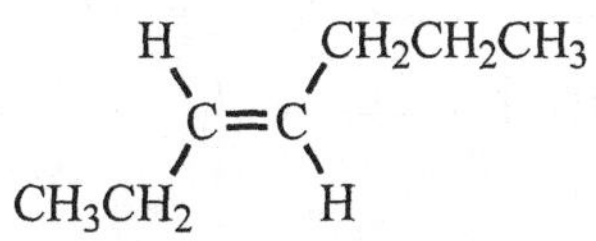

11.19 (a) $\overset{\overset{\displaystyle Br}{|}}{H_3C-CH-CH_2-Br}$ 1,2-dibromopentane

       (b) $CH_3CH_2CH_2CH_2CH_3$ pentane

11.20 (a) $H_3C-\overset{\overset{\displaystyle CH_3}{|}}{\underset{\underset{\displaystyle H}{|}}{C}}-CH_2-CH_2-CH_3$ 2-methylpentane

       (b) $H_3C-\overset{\overset{\displaystyle Br}{|}}{\underset{\underset{\displaystyle Br}{|}}{C}}-\overset{\overset{\displaystyle Br}{|}}{\underset{\underset{\displaystyle Br}{|}}{C}}-CH_2-CH_3$ 2,2,3,3-tetrabromopentane

11.21 $CH_3CH_2CH=CH_2$ 1-butene

11.22 $H_3C-\overset{\overset{\displaystyle CH_3}{|}}{C}=CHCH_2CH_2CH_3 \ + Br_2 \rightarrow \ H_3C-\overset{\overset{\displaystyle CH_3}{|}}{\underset{\underset{\displaystyle Br}{|}}{C}}-\overset{}{\underset{\underset{\displaystyle Br}{|}}{C}}HCH_2CH_2CH_3$

       2-methyl-2-hexene

11.23 $\underset{\underset{\displaystyle H}{}}{\overset{\overset{\displaystyle Cl}{}}{C}}=\underset{\underset{\displaystyle H}{}}{\overset{\overset{\displaystyle CH_3}{}}{C}}$ *cis*-1-chloropropene $\underset{\underset{\displaystyle H}{}}{\overset{\overset{\displaystyle Cl}{}}{C}}=\underset{\underset{\displaystyle CH_3}{}}{\overset{\overset{\displaystyle H}{}}{C}}$ *trans*-1-chloropropene

          $\underset{\underset{\displaystyle H}{}}{\overset{\overset{\displaystyle H}{}}{C}}=\underset{\underset{\displaystyle CH_3}{}}{\overset{\overset{\displaystyle Cl}{}}{C}}$ 2-chloropropene $\underset{\underset{\displaystyle H}{}}{\overset{\overset{\displaystyle H}{}}{C}}=\underset{\underset{\displaystyle CH_2Cl}{}}{\overset{\overset{\displaystyle H}{}}{C}}$ 3-chloropropene

11.24   If the compound is an alkene it will react with bromine to form a substituted alkane. The alkane would not
        react with bromine.

11.25 (a)   (b)

11.26 (a)   1-chloro-2-nitrobenzene (or *o*-chloronitrobenzene)
       (b)   1,4-dinitrobenzene (or *p*-dinitrobenzene)
       (c)   1-chloro-2-ethylbenzene (or *o*-chloroethylbenzene)

11.27

11.28   (benzene) $+ CH_3CH_2CH_2CH_2CH_2CH_2Cl \xrightarrow{AlCl_3}$ (benzene)$-CH_2CH_2CH_2CH_2CH_2CH_3 + HCl$

11.29   (1,4-dimethylbenzene) $+ CH_3Cl \xrightarrow{AlCl_3}$ (trimethylbenzene) $+ HCl$ 1,2,4-trimethylbenzene

11.30   (o-nitrotoluene)   (p-nitrotoluene)

11.31   (a)   1-propanol   primary

        (b)   1-butanol   primary

        (c)   2-methyl-2-propanol   tertiary

        (d)   2-methyl-2-butanol   tertiary

11.32   (a) $HO-CH_2CH_2CH_2CH_3$ primary

        (b) $CH_3\overset{\overset{OH}{|}}{C}HCH_2CH_3$ secondary

        (c) $CH_3\overset{\overset{HO}{|}}{C}H\overset{\overset{CH_3}{|}}{\underset{\underset{CH_3}{|}}{C}}CH_3$ secondary

        (c) $HO-CH_2CH_2\overset{\overset{CH_3}{|}}{\underset{\underset{CH_3}{|}}{C}}CH_3$ primary

11.33   (a) $C_2H_5NH_2$ $CH_3CH_2-\overset{\overset{\displaystyle H}{|}}{N}-H$

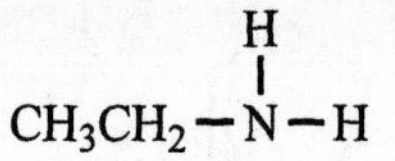

        (b) $(C_3H_7)_2NH$ $CH_3CH_2CH_2-\overset{\overset{\displaystyle CH_2CH_2CH_3}{|}}{N}-H$

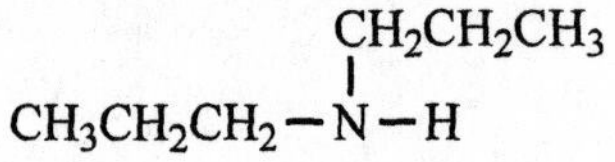

        (c) $C_4H_9N(CH_3)_2$ $CH_3CH_2CH_2CH_2-\overset{\overset{\displaystyle CH_3}{|}}{N}-CH_3$

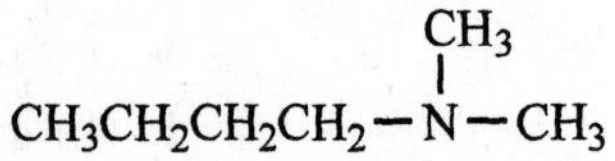

        (d) $(C_2H_5)_3N$ $CH_3CH_2-\overset{\overset{\displaystyle CH_2CH_3}{|}}{N}-CH_2CH_3$

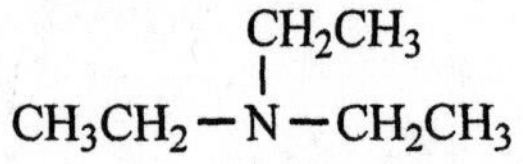

11.34   (a)   propylamine

        (b)   trimethylamine

        (c)   ethylmethylamine

        (d)   hexylamine

11.35 $HO-CH_2CH_2CH_2CH_3$ 1-butanol $CH_3\overset{\overset{\displaystyle OH}{|}}{C}HCH_2CH_3$ 2-butanol

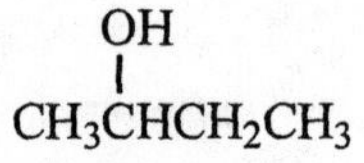

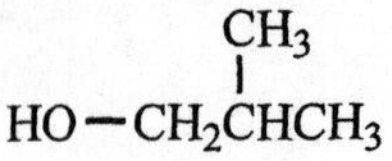

      $HO-CH_2\overset{\overset{\displaystyle CH_3}{|}}{C}HCH_3$ 2-methyl-1-propanol $CH_3\overset{\overset{\displaystyle OH}{|}}{\underset{\underset{\displaystyle CH_3}{|}}{C}}CH_3$ 2-methyl-2-propanol

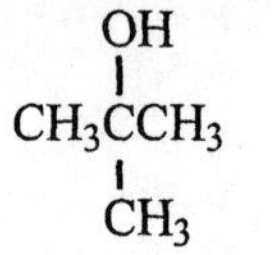

11.36 $H_2N-CH_2CH_2CH_2CH_3$ $CH_3\overset{\overset{\displaystyle NH_2}{|}}{C}HCH_2CH_3$ $H_2N-CH_2\overset{\overset{\displaystyle CH_3}{|}}{C}HCH_3$ $CH_3\overset{\overset{\displaystyle NH_2}{|}}{\underset{\underset{\displaystyle CH_3}{|}}{C}}CH_3$

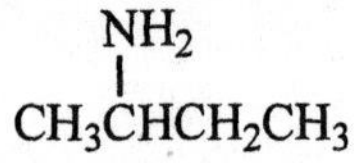

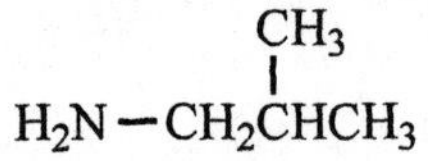

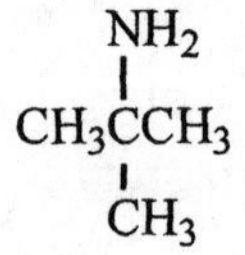

11.37   (a) $C_6H_5NH_3^+(aq) + Cl^-(aq)$

        (b) $(CH_3)_3NH^+(aq) + HSO_4^-(aq)$

11.38   (a) $CH_3CH_2CH_2CH_2-OH$ 1-butanol

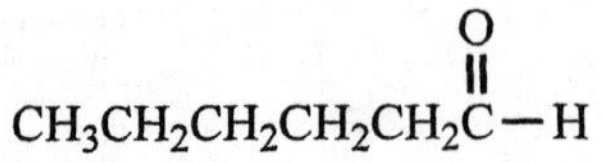

        (b) 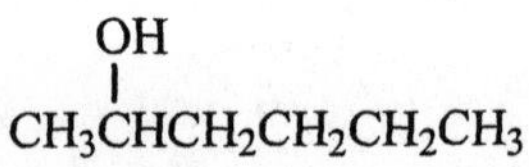 $CH_3\overset{\overset{\displaystyle OH}{|}}{C}HCH_2CH_2CH_2CH_3$ 2-hexanol

11.39   (a) 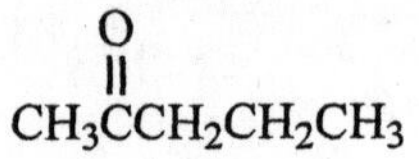 $CH_3\overset{\overset{\displaystyle O}{||}}{C}CH_2CH_2CH_3$ (b) $CH_3CH_2CH_2CH_2CH_2\overset{\overset{\displaystyle O}{||}}{C}-H$ (c) $CH_3CH_2CH_2CH_2\overset{\overset{\displaystyle O}{||}}{C}-OH$

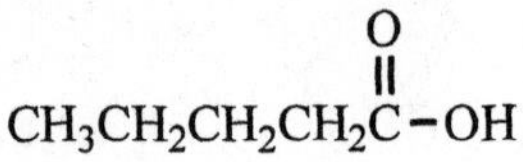

11.40   (a)   propanone; ketone   (b)   butanal; aldehyde   (c)   2-pentanone; ketone

11.41   (a) 3-methylpentanoic acid; carboxylic acid

      (b) methyl propanoate; ester

      (c) butyl acetate, ester

      (d) *p*-bromobenzoic acid; carboxylic acid

11.42   (a)
$$CH_3CH_2CH_2CH_2\overset{\underset{|}{CH_3}}{CH}-\overset{\underset{\|}{O}}{C}-OH$$

      (b)
$$CH_3CH_2CH_2\overset{\underset{\|}{O}}{C}OCH_2CH_2CH_2CH_2CH_3$$

      (c)
$$CH_3\overset{\underset{\|}{O}}{C}OCH_2CH_2CH_2CH_2CH_2CH_2CH_2CH_3$$

11.43   (a) $CH_3CH_2CH_2CH_2\overset{\underset{\|}{O}}{C}-OH$ pentanoic acid

      (b) $CH_3CH_2CH_2CH_2CH_2-OH$ 1-pentanol

      (c) $CH_3\overset{\underset{|}{OH}}{C}HCH_2CH_2CH_2CH_2CH_2CH_3$ 2-octanol

      (d) no reaction

11.44   Reduction of 2-pentanone with $LiAlH_4$ or $NaBH_4$

11.45   First oxidize 1-propanol to propanoic acid using $KMnO_4$. Next react propanoic acid with 1-propanol in the presence of a strong acid to form the ester propyl propanoate and water.

11.46 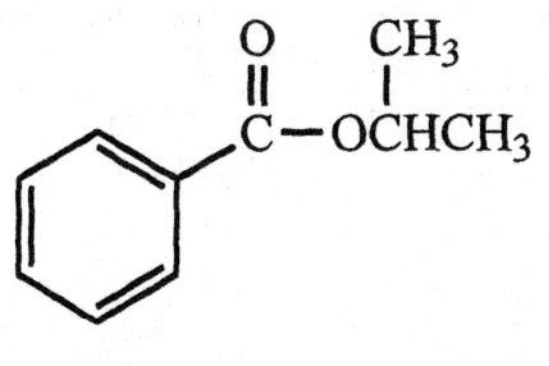   2-propyl benzoate

11.47 $CH_3\overset{\underset{\|}{O}}{C}O^-\,Na^+$ sodium acetate $HO-CH_2CH_2CH_2CH_3$ 1-butanol

11.48 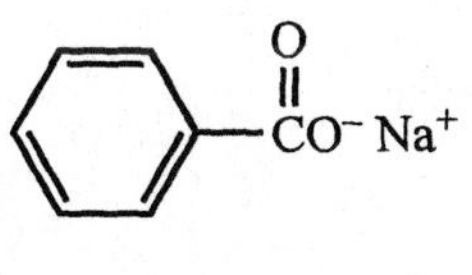   sodium benzoate $CH_3\overset{\underset{|}{OH}}{C}HCH_3$ 2-propanol

11.49   (a) trigonal planar

      (b) 120°

      (c) The molecule is chiral, carbon 2 is the chiral carbon atom

      (d) The —O—H hydrogen atom is acidic

11.50　(a)　$109°$

(b)　All of the C—O—H bond angles should be approximately $109°$

(c)　The molecule is chiral, there are two chiral carbon atoms in the molecule

(d)　C=C

(e)　alcohol, alkene, ester

11.51　(a)　alcohol

(b)　amide

(c)　carboxylic acid

(d)　ester

11.52　(a)　The ketone is reduced to an alcohol, $CH_3CH_2\overset{\overset{\displaystyle OH}{|}}{C}HCH_3$, 2-butanol

(b)　$CH_3CH_2\overset{\overset{\displaystyle O}{\|}}{C}-O\overset{\overset{\displaystyle CH_3}{|}}{C}HCH_2CH_3$　ester

(c)　$CH_3CH_2CH_2OH$　　1-propanol

(d)　$CH_3CH_2\overset{\overset{\displaystyle O}{\|}}{C}O^-\ Na^+$　　sodium propanoate

11.53　(a)

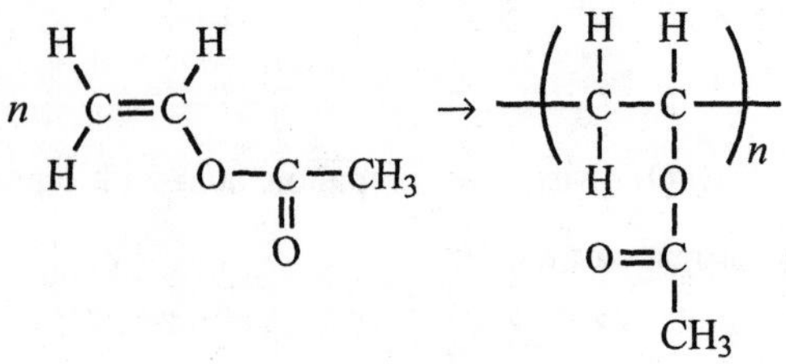

(b)

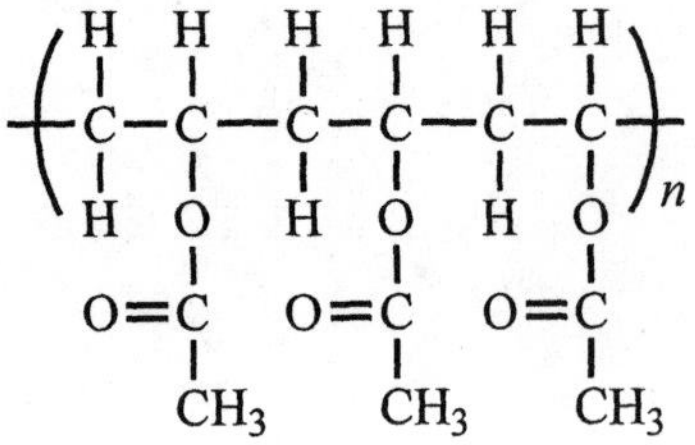

(c)　Polyvinyl alcohol is made by hydrolyzing the ester groups in polyvinyl acetate.

11.54　(a)

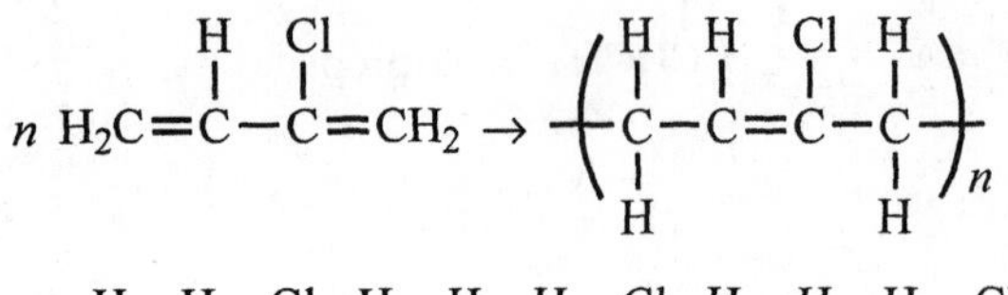

(b)

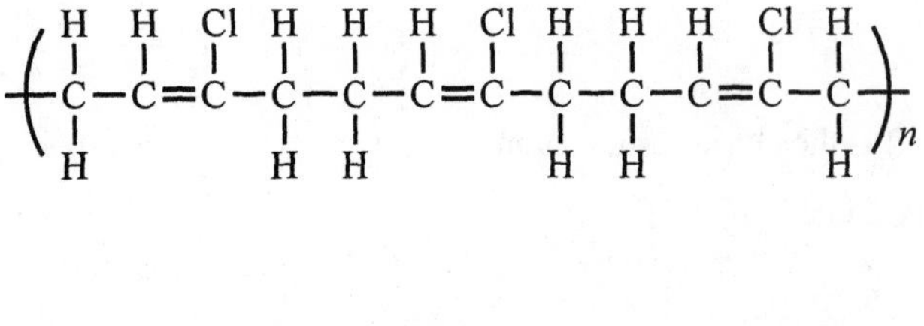

11.55

$$\left(\begin{array}{c} \text{Cl} \quad \text{H} \quad \text{H} \quad \text{Cl} \\ | \quad\; | \quad\; | \quad\; | \\ \text{C}-\text{C}-\text{C}-\text{C} \\ | \quad\; | \quad\; | \quad\; | \\ \text{Cl} \quad \text{H} \quad \text{H} \quad \text{H} \end{array}\right)_n$$

11.56

$$\left(\begin{array}{c} \text{H} \quad \text{CH}_3 \quad \text{H} \quad \text{CH}_3 \quad \text{H} \quad \text{CH}_3 \quad \text{H} \quad \text{CH}_3 \\ | \quad\; | \quad\quad | \quad\; | \quad\quad | \quad\; | \quad\quad | \quad\; | \\ \text{C}-\text{C}-\text{C}-\text{C}-\text{C}-\text{C}-\text{C}-\text{C} \\ | \quad\; | \quad\quad | \quad\; | \quad\quad | \quad\; | \quad\quad | \quad\; | \\ \text{H} \quad \text{O} \quad \text{H} \quad \text{O} \quad \text{H} \quad \text{O} \quad \text{H} \quad \text{O} \end{array}\right)_n$$

$$\text{O}=\text{C} \quad\; \text{O}=\text{C} \quad\; \text{O}=\text{C} \quad\; \text{O}=\text{C}$$
$$\quad\; | \quad\quad\quad\; | \quad\quad\quad\; | \quad\quad\quad\; |$$
$$\quad\; \text{CH}_3 \quad\quad \text{CH}_3 \quad\quad \text{CH}_3 \quad\quad \text{CH}_3$$

11.57 (a)

$$\begin{array}{cc} \text{Cl} \quad\quad \text{Cl} \\ \diagdown \quad\;\; \diagup \\ \text{C}=\text{C} \\ \diagup \quad\;\; \diagdown \\ \text{H} \quad\quad \text{H} \end{array} \qquad\qquad \begin{array}{cc} \text{Cl} \quad\quad \text{H} \\ \diagdown \quad\;\; \diagup \\ \text{C}=\text{C} \\ \diagup \quad\;\; \diagdown \\ \text{H} \quad\quad \text{Cl} \end{array}$$

$\qquad$ *cis* isomer $\qquad\qquad$ *trans* isomer

(b)

$$\begin{array}{cc} \text{H} \quad\quad \text{Cl} \\ \diagdown \quad\;\; \diagup \\ \text{C}=\text{C} \\ \diagup \quad\;\; \diagdown \\ \text{H} \quad\quad \text{Cl} \end{array}$$

11.58

$$\begin{array}{cc} \text{H} \quad\quad\quad\quad\quad\quad \text{H} \\ | \quad\quad\quad\quad\quad\quad | \\ \text{CH}_3\text{CH}_2 \;\text{C}\cdots\text{OH} \quad \text{HO}\cdots\text{C} \\ \quad\quad\quad \text{CH}_3 \quad\; \text{H}_3\text{C} \quad \text{CH}_2\text{CH}_3 \end{array}$$

The chiral C atom is the atom to which the OH group is attached. Mirror images of the molecule are not superimposable.

11.59 Three possible isomers:

$$\begin{array}{c} \text{H} \quad \text{H} \\ \diagdown \; \diagup \\ \text{H} \quad\; \text{C} \quad\; \text{CH}_3 \\ \diagdown \;\diagup \quad \diagdown \diagup \\ \text{H}-\text{C} \quad\quad \text{C}-\text{H} \\ | \quad\quad\quad\; | \\ \text{H}-\text{C}-\text{C}-\text{H} \\ | \quad\; | \\ \text{H} \quad \text{H} \end{array}$$

$$\text{CH}_3-\text{CH}=\text{CH}-\text{CH}_2-\text{CH}_2-\text{CH}_3 \qquad \begin{array}{c} \text{CH}_3 \\ | \\ \text{CH}_3-\text{CH}=\text{CH}-\text{CH}-\text{CH}_3 \end{array}$$

methylcyclopentane $\qquad\qquad$ 2-hexene $\qquad\qquad\qquad$ 4-methyl-2-pentene

None of these isomers are chiral.

11.60

$$\begin{array}{cc} \text{H}_3\text{C} \quad \text{CH}_3 \\ \diagdown \quad\; \diagup \\ \text{C}=\text{C} \\ \diagup \quad\; \diagdown \\ \text{H} \quad\quad \text{H} \end{array} \quad \begin{array}{cc} \text{H} \quad\quad \text{CH}_3 \\ \diagdown \quad\; \diagup \\ \text{C}=\text{C} \\ \diagup \quad\; \diagdown \\ \text{H}_3\text{C} \quad\; \text{H} \end{array} \quad \begin{array}{cc} \text{H} \quad\quad \text{CH}_3 \\ \diagdown \quad\; \diagup \\ \text{C}=\text{C} \\ \diagup \quad\; \diagdown \\ \text{H} \quad\quad \text{CH}_3 \end{array} \quad \begin{array}{cc} \text{H} \quad\quad \text{CH}_2\text{CH}_3 \\ \diagdown \quad\; \diagup \\ \text{C}=\text{C} \\ \diagup \quad\; \diagdown \\ \text{H} \quad\quad \text{H} \end{array}$$

$\quad$ *cis*-2-butene $\qquad\quad$ *trans*-2-butene $\qquad$ 2-methylpropene $\qquad\quad$ 1-butene

11.61 (a)
$$\underset{H_3C}{\overset{H}{>}}C=C\underset{CH_3}{\overset{H}{<}} + H_2O \rightarrow H-\underset{CH_3}{\overset{H}{\underset{|}{C}}}-\underset{CH_3}{\overset{OH}{\underset{|}{C}}}-H$$

(b)
$$\underset{H_3C}{\overset{H}{>}}C=C\underset{CH_3}{\overset{H}{<}} + HBr \rightarrow H-\underset{CH_3}{\overset{H}{\underset{|}{C}}}-\underset{CH_3}{\overset{Br}{\underset{|}{C}}}-H$$

(c)
$$\underset{H_3C}{\overset{H}{>}}C=C\underset{CH_3}{\overset{H}{<}} + Cl_2 \rightarrow H-\underset{CH_3}{\overset{Cl}{\underset{|}{C}}}-\underset{CH_3}{\overset{Cl}{\underset{|}{C}}}-H$$

11.62 (a) $CH_3CH_2CH_2\overset{O}{\overset{\|}{C}}-OH$ butanoic acid

(b) $CH_3\overset{O}{\overset{\|}{C}}CH_2CH_3$ 2-butanone

(c) NR

(d) $CH_3\underset{\underset{CH_3}{|}}{CH}\overset{O}{\overset{\|}{C}}-OH$ 2-methylpropanoic acid

11.63 (a) $H_3C-\overset{O}{\overset{\|}{C}}-OH + NaOH \rightarrow \left[H_3C-\overset{O}{\overset{\|}{C}}-O\right]^- Na^+ + H_2O$

(b) $H_3C-\underset{\underset{H}{|}}{\overset{\overset{H}{|}}{N}}-H + HCl \rightarrow \left[H_3C-\underset{\underset{H}{|}}{\overset{\overset{H}{|}}{N}}-H\right]^+ Cl^-$

11.64 (a) $H_3C-\overset{O}{\overset{\|}{C}}-OH + CH_3CH_2OH \rightarrow H_3C-\overset{O}{\overset{\|}{C}}-OCH_2CH_3$

(b)
$$\begin{array}{l} H_2C-O\overset{O}{\overset{\|}{C}}(CH_2)_{16}CH_3 \\ | \\ HC-O\overset{O}{\overset{\|}{C}}(CH_2)_{16}CH_3 \\ | \\ H_2C-O\overset{O}{\overset{\|}{C}}(CH_2)_{16}CH_3 \end{array} + 3\,H_2O \rightarrow \begin{array}{l} H_2COH \\ | \\ HCOH \\ | \\ H_2COH \end{array} + 3\,CH_3(CH_2)_{16}\overset{O}{\overset{\|}{C}}OH$$

11.65 (a) n styrene monomer $\rightarrow$ polystyrene repeat unit

(b) $n\ HOCH_2CH_2OH + n\ HOC$—⬡—$COH \rightarrow$ $\left(\!\!\begin{array}{c}O\\ \parallel\\ C\end{array}\!\!\right.$—⬡—$\left.\begin{array}{c}O\\ \parallel\\ COCH_2CH_2O\end{array}\!\!\right)_{\!n} + n\ H_2O$

11.66 (a)
$$C_6H_5\overset{\overset{\displaystyle O}{\parallel}}{\underset{\underset{\displaystyle H}{\mid}}{C}}NCH_3 + H_2O \rightarrow C_6H_5\overset{\overset{\displaystyle O}{\parallel}}{C}OH + H_2NCH_3$$

(b)
$$\left(\overset{\overset{\displaystyle O}{\parallel}}{C}-(CH_2)_4-\overset{\overset{\displaystyle O}{\parallel}}{C}-\overset{\overset{\displaystyle H}{\mid}}{N}-(CH_2)_6-\overset{\overset{\displaystyle H}{\mid}}{N}\right)_{\!x} + 2x\ H_2O \rightarrow x\ HO\overset{\overset{\displaystyle O}{\parallel}}{C}-(CH_2)_4-\overset{\overset{\displaystyle O}{\parallel}}{C}OH + x\ H_2N-(CH_2)_6-NH_2$$

11.67 (a)
$$H_3C-\overset{\overset{\displaystyle CH_3}{\mid}}{\underset{\underset{\displaystyle CH_3}{\mid}}{C}}-CH_2-CH_2-CH_3$$

(b)
$$H_3C-CH_2-\overset{\overset{\displaystyle CH_3}{\overset{\displaystyle \mid}{\overset{\displaystyle CH_2}{\mid}}}}{\underset{\underset{\displaystyle CH_3}{\underset{\displaystyle \mid}{\underset{\displaystyle CH_2}{\mid}}}}{C}}-CH_2-CH_3$$

(c)
$$H_3C-\overset{\overset{\displaystyle CH_3}{\mid}}{CH}-\overset{\overset{\displaystyle CH_2}{\overset{\displaystyle \mid}{\overset{\displaystyle CH_3}{\mid}}}}{CH}-CH_2-CH_3$$

(d)
$$H_3C-CH_2-\overset{}{\underset{\underset{\displaystyle CH_3}{\underset{\displaystyle \mid}{\underset{\displaystyle CH_2}{\mid}}}}{CH}}-CH_2-CH_2-CH_3$$

11.68 (a)

$CH_3CH_2CH_2-OH$ 1-propanol   primary alcohol

$CH_3\overset{\overset{\displaystyle OH}{\mid}}{CH}CH_3$ 2-propanol   secondary alcohol

$H_3C-O-CH_2CH_3$ ethylmethylether   ether

(b) $CH_3\overset{\overset{\displaystyle O}{\parallel}}{C}CH_2CH_3$ $CH_3CH_2CH_2\overset{\overset{\displaystyle O}{\parallel}}{C}H$

butanone   butanal

11.69

$\overset{\overset{\displaystyle Cl}{\mid}}{\underset{\underset{\displaystyle Cl}{\mid}}{HC}}-CH_2-CH_3$ $H_2\overset{\overset{\displaystyle Cl}{\mid}}{C}-\overset{\overset{\displaystyle Cl}{\mid}}{CH}-CH_3$ $H_2\overset{\overset{\displaystyle Cl}{\mid}}{C}-CH_2-\overset{\overset{\displaystyle Cl}{\mid}}{CH_2}$ $H_3C-\overset{\overset{\displaystyle Cl}{\mid}}{\underset{\underset{\displaystyle Cl}{\mid}}{C}}-CH_3$

1,1-dichloropropane   1,2-dichloropropane   1,3-dichloropropane   2,2-dichloropropane

11.70   Br
        HC—CH₂—CH₃
        |
        Cl

        Br Cl
        | |
        H₂C—CH—CH₃

        Cl Br
        | |
        H₂C—CH—CH₃

1-bromo-1-chloropropane   1-bromo-2-chloropropane   1-chloro-2-bromopropane

        Br   Cl
        | |
        H₂C—CH₂—CH₂

        Br
        |
        H₃C—C—CH₃
        |
        Cl

1-bromo-3-chlolorpropane   2-bromo-2-chloropropane

11.71

        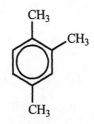

        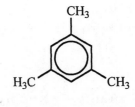

1,2,3-trimethylbenzene   1,2,4-trimethylbenzene   1,3,5-trimethylbenzene

11.72

1,2-dichlorobenzene   1,3-dichlorobenzene   1,4-dichlorobenzene

11.73   The —COOH group must be replaced with —H to convert lysine to cadaverine.

11.74
        O   O
        ‖   ‖
    ⬡—C—N—CH₂—C—OH
          |
          H

Hippuric acid is an acid because it contains a carboxylic acid group.

11.75   (a) CH₃CH₂CH₂CH₃   butane   not chiral

        (b) H
             |
        H₃C—C—CH₃
             |
             CH₃

11.76   (a) 2-pentanol   alcohol

        (b) 2-pentanone   ketone

        (c) 2-methylpropanoic acid   carboxylic acid

        (d) butanoic acid   carboxylic acid

11.77   (b) and (c)

11.78   (a) 1-propanol

$$\underset{OH}{}$$

(b) $CH_3\overset{\underset{|}{OH}}{C}HCH_3$ 2-propanol

(c) propene

(d) ethyl propanoate

11.79

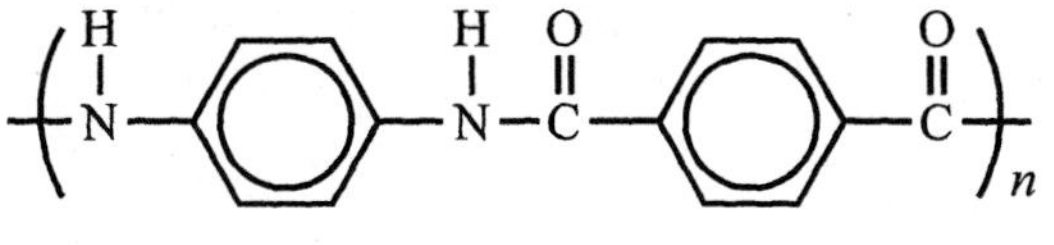

11.80

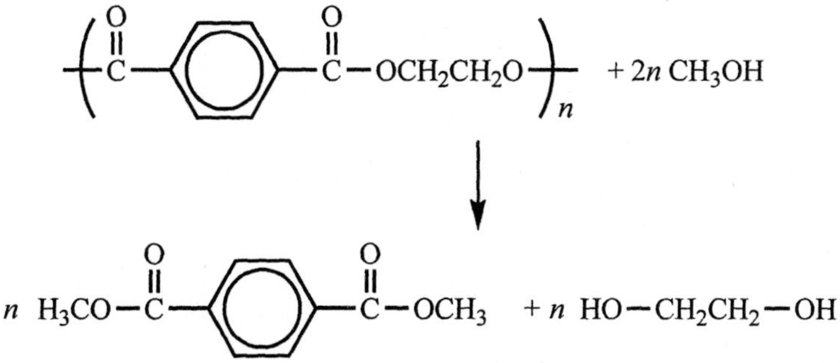

$+ 2n\ CH_3OH$

$n\ H_3CO-\overset{O}{\underset{\|}{C}}$ ⬡ $\overset{O}{\underset{\|}{C}}-OCH_3$ $+\ n\ HO-CH_2CH_2-OH$

11.81

$$\begin{array}{l} H_2C-O\overset{O}{\underset{\|}{C}}(CH_2)_{10}CH_3 \\ | \\ HC-O\overset{O}{\underset{\|}{C}}(CH_2)_{10}CH_3 \\ | \\ H_2C-O\overset{O}{\underset{\|}{C}}(CH_2)_{10}CH_3 \end{array}$$ The saponification products are glycerol and sodium laurate

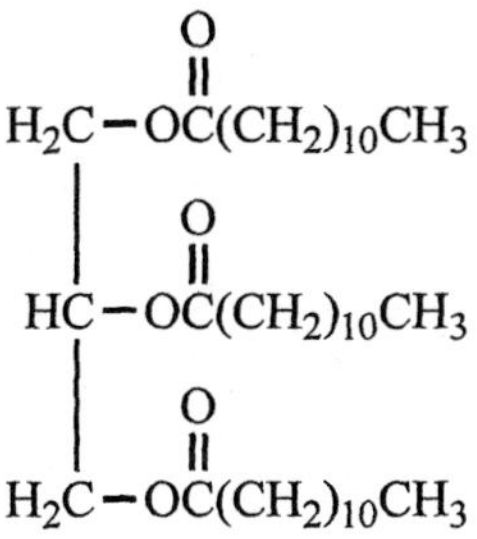

11.82

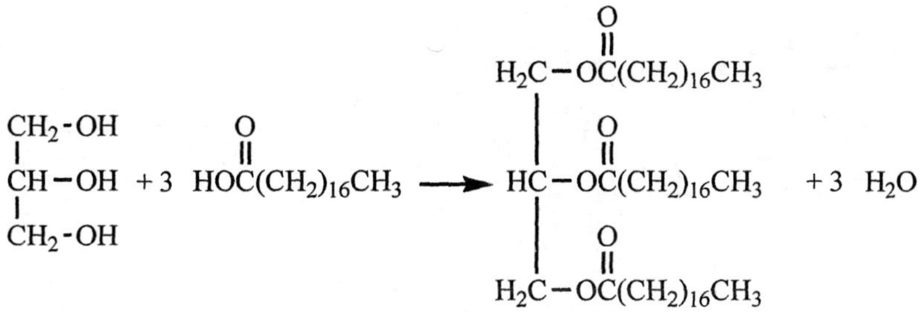

$$\begin{array}{l} CH_2\text{-}OH \\ | \\ CH-OH \\ | \\ CH_2\text{-}OH \end{array} + 3\ HO\overset{O}{\underset{\|}{C}}(CH_2)_{16}CH_3 \longrightarrow \begin{array}{l} H_2C-O\overset{O}{\underset{\|}{C}}(CH_2)_{16}CH_3 \\ | \\ HC-O\overset{O}{\underset{\|}{C}}(CH_2)_{16}CH_3 \\ | \\ H_2C-O\overset{O}{\underset{\|}{C}}(CH_2)_{16}CH_3 \end{array} + 3\ H_2O$$

11.83   The liquid is cyclohexene.

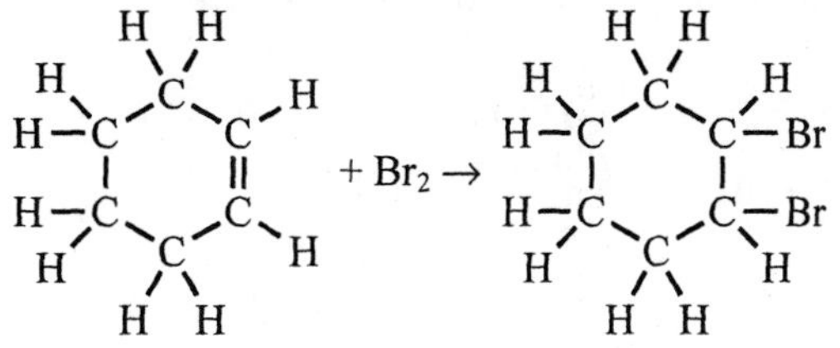

$+ Br_2 \rightarrow$

193

11.84

$$\underset{\text{2-methyl-1-propanol}}{CH_3\overset{\overset{\displaystyle H_3C}{|}}{C}HCH_2-OH} \qquad\qquad \underset{\text{2-methylpropanoic acid}}{CH_3\overset{\overset{\displaystyle H_3C}{|}}{C}H\overset{\overset{\displaystyle O}{||}}{C}OH}$$

11.85   (a) $\underset{\text{propanone}}{CH_3\overset{\overset{\displaystyle O}{||}}{C}CH_3} \qquad\qquad \underset{\text{propanal}}{CH_3CH_2\overset{\overset{\displaystyle O}{||}}{C}H}$

     (b) Only the aldehyde can be oxidized to a carboxylic acid. The correct structure is that of the aldehyde.

     (c) propanoic acid

11.86 $CH_3CH_2CH_2-OH \qquad CH_3\overset{\overset{\displaystyle OH}{|}}{C}HCH_3 \qquad H_3C-O-CH_2CH_3$

11.87 $H_2C=CH-\overset{\overset{\displaystyle CH_3}{|}}{\underset{\underset{\displaystyle CH_3}{|}}{C}}-CH_2-CH_3 \xrightarrow{\;+H_2O\;} H_3C-\overset{\overset{\displaystyle OH}{|}}{C}H-\overset{\overset{\displaystyle CH_3}{|}}{\underset{\underset{\displaystyle CH_3}{|}}{C}}-CH_2-CH_3$

             compound X   compound Y

$$H_3C-\overset{\overset{\displaystyle OH}{|}}{C}H-\overset{\overset{\displaystyle CH_3}{|}}{\underset{\underset{\displaystyle CH_3}{|}}{C}}-CH_2-CH_3 \xrightarrow[\text{agent}]{\text{oxidizing}} H_3C-\overset{\overset{\displaystyle O}{||}}{C}-\overset{\overset{\displaystyle CH_3}{|}}{\underset{\underset{\displaystyle CH_3}{|}}{C}}-CH_2-CH_3$$

11.88 $CH_3CH_2\overset{\overset{\displaystyle O}{||}}{C}-O-CH_3 \;+H_2O \rightarrow CH_3CH_2\overset{\overset{\displaystyle O}{||}}{C}-OH \;+\; HO-CH_3$

11.89   (a) $H_2C=CHCH_2OH \xrightarrow[\text{catalyst}]{+H_2} H_3C-CH_2CH_2OH$

     (b) $H_2C=CHCH_2OH \xrightarrow[\text{agent}]{\text{oxidizing}} H_2C=CH\overset{\overset{\displaystyle O}{||}}{C}OH$

     (c) $n\; H_2C=CHCH_2OH \longrightarrow \left(\!\!\begin{array}{c}\overset{\displaystyle H}{|}\;\;\overset{\displaystyle H}{|}\\ C-C\\ \underset{\displaystyle H}{|}\;\;\underset{\displaystyle CH_2OH}{|}\end{array}\!\!\right)_n$

     (d) $H_2C=CHCH_2OH + CH_3\overset{\overset{\displaystyle O}{||}}{C}OH \longrightarrow H_2C=CHCH_2O\overset{\overset{\displaystyle O}{||}}{C}CH_3 + H_2O$

11.90 $n\; HO-\overset{\overset{\displaystyle H_3C}{|}}{\underset{\underset{\displaystyle H}{|}}{C}}-\overset{\overset{\displaystyle O}{||}}{C}-OH \rightarrow \left(\!\!\begin{array}{c}\overset{\displaystyle H_3C}{|}\;\;\overset{\displaystyle O}{||}\\ C-C-O\\ \underset{\displaystyle H}{|}\end{array}\!\!\right)_n$

11.91

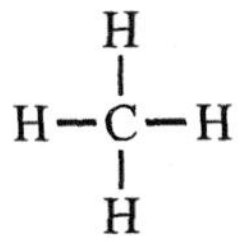

methane   four single bonds

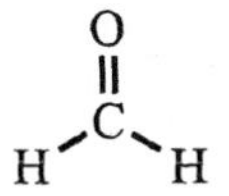

formaldehyde   one double bond and two single bonds

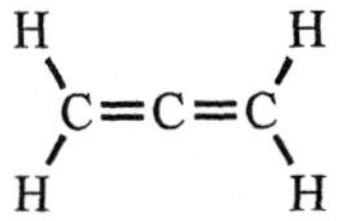

allene   two double bonds

H—C≡C—H   acetylene   one single bond and one triple bond

11.92   The restricted rotation around C=C double bonds is due to the π bond formed from overlap of unhybridized *p* orbitals on adjacent carbon atoms. Rotation around a C=C bond breaks this π bond, which requires more energy than rotation around a carbon-carbon sigma bond.

11.93   (a) Crosslinking makes the material is very rigid and inflexible.

(b) The OH groups gives the polymer a high affinity for water.

(c) Hydrogen bonding allows the chains to form coils and sheets with high tensile strength.

11.94 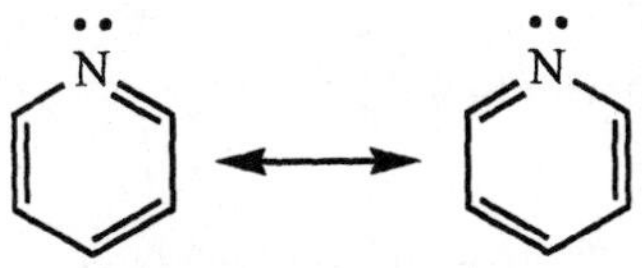   Pyridine is isoelectronic with benzene. A C—H group in benzene has been replaced by an N atom in pyridine. Both benzene and pyridine have two resonance structures.

195

11.95 $C_2H_6(g) + \frac{7}{2} O_2(g) \rightarrow 2 CO_2(g) + 3 H_2O(g)$

$C_2H_5OH(\ell) + 3 O_2(g) \rightarrow 2 CO_2(g) + 3 H_2O(g)$

(a) Ethane:

$\Delta H^{\circ}_{combustion} = 2 \Delta H_f^{\circ}[CO_2(g)] + 3 \Delta H_f^{\circ}[H_2O(g)] - \Delta H_f^{\circ}[C_2H_6(g)]$

$\Delta H^{\circ}_{combustion} = 2 \text{ mol } (-393.509 \text{ kJ/mol}) + 3 \text{ mol } (-241.83 \text{ kJ/mol}) - 1 \text{ mol } (-83.85 \text{ kJ/mol})$

$\Delta H^{\circ}_{combustion} = -1428.66 \text{ kJ}$

$\dfrac{-1428.66 \text{ kJ}}{1 \text{ mol } C_2H_6} \cdot \dfrac{1 \text{ mol } C_2H_6}{30.0694 \text{ g}} = -47.51 \text{ kJ/g } C_2H_6$

Ethanol:

$\Delta H^{\circ}_{combustion} = 2 \Delta H_f^{\circ}[CO_2(g)] + 3 \Delta H_f^{\circ}[H_2O(g)] - \Delta H_f^{\circ}[C_2H_5OH(\ell)]$

$\Delta H^{\circ}_{combustion} = 2 \text{ mol } (-393.509 \text{ kJ/mol}) + 3 \text{ mol } (-241.83 \text{ kJ/mol}) - 1 \text{ mol } (-277.0 \text{ kJ/mol})$

$\Delta H^{\circ}_{combustion} = -1235.5 \text{ kJ}$

$\dfrac{-1235.5 \text{ kJ}}{1 \text{ mol } C_2H_5OH} \cdot \dfrac{1 \text{ mol } C_2H_5OH}{46.0688 \text{ g}} = -26.82 \text{ kJ/g } C_2H_5OH$

Ethane has a more negative enthalpy of combustion per gram.

(b) The heat realized by combustion of ethanol is less negative, so partially oxidizing ethane to form ethanol decreases the amount of energy per mole available from combustion of the substance.

11.96   Cyclopentane will not react with bromine, while 1-pentene will react with bromine.

11.97   2-propanol will react with an oxidizing agent such as $KMnO_4$, while methyl ethyl ether will not. In addition, 2-propanol is soluble in water, while methyl ethyl ether is not.

11.98   Symbol   (a) polymer   (b) common use

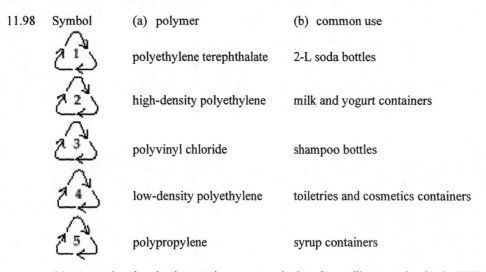

Symbol	(a) polymer	(b) common use
1	polyethylene terephthalate	2-L soda bottles
2	high-density polyethylene	milk and yogurt containers
3	polyvinyl chloride	shampoo bottles
4	low-density polyethylene	toiletries and cosmetics containers
5	polypropylene	syrup containers

(c) Assuming the plastic containers are crushed so they will not retain air, the PET plastics should sink in a water bath. HDPE and PP will float and can be skimmed off. By heating this mixture to approximately 140 °C, the HDPE will melt, allowing separation.

11.99 (a) $0.190 \text{ g CO}_2 \cdot \dfrac{1 \text{ mol CO}_2}{44.01 \text{ g}} \cdot \dfrac{1 \text{ mol C}}{1 \text{ mol CO}_2} = 0.00432 \text{ mol C}$

$0.00432 \text{ mol C} \cdot \dfrac{12.01 \text{ g}}{1 \text{ mol C}} = 0.0518 \text{ g C}$

$0.0388 \text{ g H}_2\text{O} \cdot \dfrac{1 \text{ mol H}_2\text{O}}{18.02 \text{ g}} \cdot \dfrac{2 \text{ mol H}}{1 \text{ mol H}_2\text{O}} = 0.00431 \text{ mol H}$

$0.00431 \text{ mol H} \cdot \dfrac{1.008 \text{ g}}{1 \text{ mol H}} = 0.00434 \text{ g H}$

$0.125 \text{ g acid} - 0.0518 \text{ g C} - 0.00434 \text{ g H} = 0.069 \text{ g O}$

$0.069 \text{ g O} \cdot \dfrac{1 \text{ mol O}}{16.0 \text{ g}} = 0.0043 \text{ mol O}$

$\dfrac{0.00432 \text{ mol C}}{0.0043 \text{ mol O}} = \dfrac{1 \text{ mol C}}{1 \text{ mol O}} \qquad\qquad \dfrac{0.00431 \text{ mol H}}{0.0043 \text{ mol O}} = \dfrac{1 \text{ mol H}}{1 \text{ mol O}}$

The empirical formula is CHO

(b) $0.03460 \text{ L} \cdot \dfrac{0.130 \text{ mol NaOH}}{1 \text{ L}} \cdot \dfrac{1 \text{ mol acid}}{2 \text{ mol NaOH}} = 0.00225 \text{ mol acid}$

$\dfrac{0.261 \text{ g}}{0.00225 \text{ mol}} = 116 \text{ g/mol}$

$\dfrac{116 \text{ g/mol}}{29.0 \text{ g/mol}} = 4 \qquad\qquad$ The molecular formula is $(CHO)_4$ or $C_4H_4O_4$

(c) $\text{HO} - \overset{\overset{\displaystyle O}{\|}}{C} - \underset{\underset{\displaystyle H}{|}}{C} = \underset{\underset{\displaystyle H}{|}}{C} - \overset{\overset{\displaystyle O}{\|}}{C} - \text{OH}$

(d) All four carbon atoms are sp^2 hybridized

(e) 120°

11.100 (a) The C atoms of benzene are sp^2 hybridized. The C atoms of cyclohexane, C_6H_{12}, are sp^3 hybridized.

(b) π electron delocalization can occur in benzene because each C atom has an unhybridized p orbital perpendicular to the ring. Overlap of these orbitals leads to alternating π bonds.

(c) Cyclohexane cannot be planar because the geometry around each C atom is tetrahedral with bond angles of 109°.

11.101 (a) $\text{H}_3\text{C} - \overset{\overset{\displaystyle Br}{|}}{\text{CH}} - \text{CH}_3 \qquad$ 2-bromopropane

(b) $\text{H}_3\text{C} - \overset{\overset{\displaystyle OH}{|}}{\underset{\underset{\displaystyle CH_3}{|}}{\text{C}}} - \text{CH}_2\text{CH}_3 \quad$ 2-methyl-2-butanol

(c) The product is the same.

11.102 (a) sp^3

      (b) sp^2

      (c) sp^2

      (d) sp^3

      (e) sp^3

11.103 (a) In a substitution reaction, one atom or group of atoms is substituted for another. In an elimination reaction, a small molecule is removed (eliminated) from a larger molecule.

      (b) The elimination reaction produces an alkene while the hydrogenation reaction has an alkene as a reactant. Both involve a small molecule, either H_2 or H_2O, being added to or eliminated from an organic molecule.

11.104 (a) addition

      (b) Oils generally have C=C double bonds in the long carbon chains of the fatty acids. Fats tend to have only C–C single bonds in these carbon chains (and the acid residues in fats are called saturated fatty acids).

      (c) As noted in (b), oils have unsaturated fatty acids, which makes the fatty acid chains less flexible.

11.105 (a) Double bonds.

      (b) Termination occurred when the chain reached 14 atoms. It could have been terminated earlier than this, or the chain could have continued to grow.

      (c) The termination step

      (d) Addition

11.106 (a) The molecule must contain two reactive groups, such as OH, NH, or OCl groups.

      (b) The material is white and consists of a single long strand of polymer

      (c) The two molecules combined to make nylon-6,6 each contain 6 carbon atoms.

Chapter 12
Gases and Their Properties

INSTRUCTOR'S NOTES

It is important to emphasize that *this chapter can be used almost anywhere in the sequence of topics, as long as the basic ideas of stoichiometry have been covered.* However, it works well to place it after the first 11 chapters since we can then make a very nice connection between the phases of matter by covering the chapters on gases, liquids and solids, and solutions in that order.

At the beginning of this series of topics we take the opportunity to emphasize two reasons for studying gases and their behavior:

- There are gases in the atmosphere - in every breathe we take! - and many common gases are commercially important. Therefore we must understand how to deal with them conceptually and mathematically.

- The behavior of gases is well understood and can be modeled. This has two benefits:

  a) This has led to a better understanding of other aspects of the physical world (such as the energy distribution in liquids).

  b) It is important to recognize that nature and some aspects of social behavior can be subjected to mathematical models, an approach that is important in business and industry today.

Another very useful point to make is that one can clearly see the difference between a law (the ideal gas law and the laws on which it is based) and a theory (the kinetic molecular theory).

When discussing nonideal gases, we make the point that intermolecular forces play an important role, so it is a natural transition to move from there to the discussion of liquids and solids in the next chapter.

Three to four lectures are normally given on this material.

SUGGESTED DEMONSTRATIONS

1. General Gas Demonstrations
   - deGrys, H. "Thirty Feet and Rising: Constructing and Using a Water Barometer to Explore Chemical Principles," *Journal of Chemical Education* **2003**, *80*, 1156.
   - Campbell, D. J. "An Alcohol Rocket Car—A Variation on the 'Whoosh Bottle' Theme," *Journal of Chemical Education* **2001**, *78*, 910.
   - Bare, W. D.; Andrews, L. "A Demonstration of Ideal Gas Principles Using a Football," *Journal of Chemical Education* **1999**, *76*, 622.
   - Corkern, W. H.; Hughes, E., Jr. "The Methane Balloon," *Journal of Chemical Education* **1999**, *76*, 794.
   - For a list of 26 demonstrations on "The Physical Behavior of Gases," see Shakhashiri, B. Z. *Chemical Demonstrations: A Handbook for Teachers of Chemistry*; University of Wisconsin Press, 1985; Vol. 2.

2. Boyle's Law

- To demonstrate Boyle's law, bring a bicycle pump to lecture.

- Vitz, E. "Ammonia Can Crush," *Journal of Chemical Education* **1999**, *76*, 932.

- Meyers, R. D.; Yee, G. T. "A More Dramatic Container to Crush by Atmospheric Pressure," *Journal of Chemical Education* **1999**, *76*, 933.

- Shakhashiri, B. Z. "Collapsing Can," *Chemical Demonstrations: A Handbook for Teachers of Chemistry*; University of Wisconsin Press, 1985; Vol. 2, pp. 6-8.

- Boyle's law has been demonstrated in Figure 12.3 using a large syringe. Instead of lead shot in a beaker, one can also use a pile of textbooks to provide the pressure as described in Shakhashiri, B. Z. "Boyle's Law and the Mass of a Textbook," *Chemical Demonstrations: A Handbook for Teachers of Chemistry*; University of Wisconsin Press, 1985; Vol. 2, pp. 20-23. (For more on gas law demonstrations using syringes, see Davenport, D. *Journal of Chemical Education* **1962**, *39*, 252.)

3. Charles's Law

- A favorite demonstration with the students in shown in Figure 12.5. Perhaps 15–20 balloons are passed out to students at the beginning of the lecture, and they are asked to blow them up and tie them off. When the demonstration begins, each of these students comes to the front of the room and places the inflated balloon in a large beaker of liquid nitrogen. After all the balloons have been placed in the beaker, they are poured out again and reinflate to their original volume when warmed back to room temperature. (However, a few may break, as they become twisted when frozen.)

- Krnel, D.; Glazar, S. A. "'Experiment with a Candle' Without a Candle," *Journal of Chemical Education* **2001**, *78*, 914.

- Shakhashiri, B. Z. "Charles Law," *Chemical Demonstrations: A Handbook for Teachers of Chemistry*; University of Wisconsin Press, 1985; Vol. 2, pp. 28-32.

4. Avogadro's Law

- Shakhashiri, B. Z. "Avogadro's Hypothesis," *Chemical Demonstrations: A Handbook for Teachers of Chemistry*; University of Wisconsin Press, 1985; Vol. 2, pp. 44-47.

5. Density

- Figure 12.8a illustrates the relative densities of two gases and is an easy demonstration. This can also be used to illustrate diffusion, since He atoms diffuse from a balloon much faster than Ar or air (O_2 and N_2).

6. Molar Mass Determination

- Shakhashiri, B. Z. "Determination of the Molecular Mass of the Gas from a Butane Lighter," *Chemical Demonstrations: A Handbook for Teachers of Chemistry*; University of Wisconsin Press, 1985; Vol. 2, pp. 48-50.

7. Diffusion and Effusion

- Release a small quantity of a concentrated scent (rose, lavender, or lemon oil) at the beginning of the lecture. The scent will fill the room.

- Keller, P. C. "A Simple Apparatus to Demonstrate Differing Gas Diffusion Rates (Graham's Law)," *Journal of Chemical Education* **1990**, *67*, 160.

- Shakhashiri, B. Z. "Graham's Law of Diffusion," *Chemical Demonstrations: A Handbook for Teachers of Chemistry*; University of Wisconsin Press, 1985; Vol. 2, pp. 69-71.

- Shakhashiri, B. Z. "Graham's Law of Effusion," *Chemical Demonstrations: A Handbook for Teachers of Chemistry*; University of Wisconsin Press, 1985; Vol. 2, pp. 72-74.

SOLUTIONS TO STUDY QUESTIONS

12.1   (a) $440 \text{ mm Hg} \cdot \dfrac{1 \text{ atm}}{760 \text{ mm Hg}} = 0.58 \text{ atm}$

        (b) $0.58 \text{ atm} \cdot \dfrac{1.013 \text{ bar}}{1 \text{ atm}} = 0.59 \text{ bar}$

        (c) $440 \text{ mm Hg} \cdot \dfrac{101.325 \text{ kPa}}{760 \text{ mm Hg}} = 59 \text{ kPa}$

12.2 $210 \text{ mm Hg} \cdot \dfrac{1 \text{ atm}}{760 \text{ mm Hg}} = 0.28 \text{ atm}$

        $0.28 \text{ atm} \cdot \dfrac{1.013 \text{ bar}}{1 \text{ atm}} = 0.28 \text{ bar}$

        $210 \text{ mm Hg} \cdot \dfrac{101.325 \text{ kPa}}{760 \text{ mm Hg}} = 28 \text{ kPa}$

12.3   (a) $534 \text{ mm Hg} \cdot \dfrac{1.013 \text{ bar}}{760 \text{ atm}} = 0.71 \text{ bar}$ 0.754 is the higher pressure

        (b) $534 \text{ mm Hg} \cdot \dfrac{101.325 \text{ kPa}}{760 \text{ mm Hg}} = 71.2 \text{ kPa}$ 650 kPa is the higher pressure

        (c) $1.34 \text{ bar} \cdot \dfrac{1 \times 10^2 \text{ kPa}}{1 \text{ bar}} = 134 \text{ kPa}$ 934 kPa is the higher pressure

12.4 $363 \text{ mm Hg} \cdot \dfrac{1 \text{ atm}}{760 \text{ mm Hg}} = 0.478 \text{ atm}$

        $363 \text{ kPa} \cdot \dfrac{1 \text{ atm}}{101.325 \text{ kPa}} = 3.58 \text{ atm}$

        $0.523 \text{ bar} \cdot \dfrac{1 \text{ atm}}{1.013 \text{ bar}} = 0.516 \text{ atm}$

        $0.256 \text{ atm} < 363 \text{ mm Hg} < 0.523 \text{ bar} < 363 \text{ kPa}$

12.5 $P_2 = \dfrac{P_1 V_1}{V_2} = \dfrac{(67.5 \text{ mm Hg})(500. \text{ mL})}{125 \text{ mL}} = 270. \text{ mm Hg}$

12.6 $V_2 = \dfrac{P_1 V_1}{P_2} = \dfrac{(56.5 \text{ mm Hg})(125 \text{ mL})}{62.3 \text{ mm Hg}} = 113 \text{ mL}$

12.7 $V_2 = T_2 \left(\dfrac{V_1}{T_1} \right) = (310. \text{ K}) \left(\dfrac{3.5 \text{ L}}{295.2 \text{ K}} \right) = 3.7 \text{ L}$

12.8 $V_2 = T_2 \left(\dfrac{V_1}{T_1} \right) = (273 \text{ K}) \left(\dfrac{5.0 \text{ mL}}{295 \text{ K}} \right) = 4.6 \text{ mL}$

12.9 $P_2 = P_1 \left(\dfrac{V_1}{V_2} \right) \left(\dfrac{T_2}{T_1} \right) = (380 \text{ mm Hg}) \left(\dfrac{3.6 \text{ L}}{5.0 \text{ L}} \right) \left(\dfrac{273.2 \text{ K}}{298 \text{ K}} \right) = 250 \text{ mm Hg}$

12.10 $V_2 = V_1 \left(\dfrac{P_1}{P_2}\right)\left(\dfrac{T_2}{T_1}\right) = (25.0 \text{ mL})\left(\dfrac{436.5 \text{ mm Hg}}{94.3 \text{ mm Hg}}\right)\left(\dfrac{297.7 \text{ K}}{293.7 \text{ K}}\right) = 117 \text{ mL}$

12.11 $P_2 = P_1 \left(\dfrac{T_2}{T_1}\right) = (360 \text{ mm Hg})\left(\dfrac{268.2 \text{ K}}{298.7 \text{ K}}\right) = 320 \text{ mm Hg}$

12.12 $P_2 = P_1 \left(\dfrac{V_1}{V_2}\right)\left(\dfrac{T_2}{T_1}\right) = (165 \text{ mm Hg})\left(\dfrac{135 \text{ mL}}{252 \text{ mL}}\right)\left(\dfrac{273.2 \text{ K}}{295.7 \text{ K}}\right) = 81.7 \text{ mm Hg}$

12.13 $P_2 = P_1 \left(\dfrac{V_1}{V_2}\right)\left(\dfrac{T_2}{T_1}\right) = (1.00 \text{ atm})\left(\dfrac{400. \text{ cm}^3}{50.0 \text{ cm}^3}\right)\left(\dfrac{350. \text{ K}}{288 \text{ K}}\right) = 9.72 \text{ atm}$

12.14 $V_2 = V_1 \left(\dfrac{P_1}{P_2}\right)\left(\dfrac{T_2}{T_1}\right) = (1.2 \times 10^7 \text{ L})\left(\dfrac{737 \text{ mm Hg}}{600. \text{ mm Hg}}\right)\left(\dfrac{240. \text{ K}}{289.2 \text{ K}}\right) = 1.2 \times 10^7 \text{ L}$

The volume of gas is nearly the same (to 2 significant figures) at the higher altitude.

12.15   (a) $150 \text{ mL NO} \cdot \dfrac{1 \text{ L O}_2}{2 \text{ L NO}} = 75 \text{ mL O}_2$

　　　　(b) $150 \text{ mL NO} \cdot \dfrac{2 \text{ L NO}_2}{2 \text{ L NO}} = 150 \text{ mL NO}_2$

12.16 $5.2 \text{ L C}_2\text{H}_6 \cdot \dfrac{7 \text{ L O}_2}{2 \text{ L C}_2\text{H}_6} = 18 \text{ L O}_2$

　　　　$5.2 \text{ L C}_2\text{H}_6 \cdot \dfrac{6 \text{ L H}_2\text{O}}{2 \text{ L C}_2\text{H}_6} = 16 \text{ L H}_2\text{O}$

12.17 $1.25 \text{ g} \cdot \dfrac{1 \text{ mol CO}_2}{44.01 \text{ g}} = 0.0284 \text{ mol CO}_2$

　　　　$750. \text{ mL} \cdot \dfrac{1 \text{ L}}{10^3 \text{ mL}} = 0.750 \text{ L}$

　　　　$P = \dfrac{nRT}{V} = \dfrac{(0.0284 \text{ mol})(0.082057 \text{ L} \cdot \text{atm/K} \cdot \text{mol})(295.7 \text{ K})}{0.750 \text{ L}} = 0.919 \text{ atm}$

12.18 $30.0 \text{ kg} \cdot \dfrac{1000 \text{ g}}{1 \text{ kg}} \cdot \dfrac{1 \text{ mol He}}{4.003 \text{ g}} = 7490 \text{ mol He}$

　　　　$V = \dfrac{nRT}{P} = \dfrac{(7490 \text{ mol})(0.082057 \text{ L} \cdot \text{atm/K} \cdot \text{mol})(295 \text{ K})}{1.20 \text{ atm}} = 1.51 \times 10^5 \text{ L}$

12.19 $2.2 \text{ g} \cdot \dfrac{1 \text{ mol CO}_2}{44.0 \text{ g}} = 0.050 \text{ mol CO}_2$

　　　　$313 \text{ mm Hg} \cdot \dfrac{1 \text{ atm}}{760 \text{ mm Hg}} = 0.418 \text{ atm}$

　　　　$V = \dfrac{nRT}{P} = \dfrac{(0.050 \text{ mol})(0.082057 \text{ L} \cdot \text{atm/K} \cdot \text{mol})(295 \text{ K})}{0.418 \text{ atm}} = 2.9 \text{ L}$

12.20 $1.50 \text{ g} \cdot \dfrac{1 \text{ mol } C_2H_5OH}{46.07 \text{ g}} = 0.0326 \text{ mol } C_2H_5OH$

$251 \text{ cm}^3 \cdot \dfrac{1 \text{ mL}}{1 \text{ cm}^3} \cdot \dfrac{1 \text{ L}}{10^3 \text{ mL}} = 0.251 \text{ L}$

$P = \dfrac{nRT}{V} = \dfrac{(0.0326 \text{ mol } C_2H_5OH)(0.082057 \text{ L} \cdot \text{atm/K} \cdot \text{mol})(520 \text{ K})}{0.251 \text{ L}} = 5.6 \text{ atm}$

12.21 $737 \text{ mm Hg} \cdot \dfrac{1 \text{ atm}}{760 \text{ mm Hg}} = 0.970 \text{ atm}$

$n = \dfrac{PV}{RT} = \dfrac{(0.970 \text{ atm})(1.2 \times 10^7 \text{ L})}{(0.082057 \text{ L} \cdot \text{atm/K} \cdot \text{mol})(298 \text{ K})} = 4.8 \times 10^5 \text{ mol He}$

$4.8 \times 10^5 \text{ mol He} \cdot \dfrac{4.00 \text{ g}}{1 \text{ mol He}} = 1.9 \times 10^6 \text{ g He}$

12.22 $n = \dfrac{PV}{RT} = \dfrac{(1.1 \text{ atm})(5.0 \text{ L})}{(0.082057 \text{ L} \cdot \text{atm/K} \cdot \text{mol})(298 \text{ K})} = 0.22 \text{ mol He}$

$0.22 \text{ mol He} \cdot \dfrac{4.00 \text{ g}}{1 \text{ mol He}} = 0.88 \text{ g He}$

12.23 $0.20 \text{ mm Hg} \cdot \dfrac{1 \text{ atm}}{760 \text{ mm Hg}} = 2.6 \times 10^{-4} \text{ atm}$

$d = \dfrac{PM}{RT} = \dfrac{(2.6 \times 10^{-4} \text{ atm})(28.96 \text{ g/mol})}{(0.082057 \text{ L} \cdot \text{atm/K} \cdot \text{mol})(250 \text{ K})} = 3.7 \times 10^{-4} \text{ g/L}$

12.24 $233 \text{ mm Hg} \cdot \dfrac{1 \text{ atm}}{760 \text{ mm Hg}} = 0.307 \text{ atm}$

$d = \dfrac{PM}{RT} = \dfrac{(0.307 \text{ atm})(74.12 \text{ g/mol})}{(0.082057 \text{ L} \cdot \text{atm/K} \cdot \text{mol})(298 \text{ K})} = 0.929 \text{ g/L}$

12.25 $189 \text{ mm Hg} \cdot \dfrac{1 \text{ atm}}{760 \text{ mm Hg}} = 0.249 \text{ atm}$

$M = \dfrac{dRT}{P} = \dfrac{(0.355 \text{ g/L})(0.082057 \text{ L} \cdot \text{atm/K} \cdot \text{mol})(290. \text{ K})}{0.249 \text{ atm}} = 34.0 \text{ g/mol}$

12.26 $195 \text{ mm Hg} \cdot \dfrac{1 \text{ atm}}{760 \text{ mm Hg}} = 0.257 \text{ atm}$

$M = \dfrac{dRT}{P} = \dfrac{(1.25 \text{ g/L})(0.082057 \text{ L} \cdot \text{atm/K} \cdot \text{mol})(298.2 \text{ K})}{0.257 \text{ atm}} = 119 \text{ g/mol}$

12.27 $d = \dfrac{1.007 \text{ g}}{0.452 \text{ L}} = 2.23 \text{ g/L}$

$715 \text{ mm Hg} \cdot \dfrac{1 \text{ atm}}{760 \text{ mm Hg}} = 0.941 \text{ atm}$

$M = \dfrac{dRT}{P} = \dfrac{(2.23 \text{ g/L})(0.082057 \text{ L} \cdot \text{atm/K} \cdot \text{mol})(296 \text{ K})}{0.941 \text{ atm}} = 57.5 \text{ g/mol}$

12.28 $d = \dfrac{0.0125 \text{ g}}{0.165 \text{ L}} = 0.0758 \text{ g/L}$

13.7 mm Hg $\cdot$ $\dfrac{1 \text{ atm}}{760 \text{ mm Hg}} = 0.0180 \text{ atm}$

$M = \dfrac{dRT}{P} = \dfrac{(0.0758 \text{ g/L})(0.082057 \text{ L} \cdot \text{atm/K} \cdot \text{mol})(295.7 \text{ K})}{0.0180 \text{ atm}} = 102 \text{ g/mol}$

$\dfrac{102 \text{ g/mol}}{51 \text{ g/mol}} = 2$ The molecular formula is $(CHF_2)_2$ or $C_2H_2F_4$

12.29 $d = \dfrac{12.5 \times 10^{-3} \text{ g}}{0.125 \text{ L}} = 0.100 \text{ g/L}$

24.8 mm Hg $\cdot$ $\dfrac{1 \text{ atm}}{760 \text{ mm Hg}} = 0.0326 \text{ atm}$

$M = \dfrac{dRT}{P} = \dfrac{(0.100 \text{ g/L})(0.082057 \text{ L} \cdot \text{atm/K} \cdot \text{mol})(298 \text{ K})}{0.0326 \text{ atm}} = 74.9 \text{ g/mol}$

(d) B_6H_{10}

12.30 $d = \dfrac{0.107 \text{ g}}{0.125 \text{ L}} = 0.856 \text{ g/L}$

331 mm Hg $\cdot$ $\dfrac{1 \text{ atm}}{760 \text{ mm Hg}} = 0.436 \text{ atm}$

$M = \dfrac{dRT}{P} = \dfrac{(0.856 \text{ g/L})(0.082057 \text{ L} \cdot \text{atm/K} \cdot \text{mol})(273.2 \text{ K})}{0.436 \text{ atm}} = 44.1 \text{ g/mol}$

12.31   2.2 g $\cdot$ $\dfrac{1 \text{ mol Fe}}{55.9 \text{ g}}$ $\cdot$ $\dfrac{1 \text{ mol H}_2}{1 \text{ mol Fe}} = 0.039 \text{ mol H}_2$

$P = \dfrac{nRT}{V} = \dfrac{(0.039 \text{ mol})(0.082057 \text{ L} \cdot \text{atm/K} \cdot \text{mol})(298 \text{ K})}{10.0 \text{ L}} = 0.096 \text{ atm}$

12.32   356 mm Hg $\cdot$ $\dfrac{1 \text{ atm}}{760 \text{ mm Hg}} = 0.468 \text{ atm}$

425 mm Hg $\cdot$ $\dfrac{1 \text{ atm}}{760 \text{ mm Hg}} = 0.559 \text{ atm}$

$n = \dfrac{PV}{RT} = \dfrac{(0.468 \text{ atm})(5.20 \text{ L})}{(0.082057 \text{ L} \cdot \text{atm/K} \cdot \text{mol})(298 \text{ K})} = 0.0996 \text{ mol SiH}_4$

0.0996 mol SiH_4 $\cdot$ $\dfrac{2 \text{ mol O}_2}{1 \text{ mol SiH}_4} = 0.199 \text{ mol O}_2$

$V = \dfrac{nRT}{P} = \dfrac{(0.199 \text{ mol O}_2)(0.082057 \text{ L} \cdot \text{atm/K} \cdot \text{mol})(298 \text{ K})}{0.559 \text{ atm}} = 8.71 \text{ L}$

12.33 $n = \dfrac{PV}{RT} = \dfrac{(1.3 \text{ atm})(75.0 \text{ L})}{(0.082057 \text{ L} \cdot \text{atm/K} \cdot \text{mol})(298 \text{ K})} = 4.0 \text{ mol N}_2$

4.0 mol N_2 $\cdot$ $\dfrac{2 \text{ mol NaN}_3}{3 \text{ mol N}_2}$ $\cdot$ $\dfrac{65.0 \text{ g}}{1 \text{ mol NaN}_3} = 170 \text{ g NaN}_3$

12.34 $0.095 \text{ g} \cdot \dfrac{1 \text{ mol } C_8H_{18}}{114 \text{ g}} = 8.3 \times 10^{-4} \text{ mol } C_8H_{18}$

$8.3 \times 10^{-4} \text{ mol } C_8H_{18} \cdot \dfrac{18 \text{ mol } H_2O}{2 \text{ mol } C_8H_{18}} = 0.0075 \text{ mol } H_2O$

$P_{H_2O} = \dfrac{n_{H_2O} RT}{V} = \dfrac{(0.0075 \text{ mol } H_2O)(0.082057 \text{ L} \cdot \text{atm/K} \cdot \text{mol})(303.2 \text{ K})}{4.75 \text{ L}} = 0.039 \text{ atm}$

$8.3 \times 10^{-4} \text{ mol } C_8H_{18} \cdot \dfrac{25 \text{ mol } O_2}{2 \text{ mol } C_6H_6} = 0.010 \text{ mol } O_2$

$P_{O_2} = \dfrac{n_{O_2} RT}{V} = \dfrac{(0.010 \text{ mol } O_2)(0.082057 \text{ L} \cdot \text{atm/K} \cdot \text{mol})(295 \text{ K})}{4.75 \text{ L}} = 0.053 \text{ atm}$

12.35 $1.00 \times 10^3 \text{ g} \cdot \dfrac{1 \text{ mol } N_2H_4}{32.05 \text{ g}} \cdot \dfrac{1 \text{ mol } O_2}{1 \text{ mol } N_2H_4} = 31.2 \text{ mol } O_2$

$P = \dfrac{nRT}{V} = \dfrac{(31.2 \text{ mol})(0.082057 \text{ L} \cdot \text{atm/K} \cdot \text{mol})(296 \text{ K})}{450 \text{ L}} = 1.7 \text{ atm}$

12.36 $767 \text{ mm Hg} \cdot \dfrac{1 \text{ atm}}{760 \text{ mm Hg}} = 1.01 \text{ atm}$

$n = \dfrac{PV}{RT} = \dfrac{(1.01 \text{ atm})(8.90 \text{ L})}{(0.082057 \text{ L} \cdot \text{atm/K} \cdot \text{mol})(295.2 \text{ K})} = 0.371 \text{ mol } CO_2$

$0.371 \text{ mol } CO_2 \cdot \dfrac{4 \text{ mol } KO_2}{2 \text{ mol } CO_2} \cdot \dfrac{71.10 \text{ g}}{1 \text{ mol } KO_2} = 52.7 \text{ g } KO_2$

12.37 $1.0 \text{ g} \cdot \dfrac{1 \text{ mol } H_2}{2.02 \text{ g}} = 0.50 \text{ mol } H_2$

$8.0 \text{ g} \cdot \dfrac{1 \text{ mol Ar}}{39.9 \text{ g}} = 0.20 \text{ mol Ar}$

$P_{H_2} = \dfrac{n_{H_2} RT}{V} = \dfrac{(0.50 \text{ mol})(0.082057 \text{ L} \cdot \text{atm/K} \cdot \text{mol})(300. \text{ K})}{3.0 \text{ L}} = 4.1 \text{ atm}$

$P_{Ar} = \dfrac{n_{Ar} RT}{V} = \dfrac{(0.20 \text{ mol})(0.082057 \text{ L} \cdot \text{atm/K} \cdot \text{mol})(300. \text{ K})}{3.0 \text{ L}} = 1.6 \text{ atm}$

$P_{total} = 4.1 \text{ atm} + 1.6 \text{ atm} = 5.7 \text{ atm}$

12.38 $\%N = 100.0 - (4.5\% \ H_2S + 3.0\% \ CO_2) = 92.5\% \ N$

The partial pressure of each gas is proportional to its percentage:

$P_{N_2} = (46 \text{ atm})(0.925) = 43 \text{ atm}$

$P_{H_2S} = (46 \text{ atm})(0.045) = 2.1 \text{ atm}$

$P_{CO_2} = (46 \text{ atm})(0.030) = 1.4 \text{ atm}$

12.39   (a) $\dfrac{\text{mol halothane}}{\text{mol } O_2} = \dfrac{170 \text{ mm Hg}}{570 \text{ mm Hg}} = 0.30$

(b) $160 \text{ g} \cdot \dfrac{1 \text{ mol } O_2}{32.0 \text{ g}} \cdot \dfrac{0.30 \text{ mol halothane}}{1 \text{ mol } O_2} \cdot \dfrac{197 \text{ g}}{1 \text{ mol halothane}} = 3.0 \times 10^2 \text{ g halothane}$

12.40   (a) $n = \dfrac{PV}{RT} = \dfrac{(1.00 \text{ atm})(12.5 \text{ L})}{(0.082057 \text{ L} \cdot \text{atm/K} \cdot \text{mol})(294.7 \text{ K})} = 0.517 \text{ mol He}$

$0.517 \text{ mol He} \cdot \dfrac{4.003 \text{ g}}{1 \text{ mol He}} = 2.07 \text{ g He}$

(b) $P = \dfrac{nRT}{V} = \dfrac{(0.517 \text{ mol He})(0.082057 \text{ L} \cdot \text{atm/K} \cdot \text{mol})(294.7 \text{ K})}{26 \text{ L}} = 0.48 \text{ atm}$

(c) $P_{O_2} = P_{\text{total}} - P_{He} = 1.00 \text{ atm} - 0.48 \text{ atm} = 0.52 \text{ atm}$

(d) $X_{He} = \dfrac{0.48 \text{ atm}}{1.00 \text{ atm}} = 0.48$ $X_{O_2} = \dfrac{0.52 \text{ atm}}{1.00 \text{ atm}} = 0.52$

12.41   (a)   The two gases are at the same temperature so the average kinetic energy per molecule is the same.

(b)   The molar mass of H_2 (2.02 g/mol) is less than the molar mass of CO_2 (44.0 g/mol). Flask A has molecules with higher average velocity.

(c)   At constant T and V, $n \propto P$. Flask B contains more molecules.

(d) $\dfrac{n_{H_2}}{n_{CO_2}} = \dfrac{(1 \text{ atm})(V)/(R)(273 \text{ K})}{(2 \text{ atm})(V)/(R)(298 \text{ K})} = \dfrac{0.5 \text{ mol H}_2}{1 \text{ mol CO}_2}$

1 mol CO_2 (44 g) has a greater mass than 0.5 mol H_2 (1.0 g). Flask B has a greater mass.

12.42   The molar mass of Ar (40 g/mol) is greater than the molar mass of N_2 (28 g/mol). Therefore, for samples with equal mass there are more moles of N_2 present than moles of Ar.

(a)   True. There are more moles of N_2 present, so there are more molecules of N_2 present.

(b)   False. Pressure is directly related to the number of moles of gas present. The pressure in the nitrogen flask is greater because there are more moles of N_2 present.

(c)   False. The gas with the smaller molar mass (N_2) will have a greater velocity than the gas with the greater molar mass (Ar).

(d)   True. The nitrogen molecules have a greater velocity than the argon molecules and there are more molecules of nitrogen present, so they will collide more frequently with the walls of the flask.

12.43 $\dfrac{\text{rms speed O}_2}{\text{rms speed CO}_2} = \dfrac{4.28 \times 10^4 \text{ cm/s}}{\sqrt{\overline{u^2}} \text{ (CO}_2)} = \sqrt{\dfrac{44.01 \text{ g/mol}}{32.00 \text{ g/mol}}}$

$\sqrt{\overline{u^2}} \text{ (CO}_2) = 3.65 \times 10^4 \text{ cm/s}$

12.44 $\sqrt{\overline{u^2}} = \sqrt{\dfrac{3RT}{M}} = \sqrt{\dfrac{3(8.3145 \text{ J/K} \cdot \text{mol})(298 \text{ K})}{28.01 \times 10^{-3} \text{ kg/mol}}} = 515 \text{ m/s}$

$\dfrac{\text{rms speed CO}}{\text{rms speed Ar}} = \sqrt{\dfrac{39.95 \text{ g/mol}}{28.01 \text{ g/mol}}} = 1.194$

12.45   Increasing average molecular speed: $CH_2F_2 < Ar < N_2 < CH_4$

molar mass (g/mol)   51   40   28   16

12.46   Increasing average molecular speed: $OSCl_2 < Cl_2O < Cl_2 < SO_2$

        molar mass (g/mol):   119   87   71   64

12.47   (a) F_2 (38 g/mol) effuses faster than CO_2 (44 g/mol).

        (b) N_2 (28 g/mol) effuses faster than O_2 (32 g/mol).

        (c) C_2H_4 (28.1 g/mol) effuses faster than C_2H_6 (30.1 g/mol).

        (d) $CFCl_3$ (137 g/mol) effuses faster than $C_2Cl_2F_4$ (171 g/mol).

12.48   He will effuse faster $\dfrac{\text{Rate of He effusion}}{\text{Rate of Ar effusion}} = \sqrt{\dfrac{39.9 \text{ g/mol}}{4.00 \text{ g/mol}}} = 3.16$ times faster

12.49 $\dfrac{\text{Rate of He effusion}}{\text{Rate of unknown gas effusion}} = \dfrac{\text{Rate of He effusion}}{1/3(\text{Rate of He effusion})} = \sqrt{\dfrac{\text{unknown gas molar mass}}{4.00 \text{ g/mol}}}$

        unknown gas molar mass = 36 g/mol

12.50 $\dfrac{\text{Rate of } I_2}{\text{Rate of uranium fluoride}} = \sqrt{\dfrac{M_{\text{uranium fluoride}}}{M_{I_2}}}$

        $\dfrac{\left(\dfrac{0.0150 \text{ g}}{1 \text{ hr}} \cdot \dfrac{1 \text{ mol } I_2}{253.8 \text{ g}}\right)}{\left(\dfrac{0.0177 \text{ mg}}{1 \text{ hr}} \cdot \dfrac{1}{M_{\text{uranium fluoride}}}\right)} = \sqrt{\dfrac{M_{\text{uranium fluoride}}}{253.8 \text{ g/mol}}}$

        $(0.00334)^2 (M_{\text{uranium fluoride}})^2 = \dfrac{M_{\text{uranium fluoride}}}{253.8 \text{ g/mol}}$

        $M_{\text{uranium fluoride}} = 353$ g/mol

12.51 $P_{\text{ideal}} = \dfrac{nRT}{V} = \dfrac{(8.00 \text{ mol})(0.082057 \text{ L} \cdot \text{atm/K} \cdot \text{mol})(300.2 \text{ K})}{4.00 \text{ L}} = 49.3$ atm

        $\left(P + a\left[\dfrac{n}{V}\right]^2\right)(V - bn) = nRT$

        $\left(P + (6.49 \text{ atm} \cdot \text{L}^2 / \text{mol}^2)\left[\dfrac{8.00 \text{ mol}}{4.00 \text{ L}}\right]^2\right)\left(4.00 \text{ L} - [0.0562 \text{ L/mol}][8.00 \text{ mol}]\right)$

                                                $= (8.00 \text{ mol})(0.082057 \text{ L} \cdot \text{atm/K} \cdot \text{mol})(300.2 \text{ K})$

        $P = 29.5$ atm

12.52 $165 \text{ g} \cdot \dfrac{1 \text{ mol CO}_2}{44.01 \text{ g}} = 3.75 \text{ mol CO}_2$

(a) $P = \dfrac{nRT}{V} = \dfrac{(3.75 \text{ mol})(0.082057 \text{ L} \cdot \text{atm/K} \cdot \text{mol})(298 \text{ K})}{12.5 \text{ L}} = 7.33 \text{ atm}$

(b) $\left(P + a \left[\dfrac{n}{V} \right]^2 \right) (V - bn) = nRT$

$\left(P + (3.59 \text{ atm} \cdot \text{L}^2 / \text{mol}^2) \left[\dfrac{3.75 \text{ mol}}{12.5 \text{ L}} \right]^2 \right) \left(12.5 \text{ L} - [0.0427 \text{ L/mol}][3.75 \text{ mol}] \right)$

$= (3.75 \text{ mol})(0.08206 \text{ L} \cdot \text{atm/K} \cdot \text{mol})(298 \text{ K})$

$P = 7.11 \text{ atm}$

12.53

	atm	mm Hg	kPa	bar
Standard atmosphere	1	760	101.325	1.013
Partial pressure of N_2 in the atmosphere	0.780	593	79.1	0.791
Tank of compressed H_2	131	99800	13300	133
Atmospheric pressure at the top of Mt. Everest	0.333	253	33.7	0.337

12.54 $V = \pi r^2 l = \pi \cdot (10.0 \text{ cm})^2 \cdot 20.0 \text{ m} \cdot \dfrac{10^2 \text{ cm}}{1 \text{ m}} \cdot \dfrac{1 \text{ mL}}{1 \text{ cm}^3} \cdot \dfrac{1 \text{ L}}{10^3 \text{ ml}} = 628 \text{ L}$

$865 \text{ mm Hg} \cdot \dfrac{1 \text{ atm}}{760 \text{ mm Hg}} = 1.14 \text{ atm}$

$n = \dfrac{(1.14 \text{ atm})(628 \text{ L})}{(0.082057 \text{ L} \cdot \text{atm/K} \cdot \text{mol})(298 \text{ K})} = 29.2 \text{ mol CO}_2$

$29.2 \text{ mol CO}_2 \cdot \dfrac{44.01 \text{ g}}{1 \text{ mol CO}_2} = 1290 \text{ g CO}_2$

12.55 $2.82 \text{ g H}_2\text{O} \cdot \dfrac{1 \text{ mol H}_2\text{O}}{18.02 \text{ g}} \cdot \dfrac{2 \text{ mol H}}{1 \text{ mol H}_2\text{O}} = 0.31 \text{ mol H}$

At STP, 1 mol of a gas occupies 22.414 L

$2.0 \text{ L CO}_2 \cdot \dfrac{1 \text{ mol CO}_2}{22.414 \text{ L}} \cdot \dfrac{1 \text{ mol C}}{1 \text{ mol CO}_2} = 0.089 \text{ mol C}$

$0.5 \text{ L N}_2 \cdot \dfrac{1 \text{ mol N}_2}{22.414 \text{ L}} \cdot \dfrac{2 \text{ mol N}}{1 \text{ mol N}_2} = 0.045 \text{ mol N}$

$\dfrac{0.31 \text{ mol H}}{0.045 \text{ mol N}} = \dfrac{7 \text{ mol H}}{1 \text{ mol N}}$ $\dfrac{0.089 \text{ mol C}}{0.045 \text{ mol N}} = \dfrac{2 \text{ mol C}}{1 \text{ mol N}}$ The empirical formula is C_2H_7N

12.56 $T_2 = V_2 \left(\dfrac{T_1}{V_1} \right) = (21.5 \text{ mL}) \left(\dfrac{360 \text{ K}}{25.5 \text{ mL}} \right) = 310 \text{ K} = 30 \text{ }^\circ\text{C}$

12.57 $\sqrt{\overline{u^2}} = \sqrt{\dfrac{3RT}{M}} = \sqrt{\dfrac{3(8.314 \text{ J/K} \cdot \text{mol})(240 \text{ K})}{0.00400 \text{ kg/mol}}} = 1220 \text{ m/s}$

New speed $= (1220 \text{ m/s})(1.10) = 1350 \text{ m/s}$

$1350 \text{ m/s} = \sqrt{\dfrac{3(8.314 \text{ J/K} \cdot \text{mol})T}{0.00400 \text{ kg/mol}}}$ $T = 290. \text{ K} = 17 \text{ °C}$

12.58 $n_2 = n_1\left(\dfrac{T_1}{T_2}\right)$ and $n = \dfrac{\text{mass (g)}}{32.00 \text{ g/mol}}$

$\text{mass}_2 = \text{mass}_1\left(\dfrac{T_1}{T_2}\right) = (12.0 \text{ g})\left(\dfrac{300. \text{ K}}{278.2 \text{ K}}\right) = 12.9 \text{ g}$

12.59

	Helium balloon	Hydrogen balloon
Volume	V	$2 \times V$
Pressure	2 atm	1 atm
Temperature	296 K	268 K

(a) $\dfrac{n_{\text{He}}}{n_{\text{H}_2}} = \dfrac{PV \,/\, RT}{PV \,/\, RT} = \dfrac{(2 \text{ atm})(V)/(R)(296 \text{ K})}{(1 \text{ atm})(2 \times V)/(R)(268 \text{ K})} = \dfrac{0.9 \text{ mol He}}{1 \text{ mol H}_2}$

There are more moles of H_2 than He, so there are more molecules of H_2 than He.

(b) Assume that the hydrogen balloon contains 1 mol (2.02 g) of H_2. This must mean that the helium balloon contains 0.9 mol (3.6 g) of He. Therefore, there is a greater mass of helium present.

12.60 $T = \dfrac{PV}{nR} = \dfrac{(7.25 \text{ atm})(1.52 \text{ L})}{(0.406 \text{ mol})(0.082057 \text{ L} \cdot \text{atm/K} \cdot \text{mol})} = 331 \text{ K} = 58 \text{ °C}$

12.61   Assume the Mars atmosphere behaves as an ideal gas.

$n = \dfrac{PV}{RT} = \dfrac{\left(8 \text{ mm Hg} \cdot \dfrac{1 \text{ atm}}{760 \text{ mm Hg}}\right)\left(10. \text{ m}^3 \cdot \dfrac{10^3 \text{ L}}{1 \text{ m}^3}\right)}{(0.082057 \text{ L} \cdot \text{atm/K} \cdot \text{mol})(300. \text{ K})} = 4 \text{ mol}$

12.62 $2.25 \text{ g} \cdot \dfrac{1 \text{ mol Si}}{28.09 \text{ g}} = 0.0801 \text{ mol Si}$

$n_{\text{CH}_3\text{Cl}} = \dfrac{\left(585 \text{ mm Hg} \cdot \dfrac{1 \text{ atm}}{760 \text{ mm Hg}}\right)(6.56 \text{ L})}{(0.082057 \text{ L} \cdot \text{atm/K} \cdot \text{mol})(298 \text{ K})} = 0.206 \text{ mol CH}_3\text{Cl}$

$\dfrac{0.206 \text{ mol CH}_3\text{Cl}}{0.0801 \text{ mol Si}} = \dfrac{2.58 \text{ mol CH}_3\text{Cl}}{1 \text{ mol Si}} > \dfrac{2 \text{ mol CH}_3\text{Cl}}{1 \text{ mol Si}}$ Si is the limiting reactant

$0.0801 \text{ mol Si} \cdot \dfrac{1 \text{ mol (CH}_3)_2\text{SiCl}_2}{1 \text{ mol Si}} \cdot \dfrac{129.1 \text{ g}}{1 \text{ mol (CH}_3)_2\text{SiCl}_2} = 10.3 \text{ g (CH}_3)_2\text{SiCl}_2$

$P_{(\text{CH}_3)_2\text{SiCl}_2} = \dfrac{(0.0801 \text{ mol})(0.082057 \text{ L} \cdot \text{atm/K} \cdot \text{mol})(368 \text{ K})}{6.56 \text{ L}} = 0.369 \text{ atm}$

12.63 $0.450 \text{ g} \cdot \dfrac{1 \text{ mol Ni}}{58.69 \text{ g}} = 0.00767 \text{ mol Ni}$

$n_{CO} = \dfrac{\left(418 \text{ mm Hg} \cdot \dfrac{1 \text{ atm}}{760 \text{ mm Hg}}\right)(1.50 \text{ L})}{(0.082057 \text{ L} \cdot \text{atm/K} \cdot \text{mol})(298.2 \text{ K})} = 0.0337 \text{ mol CO}$

$\dfrac{0.0337 \text{ mol CO}}{0.00767 \text{ mol Ni}} = \dfrac{4.40 \text{ mol CO}}{1 \text{ mol Ni}} > \dfrac{4 \text{ mol CO}}{1 \text{ mol Ni}}$ Ni is the limiting reactant

$0.00767 \text{ mol Ni} \cdot \dfrac{1 \text{ mol Ni(CO)}_4}{1 \text{mol Ni}} \cdot \dfrac{170.7 \text{ g}}{1 \text{ mol Ni(CO)}_4} = 1.31 \text{ g Ni(CO)}_4$

12.64   (a) $O_2 < B_2H_6 < H_2O$

(b) $P_{O_2} = 256 \text{ mm Hg} \cdot \dfrac{3 \text{ mol O}_2}{1 \text{ mol B}_2\text{H}_6} = 768 \text{ mm Hg}$

12.65   1. $1.0 \text{ L H}_2 \cdot \dfrac{1 \text{ mol H}_2}{22.414 \text{ L}} = 0.045 \text{ mol H}_2$

2. $1.0 \text{ L Ar} \cdot \dfrac{1 \text{ mol Ar}}{22.414 \text{ L}} = 0.045 \text{ mol Ar}$

3. $n = \dfrac{PV}{RT} = \dfrac{(1.0 \text{ atm})(1.0 \text{ L})}{(0.082057 \text{ L} \cdot \text{atm/K} \cdot \text{mol})(300. \text{ K})} = 0.041 \text{ mol H}_2$

4. $n = \dfrac{PV}{RT} = \dfrac{\left(900 \text{ mm Hg} \cdot \dfrac{1 \text{ atm}}{760 \text{ mm Hg}}\right)(1.0 \text{ L})}{(0.082057 \text{ L} \cdot \text{atm/K} \cdot \text{mol})(273 \text{ K})} = 0.05 \text{ mol He}$

(a) The number of molecules is proportional to number of moles, so sample 4 contains the greatest number of molecules.

(b) Sample 3 contains the smallest number of gas molecules.

(c) Argon has the greatest molar mass, so sample 2 contains the largest mass of gas ($0.045 \text{ mol Ar} \cdot 39.9 \text{ g/mol} = 1.8 \text{ g Ar}$).

12.66 $n_{\text{air}} = \dfrac{PV}{RT} = \dfrac{(3.2 \text{ atm})(17 \text{ L})}{(0.082057 \text{ L} \cdot \text{atm/K} \cdot \text{mol})(298 \text{ K})} = 2.2 \text{ mol air}$

$2.2 \text{ mol air} \cdot \dfrac{28.96 \text{ g}}{1 \text{ mol air}} = 64 \text{ g air}$

12.67 $P_{B_2H_6} = X_{B_2H_6} P_{\text{total}} = \dfrac{1 \text{ mol B}_2\text{H}_6}{4 \text{ mol total}} \cdot 228 \text{ mm Hg} = 57.0 \text{ mm Hg}$

$P_{O_2} = 228 \text{ mm Hg} - 57.0 \text{ mm Hg} = 171 \text{ mm Hg}$

When reaction is complete, H_2O is the only gas present in the flask. $P_{H_2O} = P_{O_2} = 171 \text{ mm Hg}$

12.68 $100.00\% - (11.79\% \text{ C} + 69.57\% \text{ Cl}) = 18.64\% \text{ F}$

Assume 100.00 g compound

$$11.79 \text{ g} \cdot \frac{1 \text{ mol C}}{12.011 \text{ g}} = 0.9816 \text{ mol C}$$

$$69.57 \text{ g} \cdot \frac{1 \text{ mol Cl}}{35.453 \text{ g}} = 1.962 \text{ mol Cl}$$

$$18.64 \text{ g} \cdot \frac{1 \text{ mol F}}{18.998 \text{ g}} = 0.9812 \text{ mol F}$$

$$\frac{0.9816 \text{ mol C}}{0.9812 \text{ mol F}} = \frac{1 \text{ mol C}}{1 \text{ mol F}} \qquad \frac{1.962 \text{ mol Cl}}{0.9812 \text{ mol F}} = \frac{2 \text{ mol Cl}}{1 \text{ mol F}} \qquad \text{The empirical formula is } CCl_2F$$

$$M = \frac{dRT}{P} = \frac{\left(\dfrac{0.107 \text{ g}}{0.458 \text{ L}}\right)(0.082057 \text{ L} \cdot \text{atm/K} \cdot \text{mol})(298 \text{ K})}{21.3 \text{ mm Hg} \cdot \dfrac{1 \text{ atm}}{760 \text{ mm Hg}}} = 204 \text{ g/mol}$$

$$\frac{204 \text{ g/mol}}{102 \text{ g/mol}} = 2 \qquad \text{The molecular formula is } (CCl_2F)_2 \text{ or } C_2Cl_4F_2$$

12.69 $$25.23 \text{ g} \cdot \frac{1 \text{ mol S}}{32.066 \text{ g}} = 0.7868 \text{ mol S}$$

$$74.77 \text{ g} \cdot \frac{1 \text{ mol F}}{18.998 \text{ g}} = 3.935 \text{ mol F}$$

$$\frac{3.935 \text{ mol F}}{0.7868 \text{ mol S}} = \frac{5 \text{ mol F}}{1 \text{ mol S}} \qquad \text{The empirical formula is } SF_5$$

$$M = \frac{dRT}{P} = \frac{\left(\dfrac{0.0955 \text{ g}}{0.089 \text{ L}}\right)(0.082057 \text{ L} \cdot \text{atm/K} \cdot \text{mol})(318 \text{ K})}{83.8 \text{ mm Hg} \cdot \dfrac{1 \text{ atm}}{760 \text{ mm Hg}}} = 254 \text{ g/mol}$$

$$\frac{254 \text{ g/mol}}{127 \text{ g/mol}} = 2 \qquad \text{The molecular formula is } (SF_5)_2 \text{ or } S_2F_{10}$$

12.70 $$0.95 \text{ g} \cdot \frac{1 \text{ mol } (NH_4)_2Cr_2O_7}{252 \text{ g}} \cdot \frac{5 \text{ mol gas}}{1 \text{ mol } (NH_4)_2Cr_2O_7} = 0.019 \text{ mol gas produced}$$

$$P_{\text{total}} = \frac{n_{\text{total}}RT}{V} = \frac{(0.018 \text{ mol})(0.082057 \text{ L} \cdot \text{atm/K} \cdot \text{mol})(296 \text{ K})}{15.0 \text{ L}} = 0.031 \text{ atm}$$

$$P_{N_2} = 0.031 \text{ atm} \cdot \frac{1 \text{ mol } N_2}{5 \text{ mol gas}} = 0.0061 \text{ atm}$$

$$P_{H_2O} = 0.031 \text{ atm} \cdot \frac{4 \text{ mol } H_2O}{5 \text{ mol gas}} = 0.024 \text{ atm}$$

12.71 $3.52 \text{ g} \cdot \dfrac{1 \text{ mol Fe}}{55.85 \text{ g}} = 0.0630 \text{ mol Fe}$

$$n_{CO} = \frac{PV}{RT} = \frac{\left(732 \text{ mm Hg} \cdot \dfrac{1 \text{ atm}}{760 \text{ mm Hg}}\right)(5.50 \text{ L})}{(0.082057 \text{ L} \cdot \text{atm/K} \cdot \text{mol})(296 \text{ K})} = 0.218 \text{ mol CO}$$

$\dfrac{0.218 \text{ mol CO}}{0.0630 \text{ mol Fe}} = \dfrac{3.46 \text{ mol CO}}{1 \text{ mol Fe}} < \dfrac{5 \text{ mol CO}}{1 \text{ mol Fe}}$ CO is the limiting reactant

$0.218 \text{ mol CO} \cdot \dfrac{1 \text{ mol Fe(CO)}_5}{5 \text{ mol CO}} \cdot \dfrac{195.9 \text{ g}}{1 \text{ mol Fe(CO)}_5} = 8.55 \text{ g Fe(CO)}_5$

12.72 $n_{N_2} = \dfrac{PV}{RT} = \dfrac{\left(713 \text{ mm Hg} \cdot \dfrac{1 \text{ atm}}{760 \text{ mm Hg}}\right)(0.295 \text{ L})}{(0.082057 \text{ L} \cdot \text{atm/K} \cdot \text{mol})(294.2 \text{ K})} = 0.0115 \text{ mol N}_2$

$0.0115 \text{ mol N}_2 \cdot \dfrac{1 \text{ mol NaNO}_2}{1 \text{ mol N}_2} \cdot \dfrac{69.00 \text{ g}}{1 \text{ mol NaNO}_2} = 0.791 \text{ g NaNO}_2$

$\dfrac{0.791 \text{ g NaNO}_2}{1.232 \text{ g sample}} \cdot 100\% = 64.2\%$

12.73   (a) $M = \dfrac{dRT}{P} = \dfrac{\left(\dfrac{92 \text{ g}}{1 \text{ m}^3} \cdot \dfrac{1 \text{ m}^3}{10^3 \text{ L}}\right)(0.082057 \text{ L} \cdot \text{atm/K} \cdot \text{mol})(210. \text{ K})}{42 \text{ mm Hg} \cdot \dfrac{1 \text{ atm}}{760 \text{ mm Hg}}} = 29 \text{ g/mol}$

(b) $X_{O_2} + X_{N_2} = 1$

$29 \text{ g/mol} = X_{O_2} \cdot \dfrac{32.0 \text{ g}}{1 \text{ mol O}_2} + (1 - X_{O_2}) \cdot \dfrac{28.0 \text{ g}}{1 \text{ mol N}_2}$

$X_{O_2} = 0.18$

$X_{N_2} = 0.82$

12.74   He: $P_2 = \dfrac{P_1 V_1}{V_2} = \dfrac{(145 \text{ mm Hg})(3.0 \text{ L})}{5.0 \text{ L}} = 87 \text{ mm Hg}$

Hg: $P_2 = \dfrac{P_1 V_1}{V_2} = \dfrac{(355 \text{ mm Hg})(2.0 \text{ L})}{5.0 \text{ L}} = 140 \text{ mm Hg}$

$P_{total} = 87 \text{ mm Hg} + 140 \text{ mm Hg} = 230 \text{ mm Hg}$

12.75 $7 \times 10^{-5} \text{ mg PH}_3 \cdot \dfrac{1 \text{ g}}{1000 \text{ mg}} \cdot \dfrac{1 \text{ mol PH}_3}{34 \text{ g}} = 2 \times 10^{-9} \text{ mol}$

$P = \dfrac{(2 \times 10^{-9} \text{ mol})(0.082057 \text{ L} \cdot \text{atm/K} \cdot \text{mol})(298 \text{ K})}{1 \text{ L}} = 5 \times 10^{-8} \text{ atm}$

12.76 $P_{F_2 \text{(consumed)}} = P_{\text{total}} - P_{Xe} - P_{F_2 \text{(unreacted)}} = 0.72 \text{ atm} - 0.12 \text{ atm} - 0.36 \text{ atm} = 0.24 \text{ atm}$

$$n_F = \frac{(0.24 \text{ atm})(0.25 \text{ L})}{(0.082057 \text{ L} \cdot \text{atm/K} \cdot \text{mol})(273.2 \text{ K})} \cdot \frac{2 \text{ mol F}}{1 \text{ mol F}_2} = 0.0054 \text{ mol F}$$

$$n_{Xe} = \frac{(0.12 \text{ atm})(0.25 \text{ L})}{(0.082057 \text{ L} \cdot \text{atm/K} \cdot \text{mol})(273.2 \text{ K})} = 0.0013 \text{ mol Xe}$$

$$\frac{0.0054 \text{ mol F}}{0.0013 \text{ mol Xe}} = \frac{4 \text{ mol F}}{1 \text{ mol Xe}} \qquad\qquad \text{The empirical formula is XeF}_4$$

12.77 $n = \dfrac{PV}{RT} = \dfrac{\left(17.2 \text{ mm Hg} \cdot \dfrac{1 \text{ atm}}{760 \text{ mm Hg}}\right)(1.850 \text{ L})}{(0.082057 \text{ L} \cdot \text{atm/K} \cdot \text{mol})(294 \text{ K})} = 0.00174 \text{ mol gas}$

$$M = \frac{0.150 \text{ g}}{0.00174 \text{ mol}} = 86.4 \text{ g/mol} \qquad\qquad \text{The gas is probably ClO}_2\text{F (86.4 g/mol)}$$

12.78   Helium pressure = gauge pressure + barometric pressure = 22 mm Hg + 755 mm Hg = 777 mm Hg

$$n = \frac{PV}{RT} = \frac{\left(777 \text{ mm Hg} \cdot \dfrac{1 \text{ atm}}{760 \text{ mm Hg}}\right)(0.305 \text{ L})}{(0.082057 \text{ L} \cdot \text{atm/K} \cdot \text{mol})(298 \text{ K})} = 0.0128 \text{ mol He}$$

12.79   Theoretical yield of acetylene:

$$2.65 \text{ g} \cdot \frac{1 \text{ mol CaC}_2}{64.10 \text{ g}} \cdot \frac{1 \text{ mol C}_2\text{H}_2}{1 \text{ mol CaC}_2} = 0.0413 \text{ mol C}_2\text{H}_2$$

Actual yield of acetylene:

$$n_{C_2H_2} = \frac{\left(735.2 \text{ mm Hg} \cdot \dfrac{1 \text{ atm}}{760 \text{ mm Hg}}\right)(0.795 \text{ L})}{(0.082057 \text{ L} \cdot \text{atm/K} \cdot \text{mol})(298.4 \text{ K})} = 0.0314 \text{ mol C}_2\text{H}_2$$

$$\frac{0.0314 \text{ mol C}_2\text{H}_2}{0.0413 \text{ mol C}_2\text{H}_2} \cdot 100\% = 76.0\%$$

12.80 $\dfrac{n}{V} = \dfrac{P}{RT} = \dfrac{23.8 \text{ mm Hg} \cdot \dfrac{1 \text{ atm}}{760 \text{ mm Hg}}}{(0.082057 \text{ L} \cdot \text{atm/K} \cdot \text{mol})(298 \text{ K})} \cdot \dfrac{6.022 \times 10^{23} \text{ molecules}}{1 \text{ mol}} \cdot \dfrac{1 \text{ L}}{10^3 \text{ cm}^3}$

$$= 7.71 \times 10^{17} \text{ molecules/cm}^3$$

12.81 $n_{O_2} = \dfrac{\left(735 \text{ mm Hg} \cdot \dfrac{1 \text{ atm}}{760 \text{ mm Hg}}\right)(0.327 \text{ L})}{(0.082057 \text{ L} \cdot \text{atm/K} \cdot \text{mol})(292 \text{ K})} = 0.0132 \text{ mol O}_2$

$$0.0132 \text{ mol O}_2 \cdot \frac{2 \text{ mol KClO}_3}{3 \text{ mol O}_2} \cdot \frac{122.5 \text{ g}}{1 \text{ mol KClO}_3} = 1.08 \text{ g KClO}_3$$

$$\frac{1.08 \text{ g KClO}_3}{1.56 \text{ g mixture}} \cdot 100\% = 69.1\%$$

12.82 $P_{total} = P_{H_2O} + P_{O_2} + P_{CO_2} + P_{N_2}$

$P_{N_2} = 253$ mm Hg $- 47.1$ mm Hg $- 35$ mm Hg $- 7.5$ mm Hg

$P_{N_2} = 163$ mm Hg

12.83   (a) $NO_2 < O_2 < NO$

(b)   150 mm Hg $\cdot \dfrac{1\ mol\ O_2}{2\ mol\ NO} = 75$ mm Hg

(c)   150 mm Hg $\cdot \dfrac{2\ mol\ NO_2}{2\ mol\ NO} = 150$ mm Hg

12.84   (a)   562 g $\cdot \dfrac{1\ mol\ NH_3}{17.03\ g} \cdot \dfrac{3\ mol\ H_2}{2\ mol\ NH_3} = 49.5$ mol H_2

$V_{H_2} = \dfrac{nRT}{P} = \dfrac{(49.5\ mol)(0.082057\ L \cdot atm/K \cdot mol)(329\ K)}{745\ mm\ Hg \cdot \dfrac{1\ atm}{760\ mm\ Hg}} = 1360$ L

(b)   562 g $\cdot \dfrac{1\ mol\ NH_3}{17.03\ g} \cdot \dfrac{1\ mol\ N_2}{2\ mol\ NH_3} \cdot \dfrac{100.0\ mol\ air}{78.1\ mol\ N_2} = 21.1$ mol air

$V_{air} = \dfrac{nRT}{P} = \dfrac{(21.1\ mol)(0.082057\ L \cdot atm/K \cdot mol)(302\ K)}{745\ mm\ Hg \cdot \dfrac{1\ atm}{760\ mm\ Hg}} = 534$ L

12.85 $P_{CO_2} = 1.56$ atm $- 1.34$ atm $= 0.22$ atm

$n_{CO_2} = \dfrac{PV}{RT} = \dfrac{(0.22\ atm)(0.55\ L)}{(0.082057\ L \cdot atm/K \cdot mol)(297\ K)} = 0.0050$ mol CO_2

0.0050 mol CO_2 $\cdot \dfrac{44.0\ g}{1\ mol\ CO_2} = 0.22$ g CO_2

$P_{O_2} = \dfrac{nRT}{V} = \dfrac{\left(0.0870\ g \cdot \dfrac{1\ mol\ O_2}{32.00\ g}\right)(0.082057\ L \cdot atm/K \cdot mol)(297\ K)}{0.55\ L} = 0.12$ atm

$P_{CO} = 1.56$ atm $- 0.22$ atm $- 0.12$ atm $= 1.22$ atm

$n_{CO_2} = \dfrac{PV}{RT} = \dfrac{(1.22\ atm)(0.55\ L)}{(0.082057\ L \cdot atm/K \cdot mol)(297\ K)} = 0.028$ mol CO

0.028 mol CO $\cdot \dfrac{28.0\ g}{1\ mol\ CO} = 0.77$ g CO

12.86 $CH_4(g) + 2\,O_2(g) \rightarrow CO_2(g) + 2\,H_2O(g)$

Assume a one-minute time period:

$$n_{CH_4} = \frac{\left(773\ \text{mm Hg} \cdot \dfrac{1\ \text{atm}}{760\ \text{mm Hg}}\right)(5.0\ \text{L})}{(0.082057\ \text{L} \cdot \text{atm/K} \cdot \text{mol})(301\ \text{K})} = 0.21\ \text{mol CH}_4$$

$$0.21\ \text{mol CH}_4 \cdot \frac{2\ \text{mol O}_2}{1\ \text{mol CH}_4} = 0.41\ \text{mol O}_2$$

$$V_{O_2} = \frac{(0.41\ \text{mol O}_2)(0.082057\ \text{L} \cdot \text{atm/K} \cdot \text{mol})(299\ \text{K})}{742\ \text{mm Hg} \cdot \dfrac{1\ \text{atm}}{760\ \text{mm Hg}}} = 10\ \text{L O}_2$$

The oxygen must be supplied to the burner at a rate of 10 L/min.

12.87 $$n_{CO_2} = \frac{PV}{RT} = \frac{\left(44.9\ \text{mm Hg} \cdot \dfrac{1\ \text{atm}}{760\ \text{mm Hg}}\right)(1.50\ \text{L})}{(0.082057\ \text{L} \cdot \text{atm/K} \cdot \text{mol})(298\ \text{K})} = 0.00362\ \text{mol CO}_2$$

$$0.00362\ \text{mol CO}_2 \cdot \frac{1\ \text{mol CO}}{1\ \text{mol CO}_2} \cdot \frac{28.01\ \text{g}}{1\ \text{mol CO}} = 0.102\ \text{g CO}$$

mass of Fe in sample = 0.142 g sample – 0.102 g CO = 0.040 g Fe

$$0.040\ \text{g Fe} \cdot \frac{1\ \text{mol Fe}}{55.8\ \text{g}} = 7.3 \times 10^{-4}\ \text{mol Fe}$$

$$\frac{0.00362\ \text{mol CO}}{7.3 \times 10^{-4}\ \text{mol Fe}} = \frac{5\ \text{mol CO}}{1\ \text{mol Fe}} \qquad \text{The empirical formula is Fe(CO)}_5$$

12.88 $$n_{CO_2} = n_{MCO_3} = \frac{\left(69.8\ \text{mm Hg} \cdot \dfrac{1\ \text{atm}}{760\ \text{mm Hg}}\right)(0.285\ \text{L})}{(0.082057\ \text{L} \cdot \text{atm/K} \cdot \text{mol})(298\ \text{K})} = 0.00107\ \text{mol MCO}_3$$

$$\frac{0.158\ \text{g MCO}_3}{0.00107\ \text{mol MCO}_3} = 148\ \text{g/mol}$$

148 g/mol = M_{metal} + M_{CO_3} = M_{metal} + 60.0 g/mol

M_{metal} = 88 g/mol The metal is probably Sr (87.6 g/mol)

12.89 $$P_{SiH_4} = X_{SiH_4} P_{total} = \frac{1\ \text{mol SiH}_4}{3\ \text{mol total}} \cdot 120\ \text{mm Hg} = 40.\ \text{mm Hg}$$

P_{O_2} = 120 mm Hg – 40. mm Hg = 80. mm Hg

When reaction is complete, H_2O is the only gas present in the flask. $P_{H_2O} = P_{O_2} = 80.$ mm Hg

12.90 (a) $n_{ClF_3} = \dfrac{PV}{RT} = \dfrac{\left(250 \text{ mm Hg} \cdot \dfrac{1 \text{ atm}}{760 \text{ mm Hg}}\right)(2.5 \text{ L})}{(0.082057 \text{ L} \cdot \text{atm/K} \cdot \text{mol})(293 \text{ K})} = 0.034 \text{ mol ClF}_3$

$0.034 \text{ mol ClF}_3 \cdot \dfrac{6 \text{ mol NiO}}{4 \text{ mol ClF}_3} \cdot \dfrac{74.7 \text{ g}}{1 \text{ mol NiO}} = 3.8 \text{ g NiO}$

(b) Partial pressures:

$0.034 \text{ mol ClF}_3 \cdot \dfrac{3 \text{ mol O}_2}{4 \text{ mol ClF}_3} = 0.026 \text{ mol O}_2$

$0.034 \text{ mol ClF}_3 \cdot \dfrac{2 \text{ mol Cl}_2}{4 \text{ mol ClF}_3} = 0.017 \text{ mol Cl}_2$

$P_{O_2} = \dfrac{nRT}{V} = \dfrac{(0.026 \text{ mol})(0.082057 \text{ L} \cdot \text{atm/K} \cdot \text{mol})(293 \text{ K})}{2.5 \text{ L}} = 0.25 \text{ atm} = 190 \text{ mm Hg}$

$P_{Cl_2} = \dfrac{nRT}{V} = \dfrac{(0.017 \text{ mol})(0.082057 \text{ L} \cdot \text{atm/K} \cdot \text{mol})(293 \text{ K})}{2.5 \text{ L}} = 0.16 \text{ atm} = 120 \text{ mm Hg}$

$P_{total} = 190 \text{ mm Hg} + 120 \text{ mm Hg} = 310 \text{ mm Hg}$

12.91 (a) $0.136 \text{ g} \cdot \dfrac{1 \text{ mol NaBH}_4}{37.83 \text{ g}} \cdot \dfrac{1 \text{ mol B}_2\text{H}_6}{2 \text{ mol NaBH}_4} = 0.00180 \text{ mol B}_2\text{H}_6$

$P = \dfrac{nRT}{V} = \dfrac{(0.00180 \text{ mol})(0.082057 \text{ L} \cdot \text{atm/K} \cdot \text{mol})(298 \text{ K})}{2.75 \text{ L}} = 0.0160 \text{ atm}$

(b) $P_{H_2} = 0.0160 \text{ atm} \cdot \dfrac{2 \text{ mol H}_2}{1 \text{ mol B}_2\text{H}_6} = 0.0320 \text{ atm}$

$P_{total} = 0.0160 \text{ atm} + 0.0320 \text{ atm} = 0.0480 \text{ atm}$

12.92 $13.0 \text{ g} \cdot \dfrac{1 \text{ mol CaC}_2}{64.10 \text{ g}} \cdot \dfrac{1 \text{ mol C}_2\text{H}_2}{1 \text{ mol CaC}_2} = 0.203 \text{ mol C}_2\text{H}_2$

$4.65 \text{ g} \cdot \dfrac{1 \text{ mol H}_2\text{O}}{18.02 \text{ g}} \cdot \dfrac{1 \text{ mol C}_2\text{H}_2}{2 \text{ mol H}_2\text{O}} = 0.129 \text{ mol C}_2\text{H}_2$ H$_2$O is the limiting reactant

$P = \dfrac{nRT}{V} = \dfrac{(0.129 \text{ mol})(0.082057 \text{ L} \cdot \text{atm/K} \cdot \text{mol})(296 \text{ K})}{4.66 \text{ L}} = 0.672 \text{ atm}$

12.93 $0.0120 \text{ L} \cdot \dfrac{1.50 \text{ mol HCl}}{1 \text{ L}} = 0.0180 \text{ mol HCl}$

Set up two equations with two unknowns.

$1.249 \text{ g} = x \text{ mol NaHCO}_3 \cdot \dfrac{84.007 \text{ g}}{1 \text{ mol NaHCO}_3} + y \text{ mol Na}_2\text{CO}_3 \cdot \dfrac{105.99 \text{ g}}{1 \text{ mol Na}_2\text{CO}_3}$

$0.0180 \text{ mol HCl} = \left(x \text{ mol NaHCO}_3 \cdot \dfrac{1 \text{ mol HCl}}{1 \text{ mol NaHCO}_3} \right) + \left(y \text{ mol Na}_2\text{CO}_3 \cdot \dfrac{2 \text{ mol HCl}}{1 \text{ mol Na}_2\text{CO}_3} \right)$

Substitute $(0.0180 - 2y)$ for x and solve.

$y = 0.00424 \text{ mol Na}_2\text{CO}_3; x = 0.00952 \text{ mol NaHCO}_3$

$n_{\text{CO}_2} = 0.00424 \text{ mol Na}_2\text{CO}_3 \cdot \dfrac{1 \text{ mol CO}_2}{1 \text{ mol Na}_2\text{CO}_3} + 0.00952 \text{ mol Na}_2\text{CO}_3 \cdot \dfrac{1 \text{ mol CO}_2}{1 \text{ mol NaHCO}_3} = 0.0138 \text{ mol CO}_2$

$V = \dfrac{nRT}{P} = \dfrac{(0.0138 \text{ mol})(0.082057 \text{ L} \cdot \text{atm/K} \cdot \text{mol})(298 \text{ K})}{745 \text{ mm Hg} \cdot \dfrac{1 \text{ atm}}{760 \text{ mm Hg}}} = 0.343 \text{ L}$

12.94 $n_{\text{CO}_2} = \dfrac{PV}{RT} = \dfrac{\left(735 \text{ mm Hg} \cdot \dfrac{1 \text{ atm}}{760 \text{ mm Hg}} \right)(0.665 \text{ L})}{(0.082057 \text{ L} \cdot \text{atm/K} \cdot \text{mol})(298 \text{ K})} = 0.0263 \text{ mol CO}_2$

Set up two equations with two unknowns.

$0.0263 \text{ mol CO}_2 = x \text{ mol Na}_2\text{CO}_3 \cdot \dfrac{1 \text{ mol CO}_2}{1 \text{ mol Na}_2\text{CO}_3} + y \text{ mol Na}_2\text{CO}_3 \cdot \dfrac{1 \text{ mol CO}_2}{1 \text{ mol NaHCO}_3}$

$2.50 \text{ g} = x \text{ mol NaHCO}_3 \cdot \dfrac{84.01 \text{ g}}{1 \text{ mol NaHCO}_3} + y \text{ mol Na}_2\text{CO}_3 \cdot \dfrac{106.0 \text{ g}}{1 \text{ mol Na}_2\text{CO}_3}$

Substitute $(0.0263 - y)$ for x and solve.

$y = 0.0132 \text{ mol Na}_2\text{CO}_3; x = 0.0131 \text{ mol NaHCO}_3$

$\dfrac{0.131 \text{ mol} \cdot \dfrac{84.01 \text{ g}}{1 \text{ mol NaHCO}_3}}{2.50 \text{ g mixture}} \cdot 100\% = 44.0\% \text{ NaHCO}_3$

$\dfrac{0.0132 \text{ mol} \cdot \dfrac{106.0 \text{ g}}{1 \text{ mol Na}_2\text{CO}_3}}{2.50 \text{ g mixture}} \cdot 100\% = 56.0\% \text{ Na}_2\text{CO}_3$

12.95 (a) $P_{\text{H}_2\text{O}} = (\text{relative humidity})(\text{H}_2\text{O vapor pressure}) = \left(\dfrac{45 \text{ mm Hg}}{100 \text{ mm Hg}} \right)(17.5 \text{ mm Hg}) = 7.9 \text{ mm Hg at } 20 \text{ °C}$

$d = \dfrac{PM}{RT} = \dfrac{\left(7.9 \text{ mm Hg} \cdot \dfrac{1 \text{ atm}}{760 \text{ mm Hg}} \right)(18.0 \text{ g/mol})}{(0.082057 \text{ L} \cdot \text{atm/K} \cdot \text{mol})(293 \text{ K})} = 0.0078 \text{ g/L}$

(b) $P_{\text{H}_2\text{O}} = (\text{relative humidity})(\text{H}_2\text{O vapor pressure}) = \left(\dfrac{95 \text{ mm Hg}}{100 \text{ mm Hg}} \right)(4.6 \text{ mm Hg}) = 4.4 \text{ mm Hg at } 0 \text{ °C}$

$d = \dfrac{PM}{RT} = \dfrac{\left(4.4 \text{ mm Hg} \cdot \dfrac{1 \text{ atm}}{760 \text{ mm Hg}} \right)(18.0 \text{ g/mol})}{(0.082057 \text{ L} \cdot \text{atm/K} \cdot \text{mol})(273 \text{ K})} = 0.0046 \text{ g/L}$

12.96 P_{H_2O} = (relative humidity)(H_2O vapor pressure) = $\left(\dfrac{55 \text{ mm Hg}}{100 \text{ mm Hg}}\right)$ (21.1 mm Hg) = 12 mm Hg

$$n = \frac{PV}{RT} = \frac{\left(12 \text{ mm Hg} \cdot \dfrac{1 \text{ atm}}{760 \text{ mm Hg}}\right)\left(4.5 \text{ m}^2 \cdot 3.5 \text{ m} \cdot \dfrac{1 \text{ L}}{10^{-3} \text{ m}^3}\right)}{(0.082057 \text{ L} \cdot \text{atm/K} \cdot \text{mol})(296 \text{ K})} = 9.9 \text{ mol CO}_2$$

9.9 mol $\cdot \dfrac{44.0 \text{ g}}{1 \text{ mol CO}_2} = 440 \text{ g CO}_2$

12.97   (a)   There are more moles of O_2 in the flask (oxygen has a smaller molar mass), so the oxygen has a greater partial pressure.

          (b)   Oxygen has a smaller molar mass so its molecules have the greater average speed.

          (c)   The gases are at the same temperature so the average kinetic energy is the same for both gases.

12.98   (a)   True

          (b)   False   Nitrogen (N_2) has a smaller molar mass than O_2, so an equal mass of N_2 contains more moles and more molecules than the O_2 sample

12.99   (a)   Acetylene has a smaller molar mass, so there are more moles of gas in the acetylene cylinder and thus the pressure is greater.

          (b)   The acetylene cylinder has a greater number of molecules.

12.100   At a constant pressure, the number of moles of a gas is inversely proportional to the temperature of the gas. Therefore flask B (at a lower temperature) contains more moles (and more molecules) of oxygen.

12.101   (a)   probably not a gas (a gas would expand more)

          (b)   probably not a gas (density = 8.2 g/mL, too large for a gas)

          (c)   insufficient information (could also be a liquid or a solid)

          (d)   gas

12.102   (a)   All four tires have the same pressure, temperature, and volume. They have the same number of gas molecules.

          (b)   160. g/16.0 g = 10 times heavier

          (c)   All the molecules have the same kinetic energy (they have the same temperature). Helium is the lightest gas of the four, so its molecules have the greatest average speed.

12.103   (a) $65.0 \text{ g} \cdot \dfrac{1 \text{ mol Na}}{23.00 \text{ g}} = 2.83 \text{ mol Na}$

$$n_{N_2O} = \frac{(2.12 \text{ atm})(35.0 \text{ L})}{(0.082057 \text{ L} \cdot \text{atm/K} \cdot \text{mol})(296 \text{ K})} = 3.05 \text{ mol N}_2\text{O}$$

$\dfrac{3.05 \text{ mol N}_2\text{O}}{2.83 \text{ mol Na}} = \dfrac{1.08 \text{ mol N}_2\text{O}}{1 \text{ mol Na}} > \dfrac{0.75 \text{ mol N}_2\text{O}}{1 \text{ mol Na}}$ Na is the limiting reactant

$2.83 \text{ mol Na} \cdot \dfrac{1 \text{ mol NaN}_3}{4 \text{ mol Na}} \cdot \dfrac{65.02 \text{ g}}{1 \text{ mol NaN}_3} = 45.9 \text{ g NaN}_3$

(b)

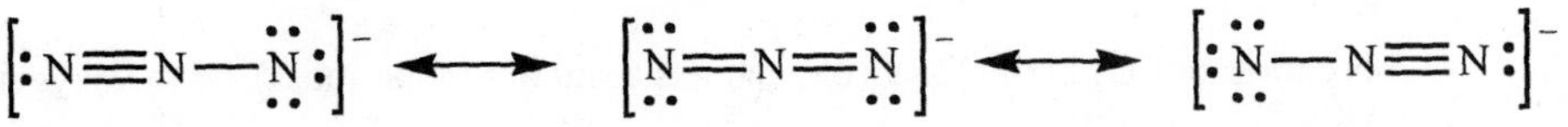

$$\left[:N\equiv N - \ddot{\underset{..}{N}}: \right]^{-} \longleftrightarrow \left[\ddot{\underset{..}{N}} = N = \ddot{\underset{..}{N}} \right]^{-} \longleftrightarrow \left[:\ddot{\underset{..}{N}} - N \equiv N: \right]^{-}$$

     0   +1   −2   −1   +1   −1   −2   +1   0

The formal charges (shown below the resonance structures) indicate that the center resonance structure is most likely.

(c)   The azide ion is linear.

12.104   (a) $7 + 2(6) = 19$ valence electrons

(b) 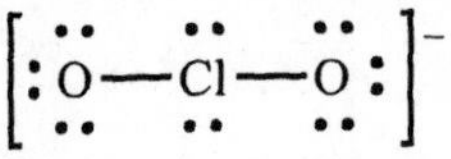 $\left[:\ddot{\underset{..}{O}} - \ddot{\underset{..}{C}}l - \ddot{\underset{..}{O}}: \right]^{-}$

(c) sp^3 The ion is bent

(d)   Ozone has a larger bond angle. The central atom is sp^2 hybridized. $\ddot{O} = \ddot{O} - \ddot{\underset{..}{O}}:$

(e) $15.6 \text{ g} \cdot \dfrac{1 \text{ mol NaClO}_2}{90.44 \text{ g}} = 0.172 \text{ mol NaClO}_2$

$$n_{Cl_2} = \frac{PV}{RT} = \frac{\left(1050 \text{ mm Hg} \cdot \dfrac{1 \text{ atm}}{760 \text{ mm Hg}} \right)(1.45 \text{ L})}{(0.082057 \text{ L} \cdot \text{atm/K} \cdot \text{mol})(295 \text{ K})} = 0.0828 \text{ mol Cl}_2$$

$\dfrac{0.172 \text{ mol NaClO}_2}{0.0828 \text{ mol Cl}_2} = \dfrac{2.08 \text{ mol NaClO}_2}{1 \text{ mol Cl}_2} > \dfrac{2 \text{ mol NaClO}_2}{1 \text{ mol Cl}_2}$ Cl_2 is the limiting reactant

$0.0828 \text{ mol Cl}_2 \cdot \dfrac{2 \text{ mol ClO}_2}{1 \text{ mol Cl}_2} \cdot \dfrac{67.45 \text{ g}}{1 \text{ mol ClO}_2} = 11.2 \text{ g ClO}_2$

12.105   Speed of gas molecules is related to the square root of the absolute temperature, so a doubling of the temperature will lead to an increase of about $(2)^{1/2}$ or 1.4.

12.106   The animation should show that as n increases, V must increase in order to maintain constant P and T.

Chapter 13
Intermolecular Forces, Liquids, and Solids

INSTRUCTOR'S NOTES

We believe the material in this chapter has been imprudently neglected in introductory courses, particularly the matter of intermolecular forces. Therefore, we set aside 5-6 lecture periods for this chapter.

These are some points to make in the coverage of this chapter:

- Polarity of molecules, as introduced in the context of molecular geometry, is a central consideration when studying intermolecular forces.

- London forces may not seem to be important, but because even non-polar atoms and molecules do condense into liquids the existence of these forces is proved.

- Although London forces are generally considered to be the weakest of the intermolecular forces, for large molecules the total energy involved may equal or exceed that of other forces.

- Hydrogen bonding, though not truly a bond, is responsible for an incredible deviation from trends in properties such as boiling points. The role of hydrogen bonding in biochemistry can also be noted.

- Although many substances are solids, there are many different ways in which the atoms and or ions can be arranged (Table 13.6).

The ionic and molecular solids pictured in this chapter can be found on the *General ChemistryNow CD-ROM* in the Molecular Modeling Database. The ionic solids pictured have been manipulated (by changing the ionic radii) in order to make the ions appear with the correct radius.

SUGGESTED DEMONSTRATIONS

1. Vapor Pressure

    - We have searched for good demonstrations of vapor pressure for some time. One of the demonstrations we use is a so-called "Love Meter", a toy that can be obtained in novelty and gift shops. The closed, thinwalled glass vessel contains methyl chloride (bp –23.7 °C). Warming the vessel in your hand raises the vapor pressure of the liquid and forces the liquid to another compartment of the vessel.

2. Solids

    - Cady, S. G. "Use of Pom Pons to Illustrate Cubic Crystal Structures," *Journal of Chemical Education*, **1997**, *74*, 794.

    - Molecular models are invaluable to show intermolecular forces and solid state structures. Various kits are available from Aldrich Chemical Company.

    - The Klinger Educational Products Corp. (112-19 14th Road, College Point, New York, NY 11356-1453) sells a very large number of models of various solids.

    - The Institute for Chemical Education (Department of Chemistry, University of Wisconsin - Madison, 1101

University Ave., Madison, WI 53706) offers a Solid State Model Kit that can be used to illustrate the variety of unit cells.

- The close packing of spheres (such as the photos on page 621) is easy to do on an overhead projector. We have also used oranges and grapefruits, as well as Styrofoam balls.

3. Colligative Properties

- Morse, J. G. "A Simple Demonstration Model of Osmosis," *Journal of Chemical Education* **1999**, *76*, 64.

4. Intermolecular Forces

- Kitson, T. M. "Purple or Colorless—Which Way Up? An Entertaining Solubility Demonstration," *Journal of Chemical Education* **2003**, *80*, 892.

5. Hydrogen Bonding

- Johnson, J. L. H.; Yalkowsky, S. H. "A Three-Dimensional Model for Water," *Journal of Chemical Education* **2002**, *79*, 1088.

6. Boiling / Phase Change

- McRae, R.; Rahn, J. A.; Beamer, T. W.; LeBret, N. "The Liquid Nitrogen Fountain," *Journal of Chemical Education* **2002**, *79*, 1220.

SOLUTIONS TO STUDY QUESTIONS

13.1   (a) hydrogen bonding

      (b) induced dipole/induced dipole

      (c) hydrogen bonding

13.2   solid iodine: induced dipole/induced dipole

      CH_3OH: hydrogen bonding

      I_2 and CH_3OH: dipole/induced dipole

13.3   (a) induced dipole/induced dipole   (c) dipole-dipole

      (b) induced dipole/induced dipole   (d) hydrogen bonding

13.4   (a) induced dipole/induced dipole   (c) dipole-dipole

      (b) hydrogen bonding   (d) induced dipole/induced dipole

13.5   Based on increasing molar mass: $CH_4 < Ne < CO < CCl_4$

                                      —increasing intermolecular forces→

      However, boiling points are in the order   Ne (–246 °C) < CO (–192 °C) < CH_4 (–162 °C) < CCl_4 (77 °C)

      CH_4, Ne, and CO are gases at 25 °C and 1 atm

13.6 $He < CH_3CH_2CH_2CH_3 < CH_3OH$

      —increasing intermolecular forces→

      He and $CH_3CH_2CH_2CH_3$ are gases at 25 °C and 1 atm

13.7   (c) HF, (d) CH_3CO_2H, and (f) CH_3OH would be expected to form intermolecular hydrogen bonds in the liquid state

13.8 HCO_2H would be expected to form intermolecular hydrogen bonds in the liquid state.

13.9   (a) LiCl   Lithium ions are smaller than cesium ions

      (b) $Mg(NO_3)_2$ Magnesium has a larger positive charge (+2) than sodium (+1)

      (c) $NiCl_2$ Nickel has a larger positive charge (+2) than rubidium (+1) and it is a smaller ion

13.10 Mg^{2+} is most strongly hydrated because of its small size and large positive charge. Cs^+ is least strongly hydrated because of its large size and smaller positive charge.

13.11 $125 \text{ mL} \cdot \dfrac{0.7849 \text{ g}}{1 \text{ mL}} \cdot \dfrac{1 \text{ mol } CH_3CH_2OH}{46.069 \text{ g}} \cdot \dfrac{42.32 \text{ kJ}}{1 \text{ mol}} = 90.1 \text{ kJ}$

13.12 $0.500 \text{ mL} \cdot \dfrac{13.6 \text{ g}}{1 \text{ mL}} \cdot \dfrac{1 \text{ mol Hg}}{200.59 \text{ g}} \cdot \dfrac{59.11 \text{ kJ}}{1 \text{ mol}} = 2.00 \text{ kJ}$

13.13   (a) Approximately 150 mm Hg. Appendix G shows a value of 149.4 mm Hg

        (b) 93 °C

        (c) Ethanol (520 mm Hg) has a higher vapor pressure at 70 °C than water (225 mm Hg)

13.14   (a) Approximately 400 mm Hg.

        (b) diethyl ether < ethanol < water

        (c) diethyl ether is a gas, and ethanol and water are in the liquid phase

13.15   The vapor pressure of diethyl ether at 30 °C is approximately 600 mm Hg.

$$n = \dfrac{PV}{RT} = \dfrac{\left(600 \text{ mm Hg} \cdot \dfrac{1 \text{ atm}}{760 \text{ mm Hg}}\right)(0.100 \text{ mL})}{(0.082057 \text{ L} \cdot \text{atm/K} \cdot \text{mol})(303 \text{ K})} = 0.0032 \text{ mol}$$

$0.0032 \text{ mol} \cdot \dfrac{74.1 \text{ g } (C_2H_5)_2O}{1 \text{ mol}} = 0.24 \text{ g diethyl ether needed to create pressure of 600 mm Hg in flask}$

There is enough diethyl ether available (1.0 g) to create a pressure of 600 mm Hg. When the flask is cooled, some ether will condense to a liquid.

13.16   (a) As the water cools, the vapor pressure of the water decreases, resulting in a decrease in the total pressure inside the bottle. The bottle will collapse because the pressure inside is less than the external pressure.

        (b) The normal boiling point of diethyl ether is 34.6 °C so the liquid will evaporate completely at body temperature (37 °C).

13.17   (a) O_2 (higher molar mass)   (c) HF (hydrogen bonding)

        (b) SO_2 (polar molecule)   (d) GeH_4 (higher molar mass)

13.18 $CH_4 < CO < NH_3 < SCl_2$ (predicted based on increasing molar mass)

        $CO < CH_4 < NH_3 < SCl_2$ (actual order of increasing boiling point)

        —increasing boiling point→

13.19   (a) CS_2:   620 mm Hg CH_3NO_2:   80 mm Hg

        (b)   induced dipole/induced dipole   dipole-dipole

        (c)   46 °C   100 °C

        (d) 39 °C

        (e) 34 °C

13.20   (a)   increases

(b)   increases

(c)   does not change

(d)   increases

13.21   (a)   80.1 °C

(b)   Using the equation for the straight line, $T = 48\ °C$ when $P = 250$ mm Hg and $T = 75\ °C$ when $P = 650$ mm Hg,

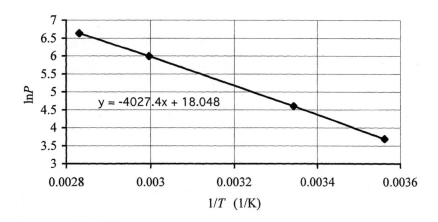

ln(vapor pressure) vs. 1/temperature

(c) $\ln\left(\dfrac{400.\ \text{mm Hg}}{100.\ \text{mm Hg}}\right) = \dfrac{\Delta H_{\text{vap}}}{0.0083145\ \text{kJ/K} \cdot \text{mol}}\left[\dfrac{1}{299.3\ \text{K}} - \dfrac{1}{333.8\ \text{K}}\right]$

$\Delta H_{\text{vap}} = 33.4$ kJ/mol

13.22 $\ln\left(\dfrac{45.3\ \text{mm Hg}}{13.6\ \text{mm Hg}}\right) = \dfrac{\Delta H_{\text{vap}}}{0.0083145\ \text{kJ/K} \cdot \text{mol}}\left[\dfrac{1}{298\ \text{K}} - \dfrac{1}{323\ \text{K}}\right]$

$\Delta H_{\text{vap}} = 38.5$ kJ/mol

Use this value to calculate the temperature when vapor pressure = 760 mm Hg

$\ln\left(\dfrac{760\ \text{mm Hg}}{13.6\ \text{mm Hg}}\right) = \dfrac{38.5\ \text{kJ/mol}}{0.0083145\ \text{kJ/K} \cdot \text{mol}}\left[\dfrac{1}{298\ \text{K}} - \dfrac{1}{T_2}\right]$

$T_2 = 402$ K (129 °C)   The actual boiling point is 126 °C

13.23   Two possible unit cells: Each unit cell contains 1 A square and 8 B squares, so the

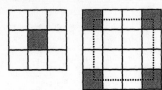

simplest formula is AB_8

13.24   The area inside the box is a unit cell. Each unit cell contains 2 A squares and 2 B squares,

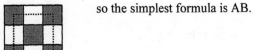

so the simplest formula is AB.

13.25   8 corner Ti $\times$ $^1/_8$ = 1 Ti   12 edge O $\times$ $^1/_4$ = 3 O   1 internal Ca = 1 Ca

The formula is $CaTiO_3$

13.26   8 corner Ti $\times$ $^1/_8$ = 1 Ti   4 face O $\times$ $^1/_2$ = 2 O

1 internal Ti   = 1 Ti   2 internal O   = 2 O
_____

                  = 2 Ti total   = 4 O total

There are two TiO_2 units per unit cell.

13.27   (a)   8 corner O $\times$ $^1/_8$ = 1 O

1 internal O   = 1 O   4 internal Cu   = 4 Cu
_____

                  = 2 O total   = 4 Cu total

There is a ratio of two copper ions to one oxide ion for a formula of Cu_2O.

(b)   The oxidation number of copper is +1.

13.28   (a)   face-centered cubic

(b)   tetrahedral holes

(c)   (8 corner Ca^{2+} $\times$ $^1/_8$) + (6 face Ca^{2+} $\times$ $^1/_2$) = 4 Ca^{2+} 8 internal F^- = 8 F^-

The formula is CaF_2

13.29   (a)   (8 corner C $\times$ $^1/_8$) + (6 face C $\times$ $^1/_2$) + (4 internal C) = 8 C atoms/unit cell

(b)   face-centered cubic arrangement with carbon atoms in tetrahedral holes

13.30   (a)   induced dipole/induced dipole

(b)   Since there are only weak intermolecular forces between the layers in graphite, the layers slide over each other easily, giving graphite a slippery feel. Pushing a pencil lead against paper causes some of the carbon layers to rub off, leaving a black mark

13.31 $15.5 \text{ g} \cdot \dfrac{1 \text{ mol } C_6H_6}{78.11 \text{ g}} \cdot \dfrac{9.95 \text{ kJ}}{1 \text{ mol}} = 1.97 \text{ kJ heat evolved } (-1.97 \text{ kJ})$

+1.97 kJ of heat must be absorbed to convert the solid to a liquid.

13.32   The total heat required is the sum of the heat required to (1) heat the solid from 25 °C to its melting point and (2) liquefy the solid at its melting point.

$q_{solid} = (5.00 \text{ g Ag})(0.235 \text{ J/g·K})(1235 \text{ K} - 298 \text{ K}) = 1.10 \times 10^3 \text{ J}$

$q_{melting} = 5.00 \text{ g} \cdot \dfrac{1 \text{ mol Ag}}{107.9 \text{ g}} \cdot \dfrac{11.3 \text{ kJ}}{1 \text{ mol}} \cdot \dfrac{10^3 \text{ J}}{1 \text{ kJ}} = 5.24 \times 10^2 \text{ J}$

$q_{total} = (1.10 \times 10^3 \text{ J}) + (5.24 \times 10^2 \text{ J}) = 1.62 \times 10^3 \text{ J}$

13.33   (a) The positive slope of the solid/liquid equilibrium line indicates that liquid CO_2 is less dense than solid CO_2.

(b) gas phase

(c) no

13.34   (a) Xenon is a gas at room temperature and 1.0 atm pressure.

(b) Xenon is a liquid at 0.75 atm pressure and –114 °C.

(c) When the pressure on a sample of liquid xenon is 380 mm Hg (0.5 atm), the temperature is between –117 and –119 °C.

(d) At –122 °C, the vapor pressure of solid xenon is 0.25 atm.

(e) The solid phase is more dense than the liquid phase because the solid–liquid equilibrium line has a positive slope.

13.35   The total heat required is the sum of the heat required to (1) heat the liquid from –50.0 °C to its boiling point, (2) vaporize the gas, and (3) heat the vapor to 0.0 °C.

$q_{liquid} = (12 \text{ kg} \cdot \dfrac{10^3 \text{ g}}{1 \text{ kg}})(4.7 \text{ J/g·K})(239.9 \text{ K} - 223.2 \text{ K}) \cdot \dfrac{1 \text{ kJ}}{10^3 \text{ J}} = 9.4 \times 10^2 \text{ kJ}$

$q_{evaporation} = 12 \text{ kg} \cdot \dfrac{10^3 \text{ g}}{1 \text{ kg}} \cdot \dfrac{1 \text{ mol } NH_3}{17.0 \text{ g}} \cdot \dfrac{23.33 \text{ kJ}}{1 \text{ mol}} = 1.6 \times 10^4 \text{ kJ}$

$q_{vapor} = (12 \text{ kg} \cdot \dfrac{10^3 \text{ g}}{1 \text{ kg}})(2.2 \text{ J/g·K})(273.2 \text{ K} - 239.9 \text{ K}) \cdot \dfrac{1 \text{ kJ}}{10^3 \text{ J}} = 8.8 \times 10^2 \text{ kJ}$

$q_{total} = 9.4 \times 10^2 \text{ kJ} + 1.6 \times 10^4 \text{ kJ} + 8.8 \times 10^2 \text{ kJ} = 1.8 \times 10^4 \text{ kJ}$

13.36   The total heat required is the sum of the heat required to (1) cool the gas from 40.0 °C to its boiling point, (2) condense the gas, and (3) cool the liquid to –40.0 °C.

$$q_{gas} = 20.0 \cdot \frac{1 \text{ mol g } CCl_2F_2}{120.9 \text{ g}} \cdot 117.2 \text{ J/mol} \cdot K \cdot (243.4 \text{ K} - 313.2 \text{ K}) = -1350 \text{ J}$$

$$q_{condensation} = 20.0 \text{ g} \cdot \frac{1 \text{ mol } CCl_2F_2}{120.9 \text{ g}} \cdot \frac{-20.11 \text{ kJ}}{1 \text{ mol}} \cdot \frac{10^3 \text{ J}}{1 \text{ kJ}} = -3330 \text{ J}$$

$$q_{liquid} = 20.0 \text{ g} \cdot \frac{1 \text{ mol } CCl_2F_2}{120.9 \text{ g}} \cdot 72.3 \text{ J/mol} \cdot K \cdot (233.2 \text{ K} - 243.4 \text{ K}) = -122 \text{ J}$$

$$q_{total} = (-1350 \text{ J}) + (-3330 \text{ J}) + (-122 \text{ J}) = -4.80 \times 10^3 \text{ J}$$

13.37   Yes, the critical temperature is well above room temperature.

13.38   The critical temperature for propane is well above room temperature, so propane can be liquefied. Liquefied propane is commonly used for heating and cooking.

13.39 $Ar < CO_2 < CH_3OH$

—increasing intermolecular forces→

13.40   (a) induced dipole/induced dipole forces

(b) hydrogen bonding

13.41

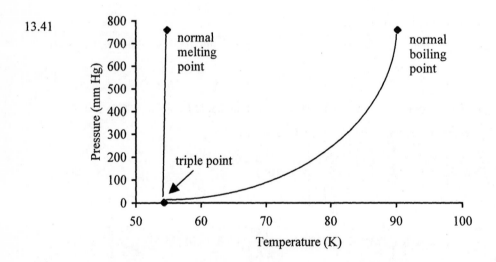

The estimated vapor pressure at 77 K is approximately 200 mmHg. The solid-liquid equilibrium line has a positive slope, so the density of liquid O_2 is less than that of solid O_2.

13.42 (8 corner $Cl^{-+} \times \frac{1}{8}$) = 1 Cl^- 1 internal Cs^+ = 1 Cs^+

Unit cell volume:

$$\frac{1 \text{ CsCl}}{\text{unit cell}} \cdot \frac{1 \text{ mol CsCl}}{6.022 \times 10^{23} \text{ atoms}} \cdot \frac{168.4 \text{ g}}{1 \text{ mol CsCl}} \cdot \frac{1 \text{ cm}^3}{3.99 \text{ g}} = 7.01 \times 10^{-23} \text{ cm}^3$$

Unit cell edge length:

$V = 7.01 \times 10^{-23} \text{ cm}^3 = (\text{edge length})^3$

edge length $= \sqrt[3]{7.01 \times 10^{-23} \text{ cm}^3} = 4.12 \times 10^{-8}$ cm

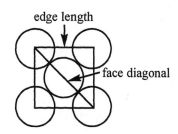

(face diagonal)^2 = (edge length)^2 + (edge length)^2

face diagonal $= \sqrt{2} \cdot$ edge length

(cube diagonal)^2 = (edge length)^2 + (face diagonal)^2

(cube diagonal)^2 = (edge length)^2 + ($\sqrt{2} \cdot$ edge length)^2

cube diagonal $= \sqrt{3} \cdot$ (edge length)

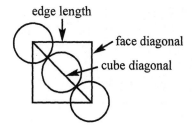

cube diagonal $= \sqrt{3} \cdot 412$ pm

cube diagonal = 714 pm

(2 × Cl^- radius) + (2 × Cs^+ radius) = cube diagonal

(2 × 181 pm) + (2 × Cs^+ radius) = 714 pm

Cs^+ radius = 176 pm

13.43 $1.0 \times 10^3 \text{ mL} \cdot \dfrac{1 \text{ cm}^3}{1 \text{ mL}} \cdot \dfrac{0.785 \text{ g}}{1 \text{ cm}^3} \cdot \dfrac{1 \text{ mol C}_2\text{H}_5\text{OH}}{46.07 \text{ g}} = 17 \text{ mol C}_2\text{H}_5\text{OH}$

$V_{\text{room}} = 3.0 \text{ m} \cdot 2.5 \text{ m} \cdot 2.5 \text{ m} \cdot \left(\dfrac{10^2 \text{ cm}}{1 \text{ m}}\right)^3 \cdot \dfrac{1 \text{ mL}}{1 \text{ cm}^3} \cdot \dfrac{1 \text{ L}}{10^3 \text{ mL}} = 1.9 \times 10^4 \text{ L}$

$n = \dfrac{PV}{RT} = \dfrac{\left(59 \text{ mm Hg} \cdot \dfrac{1 \text{ atm}}{760 \text{ mm Hg}}\right)(1.9 \times 10^4 \text{ L})}{(0.082057 \text{ L} \cdot \text{atm/K} \cdot \text{mol})(298 \text{ K})} = 60. \text{ mol ethanol}$

Less ethanol is available (17 mol) than would be required to completely fill the room with vapor (60. mol), so all of the ethanol will evaporate.

13.44 (a) ICl (polar molecule)

(b) krypton (greater molar mass)

(c) CH_3CH_2OH (hydrogen bonding)

13.45 Li_2SO_4 should have the more exothermic heat of hydration because the lithium ion is smaller than the cesium ion.

13.46 Compounds (a), (b), and (d) contain small, highly charged metal ions. These salts will most likely experience strong ion-dipole forces between the metal cation and water molecules and exist as hydrated solids.

13.47   (a) 350 mm Hg

         (b) ethanol (lower vapor pressure at every temperature)

         (c) 84 °C

         (d) CS_2: 46 °C C_2H_2OH: 78 °C C_7H_{16}: 99 °C

         (e) CS_2: gas C_2H_2OH: gas C_7H_{16}: liquid

13.48 $q_{NH_3} = \left(1.00 \text{ mol NH}_3 \cdot \dfrac{17.03 \text{ g}}{1 \text{ mol NH}_3} \right)(4.70 \text{ J/g} \cdot \text{K})(229.9 \text{ K} - 239.9 \text{ K})$

         $q_{NH_3} = -800. \text{ J}$

         $q_{H_2O} = \left(1.00 \text{ mol H}_2O \cdot \dfrac{18.02 \text{ g}}{1 \text{ mol H}_2O} \right)(4.18 \text{ J/g} \cdot \text{K})(-10.0 \text{ K})$

         $q_{H_2O} = -753 \text{ J}$

         Cooling liquid ammonia evolves more heat.

13.49 $(\text{face diagonal})^2 = (\text{edge length})^2 + (\text{edge length})^2$

         face diagonal $= \sqrt{2} \cdot$ edge length

         face diagonal $= \sqrt{2} \cdot 409$ pm

         face diagonal $= 578$ pm

         radius $= \dfrac{578 \text{ pm}}{4} = 145$ pm

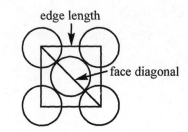

13.50   (a) body-centered cubic

         (b) (8 corner W $\times \frac{1}{8}$) + (1 internal W) = 2 W atoms/unit cell

         (c) $(\text{cube diagonal})^2 = (\text{edge length})^2 + (\text{face diagonal})^2$

              $(\text{cube diagonal})^2 = (\text{edge length})^2 + (\sqrt{2} \cdot \text{edge length})^2$

              cube diagonal $= \sqrt{3} \cdot (\text{edge length})$

              cube diagonal $= \sqrt{3} \cdot 316.5$ pm

              cube diagonal $= 548$ pm

              radius $= \dfrac{548 \text{ pm}}{4} = 137$ pm

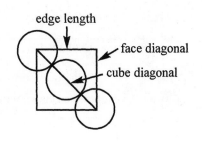

13.51   8 corner Ca $\times \frac{1}{8}$ = 1 Ca   8 edge C $\times \frac{1}{4}$ = 2 C

         1 internal Ca   = 1 Ca   2 internal C   = 2 C

                              _____   _____

                              = 2 Ca total   = 4 C total

         There is a ratio of two calcium ions to four carbon ions for a formula of CaC_2.

13.52 $CO_2 < CH_3Cl < HCO_2H$

         —increasing intermolecular forces→

13.53 $C_2H_6 < HCl < CH_3OH$

—increasing enthalpy of vaporization→

13.54   Unit cell volume:

$$\frac{40.08 \text{ g}}{1 \text{ mol Ca}} \cdot \frac{1 \text{ cm}^3}{1.54 \text{ g}} \cdot \frac{1 \text{ mol Ca}}{6.022 \times 10^{23} \text{ atoms}} \cdot \frac{4 \text{ Ca atoms}}{\text{unit cell}} = 1.73 \times 10^{-22} \text{ cm}^3$$

Unit cell edge length:

$V = 1.73 \times 10^{-22} \text{ cm}^3 = (\text{edge length})^3$

edge length $= \sqrt[3]{1.73 \times 10^{-22} \text{ cm}^3} = 5.57 \times 10^{-8}$ cm

face diagonal $= 4 \cdot \text{radius} = \sqrt{2} \cdot \text{edge length}$

$\text{radius} = \dfrac{\sqrt{2} \cdot (5.57 \times 10^{-8} \text{ cm})}{4} = 1.97 \times 10^{-8} \text{ cm} = 197 \text{ pm}$

13.55   Unit cell volume:

$$\frac{4 \text{ Ir atoms}}{\text{unit cell}} \cdot \frac{192.22 \text{ g}}{1 \text{ mol Ir}} \cdot \frac{1 \text{ cm}^3}{22.56 \text{ g}} \cdot \frac{1 \text{ mol Ir}}{6.0221 \times 10^{23} \text{ atoms}} = 5.659 \times 10^{-23} \text{ cm}^3$$

Unit cell edge length:

$V = 5.659 \times 10^{-23} \text{ cm}^3 = (\text{edge length})^3$

edge length $= \sqrt[3]{5.659 \times 10^{-23} \text{ cm}^3} = 3.839 \times 10^{-8}$ cm

face diagonal $= 4 \cdot \text{radius} = \sqrt{2} \cdot \text{edge length}$

$\text{radius} = \dfrac{\sqrt{2} \cdot (3.839 \times 10^{-8} \text{ cm})}{4} = 1.357 \times 10^{-8} \text{ cm} = 135.7 \text{ pm}$

13.56   Assume that copper has a face-centered cubic unit cell. Calculate the density of the unit cell based on this assumption and compare it with the actual density of copper:

mass of one Cu atom $= \dfrac{63.546 \text{ g}}{1 \text{ mol Cu}} \cdot \dfrac{1 \text{ mol Cu}}{6.02214 \times 10^{23} \text{ atoms}} = 1.0552 \times 10^{-22} \text{ g}$

mass of unit cell $= \dfrac{1.0552 \times 10^{-22} \text{ g}}{1 \text{ Cu atom}} \cdot \dfrac{4 \text{ Cu atoms}}{1 \text{ unit cell}} = 4.2208 \times 10^{-22} \text{ g/unit cell}$

face diagonal $= 4 \cdot \text{atom radius} = \sqrt{2} \cdot \text{edge length}$

edge length $= \dfrac{4 \cdot \text{atom radius}}{\sqrt{2}} = \dfrac{4 \cdot 127.8 \text{ pm}}{\sqrt{2}} = 361.5 \text{ pm} = 3.615 \times 10^{-8}$ cm

unit cell volume $= (\text{edge length})^3 = (3.615 \times 10^{-8} \text{ cm})^3 = 4.723 \times 10^{-23} \text{ cm}^3$

unit cell density $= \dfrac{4.2208 \times 10^{-22} \text{ g}}{4.723 \times 10^{-23} \text{ cm}^3} = 8.937 \text{ g/cm}^3$

The calculated density closely matches the actual density (8.95 g/cm^3) so the copper unit cell is most likely face-centered cubic.

13.57   Assume that vanadium metal has a face–centered cubic unit cell. Calculate the density of the unit cell

based on this assumption and compare it with the actual density of vanadium:

$$\text{mass of one V atom} = \frac{50.94 \text{ g}}{1 \text{ mol V}} \cdot \frac{1 \text{ mol V}}{6.022 \times 10^{23} \text{ atoms}} = 8.459 \times 10^{-23} \text{ g}$$

$$\text{mass of unit cell} = \frac{8.459 \times 10^{-23} \text{ g}}{1 \text{ V atom}} \cdot \frac{4 \text{ V atoms}}{1 \text{ unit cell}} = 3.384 \times 10^{-22} \text{ g/unit cell}$$

$$\text{face diagonal} = 4 \cdot \text{atom radius} = \sqrt{2} \cdot \text{edge length}$$

$$\text{edge length} = \frac{4 \cdot \text{atom radius}}{\sqrt{2}} = \frac{4 \cdot 132 \text{ pm}}{\sqrt{2}} = 373 \text{ pm} = 3.73 \times 10^{-8} \text{ cm}$$

$$\text{unit cell volume} = (\text{edge length})^3 = (3.73 \times 10^{-8} \text{ cm})^3 = 5.19 \times 10^{-23} \text{ cm}^3$$

$$\text{unit cell density} = \frac{3.384 \times 10^{-22} \text{ g}}{5.19 \times 10^{-23} \text{ cm}^3} = 6.52 \text{ g/cm}^3$$

The calculated density does not agree with the actual density (6.11 g/cm^3). If the unit cell is assumed to be

body–centered cubic, the calculated density is 5.97 g/cm^3; simple cubic results in a calculated density of

4.60 g/cm^3. The vanadium unit cell is most likely body–centered cubic.

13.58   Calculate the mass of one iron atom and compare this to the mass of one mole of iron.

$$V = \left(286.65 \text{ pm} \cdot \frac{1 \text{ m}}{10^{12} \text{ pm}} \cdot \frac{10^2 \text{ cm}}{1 \text{ m}} \right)^3 = 2.3554 \times 10^{-23} \text{ cm}^3$$

$$2.3554 \times 10^{-23} \text{ cm}^3 \cdot \frac{7.874 \text{ g}}{1 \text{ cm}^3} \cdot \frac{1 \text{ unit cell}}{2 \text{ Fe atoms}} = 9.2730 \times 10^{-23} \text{ g/Fe atom}$$

$$\frac{55.845 \text{ g/1 mol Fe}}{9.2730 \times 10^{-23} \text{ g/Fe atom}} = 6.0223 \times 10^{23} \text{ Fe atoms/mol}$$

13.59   Calculate the mass of one CaF_2 ion pair and compare this to the mass of one mole of CaF_2:

$$(5.46295 \times 10^{-8} \text{ cm})^3 \cdot \frac{3.1805 \text{ g}}{1 \text{ cm}^3} \cdot \frac{1 \text{ unit cell}}{4 \text{ CaF}_2} = 1.2963 \times 10^{-22} \text{ g/CaF}_2$$

$$\frac{78.077 \text{ g/1 mol CaF}_2}{1.2963 \times 10^{-22} \text{ g/CaF}_2} = 6.0230 \times 10^{23} \text{ CaF}_2\text{/mol}$$

13.60 $$\frac{n}{V} = \frac{P}{RT} = \frac{0.00169 \text{ mm Hg} \cdot \dfrac{1 \text{ atm}}{760 \text{ mm Hg}}}{(0.082057 \text{ L} \cdot \text{atm/K} \cdot \text{mol})(297 \text{ K})} = 9.12 \times 10^{-8} \text{ mol/L}$$

$$\frac{9.12 \times 10^{-8} \text{ mol}}{1 \text{ L}} \cdot \frac{6.022 \times 10^{23} \text{ atoms}}{1 \text{ mol}} \cdot \frac{1 \text{ L}}{10^{-3} \text{ m}^3} = 5.49 \times 10^{19} \text{ atoms/m}^3$$

13.61   Diagram A:

$$\frac{\text{area covered by circles}}{\text{total area}} = \frac{\text{area of one circle}}{(2\,r_{\text{circle}})^2} = \frac{\pi\,r^2}{4\,r^2} = 0.785 \approx 78.5\%$$

Diagram B:

$$\text{area of triangle} = \frac{1}{2} \times \text{base} \times \text{height} = \frac{1}{2}(2\,r)(\sqrt{3}\,r)$$

$$\text{area covered by circles} = \frac{1}{2} \times \text{area of circle} = \frac{1}{2}\pi\,r^2$$

$$\frac{\text{area covered}}{\text{area of triangle}} = \frac{\frac{1}{2}\pi\,r^2}{\frac{1}{2}(2\,r)(\sqrt{3}\,r)} = 0.907 = 90.7\%$$

13.62   % occupied space $= \dfrac{\text{volume occupied by spheres}}{\text{total volume of unit cell}} \cdot 100\% = \dfrac{1\ \text{sphere} \times \frac{4}{3}\pi r^3}{(2\,r)^3} \cdot 100\% = 52\%$

% empty space $= 100 - \%$ occupied space $= 48\%$

13.63   (a) 70.3 °C

(b) Using the equation for the straight line, $T = 39$ °C when $P = 250$ mm Hg and $T = 66$ °C when $P = 650$ mm Hg,

ln(vapor pressure) vs. 1/temperature

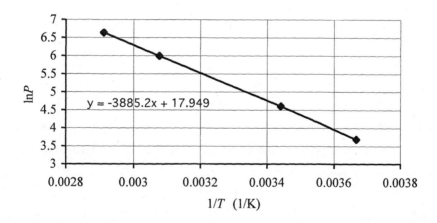

(c) $\ln\left(\dfrac{400.\ \text{mm Hg}}{100.\ \text{mm Hg}}\right) = \dfrac{\Delta H_{\text{vap}}}{0.0083145\ \text{kJ/K}\cdot\text{mol}}\left[\dfrac{1}{290.7\ \text{K}} - \dfrac{1}{325.1\ \text{K}}\right]$

$\Delta H_{\text{vap}} = 31.7$ kJ/mol

13.64 (a)

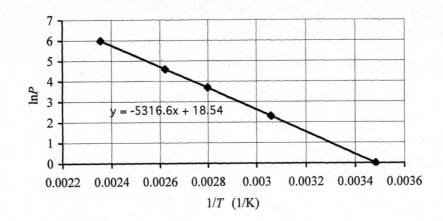

ln(vapor pressure) vs. 1/temperature

The graph shows $\ln P$ on the y-axis (0 to 7) versus $1/T$ (1/K) on the x-axis (0.0022 to 0.0036), with a straight line:

$$y = -5316.6x + 18.54$$

(b) Using the equation for the straight line, $T = 135\ °C$ when $P = 250$ mm Hg and $T = 168\ °C$ when

   $P = 650$ mm Hg

(c) $T = 173\ °C$ when $P = 760$ mm Hg

(d) $\ln\left(\dfrac{400.\ \text{mm Hg}}{100.\ \text{mm Hg}}\right) = \dfrac{\Delta H_{vap}}{0.0083145\ \text{kJ/K} \cdot \text{mol}}\left[\dfrac{1}{381.5\ \text{K}} - \dfrac{1}{424.6\ \text{K}}\right]$

   $\Delta H_{vap} = 43.3$ kJ/mol

13.65 Acetone readily absorbs water because hydrogen bonding occurs between the molecules.

$$H_3C \overset{\displaystyle :O:}{\underset{\displaystyle CH_3}{\overset{\|}{C}}} \cdots H \quad \overset{\displaystyle \cdot\cdot\ddot{O}\cdot\cdot}{\diagdown} H$$

13.66 Since cooking oil does not mix with water, the two substances have different types of intermolecular

   forces. Water is a polar molecule, and strong hydrogen bonding occurs between water molecules. The

   molecules in cooking oil are likely nonpolar.

13.67 The viscosity of ethylene glycol is greater than that of ethanol since ethylene glycol contains two O—H

   groups per molecule while ethanol has only one.

13.68 The meniscus is concave since there are adhesive forces between the methanol and the silicate of the glass.

13.69 (a) Water has two O—H bonds and two lone pairs on oxygen, and ethanol has only one O—H bond.

      This leads to less extensive hydrogen bonding in ethanol and a lower boiling point than water.

   (b) The water molecules interact extensively with the ethanol molecules (through hydrogen bonding) and

      can therefore occupy less than the anticipated 100 mL.

13.70   In a face-centered cubic lattice of anions (X) there are a total of four anions per unit cell.

Type of holes occupied by cation (M)	Number of cations per unit cell	Formula of salt
all tetrahedral holes	8	M_2X
half of the tetrahedral holes	4	MX
all octahedral holes	4	MX

It is not possible to have a cation:anion ratio of 3:1.

13.71   No. The sodium chloride unit cell contains four anions and four cations. It cannot have a 1:2 cation:anion stoichiometry.

13.72   1-propanol has stronger intermolecular forces (hydrogen bonding) than methyl ethyl ether (dipole-dipole).

13.73   Two pieces of evidence for $H_2O(\ell)$ having considerable intermolecular attractive forces:

(1) Based on the trend for Group VIA hydrides, the boiling point of water should be approximately –80 °C. The actual boiling point (100 °C) reflects the significant hydrogen bonding present.

(2) Liquid water has a heat capacity of 4.184 J/g·K, higher than almost all other liquids. This reflects the fact that it takes a relatively large amount of energy to overcome intermolecular forces in order to raise the temperature of a sample of water.

13.74   The frost–free refrigerator's freezer is warmed periodically to near the freezing point of water. This allows the vapor pressure of the ice to increase so that sublimation readily occurs, keeping the frost from accumulating in the freezer. It would therefore make the hailstones disappear over time. No such mechanism exists in the older non–frost–free refrigerator.

13.75   (a) HI

(b) The large iodine atom in HI leads to a significant polarizability for the molecule and thus to a large dispersion force.

(c) The dipole moment of HCl (1.07 D, Table 9.8) is larger than for HI (0.38 D).

(d) HI; see (b)

13.76   The volatile liquid has a low boiling point. Warming the lower compartment in your hands increases the number of molecules in the vapor phase, raising the vapor pressure of the liquid and forcing the liquid to the upper chamber.

13.77   When the water vapor in the can comes in contact with the cold water in the pan, the vapor condenses, decreasing the vapor pressure inside the can. The pressure inside the can is now lower than the atmospheric pressure outside the can, causing the can to collapse.

13.78   A gas can be liquefied at or below its critical temperature. The critical temperature for CF_4 (-45.7 °C) is below room temperature (25 °C), so it cannot be liquefied at room temperature.

13.79   (a) -27 °C

         (b) 6.5 atm

         (c) The flow is rapid at first because the liquid has vaporized to form the maximum amount of vapor possible at that temperature, with a pressure of approximately 6.5 atm. As the gas leaves the cylinder, additional liquid vaporizes in an attempt to reach liquid-vapor equilibrium. The flow becomes much slower because the pressure in the cylinder has dropped and cannot increase unless the cylinder is closed or enough heat is supplied to vaporize the remaining liquid. This vaporization requires energy, so the temperature of the cylinder drops and ice forms on the outside of the cylinder.

         (d) (2) Cool the cylinder to -78 °C and open the valve. Cooling the cylinder will condense the vapor, allowing it to be easily removed as a liquid.

13.80   Assuming the spheres are packed in an identical way, the water levels will be identical. A face–centered cubic lattice, for example, uses 74% of the available volume, regardless of sphere size.

13.81 $\bullet$ = CO_2 molecule

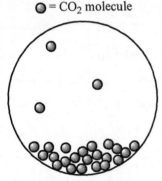

Separate liquid and vapor
phases in equilibrium.

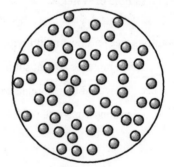

Distinct liquid and vapor
phases not visible.
Molecules closer together
than in vapor phase

13.82   (a) The Ca^{2+} ions are in a face-centered cubic arrangement and the O^{2-} ions fill octahedral holes.

         (b) There are 4 Ca^{2+} ions and 4 O^{2-} ions per unit cell, a 1:1 ratio that matches the compound formula.

         (c) Calcium oxide has the same structure as sodium chloride.

13.83   (a) The Zn^{2+} ions are in a face-centered cubic arrangement and the S^{2-} ions fill half of the tetrahedral holes.

         (b) There are 4 Zn^{2+} ions and 4 S^{2-} ions per unit cell, a 1:1 ratio that matches the compound formula.

13.84   Lead sulfide has the same structure as sodium chloride, not the same structure as ZnS. There are 4 Pb^{2+} ions and 4 S^{2-} ions per unit cell, a 1:1 ratio that matches the compound formula.

13.85   (a) The Ca^{2+} ions are in a face-centered cubic arrangement and the F^- ions fill all of the tetrahedral holes.

      (b) There are 4 Ca^{2+} ions and 8 F^- ions per unit cell, a 1:2 ratio that matches the compound formula. The CaF_2 and ZnS structures both have a face-centered cubic arrangement of cations.

      (c) The ZnS structure fills half of the tetrahedral holes with anions and the CaF_2 structure fills all of the tetrahedral holes with anions.

13.86   (a)

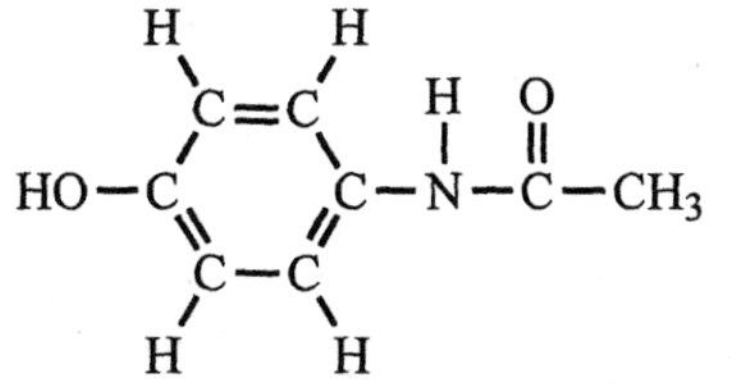

      (b) There is one C=O group that is highly polar and can interact with H atoms of water. In addition, there is one NH group and one OH group that can hydrogen bond.

13.87   (a)

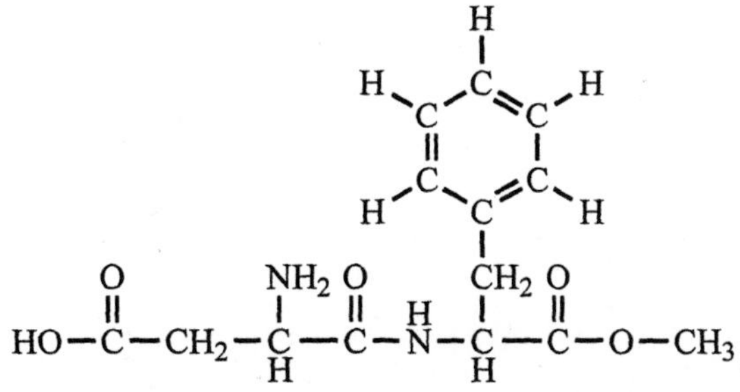

      (b) There are three C=O groups that are highly polar and can interact with H atoms of water. In addition, there are two NH groups and one —OH group than can hydrogen bond.

Chapter 14
Solutions and Their Behavior

INSTRUCTOR'S NOTES

The importance of accurately describing the relative amounts of components in mixtures such as solutions should be readily apparent to students. The consequences of errors in such descriptions can be sited (e.g., wrong dosages for medicines, dangerously inaccurate mixtures in critical engineering applications, incorrect prices for valuable commodities). Some colligative properties are familiar to students so the connection to practical matters is easy to make. In general after studying this chapter students are usually able to deal with straightforward problems and discuss solution phenomena with little difficulty.

All the topics in this chapter can generally be covered in 3-4 lectures.

SUGGESTED DEMONSTRATIONS

1. The Solution Process

    *   Several demonstrations in Volume 1 of *Chemical Demonstrations* by Shakhashiri are suitable. Suggestions include "Chemical Cold Packs," "Crystallization from Supersaturated Solutions of Sodium Acetate," "Chemical Hot Packs," and "Endothermic Reactions of Hydrated Barium Chloride and Ammonium Salts."

    *   A demonstration of Henry's Law, "Effect of Temperature and Pressure on the Solubility of Gases in Liquids," is contained in Volume 3 of the *Chemical Demonstrations* series. Also in Volume 3 are: "Getting Colder: Freezing-Point Depression," "Getting Hotter: Boiling Point Elevation by Nonvolatile Solutes," "Osmosis Through the Membrane of an Egg," and "Osmotic Pressure of a Sugar Solution."

    *   Several of the photos in the chapter represent demonstrations we do in class. For example, Figure 14.2 shows the difference between molality and molarity, and Figure 14.6, showing the preferential solubility of iodine in CCl_4, is easy to do. One of our favorites is the frozen solution in Figure 14.15b. We place an indicator in water and then allow the solution to freeze slowly in the freezer of a lab refrigerator. The result clearly shows that the solute concentrates in the solution and that the solid is pure solvent.

2. Additional demonstrations

    *   Kitson, T. M. "Purple or Colorless—Which Way Up? An Entertaining Solubility Demonstration," *Journal of Chemical Education* **2003**, *80*, 892.

    *   Mundell, D. W. "Heat of Solution and Colligative Properties: An Illustration of Enthalpy and Entropy," *Journal of Chemical Education* **1990**, *67*, 426.

    *   Levy, J. B.; Hornack, F. M.; Levy, M. A. "Simple Determination of Henry's Law Constant for Carbon Dioxide," *Journal of Chemical Education* **1987**, *64*, 260.

SOLUTIONS TO STUDY QUESTIONS

14.1 $2.56 \text{ g} \cdot \dfrac{1 \text{ mol } C_2H_4(CO_2H)_2}{118.1 \text{ g}} = 0.0217 \text{ mol } C_2H_4(CO_2H)_2$

$500. \text{ mL} \cdot \dfrac{1 \text{ cm}^3}{1 \text{ mL}} \cdot \dfrac{1.00 \text{ g}}{1 \text{ cm}^3} \cdot \dfrac{1 \text{ mol } H_2O}{18.02 \text{ g}} = 27.7 \text{ mol } H_2O$

(a) $m = \dfrac{\text{amount of solute}}{\text{kg of solvent}} = \dfrac{0.0217 \text{ mol } C_2H_4(CO_2H)_2}{500. \text{ g}} \cdot \dfrac{10^3 \text{ g}}{1 \text{ kg}} = 0.0434 \ m$

(b) $X_{acid} = \dfrac{0.0217 \text{ mol}}{0.0217 \text{ mol} + 27.7 \text{ mol}} = 0.000781$

(c)   Weight % $= \dfrac{2.56 \text{ g}}{2.56 \text{ g} + 500. \text{ g}} \cdot 100\% = 0.509\%$

14.2 $45.0 \text{ g } C_{10}H_{16}O \cdot \dfrac{1 \text{ mol } C_{10}H_{16}O}{152.2 \text{ g}} = 0.296 \text{ mol } C_{10}H_{16}O$

$425 \text{ mL } C_2H_5OH \cdot \dfrac{0.785 \text{ g}}{1 \text{ mL}} \cdot \dfrac{1 \text{ mol } C_2H_5OH}{46.07 \text{ g}} = 7.24 \text{ mol } C_2H_5OH$

(a) $m = \dfrac{\text{amount of solute}}{\text{kg of solvent}} = \dfrac{0.296 \text{ mol } C_{10}H_{16}O}{425 \text{ mL } C_2H_5OH} \cdot \dfrac{1 \text{ mL}}{0.785 \text{ g}} \cdot \dfrac{10^3 \text{ g}}{1 \text{ kg}} = 0.886 \ m$

(b) $X_{camphor} = \dfrac{0.296 \text{ mol}}{0.296 \text{ mol} + 7.24 \text{ mol}} = 0.0392$

(c)   Weight % $= \dfrac{45.0 \text{ g}}{45.0 \text{ g} + \left(425 \text{ mL} \cdot \dfrac{0.785 \text{ g}}{1 \text{ mL}} \right)} \cdot 100\% = 11.9\%$

14.3

Compound	Molality	Weight percent	Mole fraction
NaI	0.15	2.2	0.0027
C_2H_5OH	1.1	5.0	0.020
$C_{12}H_{22}O_{11}$	0.15	4.9	0.0027

NaI: 0.15 mol NaI dissolved in 1.0 kg H_2O

$0.15 \text{ mol} \cdot \dfrac{150. \text{ g}}{1 \text{ mol NaI}} = 23 \text{ g NaI}$

$1.0 \times 10^3 \text{ g} \cdot \dfrac{1 \text{ mol } H_2O}{18.0 \text{ g}} = 56 \text{ mol } H_2O$

Weight % $= \dfrac{23 \text{ g}}{23 \text{ g} + (1.0 \times 10^3 \text{ g})} \cdot 100\% = 2.2\%$

$X_{NaI} = \dfrac{0.15 \text{ mol}}{0.15 \text{ mol} + 56 \text{ mol}} = 0.0027$

C_2H_5OH: 5.0 g C_2H_5OH dissolved in 95.0 g H_2O

$$5.0 \text{ g} \cdot \frac{1 \text{ mol } C_2H_5OH}{46.1 \text{ g}} = 0.11 \text{ mol } C_2H_5OH$$

$$95.0 \text{ g} \cdot \frac{1 \text{ mol } H_2O}{18.02 \text{ g}} = 5.27 \text{ mol } H_2O$$

$$m = \frac{\text{amount of solute}}{\text{kg of solvent}} = \frac{0.11 \text{ mol } C_2H_5OH}{0.0950 \text{ kg } H_2O} = 1.1 \ m$$

$$X_{C_2H_5OH} = \frac{0.11 \text{ mol}}{0.11 \text{ mol} + 5.27 \text{ mol}} = 0.020$$

$C_{12}H_{22}O_{11}$: 0.15 mol $C_{12}H_{22}O_{11}$ dissolved in 1.0 kg H_2O

$$0.15 \text{ mol} \cdot \frac{342 \text{ g}}{1 \text{ mol } C_{12}H_{22}O_{11}} = 51.3 \text{ g } C_{12}H_{22}O_{11}$$

$$1.0 \times 10^3 \text{ g} \cdot \frac{1 \text{ mol } H_2O}{18.0 \text{ g}} = 56 \text{ mol } H_2O$$

$$\text{Weight \%} = \frac{51.3 \text{ g}}{51.3 \text{ g} + (1.0 \times 10^3 \text{ g})} \cdot 100\% = 4.9\%$$

$$X_{C_{12}H_{22}O_{11}} = \frac{0.15 \text{ mol}}{0.15 \text{ mol} + 56 \text{ mol}} = 0.0027$$

14.4

Compound	Molality	Weight percent	Mole fraction
KNO_3	1.10	10.0	0.0194
CH_3CO_2H	0.0183	0.110	3.30×10^{-4}
HOC_2H_4OH	3.54	18.0	0.0599

KNO_3: 10.0 g KNO_3 dissolved in 90.0 g H_2O

$$10.0 \text{ g} \cdot \frac{1 \text{ mol } KNO_3}{101.1 \text{ g}} = 0.0989 \text{ mol } KNO_3$$

$$90.0 \text{ g} \cdot \frac{1 \text{ mol } H_2O}{18.02 \text{ g}} = 4.99 \text{ mol } H_2O$$

$$m = \frac{\text{amount of solute}}{\text{kg of solvent}} = \frac{0.0989 \text{ mol } KNO_3}{0.0900 \text{ kg } H_2O} = 1.10 \ m$$

$$X_{KNO_3} = \frac{0.0989 \text{ mol}}{0.0989 \text{ mol} + 4.99 \text{ mol}} = 0.0194$$

CH_3CO_2H: 0.0183 mol CH_3CO_2H dissolved in 1.00 kg H_2O

$$0.0183 \text{ mol} \cdot \frac{60.05 \text{ g}}{1 \text{ mol } CH_3CO_2H} = 1.10 \text{ g } CH_3CO_2H$$

$$1.00 \times 10^3 \text{ g} \cdot \frac{1 \text{ mol } H_2O}{18.02 \text{ g}} = 55.5 \text{ mol } H_2O$$

$$\text{Weight \%} = \frac{1.10 \text{ g}}{1.10 \text{ g} + (1.00 \times 10^3 \text{ g})} \cdot 100\% = 0.110\%$$

$$X_{CH_3CO_2H} = \frac{0.0183 \text{ mol}}{0.0183 \text{ mol} + 55.5 \text{ mol}} = 3.30 \times 10^{-4}$$

HOCH$_2$CH$_2$OH: 18.0 g HOCH$_2$CH$_2$OH dissolved in 82.0 g H$_2$O

$$18.0 \text{ g} \cdot \frac{1 \text{ mol HOCH}_2\text{CH}_2\text{OH}}{62.07 \text{ g}} = 0.290 \text{ mol HOCH}_2\text{CH}_2\text{OH}$$

$$82.0 \text{ g} \cdot \frac{1 \text{ mol H}_2\text{O}}{18.02 \text{ g}} = 4.55 \text{ mol H}_2\text{O}$$

$$m = \frac{\text{amount of solute}}{\text{kg of solvent}} = \frac{0.290 \text{ mol HOCH}_2\text{CH}_2\text{OH}}{0.0820 \text{ kg H}_2\text{O}} = 3.54 \ m$$

$$X_{\text{HOCH}_2\text{CH}_2\text{OH}} = \frac{0.290 \text{ mol}}{0.290 \text{ mol} + 4.55 \text{ mol}} = 0.0599$$

14.5 $$\frac{0.200 \text{ mol Na}_2\text{CO}_3}{1 \text{ kg H}_2\text{O}} \cdot \frac{106.0 \text{ g}}{1 \text{ mol Na}_2\text{CO}_3} \cdot \frac{125 \text{ g H}_2\text{O}}{10^3 \text{ g/1 kg}} = 2.65 \text{ g Na}_2\text{CO}_3$$

$$X_{\text{Na}_2\text{CO}_3} = \frac{0.200 \text{ mol Na}_2\text{CO}_3}{0.200 \text{ mol Na}_2\text{CO}_3 + \left(10^3 \text{ g} \cdot \dfrac{1 \text{ mol H}_2\text{O}}{18.02 \text{ g}}\right)} = 0.00359$$

14.6 $$\frac{0.0512 \text{ mol NaNO}_3}{1 \text{ kg H}_2\text{O}} \cdot \frac{85.00 \text{ g}}{1 \text{ mol NaNO}_3} \cdot \frac{500. \text{ g H}_2\text{O}}{10^3 \text{ g/1 kg}} = 2.18 \text{ g NaNO}_3$$

$$X_{\text{NaNO}_3} = \frac{0.0512 \text{ mol NaNO}_3}{0.0512 \text{ mol NaNO}_3 + \left(10^3 \text{ g} \cdot \dfrac{1 \text{ mol H}_2\text{O}}{18.02 \text{ g}}\right)} = 9.22 \times 10^{-4}$$

14.7 $$0.093 = \frac{x \text{ mol C}_3\text{H}_5(\text{OH})_3}{x \text{ mol C}_3\text{H}_5(\text{OH})_3 + \left(425 \text{ g} \cdot \dfrac{1 \text{ mol H}_2\text{O}}{18.02 \text{ g}}\right)}$$

$x = 2.4 \text{ mol C}_3\text{H}_5(\text{OH})_3$

$$2.4 \text{ mol C}_3\text{H}_5(\text{OH})_3 \cdot \frac{92.1 \text{ g}}{1 \text{ mol C}_3\text{H}_5(\text{OH})_3} = 220 \text{ g C}_3\text{H}_5(\text{OH})_3$$

$$m = \frac{2.4 \text{ mol C}_3\text{H}_5(\text{OH})_3}{0.425 \text{ kg H}_2\text{O}} = 5.7 \ m$$

14.8 $$0.125 = \frac{x \text{ mol HOCH}_2\text{CH}_2\text{OH}}{x \text{ mol HOCH}_2\text{CH}_2\text{OH} + \left(955 \text{ g H}_2\text{O} \cdot \dfrac{1 \text{ mol H}_2\text{O}}{18.02 \text{ g}}\right)}$$

$x = 7.57 \text{ mol HOCH}_2\text{CH}_2\text{OH}$

$$7.57 \text{ mol HOCH}_2\text{CH}_2\text{OH} \cdot \frac{62.07 \text{ g}}{1 \text{ mol HOCH}_2\text{CH}_2\text{OH}} = 470. \text{ g HOCH}_2\text{CH}_2\text{OH}$$

$$m = \frac{7.57 \text{ mol HOCH}_2\text{CH}_2\text{OH}}{0.955 \text{ kg H}_2\text{O}} = 7.93 \ m$$

14.9   (a)   Mass of solution $= 1 \text{ L} \cdot \dfrac{1000 \text{ mL}}{1 \text{ L}} \cdot \dfrac{1.18 \text{ g}}{\text{mL}} = 1180 \text{ g solution}$

Mass of HCl $= 1 \text{ L} \cdot \dfrac{12.0 \text{ mol HCl}}{1 \text{ L}} \cdot \dfrac{36.46 \text{ g}}{1 \text{ mol HCl}} = 438 \text{ g HCl}$

Mass of $H_2O = 1180 \text{ g} - 438 \text{ g} = 742 \text{ g } H_2O$

$m = \dfrac{12.0 \text{ mol HCl}}{0.742 \text{ kg } H_2O} = 16.2 \ m$

(b)   Weight % $= \dfrac{438 \text{ g HCl}}{1180 \text{ g solution}} \cdot 100\% = 37.1\%$

14.10 $95.0 \text{ g} \cdot \dfrac{1 \text{ mol } H_2SO_4}{98.08 \text{ g}} = 0.969 \text{ mol } H_2SO_4$

$m = \dfrac{0.969 \text{ mol } H_2SO_4}{0.0050 \text{ kg } H_2O} = 194 \ m$

$100.0 \text{ g solution} \cdot \dfrac{1 \text{ cm}^3}{1.84 \text{ g}} \cdot \dfrac{1 \text{ mL}}{1 \text{ cm}^3} \cdot \dfrac{1 \text{ L}}{10^3 \text{ mL}} = 0.0543 \text{ L solution}$

$M = \dfrac{0.969 \text{ mol } H_2SO_4}{0.0543 \text{ L solution}} = 17.8 \text{ M}$

14.11 $\dfrac{0.18 \text{ g Li}^+}{1 \times 10^6 \text{ g } H_2O} \cdot \dfrac{1 \text{ mol Li}^+}{6.941 \text{ g}} \cdot \dfrac{10^3 \text{ g}}{1 \text{ kg}} = 2.6 \times 10^{-5} \ m$

14.12   1 ppm = 1 g solute/10^6 g solvent, so 1 ppb = 1 g solute/10^9 g solvent

(a) $\dfrac{28 \text{ g Ag}}{1 \times 10^9 \text{ g } H_2O} \cdot \dfrac{1 \text{ mol Ag}}{108 \text{ g}} \cdot \dfrac{1000 \text{ g}}{1 \text{ kg}} = 2.6 \times 10^{-7} \ m$

(b) $1.0 \times 10^2 \text{ g Ag} \cdot \dfrac{1 \times 10^9 \text{ g } H_2O}{28 \text{ g Ag}} \cdot \dfrac{1 \text{ L}}{1000 \text{ g}} = 3.6 \times 10^6 \text{ L } H_2O$

14.13   (b) C_6H_6 and CCl_4 both are nonpolar molecules

(c) H_2O and CH_3CO_2H both are polar molecules

14.14   Acetone is a polar molecule, so the strong dipole–dipole interactions between acetone and water molecules lead to a high solubility of acetone in water.

14.15 $LiCl(s) \rightarrow LiCl(aq)$

$\Delta H°_{soln} = \Delta H_f°[LiCl(aq)] - \Delta H_f°[LiCl(s)] = -445.6 \text{ kJ/mol} - (-408.7 \text{ kJ/mol}) = -36.9 \text{ kJ/mol}$

14.16 $NaClO_4(s) \rightarrow NaClO_4(aq)$

$\Delta H°_{soln} = \Delta H_f°[NaClO_4(aq)] - \Delta H_f°[NaClO_4(s)] = -369.5 \text{ kJ/mol} - (-382.9 \text{ kJ/mol}) = 13.4 \text{ kJ/mol}$

14.17   (c)   Raise the temperature of the solution and add some NaCl

14.18   As temperature increases the solubility of Li_2SO_4 decreases; additional solid should appear in the beaker. As temperature increases the solubility of LiCl increases; additional solid should dissolve.

14.19   (a) LiF   Lithium ions are smaller than rubidium ions

         (b) $Ca(NO_3)_2$ Calcium has a larger positive charge (+2) than potassium (+1)

         (c) $CuBr_2$ Cu has a larger positive charge (+2) than cesium (+1) and it is a smaller ion

14.20 Mg^{2+} is most strongly hydrated because of its small size and large positive charge. Cs^+ is least strongly hydrated because of its large size and smaller positive charge.

14.21 $$S_{O_2} = k_H P_{O_2} = \frac{1.66 \times 10^{-6} \text{ M}}{\text{mm Hg}} \cdot 40 \text{ mm Hg} = 7 \times 10^{-5} \text{ M}$$

         $$\frac{7 \times 10^{-5} \text{ mol } O_2}{1 \text{ L}} \cdot \frac{32 \text{ g}}{1 \text{ mol } O_2} = 0.002 \text{ g } O_2/\text{L}$$

14.22   Since the solubility of a gas generally decreases with increasing temperature, (a) 8.80×10^{-7} M/mm Hg is the only reasonable choice because it is less than the value of the constant at 25 °C.

14.23 $$P_{CO_2} = \frac{S_{CO_2}}{k_H} = \frac{0.0506 \text{ M}}{4.48 \times 10^{-5} \text{ M/mm Hg}} = 1130 \text{ mm Hg } (1.49 \text{ atm})$$

14.24 $$P_{H_2} = P_{total} - P_{H_2O} = 760.0 \text{ mm Hg} - 23.8 \text{ mm Hg} = 736.2 \text{ mm Hg}$$

         $$S_{H_2} = \frac{1.07 \times 10^{-6} \text{ M}}{\text{mm Hg}} \cdot 736.2 \text{ mm Hg} = 7.88 \times 10^{-4} \text{ M}$$

         $$\frac{7.88 \times 10^{-4} \text{ mol } H_2}{1 \text{ L}} \cdot \frac{1 \text{ L}}{1000 \text{ mL}} \cdot \frac{2.016 \text{ g}}{1 \text{ mol } H_2} = 1.59 \times 10^{-6} \text{ g/mL}$$

14.25 $$35.0 \text{ g} \cdot \frac{1 \text{ mol HOCH}_2\text{CH}_2\text{OH}}{62.07 \text{ g}} = 0.564 \text{ mol HOCH}_2\text{CH}_2\text{OH}$$

         $$500.0 \text{ g} \cdot \frac{1 \text{ mol } H_2O}{18.02 \text{ g}} = 27.75 \text{ mol } H_2O$$

         $$X_{H_2O} = \frac{27.75 \text{ mol}}{27.75 \text{ mol} + 0.564 \text{ mol}} = 0.980$$

         $$P_{H_2O} = X_{H_2O} P°_{H_2O}$$

         $$P_{H_2O} = (0.980)(35.7 \text{ mm Hg}) = 35.0 \text{ mm Hg}$$

14.26 $9.00 \text{ g} \cdot \dfrac{1 \text{ mol (NH}_2)_2\text{CO}}{60.06 \text{ g}} = 0.150 \text{ mol (NH}_2)_2\text{CO}$

$10.0 \text{ mL} \cdot \dfrac{1.00 \text{ g}}{1 \text{ mL}} \cdot \dfrac{1 \text{ mol H}_2\text{O}}{18.02 \text{ g}} = 0.555 \text{ mol H}_2\text{O}$

$X_{H_2O} = \dfrac{0.555 \text{ mol}}{0.555 \text{ mol} + 0.150 \text{ mol}} = 0.787$

$P_{H_2O} = X_{H_2O} P^\circ_{H_2O}$

$P_{H_2O} = (0.787)(22.4 \text{ mm Hg}) = 17.6 \text{ mm Hg}$

14.27 $X_{H_2O} = \dfrac{P_{H_2O}}{P^\circ_{H_2O}} = \dfrac{457 \text{ mm Hg}}{525.8 \text{ mm Hg}} = 0.869$

$2.00 \times 10^3 \text{ g} \cdot \dfrac{1 \text{ mol H}_2\text{O}}{18.02 \text{ g}} = 111 \text{ mol H}_2\text{O}$

$X_{H_2O} = 0.869 = \dfrac{111 \text{ mol H}_2\text{O}}{111 \text{ mol H}_2\text{O} + x \text{ mol HOCH}_2\text{CH}_2\text{OH}}$

$x = 16.7 \text{ mol HOCH}_2\text{CH}_2\text{OH}$

$16.7 \text{ mol HOCH}_2\text{CH}_2\text{OH} \cdot \dfrac{62.07 \text{ g}}{1 \text{ mol HOCH}_2\text{CH}_2\text{OH}} = 1040 \text{ g HOCH}_2\text{CH}_2\text{OH}$

14.28 $105 \text{ g} \cdot \dfrac{1 \text{ mol I}_2}{253.8 \text{ g}} = 0.414 \text{ mol I}_2$ $325 \text{ g} \cdot \dfrac{1 \text{ mol CCl}_4}{153.8 \text{ g}} = 2.11 \text{ mol CCl}_4$

$X_{CCl_4} = \dfrac{2.11 \text{ mol}}{2.11 \text{ mol} + 0.414 \text{ mol}} = 0.836$

$P_{CCl_4} = X_{CCl_4} P^\circ_{CCl_4} = (0.836)(531 \text{ mm Hg}) = 444 \text{ mm Hg}$

14.29 $\Delta T_{bp} = (2.53 \text{ °C}/m)\left(\dfrac{0.200 \text{ mol solute}}{0.125 \text{ kg benzene}}\right) = 4.05 \text{ °C}$

$T_{bp} = 80.10 \text{ °C} + 4.05 \text{ °C} = 84.15 \text{ °C}$

14.30 $m_{urea} = \dfrac{15.0 \text{ g} \cdot \dfrac{1 \text{ mol urea}}{60.06 \text{ g}}}{0.500 \text{ kg H}_2\text{O}} = 0.500 \ m$

$\Delta T_{bp} = (0.5121 \text{ °C}/m)(0.500 \ m) = 0.256 \text{ °C}$

$T_{bp} = 100.00 \text{ °C} + 0.256 \text{ °C} = 100.26 \text{ °C}$

14.31 $m_{C_{12}H_{10}} = \dfrac{0.515 \text{ g} \cdot \dfrac{1 \text{ mol C}_{12}\text{H}_{10}}{154.2 \text{ g}}}{0.0150 \text{ kg CHCl}_3} = 0.223 \ m$

$\Delta T_{bp} = (3.63 \text{ °C}/m)(0.223 \ m) = 0.808 \text{ °C}$

$T_{bp} = 61.70 \text{ °C} + 0.808 \text{ °C} = 62.51 \text{ °C}$

14.32 $m_{\text{caffeine}} = \dfrac{0.755 \text{ g} \cdot \dfrac{1 \text{ mol } C_8H_{10}O_2N_4}{194.2 \text{ g}}}{0.0956 \text{ kg benzene}} = 0.0407 \ m$

$\Delta T_{\text{bp}} = (2.53 \ °C/m)(0.0407 \ m) = 0.103 \ °C$

$T_{\text{bp}} = 80.10 \ °C + 0.103 \ °C = 80.20 \ °C$

14.33 $\Delta T_{\text{bp}} = 80.51 \ °C - 80.10 \ °C = 0.41 \ °C$

$m_{C_{14}H_{10}} = \dfrac{\Delta T_{\text{bp}}}{K_{\text{bp}}} = \dfrac{0.41 \ °C}{2.53 \ °C/m} = 0.16 \ m$

$\dfrac{0.16 \text{ mol } C_{14}H_{10}}{1 \text{ kg benzene}} \cdot \dfrac{178 \text{ g}}{1 \text{ mol } C_{14}H_{10}} \cdot 0.0500 \text{ kg benzene} = 1.4 \text{ g } C_{14}H_{10}$

14.34 $\Delta T_{\text{bp}} = 104.4 \ °C - 100.0 \ °C = 4.4 \ °C$

$m_{\text{solute}} = \dfrac{\Delta T_{\text{bp}}}{K_{\text{bp}}} = \dfrac{4.4 \ °C}{0.5121 \ °C/m} = 8.6 \ m$

$\dfrac{8.6 \text{ mol } C_3H_5(OH)_3}{1 \text{ kg } H_2O} \cdot 0.735 \text{ kg } H_2O = 6.3 \text{ mol } C_3H_5(OH)_3$

$6.3 \text{ mol } C_3H_5(OH)_3 \cdot \dfrac{92.1 \text{ g}}{1 \text{ mol } C_3H_5(OH)_3} = 580 \text{ g } C_3H_5(OH)_3$

$X_{\text{glycerol}} = \dfrac{6.3 \text{ mol } C_3H_5(OH)_3}{6.3 \text{ mol } C_3H_5(OH)_3 + \left(735 \text{ g} \cdot \dfrac{1 \text{ mol } H_2O}{18.02 \text{ g}} \right)} = 0.13$

14.35   (a) $m_{\text{ethanol}} = \dfrac{\Delta T_{\text{fp}}}{K_{\text{fp}}} = \dfrac{-16.0 \ °C}{-1.86 \ °C/m} = 8.60 \ m$

(b) $8.60 \text{ mol } C_2H_5OH \cdot \dfrac{46.07 \text{ g}}{1 \text{ mol } C_2H_5OH} = 396 \text{ g } C_2H_5OH$

Weight % $= \dfrac{396 \text{ g } C_2H_5OH}{396 \text{ g } C_2H_5OH + (1.00 \times 10^3 \text{ g } H_2O)} \cdot 100\% = 28.4\%$

14.36 $m_{\text{solute}} = \dfrac{\Delta T_{\text{fp}}}{K_{\text{fp}}} = \dfrac{-15.0 \ °C}{-1.86 \ °C/m} = 8.06 \ m$

$\dfrac{8.06 \text{ mol } HOCH_2CH_2OH}{1 \text{ kg } H_2O} \cdot \dfrac{62.07 \text{ g}}{1 \text{ mol } HOCH_2CH_2OH} \cdot 5.0 \text{ kg } H_2O = 2500 \text{ g } HOCH_2CH_2OH$

14.37 $m_{\text{sucrose}} = \dfrac{15.0 \text{ g} \cdot \dfrac{1 \text{ mol sucrose}}{342.3 \text{ g}}}{0.225 \text{ kg } H_2O} = 0.195 \ m$

$\Delta T_{\text{fp}} = (-1.86 \ °C/m)(0.195 \ m) = -0.362 \ °C$

$T_{\text{fp}} = -0.362 \ °C$

14.38 $11 \text{ g} \cdot \dfrac{1 \text{ mol } C_2H_5OH}{46.1 \text{ g}} = 0.24 \text{ mol } C_2H_5OH$

$m_{C_2H_5OH} = \dfrac{0.24 \text{ mol } C_2H_5OH}{0.089 \text{ kg } H_2O} = 2.7 \ m$

$\Delta T_{fp} = (-1.86 \ ^\circ C/m)(2.7 \ m) = -5.0 \ ^\circ C$

$T_{fp} = -5.0 \ ^\circ C$ The solution will begin freeze if it is chilled to $-20 \ ^\circ C$.

14.39 $\Delta T_{bp} = 80.26 \ ^\circ C - 80.10 \ ^\circ C = 0.16 \ ^\circ C$

$m_{solute} = \dfrac{\Delta T_{bp}}{K_{bp}} = \dfrac{0.16 \ ^\circ C}{2.53 \ ^\circ C/m} = 0.063 \ m$

$\dfrac{0.063 \text{ mol solute}}{1 \text{ kg benzene}} \cdot 0.01112 \text{ kg benzene} = 7.0 \times 10^{-4} \text{ mol solute}$

$\dfrac{0.255 \text{ g}}{7.0 \times 10^{-4} \text{ mol}} = 360 \text{ g/mol}$

$\dfrac{360 \text{ g/mol}}{184 \text{ g/mol}} = 2$ The molecular formula is $(C_{10}H_8Fe)_2$ or $C_{20}H_{16}Fe_2$

14.40 $\Delta T_{bp} = 62.22 \ ^\circ C - 61.70 \ ^\circ C = 0.52 \ ^\circ C$

$m_{BHA} = \dfrac{\Delta T_{bp}}{K_{bp}} = \dfrac{0.52 \ ^\circ C}{3.63 \ ^\circ C/m} = 0.14 \ m$

$\dfrac{0.14 \text{ mol BHA}}{1 \text{ kg } CHCl_3} \cdot 0.0250 \text{ kg } CHCl_3 = 0.0035 \text{ mol BHA}$

$\dfrac{0.640 \text{ g BHA}}{0.0035 \text{ mol BHA}} = 180 \text{ g/mol}$

14.41 $\Delta T_{bp} = 61.82 \ ^\circ C - 61.70 \ ^\circ C = 0.12 \ ^\circ C$

$m_{benzyl\ acetate} = \dfrac{\Delta T_{bp}}{K_{bp}} = \dfrac{0.12 \ ^\circ C}{3.63 \ ^\circ C/m} = 0.033 \ m$

$\dfrac{0.033 \text{ mol benzyl acetate}}{1 \text{ kg } CHCl_3} \cdot 0.0250 \text{ kg } CHCl_3 = 8.3 \times 10^{-4} \text{ mol benzyl acetate}$

$\dfrac{0.125 \text{ g benzyl acetate}}{8.3 \times 10^{-4} \text{ mol benzyl acetate}} = 150 \text{ g/mol}$

14.42 $\Delta T_{bp} = 80.34 \ ^\circ C - 80.10 \ ^\circ C = 0.24 \ ^\circ C$

$m_{anthracene} = \dfrac{\Delta T_{bp}}{K_{bp}} = \dfrac{0.24 \ ^\circ C}{2.53 \ ^\circ C/m} = 0.095 \ m$

$\dfrac{0.095 \text{ mol anthracene}}{1 \text{ kg benzene}} \cdot 0.0300 \text{ kg benzene} = 0.0028 \text{ mol anthracene}$

$\dfrac{0.500 \text{ g anthracene}}{0.0028 \text{ mol anthracene}} = 180 \text{ g/mol}$

$\dfrac{180 \text{ g/mol}}{89 \text{ g/mol}} = 2$ The molecular formula is $(C_7H_5)_2$ or $C_{14}H_{10}$

14.43 $m_{\text{solute}} = \dfrac{\Delta T_{\text{fp}}}{K_{\text{fp}}} = \dfrac{-0.040\ ^{\circ}\text{C}}{-1.86\ ^{\circ}\text{C}/m} = 0.022\ m$

$\dfrac{0.022\ \text{mol solute}}{1\ \text{kg H}_2\text{O}} \cdot 0.0500\ \text{kg H}_2\text{O} = 0.0011\ \text{mol solute}$

$\dfrac{0.180\ \text{g solute}}{0.0011\ \text{mol solute}} = 170\ \text{g/mol}$

14.44 $m_{\text{solute}} = \dfrac{\Delta T_{\text{fp}}}{K_{\text{fp}}} = \dfrac{-0.197\ ^{\circ}\text{C}}{-1.86\ ^{\circ}\text{C}/m} = 0.106\ m$

$\dfrac{0.106\ \text{mol aluminon}}{1\ \text{kg H}_2\text{O}} \cdot 0.0500\ \text{kg H}_2\text{O} = 0.00530\ \text{mol aluminon}$

$\dfrac{2.50\ \text{g aluminon}}{0.00530\ \text{mol aluminon}} = 472\ \text{g/mol}$

14.45 $\Delta T_{\text{fp}} = 69.40\ ^{\circ}\text{C} - 70.03\ ^{\circ}\text{C} = -0.63\ ^{\circ}\text{C}$

$m_{\text{naphthalene}} = \dfrac{\Delta T_{\text{fp}}}{K_{\text{fp}}} = \dfrac{-0.63\ ^{\circ}\text{C}}{-8.00\ ^{\circ}\text{C}/m} = 0.079\ m$

$\dfrac{0.079\ \text{mol naphthalene}}{1\ \text{kg biphenyl}} \cdot 0.0100\ \text{kg biphenyl} = 7.9 \times 10^{-4}\ \text{mol naphthalene}$

$\dfrac{0.100\ \text{g naphthalene}}{7.9 \times 10^{-4}\ \text{mol naphthalene}} = 130\ \text{g/mol}$

14.46 $m_{\text{phenylcarbinol}} = \dfrac{\Delta T_{\text{fp}}}{K_{\text{fp}}} = \dfrac{-0.36\ ^{\circ}\text{C}}{-1.86\ ^{\circ}\text{C}/m} = 0.19\ m$

$\dfrac{0.19\ \text{mol phenylcarbinol}}{1\ \text{kg H}_2\text{O}} \cdot 0.0250\ \text{kg H}_2\text{O} = 0.048\ \text{mol phenylcarbinol}$

$\dfrac{0.52\ \text{g phenylcarbinol}}{0.048\ \text{mol phenylcarbinol}} = 110\ \text{g/mol}$

14.47 $m_{\text{LiF}} = \dfrac{52.5\ \text{g} \cdot \dfrac{1\ \text{mol LiF}}{25.94\ \text{g}}}{0.306\ \text{kg H}_2\text{O}} = 6.61\ m$

$\Delta T_{\text{fp}} = (-1.86\ ^{\circ}\text{C}/m)(6.61\ m)(2) = -24.6\ ^{\circ}\text{C}$

$T_{\text{fp}} = -24.6\ ^{\circ}\text{C}$

14.48 $m_{\text{NaCl}} = \dfrac{\Delta T_{\text{fp}}}{K_{\text{fp}} \cdot i} = \dfrac{-10.\ ^{\circ}\text{C}}{(-1.86\ ^{\circ}\text{C}/m)(1.85)} = 2.9\ m$

$\dfrac{2.9\ \text{mol NaCl}}{1\ \text{kg H}_2\text{O}} \cdot \dfrac{58.5\ \text{g}}{1\ \text{mol NaCl}} \cdot 3.0\ \text{kg H}_2\text{O} = 510\ \text{g NaCl}$

14.49

solute	solution concentration	particle concentration
(a) sugar	0.1 m	$(0.1 \times 1) = 0.1\ m$
(b) NaCl	0.1 m	$(0.1 \times 2) = 0.2\ m$
(c) $CaCl_2$	0.08 m	$(0.08 \times 3) = 0.24\ m$
(d) Na_2SO_4	0.04 m	$(0.04 \times 3) = 0.12\ m$

Freezing point increases as the particle concentration decreases:

0.08 m $CaCl_2$ < 0.1 m NaCl < 0.04 m Na_2SO_4 < 0.1 m sugar

14.50

solute	solution concentration	particle concentration
(a) ethylene glycol	0.20 m	$(0.20 \times 1) = 0.20\ m$
(b) K_2SO_4	0.12 m	$(0.12 \times 3) = 0.36\ m$
(c) $MgCl_2$	0.10 m	$(0.10 \times 3) = 0.30\ m$
(d) KBr	0.12 m	$(0.12 \times 2) = 0.24\ m$

Freezing point decreases as the particle concentration increases:

0.20 m ethylene glycol > 0.12 m KBr > 0.10 m $MgCl_2$ > 0.12 m K_2SO_4

14.51 $3.00\,\text{g C}_9\text{H}_{11}\text{NO}_2 \cdot \dfrac{1\ \text{mol C}_9\text{H}_{11}\text{NO}_2}{165.2\ \text{g}} = 0.0182\ \text{mol C}_9\text{H}_{11}\text{NO}_2$

$m_{C_9H_{11}NO_2} = \dfrac{0.0182\ \text{mol C}_9\text{H}_{11}\text{NO}_2}{0.09700\ \text{kg H}_2\text{O}} = 0.187\ m$

(a) $\Delta T_{fp} = K_{fp} m_{C_9H_{11}NO_2} = (-1.86\ °C/m)(0.187\ m) = -0.348\ °C$

$T_{fp} = -0.348\ °C$

(b) $\Delta T_{bp} = K_{bp} m_{C_9H_{11}NO_2} = (0.5121\ °C/m)(0.187\ m) = 0.0959\ °C$

$T_{bp} = 100.0959\ °C$

(c) $\Pi = cRT = \left(\dfrac{0.0182\ \text{mol}}{0.09700\ \text{L}} \right)(0.082057\ \text{L} \cdot \text{atm/K} \cdot \text{mol})(298\ \text{K}) = 4.58\ \text{atm}$

The osmotic pressure is large and can be measured with the least experimental error.

14.52 Concentration of ions in solution = (0.16 M)(1.9) = 0.30 M

$\Pi = cRT = (0.30\ \text{mol/L})(0.082057\ \text{L·atm/K·mol})(310.\ \text{K}) = 7.7\ \text{atm}$

14.53 $n = \dfrac{\Pi V}{RT} = \dfrac{\left(3.1\ \text{mm Hg} \cdot \dfrac{1\ \text{atm}}{760\ \text{mm Hg}} \right)(1.00\ \text{L})}{(0.082057\ \text{L} \cdot \text{atm/K} \cdot \text{mol})(298\ \text{K})} = 1.7 \times 10^{-4}\ \text{mol bovine insulin}$

$\dfrac{1.00\ \text{g}}{1.7 \times 10^{-4}\ \text{mol}} = 6.0 \times 10^3\ \text{g/mol}$

14.54   Concentration of ions in solution = (0.0120 M)(1.94) = 0.0233 M

$\Pi = cRT$ = (0.0233 mol/L)(0.08257 L·atm/K·mol)(273 K) = 0.522 atm

14.55   (a) $BaCl_2(aq) + Na_2SO_4(aq) \rightarrow BaSO_4(s) + 2\ NaCl(aq)$

(b) Initially the $BaSO_4$ particles form a colloidal suspension.

(c) Over time the particles of solid $BaSO_4$ grow and precipitate.

14.56   diameter = 1.0×10^2 nm, radius = 50. nm

(a) $V = \frac{4}{3}\pi r^3 = \frac{4}{3}\pi (50.\ nm)^3 = 5.2 \times 10^5\ nm^3$

$A = 4\pi r^2 = 4\pi (50.\ nm)^2 = 3.1 \times 10^4\ nm^2$

(b) $1.0\ cm^3 \cdot \dfrac{1\ sphere}{5.2 \times 10^5\ nm^3} \cdot \left(\dfrac{10^7\ nm}{1\ cm}\right)^3 = 1.9 \times 10^{15}$ spheres

$1.9 \times 10^{15}\ spheres \cdot \dfrac{3.1 \times 10^4\ nm^2}{1\ sphere} \cdot \left(\dfrac{1\ m}{10^9\ nm}\right)^2 = 60.\ m^2$

14.57 Li_2SO_4 should have the more exothermic heat of hydration because the lithium ion is smaller than the cesium ion.

14.58   (a) The 0.10 m Na_2SO_4 solution has a higher particle concentration (0.30 m) so it should have the higher boiling point.

(b) The 0.30 m NH_4NO_3 solution has a lower particle concentration (0.60 m) so it should have the higher water vapor pressure.

14.59

solute	solution concentration	particle concentration
(a) $HOCH_2CH_2OH$	0.35 m	$(0.35 \times 1) = 0.35\ m$
(b) sugar	0.50 m	$(0.50 \times 1) = 0.50\ m$
(c) KBr	0.20 m	$(0.20 \times 2) = 0.40\ m$
(d) Na_2SO_4	0.20 m	$(0.20 \times 3) = 0.60\ m$

(i)   Vapor pressure increases as the particle concentration decreases:

0.20 m Na_2SO_4 < 0.50 m sugar < 0.20 m KBr < 0.35 m $HOCH_2CH_2OH$

(ii) Boiling point increases as the particle concentration increases:

0.35 m $HOCH_2CH_2OH$ < 0.20 m KBr < 0.50 m sugar < 0.20 m Na_2SO_4

14.60   (a)   Weight % = $\dfrac{1130 \text{ g NaCl}}{1130 \text{ g NaCl} + 7250 \text{ g H}_2\text{O}}$ · 100% = 13.5%

     (b)   1130 g NaCl · $\dfrac{1 \text{ mol NaCl}}{58.44 \text{ g}}$ = 19.3 mol NaCl

            7250 g H$_2$O · $\dfrac{1 \text{ mol H}_2\text{O}}{18.02 \text{ g}}$ = 402 mol H$_2$O

            $X_{\text{NaCl}} = \dfrac{19.3 \text{ mol NaCl}}{19.3 \text{ mol NaCl} + 402 \text{ mol H}_2\text{O}}$ = 0.0459

     (c) $m_{\text{NaCl}} = \dfrac{19.3 \text{ mol NaCl}}{7.25 \text{ kg H}_2\text{O}}$ = 2.67 m

14.61   53.0 g DMG · $\dfrac{1 \text{ mol DMG}}{116.1 \text{ g}}$ = 0.457 mol DMG

        525 g C$_2$H$_5$OH · $\dfrac{1 \text{ mol C}_2\text{H}_5\text{OH}}{46.07 \text{ g}}$ = 11.4 mol C$_2$H$_5$OH

     (a) $X_{\text{DMG}} = \dfrac{0.457 \text{ mol DMG}}{0.457 \text{ mol DMG} + 11.4 \text{ mol C}_2\text{H}_5\text{OH}}$ = 0.0385

     (b) $m_{\text{DMG}} = \dfrac{0.457 \text{ mol DMG}}{0.525 \text{ kg C}_2\text{H}_5\text{OH}}$ = 0.870 m

     (c) $P_{\text{C}_2\text{H}_5\text{OH}} = X_{\text{C}_2\text{H}_5\text{OH}} P^{\circ}_{\text{C}_2\text{H}_5\text{OH}}$ = (1 − 0.0386)(760 mm Hg) = 730.7 mm Hg

     (d) $\Delta T_{\text{bp}} = K_{\text{bp}} m_{\text{C}_2\text{H}_5\text{OH}}$ = (1.22 °C/m)(0.870 m) = 1.06 °C

         T_{bp} = 78.4 °C + 1.06 °C = 79.5 °C

14.62   10.7 mol NaOH · $\dfrac{40.00 \text{ g}}{1 \text{ mol NaOH}}$ = 428 g NaOH

        1 × 10^3 g H$_2$O · $\dfrac{1 \text{ mol H}_2\text{O}}{18.02 \text{ g}}$ = 55.5 mol H$_2$O

        (428 g + 1000 g) · $\dfrac{1 \text{ cm}^3}{1.33 \text{ g}}$ · $\dfrac{1 \text{ mL}}{1 \text{ cm}^3}$ · $\dfrac{1 \text{ L}}{10^3 \text{ mL}}$ = 1.07 L solution

     (a) $X_{\text{NaOH}} = \dfrac{10.7 \text{ mol NaOH}}{10.7 \text{ mol NaOH} + 55.5 \text{ mol H}_2\text{O}}$ = 0.162

     (b)   Weight % = $\dfrac{428 \text{ g NaOH}}{428 \text{ g NaOH} + 1000 \text{ g H}_2\text{O}}$ · 100% = 30.0%

     (c) $M_{\text{NaOH}} = \dfrac{10.7 \text{ mol NaOH}}{1.07 \text{ L solution}}$ = 9.97 M

14.63 $14.8 \text{ mol NH}_3 \cdot \dfrac{17.03 \text{ g}}{1 \text{ mol NH}_3} = 252 \text{ g NH}_3$

$1000 \text{ mL solution} \cdot \dfrac{0.90 \text{ g}}{1 \text{ mL}} = 9.0 \times 10^2 \text{ g} = 0.90 \text{ kg}$

$9.0 \times 10^2 \text{ g solution} - 252 \text{ g NH}_3 = 650 \text{ g H}_2\text{O}$

$650 \text{ g H}_2\text{O} \cdot \dfrac{1 \text{ mol H}_2\text{O}}{18.0 \text{ g}} = 36 \text{ mol H}_2\text{O}$

$m = \dfrac{14.8 \text{ mol NH}_3}{0.65 \text{ kg}} = 23 \ m$

$X_{\text{NH}_3} = \dfrac{14.8 \text{ mol NH}_3}{14.8 \text{ mol NH}_3 + 36 \text{ mol H}_2\text{O}} = 0.29$

$\text{Weight \%} = \dfrac{252 \text{ g NH}_3}{9.0 \times 10^2 \text{ g solution}} \cdot 100\% = 28\%$

14.64 $m_{\text{Ca(NO}_3)_2} = \dfrac{2.00 \text{ g} \cdot \dfrac{1 \text{ mol Ca(NO}_3)_2}{164.1 \text{ g}}}{0.75 \text{ kg H}_2\text{O}} = 0.016 \ m$

$m_{\text{ions}} = \dfrac{0.016 \text{ mol Ca(NO}_3)_2}{1 \text{ kg H}_2\text{O}} \cdot \dfrac{3 \text{ mol ions}}{1 \text{ mol Ca(NO}_3)_2} = 0.049 \ m$

14.65 $\text{Na}_2\text{SO}_4(s) \rightarrow 2 \text{ Na}^+(aq) + \text{SO}_4^{2-}(aq)$

$\dfrac{0.100 \text{ mol ions}}{1 \text{ kg H}_2\text{O}} \cdot 0.125 \text{ kg H}_2\text{O} = 0.0125 \text{ mol ions}$

$0.0125 \text{ mol ions} \cdot \dfrac{1 \text{ mol Na}_2\text{SO}_4}{3 \text{ mol ions}} \cdot \dfrac{142.0 \text{ g}}{1 \text{ mol Na}_2\text{SO}_4} = 0.592 \text{ g Na}_2\text{SO}_4$

14.66

solute	solution concentration	particle concentration
(i) $HOCH_2CH_2OH$	0.20 m	$(0.20 \times 1) = 0.20 \ m$
(ii) $CaCl_2$	0.10 m	$(0.10 \times 3) = 0.30 \ m$
(iii) KBr	0.12 m	$(0.12 \times 2) = 0.24 \ m$
(iv) Na_2SO_4	0.12 m	$(0.12 \times 3) = 0.36 \ m$

(a) 0.12 m Na_2SO_4 Boiling point increases as the particle concentration increases

(b) 0.12 m Na_2SO_4 Freezing point decreases as the particle concentration increases

(c) 0.20 m $HOCH_2CH_2OH$ Vapor pressure increases as particle concentration decreases

14.67   (a) 0.20 m KBr (higher particle concentration, 0.40 m)

(b) 0.10 m Na_2CO_3 (higher particle concentration, 0.30 m)

14.68 $\quad m_{NaCl} = \dfrac{39.1 \text{ g} \cdot \dfrac{1 \text{ mol NaCl}}{58.44 \text{ g}}}{0.100 \text{ kg } H_2O} = 6.69 \, m$

$\Delta T_{bp} = K_{bp} m_{NaCl} i = (0.5121 \, ^\circ C/m)(6.69 \, m)(1.85) = 6.34 \, ^\circ C$

$T_{bp} = 100.00 \, ^\circ C + 6.34 \, ^\circ C = 106.34 \, ^\circ C$

14.69 $\quad m_{CaCl_2} = \dfrac{35.0 \text{ g} \cdot \dfrac{1 \text{ mol } CaCl_2}{111.0 \text{ g}}}{0.150 \text{ kg } H_2O} = 2.10 \, m$

$\Delta T_{fp} = K_{fp} m_{CaCl_2} i = (-1.86 \, ^\circ C/m)(2.10 \, m)(2.7) = -11 \, ^\circ C$

$T_{fp} = -11 \, ^\circ C$

14.70 $\quad \Delta T_{bp} = 61.82 \, ^\circ C - 61.70 \, ^\circ C = 0.12 \, ^\circ C$

$m_{solute} = \dfrac{\Delta T_{bp}}{K_{bp}} = \dfrac{0.12 \, ^\circ C}{3.63 \, ^\circ C/m} = 0.033 \, m$

$\dfrac{0.033 \text{ mol solute}}{1 \text{ kg } CHCl_3} \cdot 0.0250 \text{ kg } CHCl_3 = 8.3 \times 10^{-4} \text{ mol solute}$

$\dfrac{0.135 \text{ g solute}}{8.3 \times 10^{-4} \text{ mol solute}} = 160 \text{ g/mol}$

$\dfrac{160 \text{ g/mol}}{82 \text{ g/mol}} = 2 \qquad\qquad$ The molecular formula is $(C_5H_6O)_2$ or $C_{10}H_{12}O_2$

14.71 $\quad \Delta T_{bp} = 61.93 \, ^\circ C - 61.70 \, ^\circ C = 0.23 \, ^\circ C$

$m_{solute} = \dfrac{\Delta T_{bp}}{K_{bp}} = \dfrac{0.23 \, ^\circ C}{3.63 \, ^\circ C/m} = 0.063 \, m$

$\dfrac{0.063 \text{ mol hexachlorophene}}{1 \text{ kg } CHCl_3} \cdot 0.0250 \text{ kg } CHCl_3 = 0.0016 \text{ mol hexachlorophene}$

$\dfrac{0.640 \text{ g hexachlorophene}}{0.0016 \text{ mol hexachlorophene}} = 4.0 \times 10^2 \text{ g/mol}$

14.72 $\quad$ At 80 °C 1092 g NH_4CHO_2 will dissolve in 200 g of water (546 g/100 g). At 0 °C only 204 g NH_4CHO_2 will dissolve in 200 g of water (102 g/100 g).

1092 g – 204 g = 888 g NH_4CHO_2 precipitates at 0 °C

14.73 $\quad S_{N_2} = (8.42 \times 10^{-7} \text{ M/mm Hg})(585 \text{ mm Hg}) = 4.93 \times 10^{-4} \text{ mol/L}$

14.74   (15.5 mm Hg)(0.55) = 8.53 mm Hg

$$X_{H_2O} = \frac{P_{H_2O}}{P^{\circ}_{H_2O}} = \frac{8.53 \text{ mm Hg}}{15.5 \text{ mm Hg}} = 0.550 \qquad\qquad X_{C_3H_5(OH)_3} = 1 - 0.550 = 0.450$$

$$0.550 \text{ mol } H_2O \cdot \frac{18.02 \text{ g}}{1 \text{ mol } H_2O} = 9.91 \text{ g } H_2O$$

$$0.450 \text{ mol } C_3H_5(OH)_3 \cdot \frac{92.09 \text{ g}}{1 \text{ mol } C_3H_5(OH)_3} = 41.4 \text{ g } C_3H_5(OH)_3$$

$$\text{Weight \%} = \frac{41.4 \text{ g } C_3H_5(OH)_3}{41.4 \text{ g } C_3H_5(OH)_3 + 9.91 \text{ g } H_2O} \cdot 100\% = 80.7\%$$

14.75   (a) $c_{starch} = \dfrac{\Pi}{RT} = \dfrac{3.8 \text{ mm Hg} \cdot \dfrac{1 \text{ atm}}{760 \text{ mm Hg}}}{(0.082057 \text{ L} \cdot \text{atm/K} \cdot \text{mol})(298 \text{ K})} = 2.0 \times 10^{-4} \text{ mol/L}$

$$\frac{10.0 \text{ g/L}}{0.00020 \text{ mol/L}} = 4.9 \times 10^4 \text{ g/mol}$$

(b) $\Delta T_{fp} = K_{fp} m_{solute} = (-1.86 \text{ °C}/m)(2.0 \times 10^{-4} \text{ } m) = -3.8 \times 10^{-4} \text{ °C}$

The very small change in the freezing point would make it very difficult to determine the molar mass of starch using freezing-point depression.

14.76 $5 \text{ g} \cdot \dfrac{1 \text{ mol } CH_3CO_2H}{60.0 \text{ g}} = 0.08 \text{ mol } CH_3CO_2H$

$$95 \text{ g} \cdot \frac{1 \text{ mol } H_2O}{18.0 \text{ g}} = 5.3 \text{ mol } H_2O$$

$$X_{CH_3CO_2H} = \frac{0.08 \text{ mol } CH_3CO_2H}{0.08 \text{ mol } CH_3CO_2H + 5.8 \text{ mol } H_2O} = 0.016$$

$$m_{CH_3CO_2H} = \frac{0.08 \text{ mol } CH_3CO_2H}{0.095 \text{ kg } H_2O} = 0.9 \text{ } m$$

$$\frac{5 \times 10^{-3} \text{ mg } CH_3CO_2H}{100 \text{ g solution} \cdot \dfrac{1 \text{ mL}}{1 \text{ g}} \cdot \dfrac{1 \text{ L}}{10^3 \text{ mL}}} = 0.05 \text{ mg/L} = 0.05 \text{ ppm}$$

Calculating molarity requires knowing the total volume of the solution. Without knowing the density of the acetic acid solution it is impossible to calculate the molarity of the solution.

14.77   Benzene solution:

$$\Delta T_{fp} = 3.37 \text{ °C} - 5.50 \text{ °C} = -2.13 \text{ °C}$$

$$m_{solute} = \frac{\Delta T_{fp}}{K_{fp}} = \frac{-2.13 \text{ °C}}{-5.12 \text{ °C}/m} = 0.416 \text{ } m$$

$$\frac{0.416 \text{ mol acetic acid}}{1 \text{ kg benzene}} \cdot 0.100 \text{ kg benzene} = 0.0416 \text{ mol acetic acid}$$

$$\frac{5.00 \text{ g acetic acid}}{0.0416 \text{ mol acetic acid}} = 120. \text{ g/mol}$$

Aqueous solution:

$\Delta T_{fp} = -1.49\ °C$

$$m_{solute} = \frac{\Delta T_{fp}}{K_{fp}} = \frac{-1.49\ °C}{-1.86\ °C/m} = 0.801\ m$$

$$\frac{0.801\ mol\ acetic\ acid}{1\ kg\ H_2O} \cdot 0.100\ kg\ H_2O = 0.0801\ mol\ acetic\ acid$$

$$\frac{5.00\ g\ acetic\ acid}{0.0801\ mol\ acetic\ acid} = 62.4\ g/mol$$

The actual molar mass of acetic acid is 60.05 g/mol. The aqueous solution calculated molar mass is slightly higher, suggesting that the i value for acetic acid is slightly greater than 1 (the acid is weakly ionized in solution). This is consistent with acetic acid being a weak acid in aqueous solution. The benzene solution calculated molar mass is twice the actual molar mass, suggesting that the acetic acid molecules form dimers in benzene.

14.78 $$m_{HOCH_2CH_2OH} = \frac{\Delta T_{fp}}{K_{fp}} = \frac{-15.0\ °C}{-1.86\ °C/m} = 8.06\ m$$

$\Delta T_{bp} = K_{bp} m_{HOCH_2CH_2OH} = (+0.5121\ °C/m)(8.06\ m) = 4.13\ °C$

$T_{bp} = 100.00\ °C + 4.13\ °C = 104.13\ °C$

14.79 $Li_2SO_4(s) \rightarrow Li_2SO_4(aq)$

$\Delta H°_{soln} = \Delta H_f°[Li_2SO_4(aq)] - \Delta H_f°[Li_2SO_4(s)] = -1464.4\ kJ/mol - (-1436.4\ kJ/mol) = -28.0\ kJ/mol$

$K_2SO_4(s) \rightarrow K_2SO_4(aq)$

$\Delta H°_{soln} = \Delta H_f°[K_2SO_4(aq)] - \Delta H_f°[K_2SO_4(s)] = -1414.0\ kJ/mol - (-1437.7\ kJ/mol) = 23.7\ kJ/mol$

The enthalpy of solution for Li_2SO_4 is exothermic, and that for K_2SO_4 is endothermic

$LiCl(s) \rightarrow LiCl(aq)$

$\Delta H°_{soln} = \Delta H_f°[LiCl(aq)] - \Delta H_f°[LiCl(s)] = -445.6\ kJ/mol - (-408.6\ kJ/mol) = -37.0\ kJ/mol$

$KCl(s) \rightarrow KCl(aq)$

$\Delta H°_{soln} = \Delta H_f°[KCl(aq)] - \Delta H_f°[KCl(s)] = -419.5\ kJ/mol - (-436.7\ kJ/mol) = 17.2\ kJ/mol$

Again, the lithium salt has an exothermic enthalpy of solution and the potassium salt enthalpy of solution is endothermic.

14.80   The density of water is 0.997 g/cm^3, so 1000. mL of water will have a mass of 997 g.

$$\frac{997 \text{ g H}_2\text{O}}{1 \text{ L}} \cdot \frac{1 \text{ mol H}_2\text{O}}{18.02 \text{ g}} = 55.3 \text{ M}$$

$$\frac{55.3 \text{ mol H}_2\text{O}}{0.997 \text{ kg}} = 55.5 \ m$$

14.81   liquid: $X_{\text{toluene}} = \dfrac{1.0 \text{ mol}}{1.0 \text{ mol} + 2.0 \text{ mol}} = 0.33$ $X_{\text{benzene}} = \dfrac{2.0 \text{ mol}}{2.0 \text{ mol} + 1.0 \text{ mol}} = 0.67$

$P_{\text{total}} = P_{\text{toluene}} + P_{\text{benzene}} = X_{\text{toluene}}P^{\text{o}}_{\text{toluene}} + X_{\text{benzene}}P^{\text{o}}_{\text{benzene}}$

$P_{\text{total}} = (0.33)(22 \text{ mm Hg}) + (0.67)(75 \text{ mm Hg}) = 7.3 \text{ mm Hg} + 50. \text{ mm Hg} = 57 \text{ mm Hg}$

vapor: $X_{\text{toluene}} = \dfrac{P_{\text{toluene}}}{P^{\text{o}}_{\text{toluene}}} = \dfrac{7.3 \text{ mm Hg}}{57 \text{ mm Hg}} = 0.13$ $X_{\text{benzene}} = \dfrac{P_{\text{benzene}}}{P^{\text{o}}_{\text{benzene}}} = \dfrac{50. \text{ mm Hg}}{57 \text{ mm Hg}} = 0.87$

14.82 $50.0 \text{ mL C}_2\text{H}_5\text{OH} \cdot \dfrac{0.785 \text{ g}}{1 \text{ mL}} \cdot \dfrac{1 \text{ mol C}_2\text{H}_5\text{OH}}{46.07 \text{ g}} = 0.852 \text{ mol C}_2\text{H}_5\text{OH}$

$50.0 \text{ mL H}_2\text{O} \cdot \dfrac{1.00 \text{ g}}{1 \text{ mL}} \cdot \dfrac{1 \text{ mol H}_2\text{O}}{18.02 \text{ g}} = 2.77 \text{ mol H}_2\text{O}$

$X_{\text{C}_2\text{H}_5\text{OH}} = \dfrac{0.852 \text{ mol}}{0.852 \text{ mol} + 2.77 \text{ mol}} = 0.235$

$P_{\text{total}} = P_{\text{C2H5OH}} + P_{\text{H2O}} = X_{\text{C2H5OH}}P^{\text{o}}_{\text{C2H5OH}} + (1 - X_{\text{C2H5OH}})P^{\text{o}}_{\text{H2O}}$

$P_{\text{total}} = (0.235)(43.6 \text{ mm Hg}) + (1 - 0.235)(17.5 \text{ mm Hg}) = 23.6 \text{ mm Hg}$

14.83 $\Delta T_{\text{fp}} = 3.1 \ ^{\circ}\text{C} - 5.50 \ ^{\circ}\text{C} = -2.4 \ ^{\circ}\text{C}$

$m_{\text{solute}} = \dfrac{\Delta T_{\text{fp}}}{K_{\text{fp}}} = \dfrac{-2.4 \ ^{\circ}\text{C}}{-5.12 \ ^{\circ}\text{C}/m} = 0.47 \ m$

$\Delta T_{\text{bp}} = 82.6 \ ^{\circ}\text{C} - 80.10 \ ^{\circ}\text{C} = 2.5 \ ^{\circ}\text{C}$

$m_{\text{solute}} = \dfrac{\Delta T_{\text{bp}}}{K_{\text{bp}}} = \dfrac{2.5 \ ^{\circ}\text{C}}{2.53 \ ^{\circ}\text{C}/m} = 0.99 \ m$

The calculated molality at the freezing point of benzene is 0.47 m, whereas it is 0.99 m at the boiling point. A higher molality at the higher temperature indicates more molecules are dissolved. Therefore, assuming benzoic acid forms dimers like acetic acid, dimer formation is more prevalent at the lower temperature.

14.84 $\dfrac{\text{I}_2 \text{ solubility in CCl}_4}{\text{I}_2 \text{ solubility in H}_2\text{O}} = \dfrac{85}{1}$

x = mass of I_2 that dissolves in H_2O

$\dfrac{(5.0 \text{ mg} - x)/10. \text{ mL}}{x/25 \text{ mL}} = \dfrac{85}{1}$

$x = 0.14 \text{ mg I}_2$ dissolved in H_2O

$5.0 - x = 4.9 \text{ mg I}_2$ dissolved in CCl_4

14.85 $\quad m = \dfrac{2.0 \text{ g} \cdot \dfrac{1 \text{ mol } C_{13}H_{21}ClN_2O_2}{273 \text{ g}}}{0.0980 \text{ kg } H_2O} = 0.075 \ m$

$i = \dfrac{\Delta T_{fp}}{K_{fp}m} = \dfrac{-0.237 \ ^\circ C}{(-1.86 \ ^\circ C/m)(0.075 \ m)} = 1.7$

There are approximately 2 moles of ions in solution per mole of compound.

14.86 (a) $\quad m_{\text{maltose}} = \dfrac{\Delta T_{fp}}{K_{fp}} = \dfrac{-0.229 \ ^\circ C}{-1.86 \ ^\circ C/m} = 0.123 \ m$

$\dfrac{0.123 \text{ mol maltose}}{1 \text{ kg } H_2O} \cdot 0.09600 \text{ kg } H_2O = 0.0118 \text{ mol maltose}$

$\dfrac{4.00 \text{ g maltose}}{0.0118 \text{ mol maltose}} = 338 \text{ g/mol}$

(b) $\quad 100.00 \text{ g solution} \cdot \dfrac{1 \text{ mL}}{1.014 \text{ g}} = 98.62 \text{ mL}$

$c_{\text{maltose}} = \dfrac{4.00 \text{ g} \cdot \dfrac{1 \text{ mol maltose}}{338 \text{ g}}}{0.09862 \text{ L}} = 0.120 \text{ mol/L}$

at 25 $^\circ$C: $\Pi = cRT = (0.120 \text{ mol/L})(0.082057 \text{ L} \cdot \text{atm/K} \cdot \text{mol})(298 \text{ K}) = 2.93 \text{ atm}$

14.87 (a) Assume a mass of 1×10^6 g seawater

Cl^- $\quad 1.95 \times 10^4 \text{ g} \cdot \dfrac{1 \text{ mol}}{35.45 \text{ g}} = 550. \text{ mol } Cl^-$

Na^+ $\quad 1.08 \times 10^4 \text{ g} \cdot \dfrac{1 \text{ mol}}{22.99 \text{ g}} = 470. \text{ mol } Na^+$

Mg^{2+} $\quad 1.29 \times 10^3 \text{ g} \cdot \dfrac{1 \text{ mol}}{24.31 \text{ g}} = 53.1. \text{ mol } Mg^{2+}$

SO_4^{2-} $\quad 9.05 \times 10^2 \text{ g} \cdot \dfrac{1 \text{ mol}}{96.06 \text{ g}} = 9.42 \text{ mol } SO_4^{2-}$

Ca^{2+} $\quad 4.12 \times 10^2 \text{ g} \cdot \dfrac{1 \text{ mol}}{40.08 \text{ g}} = 10.3 \text{ mol } Ca^{2+}$

K^+ $\quad 3.80 \times 10^2 \text{ g} \cdot \dfrac{1 \text{ mol}}{39.10 \text{ g}} = 9.72 \text{ mol } K^+$

Br^- $\quad 67 \text{ g} \cdot \dfrac{1 \text{ mol}}{79.90 \text{ g}} = 0.84 \text{ mol } Br^-$

$m_{\text{ions}} = \dfrac{1103 \text{ mol ions}}{1 \times 10^3 \text{ kg } H_2O} = 1.103 \ m$

$\Delta T_{fp} = K_{fp}m_{\text{ions}} = (-1.86 \ ^\circ C/m)(1.103 \ m) = -2.05 \ ^\circ C$

$T_{fp} = -2.05 \ ^\circ C$

(b) $\Pi = cRT = \left(\dfrac{1.103 \text{ mol ions}}{1 \text{ L}} \right)(0.082057 \text{ L} \cdot \text{atm/K} \cdot \text{mol})(298 \text{ K}) = 27.0 \text{ atm}$

A pressure greater than 27.0 atm is required to purify seawater by reverse osmosis.

14.88   (a) The 10 m tree is equal to a column of water 10^4 mm tall. The equivalent column of mercury would be

$$10^4 \text{ mm Hg} \cdot \frac{1.0 \text{ mm Hg}}{13.6 \text{ mm H}_2\text{O}} = 735 \text{ mm Hg}$$

$$c = \frac{\Pi}{RT} = \frac{735 \text{ mm Hg} \cdot \dfrac{1 \text{ atm}}{760 \text{ mm Hg}}}{(0.082057 \text{ L} \cdot \text{atm/K} \cdot \text{mol})(293 \text{ K})} = 0.0402 \text{ M}$$

   (b) Assuming the density of sap is 1.0 g/mL, the mass of 1 L of sap is 10^3 g

$$\text{Weight \%} = \frac{(0.0402 \text{ mol/L})(342.3 \text{ g/mol})}{1.0 \times 10^3 \text{ g/L}} \cdot 100\% = 1.38\%$$

14.89   (a) $m = \dfrac{2.00 \text{ g} \cdot \dfrac{1 \text{ mol H}_2\text{SO}_4}{98.08 \text{ g}}}{0.09800 \text{ kg H}_2\text{O}} = 0.208 \; m$

$$i = \frac{\Delta T_{fp}}{K_{fp} m} = \frac{-0.796 \text{ °C}}{(-1.86 \text{ °C}/m)(0.208 \; m)} = 2.06$$

   (b) $H^+ + HSO_4^-$

14.90 $m = \dfrac{\Delta T_{fp}}{K_{fp} i} = \dfrac{-1.28 \text{ °C}}{(-1.86 \text{ °C}/m)(2)} = 0.344 \; m$

$$\frac{0.344 \text{ mol KX}}{1 \text{ kg H}_2\text{O}} \cdot 0.100 \text{ kg H}_2\text{O} = 0.0344 \text{ mol KX}$$

$$\frac{4.00 \text{ g KX}}{0.344 \text{ mol KX}} = 116 \text{ g/mol}$$

116 g/mol – 39 g/mol = 77 g/mol   The halide ion is probably Br^-

14.91   (a) Assume 100.0 g compound

$$22.1 \text{ g} \cdot \frac{1 \text{ mol B}}{10.81 \text{ g}} = 2.04 \text{ mol B} \qquad\qquad 77.9 \text{ g} \cdot \frac{1 \text{ mol F}}{19.00 \text{ g}} = 4.10 \text{ mol F}$$

$$\frac{4.10 \text{ mol F}}{2.04 \text{ mol B}} = \frac{2 \text{ mol F}}{1 \text{ mol B}} \qquad\qquad \text{The empirical formula is } BF_2$$

$$X_{C_6H_6} = \frac{P_{C_6H_6}}{P^\circ_{C_6H_6}} = \frac{94.16 \text{ mm Hg}}{95.26 \text{ mm Hg}} = 0.9885$$

$$10.0 \text{ g} \cdot \frac{1 \text{ mol } C_6H_6}{78.11 \text{ g}} = 0.128 \text{ mol } C_6H_6$$

$$0.9885 = \frac{0.128 \text{ mol } C_6H_6}{0.128 \text{ mol } C_6H_6 + x \text{ mol solute}}$$

$$x = 0.00150 \text{ mol solute}$$

$$\frac{0.146 \text{ g solute}}{0.00150 \text{ mol solute}} = 97.6 \text{ g/mol}$$

$$\frac{97.6 \text{ g/mol}}{48.81 \text{ g/mol}} = 2 \qquad\qquad \text{The molecular formula is } (BF_2)_2 \text{ or } B_2F_4$$

(b)

All bond angles are 120°; the boron atom is sp^2 hybridized

14.92   Compound contains 73.94% C, 8.27% H, and 17.79% Cr

$$73.94 \text{ g} \cdot \frac{1 \text{ mol C}}{12.011 \text{ g}} = 6.156 \text{ mol C}$$

$$8.27 \text{ g} \cdot \frac{1 \text{ mol H}}{1.008 \text{ g}} = 8.20 \text{ mol H}$$

$$17.79 \text{ g} \cdot \frac{1 \text{ mol Cr}}{51.996 \text{ g}} = 0.3421 \text{ mol Cr}$$

$$\frac{6.156 \text{ mol C}}{0.3421 \text{ mol Cr}} = \frac{18 \text{ mol C}}{1 \text{ mol Cr}} \qquad\qquad \frac{8.20 \text{ mol H}}{0.3421 \text{ mol Cr}} = \frac{24 \text{ mol H}}{1 \text{ mol Cr}}$$

The empirical formula is $C_{18}H_{24}Cr$

$$n = \frac{\Pi V}{RT} = \frac{\left(3.17 \text{ mm Hg} \cdot \dfrac{1 \text{ atm}}{760 \text{ mm Hg}} \right)(0.100 \text{ L})}{(0.082057 \text{ L} \cdot \text{atm/K} \cdot \text{mol})(298.2 \text{ K})} = 1.70 \times 10^{-5} \text{ mol}$$

$$\frac{5.00 \times 10^{-3} \text{ g compound}}{1.70 \times 10^{-5} \text{ mol}} = 293 \text{ g/mol}$$

The empirical formula weight is 292.4 g/mol, so the molecular formula is also $C_{18}H_{24}Cr$

14.93   When the solids dissolve in water, $CaCl_2$ produces three ions per mole of solute while NaCl produces only two moles of ions per mole of solute. The solution with a higher concentration of ions (particles) will have a lower freezing point.

14.94   The solution inside the cucumber has a higher solvent concentration than the concentrated salt solution. The solvent molecules flow out of the cucumber, and the cucumber shrivels.

14.95   At the particulate level, Na^+ and Cl^- ions are still leaving the solid state and entering solution. Concurrently, solid NaCl is forming from Na^+ and Cl^- ions in solution.

14.96   Make a solution from a known quantity of solute (with unknown molar mass) and solvent. Measure the freezing point depression of the solution and use this to calculate the molality of the solution. From this determine the amount of solute (mol) in the solution. The ratio of the mass and amount of solute gives the molar mass.

14.97   (a) ionic solid, soluble in water

         (b) polar, soluble in water

         (c) nonpolar, soluble in benzene

         (d) ionic solid, soluble in water

14.98   All of the alcohols contain a polar —OH group that can interact with polar water molecules. The smaller alcohols are miscible with water because of this polar group. However, with an increase in the size of the hydrocarbon group, the organic group (the nonpolar part of the molecule) has become a larger fraction of the molecule, and properties associated with nonpolarity begin to dominate.

14.99   The C—C and C—H bonds in hydrocarbons being nonpolar would tend to make such dispersions hydrophobic. The C—O and O—H bonds in starch present opportunities for hydrogen bonding with water, and hence such dispersions are expected to be hydrophilic.

14.100   10.0 g of ethylene glycol contains more moles of solute, so it has a greater influence on the vapor pressure.

14.101 $$M_{NaCl} = \frac{5.85 \text{ g} \cdot \dfrac{1 \text{ mol NaCl}}{58.44 \text{ g}}}{100 \times 10^{-3} \text{ L}} = 1 \text{ M}$$

$$M_{KNO_3} = \frac{8.88 \text{ g} \cdot \dfrac{1 \text{ mol KNO}_3}{101.1 \text{ g}}}{100 \times 10^{-3} \text{ L}} = 0.9 \text{ M}$$

The KNO_3 solution has a lower solute concentration and a higher solvent concentration, so solvent will flow from the KNO_3 solution to the NaCl solution.

14.102   Solvent (water) concentration is higher in fresh water than in ocean water, so solvent will flow into the protozoan and it will burst.

Chapter 15
Principles of Reactivity: Chemical Kinetics

INSTRUCTOR'S NOTES

The discussion of kinetics and mechanisms has been receiving more attention lately in introductory chemistry, although there is still some argument about its value at this level.

Students can recognize the need to be concerned with rates in such circumstances as:

- Biological systems (oxidation, energy release, protein synthesis – all to support living systems)

- Industrial production (producing a product fast enough to be profitable)

- Air pollution (smog development and dissipation)

Our emphasis is on the contrast in speeds of chemical reactions and the factors that go into determining those speeds. We also discuss the idea of a rate law and the important point that it must be experimentally determined. After discussing the first order rate law in particular, we spend about one half a lecture or so on catalysis.

In talking about kinetics our preference might have been to first describe common mechanisms and then see how they are evidenced by rate laws. One might think that students would come to a better appreciation of kinetics by taking such an approach. However, this does not seem to work in practice. The idea of a mechanism, as a hypothetical pathway for the reaction, is not an easy concept for them to grasp. It is good to note the insight gained from mechanisms developed from experimental rates, particularly when a proposed mechanism can be eliminated based on data. The connection between experiment and theory in kinetics is a great example of the complementary aspect of these two aspects of characterizing nature.

One area of difficulty for students when studying kinetics is the contrast between the fact that the rate law is related to the mechanism but not necessarily related to the stoichiometric equation. When discussing mechanisms, we always stress this point. As in previous chapters, there are several problem-solving tips and ideas.

The dramatic increase in rate caused by enzymes will be of interest to the life science students.

Graphing is central of some of the topics in kinetics. Spreadsheet programs can be used to produce plots as well as to experiment with various parameters to see the effect on rates and/or concentrations.

We believe these ideas are important in the course so we spend 3-4 lectures on the material.

SUGGESTED DEMONSTRATIONS

1. Effect of Concentration on Reaction Rate

- Figures 15.1 and 15.3 illustrate the measurement of reaction rate and the effect of reactant concentration and temperature on the rate.

- The burning of lycopodium powder in Figure 15.5 is a good demonstration showing the effect of surface area, although it is certainly more dramatic to explode lycopodium powder as outlined in Volume 1 of *Chemical Demonstrations* by Shakhashiri (page 103).

- Creary, X.; Morris, K. M. "A New Twist on the Iodine Clock Reaction: Determining the Order of a Reaction," *Journal of Chemical Education* **1999**, *76*, 530.

2.   Relationships Between Concentration and Time

- Some of the examples in this chapter are based on hydrogen peroxide decomposition because we commonly do this reaction as a demonstration. The details were outlined in Chapter 4 of this *Manual*.

3.   A Microscopic View of Reactions

- Eliason, R.; McMahon, T. "Temperature effect on reaction rates," *Journal of Chemical Education* **1981**, *58*, 354.

4.   Catalysts and Reaction Rate

- Mattson, B.; Fujita, J.; Catahan, R.; Cheng, W.; Greimann, J.; Hoette, T.; Khandhar, P.; Mattson, A.; Rajani, A.; Sullivan, P.; Perkins, R. "Demonstrating Heterogeneous Gas-Phase Catalysis with the Gas Reaction Catalyst Tube," *Journal of Chemical Education* **2003**, *80*, 768.

- White, C. "A Reaction That Takes Places in Beakers But Not in Conical Flasks," *Journal of Chemical Education* **2004**, *81*, 364.

- Summerlin, L.R.; Borgford, C.L.; Ealy, J.B. "Enzyme Kinetics: Effects of Temperature and an Inhibitor on Catalase Extracted from Potato," *Chemical Demonstrations: A Sourcebook for Teachers; 2nd Edition*, Vol. 2, p. 152.

5.   Additional Demonstrations

- In Volume 2 of *Chemical Demonstrations* by Shakhashiri the last chapter outlines many oscillating chemical reactions, which could be used as demonstrations in lectures on kinetics.

- Wilkinson, L. E. "Old Nassau Demonstration with Wilkinson Modification," *Journal of Chemical Education* **2004**, *81*, 1474.

- Wellman, W. E.; Noble, M. E. "Greening the Blue Bottle," *Journal of Chemical Education* **2003**, *80*, 537.

- Harrison, J. A.; Buckley, P. D. "Simulating Dynamic Equilibria," *Journal of Chemical Education* **2000**, *77*, 1013.

- Fortman, J.J. "The Old Nassau Demonstration: Educational and Entertaining Variations," *Journal of Chemical Education* **1992**, *69*, 236.

- Steffel, M.J. "Reduction of permanganate: A kinetics demonstration for general chemistry," *Journal of Chemical Education* **1990**, *67*, 598.

SOLUTIONS TO STUDY QUESTIONS

15.1   (a) $-\dfrac{1}{2}\left(\dfrac{\Delta[O_3]}{\Delta t}\right) = \dfrac{1}{3}\left(\dfrac{\Delta[O_2]}{\Delta t}\right)$

(b) $-\dfrac{1}{2}\left(\dfrac{\Delta[HOF]}{\Delta t}\right) = \dfrac{1}{2}\left(\dfrac{\Delta[HF]}{\Delta t}\right) = \dfrac{\Delta[O_2]}{\Delta t}$

15.2   (a) $-\dfrac{1}{2}\left(\dfrac{\Delta[NO]}{\Delta t}\right) = -\dfrac{\Delta[Br_2]}{\Delta t} = \dfrac{1}{2}\left(\dfrac{\Delta[NOBr]}{\Delta t}\right)$

(b) $-\dfrac{\Delta[N_2]}{\Delta t} = -\dfrac{1}{3}\left(\dfrac{\Delta[H_2]}{\Delta t}\right) = \dfrac{1}{2}\left(\dfrac{\Delta[NH_3]}{\Delta t}\right)$

15.3 $-\dfrac{\Delta[O_3]}{\Delta t} = -\dfrac{\Delta[O_2]}{\Delta t} \cdot \dfrac{2\ \text{mol}\ O_3}{3\ \text{mol}\ O_2} = -\dfrac{1.5\ \times\ 10^{-3}\ \text{mol/L}}{s} \cdot \dfrac{2\ \text{mol}\ O_3}{3\ \text{mol}\ O_2} = -1.0\ \times\ 10^{-3}\ \text{mol/L} \cdot s$

15.4 $\dfrac{\Delta[NH_3]}{\Delta t} = -\dfrac{\Delta[H_2]}{\Delta t} \cdot \dfrac{2\ \text{mol}\ NH_3}{3\ \text{mol}\ H_2} = \dfrac{4.5\ \times\ 10^{-4}\ \text{mol/L}}{\min} \cdot \dfrac{2\ \text{mol}\ NH_3}{3\ \text{mol}\ H_2} = 3.0\ \times\ 10^{-4}\ \text{mol/L} \cdot \min$

15.5   (a)

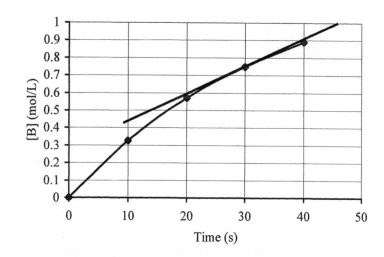

$\dfrac{\Delta[B]}{\Delta t} = \dfrac{(0.326 - 0.000)\ \text{mol/L}}{(10.0 - 0.00)\ s} = 0.0326\ \text{mol/L} \cdot s$

$= \dfrac{(0.572 - 0.326)\ \text{mol/L}}{(20.0 - 10.0)\ s} = 0.0246\ \text{mol/L} \cdot s$

$= \dfrac{(0.750 - 0.572)\ \text{mol/L}}{(30.0 - 20.0)\ s} = 0.0178\ \text{mol/L} \cdot s$

$= \dfrac{(0.890 - 0.750)\ \text{mol/L}}{(40.0 - 30.0)\ s} = 0.0140\ \text{mol/L} \cdot s$

The rate of change decreases from one time interval to the next due to the decrease in the amount of A remaining.

(b) A is consumed at half the rate B is formed. $\dfrac{\Delta[A]}{\Delta t} = -(0.0246 \text{ mol/L·s})(^1/_2) = -0.0123 \text{ mol/L·s}$

(c) Instantaneous rate is determined by drawing a tangent line to the plot at [B] = 0.750 mol/L. The slope of this line is approximately 0.016 mol/L·s

15.6   (a) The curve is a decreasing exponential curve.

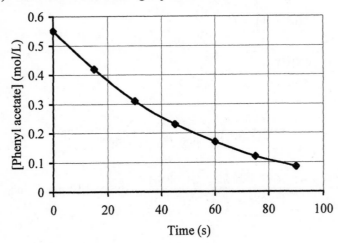

(b) $-\dfrac{\Delta[\text{phenyl acetate}]}{\Delta t} = -\dfrac{(0.31 - 0.42) \text{ mol/L}}{(30.0 - 15.0) \text{ s}} = 0.0073 \text{ mol/L} \cdot \text{s}$

$-\dfrac{\Delta[\text{phenyl acetate}]}{\Delta t} = -\dfrac{(0.085 - 0.12) \text{ mol/L}}{(90.0 - 75.0) \text{ s}} = 0.0023 \text{ mol/L} \cdot \text{s}$

The second rate is slower than the first because the rate depends on the concentration of phenyl acetate, which is smaller during the second time period.

(c) $-\dfrac{\Delta[\text{phenyl acetate}]}{\Delta t} = -\dfrac{(0.12 - 0.17) \text{ mol/L}}{(75.0 - 60.0) \text{ s}} = 0.0033 \text{ mol/L} \cdot \text{s}$

(d) Using the slope of a tangent drawn at 15 seconds, rate is approximately 0.008 mol/L·s

15.7   The reaction is second order in A and first order in B. The reaction is third order overall.

15.8   The rate will increase by a factor of 9 if the concentration of A is tripled. The rate will decrease by a factor of $^1/_4$ if the concentration of A is halved.

15.9   (a) Rate = $k[NO_2][O_3]$

(b) If the concentration of NO_2 is tripled, the rate will triple.

(c) If the concentration of O_3 is halved, the rate is halved.

15.10 (a) Rate = $k[NO]^2[Br_2]$

(b) If the concentration of Br_2 is tripled, the rate will triple.

(c) If the concentration of NO decreases by $^1/_2$, the rate will decrease by a factor of $^1/_4$.

15.11 (a) In the first two sets of data, $[O_2]$ is constant while $[NO]$ is doubled. The rate increases by a factor of four on going from the first set of data to the second, so the reaction is second order in NO. Looking at the first and third data sets, $[NO]$ is constant and $[O_2]$ doubles. The rate also doubles from the first data set to the third, so the reaction is first order in O_2.

(b) Rate $= k[NO]^2[O_2]$

(c) Rate $= \dfrac{1}{2}\left(\dfrac{\Delta[NO]}{\Delta t}\right) = \dfrac{1}{2}(2.5 \times 10^{-5}\ \text{mol/L} \cdot \text{s}) = 1.3 \times 10^{-5}\ \text{mol/L} \cdot \text{s}$

$k = \dfrac{\text{Rate}}{[NO]^2[O_2]} = \dfrac{1.3 \times 10^{-5}\ \text{mol/L} \cdot \text{s}}{(0.010\ \text{mol/L})^2(0.010\ \text{mol/L})} = 13\ \text{L}^2/\text{mol}^2 \cdot \text{s}$

(d) Rate $= k[NO]^2[O_2] = (13\ \text{L}^2/\text{mol}^2 \cdot \text{s})(0.015\ \text{mol/L})^2(0.0050\ \text{mol/L}) = 1.4 \times 10^{-5}\ \text{mol/L·s}$

(e) Rate at which O_2 is reacting $= \dfrac{1.0 \times 10^{-4}\ \text{mol/L}}{\text{s}} \cdot \dfrac{1\ \text{mol}\ O_2}{2\ \text{mol}\ NO} = 5.0 \times 10^{-5}\ \text{mol/L} \cdot \text{s}$

Rate at which NO_2 is forming $= \dfrac{1.0 \times 10^{-4}\ \text{mol/L}}{\text{s}} \cdot \dfrac{2\ \text{mol}\ NO_2}{2\ \text{mol}\ NO} = 1.0 \times 10^{-4}\ \text{mol/L} \cdot \text{s}$

15.12 (a) In the first two sets of data, $[H_2]$ is constant while $[NO]$ is halved. The rate decreases by a factor of four on going from the first set of data to the second, so the reaction is second order in NO. Looking at the second and third data sets, $[NO]$ is constant and $[H_2]$ doubles. The rate also doubles from the second data set to the third, so the reaction is first order in H_2.

(b) Rate $= k[NO]^2[H_2]$.

(c) Rate $= \dfrac{\Delta[N_2]}{\Delta t} = 0.136\ \text{mol/L} \cdot \text{s}$

$k = \dfrac{\text{Rate}}{[NO]^2[H_2]} = \dfrac{0.136\ \text{mol/L} \cdot \text{s}}{(0.420\ \text{mol/L})^2(0.122\ \text{mol/L})} = 6.32\ \text{L}^2/\text{mol}^2 \cdot \text{s}$

(d) Rate $= (6.32\ \text{L}^2/\text{mol}^2 \cdot \text{s})(0.350\ \text{mol/L})^2(0.205\ \text{mol/L}) = 0.159\ \text{mol/L·s}$

15.13 (a) In the first two data sets, $[NO]$ is constant while $[O_2]$ doubles. The rate doubles from experiment 1 to experiment 2, so the reaction is first order in O_2. Comparing experiments 2 and 3, $[O_2]$ is constant while $[NO]$ is halved. The rate decreases by a factor of $^1/_4$ from experiment 2 to experiment 3, so the reaction is second order in NO.

Rate $= k[NO]^2[O_2]$

(b) $k = \dfrac{\text{Rate}}{[NO]^2[O_2]} = \dfrac{3.4 \times 10^{-8}\ \text{mol/L} \cdot \text{h}}{(3.6 \times 10^{-4}\ \text{mol/L})^2(5.2 \times 10^{-3}\ \text{mol/L})} = 50.\ \text{L}^2/\text{mol}^2 \cdot \text{h}$

(c) Rate $= (50.\ \text{L}^2/\text{mol}^2 \cdot \text{s})(1.8 \times 10^{-4}\ \text{mol/L})^2(5.2 \times 10^{-3}\ \text{mol/L}) = 8.5 \times 10^{-9}\ \text{mol/L·h}$

15.14   (a) In the first two data sets, [CO] is constant while $[NO_2]$ is halved. The rate also halves from experiment 1 to experiment 2, so the reaction is first order in NO_2. Comparing experiments 1 and 3, $[NO_2]$ is constant while [CO] doubles. The rate doubles from experiment 1 to experiment 3, so the reaction is first order in NO.

Rate $= k[CO][NO_2]$

(b) $k = \dfrac{Rate}{[CO][NO_2]} = \dfrac{3.4 \times 10^{-8} \text{ mol/L} \cdot \text{h}}{(5.0 \times 10^{-4} \text{ mol/L})(0.36 \times 10^{-4} \text{ mol/L})} = 1.9 \text{ L/mol} \cdot \text{h}$

(c) Rate $= (1.9. \text{ L/mol} \cdot \text{h})(1.5 \times 10^{-3} \text{ mol/L})(0.72 \times 10^{-4} \text{ mol/L}) = 2.0 \times 10^{-7} \text{ mol/L} \cdot \text{h}$

15.15   (a) Comparing experiment 1 to experiment 2, $[O_2]$ remains constant, [CO] doubles, and the rate increases by a factor of four. The reaction is second order in CO. Comparing experiment 1 to experiment 3, [CO] is constant, $[O_2]$ doubles, and the rate doubles. The reaction is first order in O_2.

Rate $= k[CO]^2[O_2]$

(b) The reaction is second order in CO, first order in O_2, and third order overall.

(c) $k = \dfrac{Rate}{[CO]^2[O_2]} = \dfrac{3.68 \times 10^{-5} \text{ mol/L} \cdot \text{min}}{(0.02 \text{ mol/L})^2 (0.02 \text{ mol/L})} = 5 \text{ L}^2/\text{mol}^2 \cdot \text{min}$

15.16   (a) Comparing experiment 1 to experiment 2, $[H_2PO_4^-]$ remains constant, $[OH^-]$ doubles, and the rate increases by a factor of four. The reaction is second order in OH^-. Comparing experiment 1 to experiment 3, $[OH^-]$ is constant, $[H_2PO_4^-]$ triples, and the rate triples. The reaction is first order in $H_2PO_4^-$.

Rate $= k[H_2PO_4^-][OH^-]^2$

(b) $k = \dfrac{Rate}{[H_2PO_4^-][OH^-]^2} = \dfrac{0.0020 \text{ mol/L} \cdot \text{min}}{(0.0030 \text{ mol/L})(0.00040 \text{ mol/L})^2} = 4.2 \times 10^6 \text{ L}^2/\text{mol}^2 \cdot \text{min}$

(c) $[H_2PO_4^-] = \dfrac{Rate}{k[OH^-]^2} = \dfrac{0.0020 \text{ mol/L} \cdot \text{min}}{(4.2 \times 10^6 \text{ L}^2/\text{mol}^2 \cdot \text{min})(0.00033 \text{ mol/L})^2} = 0.0044 \text{ mol/L}$

15.17   The reaction is first order in sucrose

$\ln \dfrac{[C_{12}H_{22}O_{11}]}{[C_{12}H_{22}O_{11}]_0} = -kt$

$\ln \left(\dfrac{0.0132 \text{ M}}{0.0146 \text{ M}} \right) = -k(2.57 \text{ h})$

$k = 0.0392 \text{ h}^{-1}$

15.18 $\ln \dfrac{[N_2O_5]}{[N_2O_5]_0} = -kt$

$\ln \left(\dfrac{2.50 \text{ mg}}{2.56 \text{ mg}} \right) = -k(4.26 \text{ min})$

$k = 0.00557 \text{ min}^{-1}$

15.19 $\ln \dfrac{[SO_2Cl_2]}{[SO_2Cl_2]_0} = -kt$

$\ln\left(\dfrac{0.31 \times 10^{-3}\ \text{mol/L}}{1.24 \times 10^{-3}\ \text{mol/L}}\right) = -(2.8 \times 10^{-3}\ \text{min}^{-1})t$

$t = 5.0 \times 10^2\ \text{min}$

15.20 $\ln \dfrac{[C_3H_6]}{[C_3H_6]_0} = -kt$

$\ln\left(\dfrac{0.020\ \text{M}}{0.080\ \text{M}}\right) = -(5.4 \times 10^{-2}\ \text{h}^{-1})t$

$t = 26\ \text{h}$

15.21   The reaction is second order in ammonium cyanate

$\dfrac{1}{[NH_4NCO]} - \dfrac{1}{[NH_4NCO]_0} = kt$

$\dfrac{1}{0.180\ \text{mol/L}} - \dfrac{1}{0.229\ \text{mol/L}} = (0.0113\ \text{L/mol} \cdot \text{min})t$

$t = 105\ \text{min}$

15.22 $\dfrac{1}{[NO_2]} - \dfrac{1}{[NO_2]_0} = kt$

$\dfrac{1}{1.50\ \text{mol/L}} - \dfrac{1}{2.00\ \text{mol/L}} = (3.40\ \text{L/mol} \cdot \text{min})t$

$t = 0.0490\ \text{min}$

15.23   (a) When 15% has decomposed, the fraction remaining is 85/100

$\ln\left(\dfrac{85}{100}\right) = -(1.06 \times 10^{-3}\ \text{min}^{-1})t$

$t = 153\ \text{min}$

(b) When 85% has decomposed, the fraction remaining is 15/100

$\ln\left(\dfrac{15}{100}\right) = -(1.06 \times 10^{-3}\ \text{min}^{-1})t$

$t = 1790\ \text{min}$

15.24   When three-fourths of the sample has decomposed, the fraction remaining is $^1/_4$

$\ln\left(\dfrac{1}{4}\right) = -(2.4 \times 10^{-3}\ \text{s}^{-1})t$

$t = 580\ \text{s}$

15.25   The reaction is first order in N_2O_5

(a) $t_{1/2} = \dfrac{0.693}{k} = \dfrac{0.693}{5.0 \times 10^{-4} \text{ s}^{-1}} = 1400 \text{ s}$

(b) $\ln\left(\dfrac{1}{10}\right) = -(5.0 \times 10^{-4} \text{ s}^{-1})t$

$t = 4600 \text{ s}$

15.26 $k = \dfrac{0.693}{t_{1/2}} = \dfrac{0.693}{245 \text{ min}} = 2.83 \times 10^{-3} \text{ min}^{-1}$

$\ln\left(\dfrac{2.00 \times 10^{-4} \text{ mol}}{3.6 \times 10^{-3} \text{ mol}}\right) = -(2.83 \times 10^{-3} \text{ min}^{-1})t$

$t = 1.0 \times 10^{3} \text{ min}$

15.27 $\ln\left(\dfrac{x}{2.00 \text{ g}}\right) = -(40.8 \text{ min}^{-1})(0.0500 \text{ min})$

$\ln(x) - \ln(2.00 \text{ g}) = -(40.8 \text{ min}^{-1})(0.0500 \text{ min})$

$\ln(x) = -1.35$

$x = e^{-1.35} = 0.260 \text{ g azomethane remains}$

$(2.00 \text{ g} - 0.260 \text{ g}) \cdot \dfrac{1 \text{ mol CH}_3\text{NNCH}_3}{58.08 \text{ g}} \cdot \dfrac{1 \text{ mol N}_2}{1 \text{ mol CH}_3\text{NNCH}_3} \cdot \dfrac{28.01 \text{ g}}{1 \text{ mol N}_2} = 0.839 \text{ g N}_2$

15.28 $k = \dfrac{0.693}{t_{1/2}} = \dfrac{0.693}{30. \text{ min}} = 0.023 \text{ min}^{-1}$

$\ln\left(\dfrac{0.25 \text{ mg}}{7.50 \text{ mg}}\right) = -(0.023 \text{ min}^{-1})t$

$t = 150 \text{ min}$

15.29 $k = \dfrac{0.693}{t_{1/2}} = \dfrac{0.693}{12.70 \text{ h}} = 0.05457 \text{ h}^{-1}$

$\ln\dfrac{[^{64}\text{Cu}]}{[^{64}\text{Cu}]_0} = -(0.05457 \text{ h}^{-1})(64 \text{ h})$

$\text{fraction remaining} = \dfrac{[^{64}\text{Cu}]}{[^{64}\text{Cu}]_0} = 0.030$

15.30 $k = \dfrac{0.693}{t_{1/2}} = \dfrac{0.693}{2.7 \text{ days}} = 0.26 \text{ days}^{-1}$

$\ln\left(\dfrac{x}{5.6 \text{ mg}}\right) = -(0.26 \text{ days}^{-1})(1.0 \text{ day})$

$\ln(x) - \ln(5.6 \text{ mg}) = -(0.26 \text{ days}^{-1})(1.0 \text{ day})$

$\ln(x) = 1.46$

$x = e^{1.46} = 4.3 \text{ mg}$

15.31 $\ln\left(\dfrac{25}{100}\right) = -k(72 \text{ s})$

$k = 0.019 \text{ s}^{-1}$

$t_{1/2} = \dfrac{0.693}{k} = \dfrac{0.693}{0.019 \text{ s}^{-1}} = 36 \text{ s}$

Alternately, in a first-order reaction a sample decomposes 75% in two half-lives. $t_{1/2} = \dfrac{72 \text{ s}}{2} = 36 \text{ s}$

15.32 $k = \dfrac{0.693}{t_{1/2}} = \dfrac{0.693}{2.5 \times 10^3 \text{ min}} = 2.8 \times 10^{-4} \text{ min}^{-1}$

$\ln\dfrac{[SO_2Cl_2]}{[SO_2Cl_2]_0} = -(2.8 \times 10^{-4} \text{ min}^{-1})(750 \text{ min})$

fraction remaining $= \dfrac{[SO_2Cl_2]}{[SO_2Cl_2]_0} = 0.81$

15.33 (a) The plot of ln[sucrose] versus time is linear so the reaction is first order in sucrose.

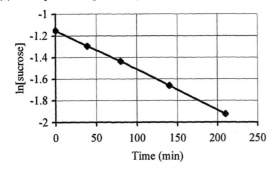 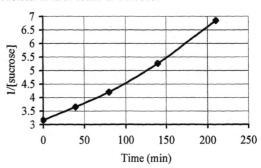

(b) Rate $= k[C_{12}H_{11}O_{22}]$

$\ln\left(\dfrac{0.274 \text{ mol/L}}{0.316 \text{ mol/L}}\right) = -k(39 \text{ min})$

$k = 0.0037 \text{ min}^{-1}$

(c) Using the ln[sucrose] versus time plot, ln[sucrose] $= -1.79$ when $t = 175$

$[C_{12}H_{11}O_{22}] = e^{-1.79} = 0.167 \text{ mol/L}$

15.34   The plot of ln[phenyl acetate] versus time is linear, so the reaction is first order in phenyl acetate.

$k = -$slope $= -(-0.0207$ min$^{-1}) = 0.0207$ min^{-1}

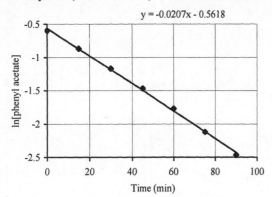
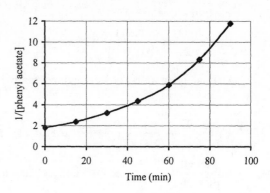

15.35   The plot of ln[N$_2$O] versus time is linear. $k = -$slope $= -(-0.0128$ min$^{-1}) = 0.0128$ min^{-1}

Rate $= k[$N$_2$O$] = (0.0128$ min$^{-1})(0.035$ mol/L$) = 4.5 \times 10^{-4}$ mol/L·min

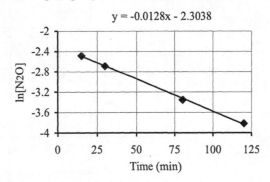

15.36   The plot of 1/[NH$_3$] versus time is linear, indicating that the reaction is second-order in [NH$_3$]. The slope of the line $= k = 9220$ L/mol·h.

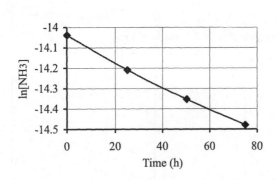
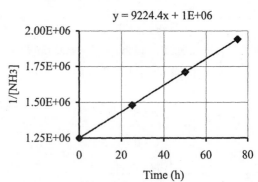

15.37   The reaction is second order in NO$_2$ Rate $= k[$NO$_2]^2$

$k =$ slope $= 1.1$ L/mol·s

15.38   The plot of ln[HOF] versus time is linear, indicating that the reaction is first order in HOF.

Rate = k[HOF] $k = -\text{slope} = -(-0.025\ \text{min}^{-1}) = 0.025\ \text{min}^{-1}$

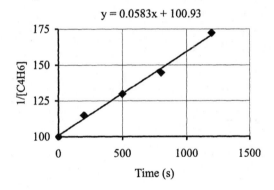

15.39   Rate = $(0.04\ \text{L/mol·s})[C_2F_4]^2$

15.40   (a) The plot of $1/[C_4H_6]$ versus time is linear, indicating that the reaction is second order in C_4H_6.

(b) $k = \text{slope} = 0.0583\ \text{L/mol·s}$

15.41 $\ln\dfrac{k_2}{k_1} = -\dfrac{E_a}{R}\left(\dfrac{1}{T_2} - \dfrac{1}{T_1}\right)$

$\ln\left(\dfrac{1.5 \times 10^{-3}\ \text{s}^{-1}}{3.46 \times 10^{-5}\ \text{s}^{-1}}\right) = -\dfrac{E_a}{8.3145 \times 10^{-3}\ \text{kJ/K·mol}}\left(\dfrac{1}{328\ \text{K}} - \dfrac{1}{298\ \text{K}}\right)$

$E_a = 102\ \text{kJ/mol}$

15.42 $\ln\dfrac{k_2}{k_1} = -\dfrac{E_a}{R}\left(\dfrac{1}{T_2} - \dfrac{1}{T_1}\right)$

$\ln\left(\dfrac{3k_1}{k_1}\right) = -\dfrac{E_a}{8.3145 \times 10^{-3}\ \text{kJ/K·mol}}\left(\dfrac{1}{310.\ \text{K}} - \dfrac{1}{300.\ \text{K}}\right)$

$E_a = 85\ \text{kJ/mol}$

15.43 $\ln\dfrac{k_2}{k_1} = -\dfrac{E_a}{R}\left(\dfrac{1}{T_2} - \dfrac{1}{T_1}\right)$

$\ln\dfrac{k_2}{0.0315\ \text{s}^{-1}} = -\dfrac{260\ \text{kJ/mol}}{8.3145\times10^{-3}\ \text{kJ/K}\cdot\text{mol}}\left(\dfrac{1}{850\ \text{K}} - \dfrac{1}{800\ \text{K}}\right)$

$\ln(k_2) - \ln(0.0315\ \text{s}^{-1}) = -\dfrac{260\ \text{kJ/mol}}{8.3145\times10^{-3}\ \text{kJ/K}\cdot\text{mol}}\left(\dfrac{1}{850\ \text{K}} - \dfrac{1}{800\ \text{K}}\right)$

$k_2 = 0.3\ \text{s}^{-1}$

15.44 $\ln\dfrac{k_2}{k_1} = -\dfrac{E_a}{R}\left(\dfrac{1}{T_2} - \dfrac{1}{T_1}\right)$

$\ln\left(\dfrac{1.02\times10^{-3}}{1.10\times10^{-4}}\right) = -\dfrac{E_a}{8.3145\times10^{-3}\ \text{kJ/mol}\cdot\text{K}}\left(\dfrac{1}{783\ \text{K}} - \dfrac{1}{743\ \text{K}}\right)$

$E_a = 270\ \text{kJ/mol}$

15.45

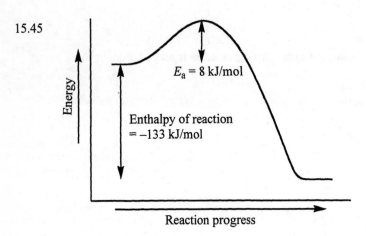

15.46   (a) The reaction is endothermic

(b) Yes, the reaction occurs in two steps

15.47   (a) Rate = $k[\text{NO}][\text{NO}_3]$

(b) Rate = $k[\text{Cl}][\text{H}_2]$

(c) Rate = $k[(\text{CH}_3)_3\text{CBr}]$

15.48   (a) Rate = $k[\text{Cl}][\text{ICl}]$

(b) Rate = $k[\text{O}][\text{O}_3]$

(c) Rate = $k[\text{NO}_2]^2$

15.49   (a) The second step (the slow step) is rate-determining

(b) Rate = $k[\text{O}_3][\text{O}]$

15.50   (a) $NO_2(g) + \cancel{NO_2(g)} \rightarrow NO(g) + \cancel{NO_3(g)}$

$\cancel{NO_3(g)} + CO(g) \rightarrow \cancel{NO_2(g)} + CO_2(g)$

_____

$NO_2(g) + CO(g) \rightarrow NO(g) + CO_2(g)$

(b) Both steps are bimolecular

(c) Rate $= k[NO_2]^2$

(d) $NO_3(g)$ is an intermediate

15.51   (a) $H_2O_2(aq) + I^-(aq) \rightarrow H_2O(\ell) + \cancel{OI^-(aq)}$

$H^+(aq) + \cancel{OI^-(aq)} \rightarrow \cancel{HOI(aq)}$

$\cancel{HOI(aq)} + H^+(aq) + I^-(aq) \rightarrow I_2(aq) + H_2O(\ell)$

_____

$H_2O_2(aq) + 2\,I^-(aq) + 2\,H^+(aq) \rightarrow I_2(aq) + 2\,H_2O(\ell)$

(b) Step 1 and Step 2 are bimolecular, Step 3 is termolecular.

(c) rate $= k[H_2O_2][I^-]$

(d) $OI^-(aq)$ and $HOI(aq)$ are intermediates.

15.52   (a) $CH_3OH + H^+ + Br^- \rightarrow CH_3Br + H_2O$

(b)

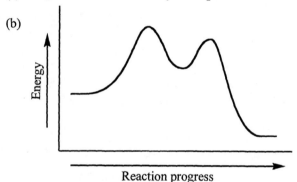

(c) Using the rate-determining step, the rate law is $-\dfrac{\Delta[CH_3OH]}{\Delta t} = k_2[CH_3OH_2^+][Br^-]$.

However, this rate law contains an intermediate, $CH_3OH_2^+$

Rate of production of $CH_3OH_2^+ = k_1[CH_3OH][H^+]$

$-\dfrac{\Delta[CH_3OH]}{\Delta t} = k_2\{k_1[CH_3OH][H^+]\}[Br^-] = k[CH_3OH][H^+][Br^-]$ $(k = k_1 \cdot k_2)$

15.53   (a) Reactants: $NO_2(g)$, $CO(g)$ Products: $NO(g)$, $CO_2(g)$ Intermediate: NO_3

(b)

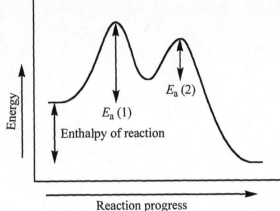

15.54   (a) $(CH_3)_3CBr + H_2O \rightarrow (CH_3)_3COH + HBr$

(b) Step 1, the slow step, is rate-determining.

(c) Rate = $k[(CH_3)_3CBr]$

15.55   The rate will double.

15.56 $(^1/_2)^5 = {}^1/_{32}$ remains

15.57   To prove a second-order rate dependence, plot $1/[OH^-]$ versus time. If the plot produces a straight line, the reaction is second order in OH^-.

15.58   (a) Comparing experiment 1 to experiment 2, $[H_2]$ remains constant, $[N_2]$ doubles, and the rate increases by a factor of four. The reaction is second order in N_2. Comparing experiment 1 to experiment 3, $[N_2]$ is constant, $[H_2]$ doubles, and the rate increases by a factor of eight. The reaction is third order in H_2.

Rate = $k[N_2]^2[H_2]^3$

(b) $k = \dfrac{Rate}{[N_2]^2[H_2]^3} = \dfrac{4.21 \times 10^{-5} \text{ mol/L} \cdot \text{min}}{(0.030 \text{ mol/L})^2(0.010 \text{ mol/L})^3} = 4.7 \times 10^4 \text{ L}^4/\text{mol}^4 \cdot \text{min}$

(c) third order

(d) fifth order

15.59   (a) Rate = $k[NH_3]$

(b) $\ln\left(\dfrac{0.26 \text{ mol/L}}{0.67 \text{ mol/L}}\right) = -k(19 \text{ s})$

$k = 0.050 \text{ s}^{-1}$

(c) $t_{1/2} = \dfrac{0.693}{k} = \dfrac{0.693}{0.050 \text{ s}^{-1}} = 14 \text{ s}$

15.60 (a) Comparing experiment 1 to experiment 2, $[Br_2]$ remains constant, $[NO]$ increases by a factor of four, and the rate increases by a factor of sixteen. The reaction is second order in NO.

(b) Comparing experiment 1 to experiment 3, $[NO]$ is constant, $[Br_2]$ increases by a factor of 2.5, and the rate increases by a factor of 2.5. The reaction is first order in Br_2.

(c) third order

15.61 (a) Rate $= k[CO_2]$

(b) $\ln\left(\dfrac{0.27 \text{ mol/L}}{0.38 \text{ mol/L}}\right) = -k(12 \text{ s})$

$k = 0.028 \text{ s}^{-1}$

(c) $t_{1/2} = \dfrac{0.693}{k} = \dfrac{0.693}{0.028 \text{ s}^{-1}} = 24 \text{ s}$

15.62 (a) The reaction is first order in CH_3NC. Rate $= k[CH_3NC]$

(b) $\ln[CH_3NC]_t = \ln[CH_3NC]_0 - kt$

(c) Estimating slope from the graph, $k = -\text{slope} = -(-2 \times 10^{-4} \text{ s}^{-1}) = 2 \times 10^{-4} \text{ s}^{-1}$

(d) $t_{1/2} = \dfrac{0.693}{k} = \dfrac{0.693}{2 \times 10^{-4} \text{ s}^{-1}} = 3 \times 10^3 \text{ s}$

(e) $[CH_3NC]_0 = e^{-4.1} = 0.0166 \text{ mol/L}$

$\ln\dfrac{[CH_3NC]}{0.0166 \text{ mol/L}} = -(2 \times 10^{-4} \text{ s}^{-1})(10{,}000 \text{ s})$

$\ln[CH_3NC] - \ln(0.0166 \text{ mol/L}) = -(2 \times 10^{-4} \text{ s}^{-1})(10{,}000 \text{ s})$

$[CH_3NC] = 0.002 \text{ mol/L}$

15.63 (a) The reaction is second order in C_2F_4. Rate $= k[C_2F_4]^2$

(b) $\dfrac{1}{0.080 \text{ M}} - \dfrac{1}{0.100 \text{ M}} = k(56 \text{ s})$ $\qquad\qquad$ $k = 0.045 \text{ L/mol} \cdot \text{s}$

(c) $\dfrac{1}{[C_2F_4]} - \dfrac{1}{0.100 \text{ M}} = (0.045 \text{ L/mol} \cdot \text{s})(600 \text{ s})$ $\qquad$ $[C_2F_4] = 0.03 \text{ M}$

(d) $\dfrac{1}{0.010 \text{ M}} - \dfrac{1}{0.100 \text{ M}} = (0.045 \text{ L/mol} \cdot \text{s})t$ $\qquad$ $t = 2000 \text{ s}$

15.64 (a) Comparing experiment 1 to experiment 2, $[CO]$ remains constant, $[NO_2]$ doubles, and the rate doubles. The reaction is first order in NO_2. Comparing experiment 1 to experiment 4, $[NO_2]$ is constant, $[CO]$ doubles, and the rate doubles. The reaction is first order in CO. Rate $= k[CO][NO_2]$

(b) The reaction is first order in NO_2 and first order in CO.

(c) $k = \dfrac{\text{Rate}}{[CO][NO_2]} = \dfrac{3.4 \times 10^{-8} \text{ mol/L} \cdot \text{h}}{(5.1 \times 10^{-4} \text{ mol/L})(0.35 \times 10^{-4} \text{ mol/L})} = 1.9 \text{ L/mol} \cdot \text{h}$

15.65   (a) Plot 1/[NH$_4$NCO] versus time and ln[NH$_4$NCO] versus time:

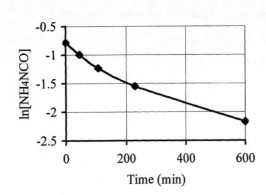
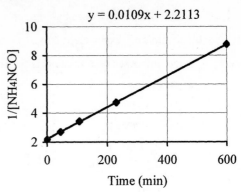

The plot of 1/[NH$_4$NCO] versus time is linear. The reaction is second-order in NH$_4$NCO.

(b) From the slope of the 1/[NH$_4$NCO] versus time plot, $k = 0.0109$ L/mol·min.

(c) $t_{1/2} = \dfrac{1}{[NH_4NCO]_0 k} = \dfrac{1}{(0.458 \text{ mol/L})(0.0109 \text{ L/mol} \cdot \text{min})} = 200. \text{ min}$

(d) $\dfrac{1}{[NH_4NCO]} - \dfrac{1}{0.458 \text{ mol/L}} = (0.0109 \text{ L/mol} \cdot \text{min})(720 \text{ min})$

$[NH_4NCO] = 0.0997 \text{ mol/L}$

15.66   (a) $k = \dfrac{0.693}{t_{1/2}} = \dfrac{0.693}{3.9 \text{ h}} = 0.18 \text{ h}^{-1}$

$\ln\left(\dfrac{x}{1.50 \text{ mg}}\right) = -(0.18 \text{ h}^{-1})(5.25 \text{ h})$

$\ln(x) - \ln(1.50 \text{ mg}) = -(0.18 \text{ h}^{-1})(5.25 \text{ h})$

$x = 0.59 \text{ mg}$

(b) $\ln\left(\dfrac{2.50 \times 10^{-6} \text{ mg}}{1.50 \text{ mg}}\right) = -(0.18 \text{ h}^{-1})t$

$t = 75 \text{ h}$

15.67   Mechanism 2: Rate $= k[NO_2][NO_2] = k[NO_2]^2$

The rate equation derived from Mechanism 2 matches the experimentally observed rate equation. Also, the two steps in Mechanism 2 add up to the overall reaction.

15.68   (a) In experiments 1 and 2, [F$_2$] and [NO$_2$F] are constant while the concentration of NO$_2$ doubles. The rate also doubles, so the reaction is first order in NO$_2$. In experiments 3 and 4, [F$_2$] doubles while [NO$_2$F] and [NO$_2$] remain constant. The rate also doubles, so the reaction is first order in F$_2$. Finally, in experiments 5 and 6 [F$_2$] and [NO$_2$] remain constant while [NO$_2$F] doubles. The rate remains constant, so the reaction is zero order in NO$_2$F. Rate $= k[F_2][NO_2]$

(b) The reaction is first order in F_2, first order in NO_2, and zero order in NO_2F.

(c) $k = \dfrac{2 \times 10^{-4} \text{ mol/L} \cdot \text{s}}{(0.001 \text{ mol/L})(0.005 \text{ mol/L})} = 40 \text{ L/mol} \cdot \text{s}$

15.69 $\ln\left(\dfrac{0.8}{1.0}\right) = -k(6.0 \text{ h})$

$k = 0.037 \text{ h}^{-1}$

$t_{1/2} = \dfrac{\ln 2}{k} = \dfrac{0.693}{0.037 \text{ h}^{-1}} = 19 \text{ hours}$

15.70 Plot $1/T$ versus $\ln k$

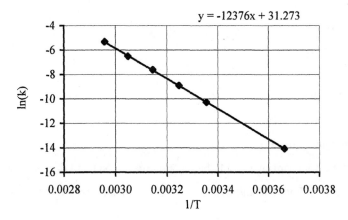

$y = -12376x + 31.273$

slope $= -12400 = -\dfrac{E_a}{R} = -\dfrac{E_a}{8.3145 \times 10^{-3} \text{ kJ/K} \cdot \text{mol}}$

$E_a = 103 \text{ kJ/mol}$

15.71 (a) $k = \dfrac{\ln 2}{t_{1/2}} = \dfrac{0.693}{25.0 \text{ min}} = 0.0277 \text{ min}^{-1}$

$\ln\dfrac{[CH_3OCH_3]}{8.00 \text{ g}} = -(0.0277 \text{ min}^{-1})(125 \text{ min})$

After 125 min, 0.251 g CH_3OCH_3 remain

After 145 min, 0.144 g CH_3OCH_3 remain

(b) $\ln\left(\dfrac{2.25 \text{ ng}}{7.60 \text{ ng}}\right) = -(0.0277 \text{ min}^{-1})t$

$t = 43.9 \text{ min}$

(c) $\ln\dfrac{[CH_3OCH_3]}{[CH_3OCH_3]_0} = -(0.0277 \text{ min}^{-1})(150 \text{ min})$

fraction remaining $= \dfrac{[CH_3OCH_3]}{[CH_3OCH_3]_0} = 0.016$

15.72   (a) When $^3/_4$ of the PH$_3$ has decomposed, $^1/_4$ remains and two half-lives have passed.

$$2(t_{1/2}) = 2(37.9 \text{ s}) = 75.8 \text{ s}$$

(b) $k = \dfrac{0.693}{t_{1/2}} = \dfrac{0.693}{37.9 \text{ s}} = 0.0183 \text{ s}^{-1}$

$$\ln \frac{[\text{PH}_3]}{[\text{PH}_3]_0} = -(0.0183 \text{ s}^{-1})(1 \text{ min})\left(\frac{60 \text{ s}}{1 \text{ min}}\right)$$

fraction remaining $= \dfrac{[\text{PH}_3]}{[\text{PH}_3]_0} = 0.33$

15.73   (a) $2 \text{ NO}(g) + \text{Br}_2(g) \rightarrow 2 \text{ BrNO}(g)$

(b) Mechanism 1:   termolecular

Mechanism 2:   Step 1: bimolecular

Step 2: bimolecular

Mechanism 3:   Step 1: bimolecular

Step 2: bimolecular

(c) Mechanism 2:   Br$_2$NO(g) is an intermediate

Mechanism 3   N$_2$O$_2$(g) is an intermediate

(d) The rate equations will all differ. Mechanism 1 would be second order in NO and first order in Br$_2$. Mechanism 2 would be first order in both NO and Br$_2$. Finally, Mechanism 3 would be second order in NO and zero order in Br$_2$.

15.74 $k = \dfrac{0.693}{8.04 \text{ days}} = 0.0862 \text{ days}^{-1}$

$$\ln\left(\frac{x}{25.0 \text{ mg}}\right) = -(0.0862 \text{ days}^{-1})(31 \text{ days})$$

$x = 1.7 \text{ mg}$

15.75   The steps in the mechanism add up to give the overall equation.

Step 2 is rate-determining: $-\dfrac{\Delta[\text{O}_3]}{\Delta t} = k_2[\text{O}_3][\text{O}]$

However, O is an intermediate

Step 1: $K_1 = \dfrac{[\text{O}_2][\text{O}]}{[\text{O}_3]}$, so $[\text{O}] = \dfrac{K_1[\text{O}_3]}{[\text{O}_2]}$

Substitute into the rate equation: $-\dfrac{\Delta[\text{O}_3]}{\Delta t} = k_2[\text{O}_3]\left(\dfrac{K_1[\text{O}_3]}{[\text{O}_2]}\right) = k_2 K_1 \dfrac{[\text{O}_3]^2}{[\text{O}_2]} = k\dfrac{[\text{O}_3]^2}{[\text{O}_2]}$

The mechanism agrees with the experimental rate law.

15.76   The slowest reaction has the smallest k (d) $\text{Cl} + \text{CH}_2\text{FCl} \rightarrow \text{HCl} + \text{CHFCl}$

The fastest reaction has the largest k (c) $\text{Cl} + \text{C}_3\text{H}_8 \rightarrow \text{HCl} + \text{C}_3\text{H}_7$

15.77   Plot $\ln k$ vs. $1/T$

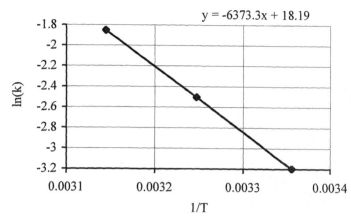

$$\text{slope} = -6370 = -\frac{E_a}{R} = -\frac{E_a}{8.3145 \times 10^{-3} \text{ kJ/K} \cdot \text{mol}}$$

$E_a = 53.0 \text{ kJ/mol}$

15.78 $\ln \dfrac{k_2}{k_1} = -\dfrac{E_a}{R}\left(\dfrac{1}{T_2} - \dfrac{1}{T_1}\right)$

$$\ln\left(\frac{k_2}{0.0900 \text{ min}^{-1}}\right) = -\frac{103 \text{ kJ/mol}}{8.3145 \times 10^{-3} \text{ kJ/K} \cdot \text{mol}}\left(\frac{1}{318.0 \text{ K}} - \frac{1}{328.0 \text{ K}}\right)$$

$k_2 = 0.0274 \text{ min}^{-1}$

15.79   Recognizing that $\dfrac{t_{90}}{t_{100}} = \dfrac{k_{100}}{k_{90}}$:

$$\ln \frac{k_{100}}{k_{90}} = \ln \frac{t_{90}}{t_{100}} = -\frac{E_a}{R}\left(\frac{1}{T_2} - \frac{1}{T_1}\right)$$

$$\ln \frac{t_{90}}{t_{100}} = -\frac{52.0 \text{ kJ/mol}}{8.3145 \times 10^{-3} \text{ kJ/K} \cdot \text{mol}}\left(\frac{1}{373 \text{ K}} - \frac{1}{363 \text{ K}}\right)$$

$\dfrac{t_{90}}{t_{100}} = 1.59$

$t_{90} = (1.59)(3 \text{ min}) = 4.76 \text{ min}$

15.80   Calculate $P_{C_4H_6\text{(unreacted)}}$ at each time (min) and plot the data to determine the reaction order:

$$P_{C_4H_6\text{(unreacted)}} = P_{\text{total}(t\,=\,0)} - P_{C_4H_6\text{(reacted)}} = P_{\text{total}(t\,=\,0)} - (2 \cdot P_{C_8H_{12}})$$

$$P_{\text{total}(t\,=\,\text{time})} = P_{C_4H_6\text{(unreacted)}} + P_{C_8H_{12}}$$

Solve for $P_{C_4H_6\text{(unreacted)}}$

$$P_{C_4H_6\text{(unreacted)}} = 2 \cdot P_{\text{total}(t\,=\,\text{time})} - P_{\text{total}(t\,=\,0)}$$

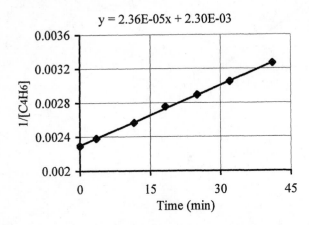

y = 2.36E-05x + 2.30E-03

The reaction is second order; k = slope = 2.36×10^{-5} L/mol·min

15.81   After 30 min (one half-life):

$P_{HOF} = 50.0$ mm Hg $P_{HF} = P_{HOF} = 50.0$ mm Hg $P_{O_2} = \tfrac{1}{2}\,P_{HF} = 25.0$ mm Hg

$P_{\text{total}} = 50.0$ mm Hg + 50.0 mm Hg + 25.0 mm Hg = 125.0 mm Hg

After 45 min:

$$k = \frac{0.693}{t_{1/2}} = \frac{0.693}{30 \text{ min}} = 0.0231 \text{ min}^{-1}$$

$$\ln\!\left(\frac{x}{100.\ \text{mm Hg}}\right) = -(0.0231 \text{ min}^{-1})(45 \text{ min})$$

$\ln(x) - \ln(100.\ \text{mm Hg}) = -(0.0231 \text{ min}^{-1})(45 \text{ min})$

$x = 35.4$ mm Hg

$P_{HOF} = 35.4$ mm Hg $P_{HF} = P_{HOF}$ consumed = 100. − 35.4 mm Hg = 65 mm Hg

$P_{O_2} = \tfrac{1}{2}\,P_{HF} = 32$ mm Hg

$P_{\text{total}} = 35.4$ mm Hg + 65 mm Hg + 32 mm Hg = 132 mm Hg

15.82   After 245 minutes (one half-life): $P_{SO_2Cl_2} = 13$ mm Hg $P_{SO_2} = 13$ mm Hg $P_{Cl_2} = 13$ mm Hg

$P_{total} = 38$ mm Hg

After 12 hours (720 min):

$$k = \frac{0.693}{t_{1/2}} = \frac{0.693}{245 \text{ min}} = 0.00283 \text{ min}^{-1}$$

$$\ln\left(\frac{x}{25 \text{ mm Hg}}\right) = -(0.00283 \text{ min}^{-1})(720 \text{ minutes})$$

$\ln(x) - \ln(25 \text{ mm Hg}) = -(0.00283 \text{ min}^{-1})(720 \text{ minutes})$

$x = 3.3$ mm Hg

$P_{SO_2Cl_2} = 3.3$ mm Hg $P_{SO_2} = P_{SO_2Cl_2}$ consumed $= 25 - 3.3 = 22$ mm Hg $P_{Cl_2} = P_{SO_2} = 22$ mm Hg

$P_{total} = 47$ mm Hg

15.83   (a)   The slow step is unimolecular and the fast step is bimolecular

(b)   Rate $= k[Ni(CO)_4]$ Yes, this rate law matches the stoichiometry of the slow step in the mechanism.

(c) $\ln\dfrac{[Ni(CO)_4]}{[Ni(CO)_4]_0} = -kt$

$$\ln\frac{[Ni(CO)_4]}{0.025 \text{ mol/L}} = -(9.3 \times 10^{-3} \text{ s}^{-1})(5.0 \text{ min})\left(\frac{60 \text{ s}}{1 \text{ min}}\right)$$

$$\ln[Ni(CO)_4] - \ln(0.025 \text{ mol/L}) = -(9.3 \times 10^{-3} \text{ s}^{-1})(5.0 \text{ min})\left(\frac{60 \text{ s}}{1 \text{ min}}\right)$$

$[Ni(CO)_4] = 0.0015$ mol/L

$[Ni(CO)_3L] = [Ni(CO)_4]$ consumed $= 0.025$ mol/L $- 0.0015$ mol/L $= 0.023$ M

15.84   (a)   Chemists use initial rates because the presence of products can affect the mechanism of the reaction.

(b)   Rate $= (0.011 \text{ L/mol·min})(0.18 \text{ mol/L})^2 = 3.6 \times 10^{-4}$ mol/L·min

15.85   The finely divided rhodium will have a significantly greater surface area than the small block of metal, which creates a huge increase in the number of reaction sites and vastly increases the reaction rate.

15.86   Accounting for the edge and corner cubes, there are 488 cubes with at least one surface on the outside surface of the 10. cm by 10. cm cube (48.8%). Splitting the cubes into eight piles of 125 blocks results in 784 blocks with at least one surface on the outside surface of the smaller cubes (78.4%). This model demonstrates that the surface area for a finely divided substance is much greater than that for a large lump of substance having the same mass.

15.87   (a) False. The reaction might occur in a single step, but this does not have to be true.

(b) True

(c) False. Raising the temperature increases the value of k.

(d) False. Temperature has no effect on the value of E_a.

(e) False. If the concentrations of both reactants are doubled the rate will increase by a factor of four.

(f) True

15.88 $\cancel{Cl} + O_3 \rightarrow \cancel{ClO} + O_2$

$\cancel{ClO} + \cancel{O} \rightarrow \cancel{Cl} + O_2$

$O_3 \rightarrow \cancel{O} + O_2$

_____

$2\,O_3 \rightarrow 3\,O_2$

The overall process consumes two moles of ozone, and since the Cl atoms are not consumed in the process (Cl is a catalyst), it can be repeated many times. ClO is an intermediate.

15.89   (a) True

(b) True

(c) False. As a reaction proceeds at constant temperature, the rate decreases.

(d) False. It is possible to have a one step mechanism for a third order reaction if the slow, rate-determining step is termolecular.

15.90   (a) Incorrect. Reactions are faster at a higher temperature because the fraction of molecules with higher energies increases.

(b) Correct

(c) Correct

(d) Incorrect. The function of a catalyst is to provide a different pathway with a lower activation energy for the reaction.

15.91   (a) decrease

(b) increase

(c) no change

(d) no change

(e) no change

(f) no change

15.92   Assume that you begin with labeled oxygen in methanol, $CH_3{}^{18}OH$. If we represent the labeled oxygen with a *, you can see from the equation below that labeled oxygen (in the water) results if the O originated from the methanol.

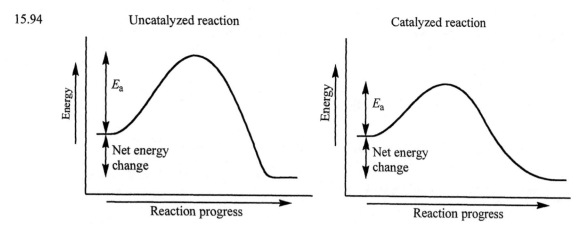

15.93   (a) There are three steps in the mechanism

        (b) The overall reaction is exothermic

15.94
        Uncatalyzed reaction   Catalyzed reaction

The activation energy in the catalyzed reaction is less than the activation energy in the uncatalyzed reaction. The net energy change is the same in both reactions.

15.95   (a) The average rate is calculated over a period of time, whereas the instantaneous rate is the rate of reaction at some instant in time.

        (b) The reaction rate decreases with time as the dye concentration decreases.

        (c) See (b) above.

15.96   (a) An increase in HCl concentration increases the reaction rate.

        (b) Initial rate and concentration are directly related.

15.97   (a) Molecules must collide with enough energy to overcome the activation energy and in the correct orientation.

        (b) In animation 2 the molecules are moving faster, so they are at a higher temperature.

        (c) Less sensitive. The O_3 and NO must collide with NO in the correct orientation. The O_3 and N_2 collision does not depend as much on orientation because N_2 is a homonuclear diatomic molecule.

15.98   (a) The stoichiometric coefficient of a reactant in an elementary step is the order of the reaction for that reactant in that step.

(b) Rate = $k[NO_3][CO]$

(c) No. Only in the two-step mechanism is there O atom exchange between NO_2 molecules. If CO reacts directly with NO_2, the CO_2 can have either ^{16}O or ^{18}O, and the product NO molecules will be either $N^{16}O$ or $N^{18}O$.

15.99   (a) I^- is regenerated during the second step in the mechanism

(b) The activation energy is smaller for the catalyzed reaction.

15.100   Overall reaction: $HA + X \rightarrow A^- + products$

Step 3 is rate-determining: Rate = $k[XH^+]$ but XH^+ is an intermediate

Step 1: $K_1 = \dfrac{[H^+][A^-]}{[HA]}$, so $[H^+] = \dfrac{K_1[HA]}{[A^-]}$

Step 2: $K_2 = \dfrac{[XH^+]}{[X][H^+]}$, so $[XH^+] = K_2[X][H^+]$

Substitute into rate equation: Rate = $k[XH^+] = k\left(K_2[X]\right)\left(\dfrac{K_1[HA]}{[A^-]}\right) = kK_1K_2\dfrac{[X][HA]}{[A^-]}$

The reaction is first order with respect to HA

Doubling the HA concentration would double the rate

Chapter 16
Principles of Reactivity: Chemical Equilibria

INSTRUCTOR'S NOTES

Introductory courses have always been the point at which students began their study of chemical equilibria, so Chapters 16-18 are quite important. Chapter 16 covers the most basic aspects of equilibria, and we usually spend about 3 lecture hours on the material.

The ICE format for concentration calculations is used consistently in order to instill the importance of characterizing the complementary changes in concentrations which the balanced chemical equation requires.

The chapter is not restricted to gas phase equilibrium systems, but also a few simple systems in aqueous solution have been introduced. This was done deliberately so that students see that the principles apply to all types of chemical systems.

The application of the quadratic equation – and deciding when the approximation is justified – can be a troublesome matter for some students. A tip box is included for the latter concept.

Approximately 10 lectures will need to be devoted to the entire subject of equilibrium (Chapters 16-18) with 3-4 lectures for each of the chapters.

SUGGESTED DEMONSTRATIONS

1. The Nature of the Equilibrium State
    - We have demonstrated the CO_2/$Ca(OH)_2$ system shown in Figure 16.2 in class with reasonable success. (This is taken from Volume 1 of *Chemical Demonstrations* by Shakhashiri, page 329.)
2. Disturbing a Chemical Equilibrium: Le Chatelier's Principle
    - Zingales, R. "Chemical Equilibria Involving Reactions of Silver(I) Ions," *Journal of Chemical Education* **2003**, *80*, 534.
    - Zingales, R. "Chemical Equilibria Involving Copper(II) Ethylenediamine Complexes," *Journal of Chemical Education* **2003**, *80*, 535.
    - Cortel, A. "Equilibrium with Fried Eggs of PbI_2 and $KPbI_3$," *Journal of Chemical Education*, **1998**, *75*, 297.
    - The equilibrium system between $[Co(H_2O)_6]^{2+}$ and $[CoCl_4]^{2-}$ is an effective demonstration. See L. R. Summerlin, J. L. Ealy, Jr. *Chemical Demonstrations: A Sourcebook for Teachers, 2nd Edition*, Vol. 1: "Effects of Temperature Change on Equilibrium: Cobalt Complex." Also in this book: "Equilibrium and Le Chatelier's Principle" and "Effect of Concentration on Equilibrium: Cobalt Complex."

- A simple demonstration which relates an equilibrium shift to a change in pressure is the effect of pressure on the melting point of ice. (Ellis, A. B.; Geselbracht, M. J.; Johnson, B. J.; Lisensky, G. C; Robinson, W. R. *Teaching General Chemistry: A Materials Science Companion*; American Chemical Society: Washington, D.C., 1993, p. 279.)

- The illustration of the NO_2/N_2O_4 equilibrium system in Figure 16.8 is simple to perform. Nitrogen dioxide, generated in the copper/nitric acid reaction, can be sealed into flasks. To see a distinct color difference it is necessary to have as large a temperature difference as possible.

SOLUTIONS TO STUDY QUESTIONS

16.1   (a) $K = \dfrac{[H_2O]^2[O_2]}{[H_2O_2]^2}$ $K_p = \dfrac{P^2_{H_2O}P_{O_2}}{P^2_{H_2O_2}}$

(b) $K = \dfrac{[CO_2]}{[CO][O_2]^{1/2}}$ $K_p = \dfrac{P_{CO_2}}{P_{CO}P^{1/2}_{O_2}}$

(c) $K = \dfrac{[CO]^2}{[CO_2]}$ $K_p = \dfrac{P^2_{CO}}{P_{CO_2}}$

(d) $K = \dfrac{[CO_2]}{[CO]}$ $K_p = \dfrac{P_{CO_2}}{P_{CO}}$

16.2   (a) $K = \dfrac{[O_3]^2}{[O_2]^3}$ $K_p = \dfrac{P^2_{O_3}}{P^3_{O_2}}$

(b) $K = \dfrac{[Fe(CO)_5]}{[CO]^5}$ $K_p = \dfrac{P_{Fe(CO)_5}}{P^5_{CO}}$

(c) $K = [NH_3]^2[CO_2][H_2O]$ $K_p = P^2_{NH_3}P_{CO_2}P_{H_2O}$

(d) $K = [Ag^+]^2[SO_4^{2-}]$

16.3 $Q = \dfrac{[I]^2}{[I_2]} = \dfrac{(2.0 \times 10^{-8})^2}{0.020} = 2.0 \times 10^{-14}$

$Q < K$ The reaction is not at equilibrium. The reaction will proceed to the right, to form more product.

16.4 $[NO_2] = \dfrac{2.0 \times 10^{-3} \text{ mol}}{10. \text{ L}} = 2.0 \times 10^{-4} \text{ mol/L}$

$[N_2O_4] = \dfrac{1.5 \times 10^{-3} \text{ mol}}{10. \text{ L}} = 1.5 \times 10^{-4} \text{ mol/L}$

$Q = \dfrac{[N_2O_4]}{[NO_2]^2} = \dfrac{1.5 \times 10^{-4}}{(2.0 \times 10^{-4})^2} = 3800$

$Q > K$ The reaction is not at equilibrium. The concentration of NO_2 will increase as the system proceeds to equilibrium.

16.5 $Q = \dfrac{[SO_3]^2}{[SO_2]^2[O_2]} = \dfrac{(6.9 \times 10^{-3})^2}{(5.0 \times 10^{-3})^2(1.9 \times 10^{-3})} = 1.0 \times 10^3$

$Q > K$ The reaction is not at equilibrium. The reaction will proceed to the left, to form more reactants.

16.6 $Q = \dfrac{[NO]^2[Cl_2]}{[NOCl]^2} = \dfrac{(2.5 \times 10^{-3})^2(2.0 \times 10^{-3})}{(5.0 \times 10^{-3})^2} = 5.0 \times 10^{-4}$

$Q < K$ The reaction is not at equilibrium. The reaction will proceed to the right, to form more products.

16.7 $K = \dfrac{[PCl_3][Cl_2]}{[PCl_5]} = \dfrac{(1.3 \times 10^{-2})(3.9 \times 10^{-3})}{4.2 \times 10^{-5}} = 1.2$

16.8 $K = \dfrac{[SO_3]^2}{[SO_2]^2[O_2]} = \dfrac{(4.13 \times 10^{-3})^2}{(3.77 \times 10^{-3})^2(4.30 \times 10^{-3})} = 279$

16.9 $[CO] = \dfrac{0.10 \text{ mol}}{2.0 \text{ L}} = 0.050 \text{ mol/L}$ $[CO_2] = \dfrac{0.20 \text{ mol}}{2.0 \text{ L}} = 0.10 \text{ mol/L}$

(a) $K = \dfrac{[CO]^2}{[CO_2]} = \dfrac{(0.050)^2}{0.10} = 0.025$

(b)   Only the amount of C has changed, and solids do not appear in equilibrium constant expressions.

     $K = 0.025$

(c)   The value of K is independent of the quantity of solid present.

16.10   (a) $K = \dfrac{[H_2O][CO]}{[H_2][CO_2]} = \dfrac{(0.11)(0.11)}{(0.087)(0.087)} = 1.6$

(b)

	H_2	+	CO_2	$\rightleftharpoons$	H_2O	+	CO
Initial (M)	0.050 mol/2.0 L		0.050 mol/2.0 L		0		0
	= 0.025 M		= 0.025 M				
Change (M)	$-x$		$-x$		$+x$		$+x$
Equilibrium (M)	$0.025 - x$		$0.025 - x$		x		x

$K = 1.6 = \dfrac{(x)(x)}{(0.025 - x)(0.025 - x)} = \dfrac{x^2}{(0.025 - x)^2}$

$\sqrt{1.6} = \sqrt{\dfrac{x^2}{(0.025 - x)^2}} = \dfrac{x}{0.025 - x}$

$x = 0.014 \text{ mol/L}$

$\dfrac{0.014 \text{ mol}}{1 \text{ L}} \cdot 2.0 \text{ L} = 0.028 \text{ mol } H_2O = 0.028 \text{ mol CO}$

16.11   (a)

	CO	+	Cl_2	$\rightleftharpoons$	$COCl_2$
Initial (M)	0.0102		0.00609		0
Change (M)	-0.00308		-0.00308		$+0.00308$
Equilibrium (M)	0.0071		0.00301		0.00308

(b) $K = \dfrac{(0.00308)}{(0.00301)(0.0071)} = 140$

16.12 $[SO_3] = \dfrac{3.00 \text{ mol}}{8.00 \text{ L}} = 0.375 \text{ M}$ $[O_2] = \dfrac{0.58 \text{ mol}}{8.00 \text{ L}} = 0.073 \text{ M}$

	2 SO$_3$ $\rightleftharpoons$	2 SO$_2$ +	O$_2$
Initial (M)	0.375	0	0
Change (M)	−2(0.073)	+2(0.073)	+0.073
Equilibrium (M)	0.230	0.15	0.073

$K = \dfrac{(0.15)^2(0.073)}{(0.230)^2} = 0.029$

16.13 $[\text{butane}] = \dfrac{0.017 \text{ mol}}{0.50 \text{ L}} = 0.034 \text{ M}$

	butane $\rightleftharpoons$	isobutane
Initial (M)	0.034	0
Change (M)	−x	+x
Equilibrium (M)	0.034 − x	x

$K = 2.5 = \dfrac{x}{0.034 - x}$

$[\text{isobutane}] = x = 0.024 \text{ M}$

$[\text{butane}] = 0.034 \text{ M} - x = 0.010 \text{ M}$

16.14 $[C_6H_{12}] = \dfrac{0.045 \text{ mol}}{2.8 \text{ L}} = 0.016 \text{ M}$

	$[C_6H_{12}]$ $\rightleftharpoons$	$[C_5H_9CH_3]$
Initial (M)	0.016	0
Change (M)	−x	+x
Equilibrium (M)	0.016 − x	x

$K = 0.12 = \dfrac{[C_5H_9CH_3]}{[C_6H_{12}]} = \dfrac{x}{0.016 - x}$

$[C_5H_9CH_3] = x = 1.7 \times 10^{-3} \text{ M}$

$[C_6H_{12}] = 0.016 - x = 0.014$

16.15 $[I_2] = \dfrac{0.105 \text{ mol}}{12.3 \text{ L}} = 0.00854 \text{ M}$

	I$_2$ $\rightleftharpoons$	2 I
Initial (M)	0.00845	0
Change (M)	−x	+2x
Equilibrium (M)	0.00845 − x	2x

$$K = \frac{[I]^2}{[I_2]} = 3.76 \times 10^{-3} = \frac{(2x)^2}{0.00845 - x}$$

$$0 = 4x^2 + (3.76 \times 10^{-3})x - (3.76 \times 10^{-3})(0.00845)$$

Solve using the quadratic equation. $x = 0.00240$ and -0.00334

$[I_2] = 0.00845 - x = 0.00614$ M

$[I] = 2x = 0.00480$ M

16.16 $[N_2O_4] = \dfrac{15.6 \text{ g}}{5.00 \text{ L}} \cdot \dfrac{1 \text{ mol } N_2O_4}{92.01 \text{ g}} = 0.0339$ M

	N_2O_4 $\rightleftharpoons$	$2 NO_2$
Initial (M)	0.0339	0
Change (M)	$-x$	$+2x$
Equilibrium (M)	$0.0339 - x$	$2x$

$$K = \frac{[NO_2]^2}{[N_2O_4]} = 5.88 \times 10^{-3} = \frac{(2x)^2}{0.0339 - x}$$

$$0 = 4x^2 - (5.88 \times 10^{-3})(0.0339 - x)$$

Solve using the quadratic equation. $x = 0.00636$ and -0.00783

(a) Amount of NO_2 present at equilibrium $= 2x = 2(0.00636 \text{ mol/L})(5.00 \text{ L}) = 0.0636$ moles NO_2

(b) % N_2O_4 dissociated $= \dfrac{0.00636 \text{ M}}{0.0339 \text{ M}} \cdot 100\% = 18.8\%$

16.17 $[COBr_2] = \dfrac{0.500 \text{ mol}}{2.00 \text{ L}} = 0.250$ M

	$COBr_2$ $\rightleftharpoons$	CO +	Br_2
Initial (M)	0.250	0	0
Change (M)	$-x$	$+x$	$+x$
Equilibrium (M)	$0.250 - x$	x	x

$$K = 0.190 = \frac{(x)(x)}{0.250 - x}$$

$$0 = x^2 - (0.190)(0.250 - x)$$

Solve using the quadratic equation. $x = 0.143$ and -0.333

$[COBr_2] = 0.250 - x = 0.107$ M $[CO] = [Br_2] = 0.143$ M

% $COBr_2$ decomposed $= \dfrac{0.143 \text{ M}}{0.250 \text{ M}} \cdot 100\% = 57.1\%$

16.18 $[I_2(aq)] = \dfrac{0.0340 \text{ g}}{0.1000 \text{ L}} \cdot \dfrac{1 \text{ mol } I_2}{253.8 \text{ g}} = 0.00134 \text{ M}$

	$I_2(aq)$	$\rightleftharpoons$	$I_2(CCl_4)$
Initial (M)	0.00134		0
Change (M)	$-x$		$+x$
Equilibrium (M)	$0.00134 - x$		x

$K = 85.0 = \dfrac{x}{0.00134 - x}$

$x = 0.00132$

$[I_2(aq)] = 0.00134 - x = 2 \times 10^{-5} \text{ M}$

amount of I_2 remaining in water $= (2 \times 10^{-5} \text{ mol/L})(0.1000 \text{ L})(253.8 \text{ g/mol}) = 4 \times 10^{-4} \text{ g } I_2$

16.19   The second equation has been multiplied by 2

(b) $K_2 = K_1^2$

16.20   The second equation has been reversed and multiplied by $^1/_2$

(a) $K_2 = 1/(K_1)^{1/2}$

16.21   The second equation has been reversed and multiplied by 2

(e) $K_2 = 1/K_1^2$

16.22   The second equation has been reversed and multiplied by 2

$K_{new} = 1/K^2 = 1/(6.66 \times 10^{-12})^2 = 2.25 \times 10^{22}$

16.23 $SnO_2(s) + 2 H_2(g) \rightleftharpoons Sn(s) + 2 H_2O(g)$ $K = 8.12$

$2 H_2O(g) + 2 CO(g) \rightleftharpoons 2 H_2(g) + 2 CO_2(g)$ $K = 1/(0.771)^2$

$SnO_2(s) + 2 CO(g) \rightleftharpoons Sn(s) + 2 CO_2(g)$ $K_{net} = (8.12)/(0.771)^2 = 13.7$

16.24 $H_2O(g) + CO(g) \rightleftharpoons H_2(g) + CO_2(g)$ $K = 1.6$

$Fe(s) + CO_2(g) \rightleftharpoons FeO(s) + CO(g)$ $K = 1/(0.67)$

$Fe(s) + H_2O(g) \rightleftharpoons FeO(s) + H_2(g)$ $K_{net} = (1.6)/(0.67) = 2.4$

16.25   (a) Adding more $N_2O_3(g)$ will shift the equilibrium to the right

(b) Adding more $NO_2(g)$ will shift the equilibrium to the left

(c) Increasing the volume of the reaction flask will shift the equilibrium to the right

(d) Lowering the temperature will shift the equilibrium to the left

16.26   (a) Adding more $Br_2(g)$ will shift the equilibrium to the left

(b) Removing some $NOBr(g)$ will shift the equilibrium to the left

(c) Decreasing the temperature will shift the equilibrium to the left

(d) Increasing the container volume will shift the equilibrium to the right

16.27   (a)

	butane $\rightleftharpoons$	isobutane
Initial (M)	1.0	2.5
Concentration immediately on adding isobutane (M)	1.0	2.5 + 0.50
Change in concentration to reestablish equilibrium (M)	+x	−x
Equilibrium (M)	1.0 + x	3.0 − x

$$K = 2.5 = \frac{3.0 - x}{1.0 + x} \qquad x = 0.14$$

[butane] = 1.0 + x = 1.1 M   [isobutane] = 3.0 − x = 2.9 M

(b)

	butane $\rightleftharpoons$	isobutane
Initial (M)	1.0	2.5
Concentration immediately on adding isobutane (M)	1.0 + 0.50	2.5
Change in concentration to reestablish equilibrium (M)	−x	+x
Equilibrium (M)	1.5 − x	2.5 + x

$$K = 2.5 = \frac{2.5 + x}{1.5 - x} \qquad x = 0.36$$

[butane] = 1.5 − x = 1.1 M   [isobutane] = 2.5 + x = 2.9 M

16.28   When the temperature is raised, the reaction adjusts to the added heat by consuming reactants and forming more products. The equilibrium shifts to the right. Adding NH_4HS, a solid, will have no effect on the equilibrium. Adding $NH_3(g)$, a product, will shift the equilibrium to the left. Removing H_2S, a product, will shift the reaction to the right, increasing the NH_3 pressure.

16.29 $[Br_2] = \dfrac{0.086 \, mol}{1.26 \, L} = 0.068 \, M$ 3.7% of $[Br_2]$ = (0.068 M)(0.037) = 0.0025 M

	Br_2 $\rightleftharpoons$	2 Br
Initial (M)	0.068	0
Change (M)	−0.0025	+2(0.0025)
Equilibrium (M)	0.066	0.0051

$$K = \frac{[Br]^2}{[Br_2]} = \frac{(0.0051)^2}{0.066} = 3.9 \times 10^{-4}$$

16.30   (a) The equation has been multiplied by $^1/_2$

$K_{new} = K^{1/2} = (1.7 \times 10^{-3})^{1/2} = 0.041$

(b) The equation has been reversed

$K_{new} = 1/K = 1/(1.7 \times 10^{-3}) = 590$

16.31   The equation has been reversed

$K_p(dissociation) = 1/[K_p(formation)] = 1/(6.5 \times 10^{11}) = 1.5 \times 10^{-12}$

16.32 $K = \dfrac{[CH_4][CCl_4]}{[CH_2Cl_2]^2}$

$1.05 = \dfrac{(0.0163)[CCl_4]}{(0.0206)^2}$

$[CCl_4] = 0.0273$ M

16.33

	CS_2	$+$	$3\,Cl_2$	$\rightleftharpoons$	S_2Cl_2	$+$	CCl_4
Initial (M)	1.2		3.6		0		0
Change (M)	−0.90		−3(0.90)		+0.90		+0.90
Equilibrium (M)	0.3		0.9		0.90		0.90

$K = \dfrac{[CCl_4][S_2Cl_2]}{[CS_2][Cl_2]^3} = \dfrac{(0.90)(0.90)}{(0.3)(0.9)^3} = 4$

16.34

	H_2	$+$	I_2	$\rightleftharpoons$	$2\,HI$
Initial (M)	0.0088		0.0088		0
Change (M)	−(0.786)(0.0088)		−(0.786)(0.0088)		+2(0.786)(0.0088)
Equilibrium (M)	0.0019		0.0019		0.014

$K = \dfrac{[HI]^2}{[H_2][I_2]} = \dfrac{(0.014)^2}{(0.0019)(0.0019)} = 54$

16.35   Assume volume is 1.00 L

$$Q = \frac{[\text{isobutane}]}{[\text{butane}]} = \frac{1.25}{1.75} = 0.714$$

Q is less than K, so the system shifts to form more isobutane.

	butane	$\rightleftharpoons$	isobutane
Initial (M)	1.75		1.25
Change (M)	$-x$		$+x$
Equilibrium (M)	$1.75 - x$		$1.25 + x$

$$K = 2.5 = \frac{[\text{isobutane}]}{[\text{butane}]} = \frac{1.25 + x}{1.75 - x} \qquad x = 0.89$$

[butane] = $1.75 - x$ = 0.86 M   [isobutane] = $1.25 + x$ = 2.14 M

16.36   (a) $Q = \dfrac{[\text{NO}]^2}{[\text{N}_2][\text{O}_2]} = \dfrac{(0.0042)^2}{(0.25)(0.25)} = 2.8 \times 10^{-4}$

$Q < K$, so the system is not at equilibrium.

(b) $Q < K$; the reaction proceeds to the right.

(c)

	N_2	$+$	O_2	$\rightleftharpoons$	2 NO
Initial (M)	0.25		0.25		0.0042
Change (M)	$-x$		$-x$		$+2x$
Equilibrium (M)	$0.25 - x$		$0.25 - x$		$0.0042 + 2x$

$$K = 1.7 \times 10^{-3} = \frac{[\text{NO}]^2}{[\text{N}_2][\text{O}_2]} = \frac{(0.0042 + 2x)^2}{(0.25 - x)^2}$$

Take the square root of both sides of the equation and solve for x

$x = 0.0030$

$[\text{N}_2] = [\text{O}_2] = 0.25 - x = 0.25$ M

$[\text{NO}] = 0.0042 + 2x = 0.0102$ M

16.37   The second equation has been reversed and multiplied by 2

(c) $K_2 = 1/K_1^{\,2}$

16.38 $3.00 \text{ g} \cdot \dfrac{1 \text{ mol SO}_2}{64.06 \text{ g}} \cdot \dfrac{1 \text{ mol O}_2}{2 \text{ mol SO}_2} \cdot \dfrac{32.00 \text{ g}}{1 \text{ mol O}_2} = 0.749 \text{ g O}_2$ required   SO$_2$ is the limiting reactant

Assume that the reaction proceeds completely to the right (because K is large).

$3.00 \text{ g} \cdot \dfrac{1 \text{ mol SO}_2}{64.06 \text{ g}} \cdot \dfrac{2 \text{ mol SO}_3}{2 \text{ mol SO}_2} \cdot \dfrac{80.06 \text{ g}}{1 \text{ mol SO}_3} = 3.75 \text{ g SO}_3$ produced

Because the value of K is not infinite, however, we know the reaction does not proceed completely to the

right, so (c) 3.61 g is the only reasonable answer.

16.39   (a) no change

        (b) shifts left

        (c) no change

        (d) shifts right

        (e) shifts right

16.40   (a) The addition of CO, a product, will shift the equilibrium to the left.

        (b) $[CO] = \dfrac{2.00 \text{ mol}}{2.00 \text{ L}} = 1.00 \text{ M}$

	COBr$_2$ $\rightleftharpoons$	CO	+	Br$_2$
Initial (M) (values from 16.17)	0.107	0.143		0.143
Concentration on adding CO (M)	0.107	0.143 + 1.00		0.143
Change to reestablish equilibrium (M)	+x	$-x$		$-x$
Equilibrium (M)	0.107 + x	1.143 − x		0.143 − x

$K = 0.190 = \dfrac{(1.143 - x)(0.143 - x)}{0.107 + x}$

$0 = x^2 - 1.48x + 0.143$

Solve using the quadratic equation. $x = 1.37$ and 0.104

$[COBr_2] = 0.107 + x = 0.211 \text{ M}$

$[CO] = 1.143 - x = 1.039$

$[Br_2] = 0.143 - x = 0.039$

        (c) The COBr$_2$ was 57.1% decomposed before the addition of CO(g).

        $\dfrac{0.250 \text{ M} - 0.211 \text{ M}}{0.250 \text{ M}} \cdot 100\% = 16\%$

        Adding CO(g) has decreased the amount of COBr$_2$ decomposed.

16.41   Adding Cl$_2$, a product, will shift the equilibrium to the left.

        $[PCl_5] = \dfrac{3.120 \text{ g}}{1.00 \text{ L}} \cdot \dfrac{1 \text{ mol PCl}_5}{208.24 \text{ g}} = 0.0150 \text{ M}$ $[PCl_3] = \dfrac{3.845 \text{ g}}{1.00 \text{ L}} \cdot \dfrac{1 \text{ mol PCl}_3}{137.33 \text{ g}} = 0.0280 \text{ M}$

        $[Cl_2] = \dfrac{1.787 \text{ g}}{1.00 \text{ L}} \cdot \dfrac{1 \text{ mol Cl}_2}{70.905 \text{ g}} = 0.0252 \text{ M}$ $[Cl_2](added) = \dfrac{1.418 \text{ g}}{1.00 \text{ L}} \cdot \dfrac{1 \text{ mol Cl}_2}{70.905 \text{ g}} = 0.0200 \text{ M}$

        $K = \dfrac{[PCl_3][Cl_2]}{[PCl_5]} = \dfrac{(0.0280)(0.0252)}{0.0150} = 0.0471$

	PCl$_5$ $\rightleftharpoons$	PCl$_3$	+	Cl$_2$
Initial (M)	0.0150	0.0280		0.0252
Concentration on adding Cl$_2$ (M)	0.0150	0.0280		0.0252 + 0.0200
Change to reestablish equilibrium (M)	+x	$-x$		$-x$
Equilibrium (M)	0.0150 + x	0.0280 − x		0.0452 − x

$$K = 0.0471 = \frac{(0.0280 - x)(0.0452 - x)}{0.0150 + x}$$

$$0 = x^2 - 0.1203x + 0.00559$$

Solve using the quadratic equation. $x = 0.115$ and 0.00485

$[PCl_5] = 0.0150 + x = 0.0199$ M

$[PCl_3] = 0.0280 - x = 0.0232$ M

$[Cl_2] = 0.0452 - x = 0.0404$ M

16.42 $K_p = P_{NH_3}P_{H_2S} = 0.11$

$P_{NH_3} = P_{H_2S}$, so $K_p = 0.11 = P_{NH_3}{}^2 = P_{H_2S}{}^2$

$P_{NH_3} = P_{H_2S} = \sqrt{0.11} = 0.33$ atm

$P_{total} = 0.33$ atm $+ 0.33$ atm $= 0.66$ atm

16.43 $P_{total} = 705$ mm Hg $\cdot \dfrac{1\ atm}{760\ mm\ Hg} = 0.928$ atm $= P_{NH_3} + P_{HI}$

$P_{NH_3} = P_{HI} = {}^1/_2(0.928\ atm) = 0.464$ atm

$K_p = (0.464)^2 = 0.215$

16.44 $P_{total} = 0.116$ atm $= P_{NH_3} + P_{CO_2}$

$P_{NH_3} = 2 \times P_{CO_2}$, so $P_{CO_2} = {}^1/_3\ P_{total} = 0.0387$ atm and $P_{NH_3} = 0.0774$ atm

$K_p = (P_{NH_3})^2 P_{CO_2} = (0.0774)^2(0.0387) = 2.31 \times 10^{-4}$

16.45 $K = 0.15 = \dfrac{P_{NO_2}{}^2}{0.85}$

$P_{NO_2} = 0.36$ atm

$P_{total} = 0.36$ atm $+ 0.85$ atm $= 1.21$ atm

16.46   (a)

	2 CH₃CO₂H ⇌ (CH₃CO₂H)₂	
Initial (M)	5.4×10^{-4}	0
Change (M)	$-2x$	$+x$
Equilibrium (M)	$5.4 \times 10^{-4} - 2x$	x

$$K = 3.2 \times 10^4 = \frac{x}{(5.4 \times 10^{-4} - 2x)^2}$$

$$0 = (1.3 \times 10^5)x^2 - 70.x + 9.3 \times 10^{-3}$$

Solve using the quadratic equation. $x = 3.2 \times 10^{-4}$ and 2.3×10^{-4}

$$\frac{2(2.3 \times 10^{-4}\ M)}{5.4 \times 10^{-4}\ M} \cdot 100\% = 84\%$$

(b) Increasing the temperature will shift the equilibrium to the left.

16.47

	$2 NH_3$	$\rightleftharpoons$	N_2	$+$	$3 H_2$
Initial (M)	1.80		0		0
Change (M)	$-2x$		$+x$		$+3x$
Equilibrium (M)	$1.80 - 2x$		x		$3x$

$$K = 6.3 = \frac{[N_2][H_2]^3}{[NH_3]^2} = \frac{(x)(3x)^3}{(1.80-2x)^2} = \frac{27x^4}{(1.80-2x)^2}$$

Take the square root of both sides of the equation and simplify.

$$0 = 5.20x^2 + 5.02x - 4.52$$

Solve using the quadratic equation. $x = 0.57$ and -1.5

$[NH_3] = 1.80 - 2x = 0.67$ M $[N_2] = x = 0.57$ M

$[H_2] = 3x = 1.7$ M

$$P_{total} = \frac{n}{V}RT = [(0.57 + 1.7 + 0.67) \text{ mol/L}](0.082057 \text{ L} \cdot \text{atm/K} \cdot \text{mol})(723 \text{ K}) = 180 \text{ atm}$$

16.48 $P_{total} = P_{NO_2} + P_{N_2O_4}$ $P_{N2O4} = 1.5 - P_{NO_2}$

$$K_p = 6.75 = \frac{1.5 - P_{NO_2}}{P_{NO_2}{}^2}$$

$$0 = 6.75P_{NO_2}{}^2 + P_{NO_2} - 1.5$$

Solve using the quadratic equation. $P_{NO_2} = 0.40$ atm $P_{N2O4} = 1.5 - P_{NO_2} = 1.1$ atm

16.49   (a) $K_c = 1.8 \times 10^{-4} = [NH_3][H_2S]$

          $[NH_3] = [H_2S]$, so $K = [NH_3]^2 = [H_2S]^2$

          $[NH_3] = [H_2S] = (1.8 \times 10^{-4})^{1/2} = 0.013$ M

(b)

	NH_4HS	$\rightleftharpoons$	NH_3	$+$	H_2S
Initial (M)			0.020		0
Change (M)			$+x$		$+x$
Equilibrium (M)			$0.020 + x$		x

$K_c = 1.8 \times 10^{-4} = [NH_3][H_2S] = (0.020 \text{ M} + x)x$

$x = [H_2S] = 0.0067$ M

$[NH_3] = 0.020 + x = 0.027$ M

16.50   (a) $Q = \dfrac{[O_2][NO_2]}{[O_3][NO]} = \dfrac{(8.2 \times 10^{-3})(2.5 \times 10^{-4})}{(1.0 \times 10^{-6})(1.0 \times 10^{-5})} = 2.1 \times 10^5$

$Q < K$ so the reaction will proceed to the right to reach equilibrium

(b) $\Delta H^\circ = \Delta H_f^\circ[NO_2(g)] - (\Delta H_f^\circ[O_3(g)] + \Delta H_f^\circ[NO(g)])$

$\Delta H^\circ = 1 \text{ mol } (33.1 \text{ kJ/mol}) - [1 \text{ mol } (142.67 \text{ kJ/mol}) + 1 \text{ mol } (90.29 \text{ kJ/mol})]$

$\Delta H^\circ = -199.9 \text{ kJ}$

Increasing the temperature shifts the equilibrium to the left. The product concentrations will decrease.

16.51   (a) $P_{total} = 1.50 \text{ atm} = P_{NO_2} + P_{N_2O_4}$ $P_{N_2O_4} = 1.50 - P_{NO_2}$

$K_p = 0.148 = \dfrac{P_{NO_2}^2}{1.50 - P_{NO_2}}$

Solve using the quadratic equation.

$P_{NO_2} = 0.403 \text{ atm}$

$P_{N_2O_4} = 1.50 - P_{NO_2} = 1.10 \text{ atm}$

$P_{N_2O_4}(\text{initial}) = 1.10 \text{ atm} + (0.403 \text{ atm})\left(\dfrac{1 \text{ mol } N_2O_4}{2 \text{ mol } NO_2}\right) = 1.30 \text{ atm}$

fraction dissociated $= \dfrac{1.30 \text{ atm} - 1.10 \text{ atm}}{1.30 \text{ atm}} = 0.15$

(b) $K_p = \dfrac{P_{NO_2}^2}{P_{N_2O_4}} = 0.148 = \dfrac{P_{NO_2}^2}{1.00 - P_{NO_2}}$

Solve using the quadratic equation. $P_{NO_2} = 0.318 \text{ atm}$ $P_{N_2O_4} = 1.00 - P_{NO_2} = 0.682 \text{ atm}$

$P_{N_2O_4}(\text{initial}) = 0.682 \text{ atm} + (0.318 \text{ atm})\left(\dfrac{1 \text{ mol } N_2O_4}{2 \text{ mol } NO_2}\right) = 0.841 \text{ atm}$

fraction dissociated $= \dfrac{0.841 \text{ atm} - 0.682 \text{ atm}}{0.841 \text{ atm}} = 0.189$

If pressure decreases, the equilibrium will shift to the right, increasing the fraction of N_2O_4 dissociated.

16.52   (a) $P_{total} = 0.200 \text{ atm} = P_{CO} + P_{CO_2}$

$P_{CO} = P_{CO_2} = {}^1/_2(0.200 \text{ atm}) = 0.100 \text{ atm}$

$K_p = (0.100 \text{ atm})^3(0.100 \text{ atm})^3 = 1.00 \times 10^{-6}$

(b) $n_{CO} = \dfrac{PV}{RT} = \dfrac{(0.100 \text{ atm})(10.0 \text{ L})}{(0.082057 \text{ L} \cdot \text{atm/K} \cdot \text{mol})(373 \text{ K})} = 0.0327 \text{ mol CO}$

$0.0327 \text{ mol CO} \cdot \dfrac{1 \text{ mol } La_2(C_2O_4)_3}{3 \text{ mol CO}} = 0.0109 \text{ mol } La_2(C_2O_4)_3$

$(0.100 \text{ mol} - 0.0109 \text{ mol}) = 0.089 \text{ mol } La_2(C_2O_4)_3 \text{ remains}$

16.53   (a) The flask containing the complex with the largest K for the dissociation reaction, $(H_3N)B(CH_3)_3$, will

have the largest partial pressure of $B(CH_3)_3$.

(b) $P_{(NH_3)B(CH_3)_3} = \dfrac{nRT}{V} = \dfrac{(0.010 \text{ mol})(0.082057 \text{ L} \cdot \text{atm/K} \cdot \text{mol})(373 \text{ K})}{0.100 \text{ L}} = 3.1 \text{ atm}$

	$(NH_3)B(CH_3)_3$	$\rightleftarrows$	$B(CH_3)_3$	+	NH_3
Initial (atm)	3.1		0		0
Change (atm)	$-x$		$+x$		$+x$
Equilibrium (atm)	$3.1 - x$		x		x

$K_p = 4.62 = \dfrac{(x)(x)}{3.1 - x}$

Solve using the quadratic equation. $x = 2.1$ and -6.7

$P_{B(CH_3)_3} = P_{NH_3} = x = 2.1 \text{ atm}$ $P_{(NH_3)B(CH_3)_3} = 3.1 - x = 1.0 \text{ atm}$

$P_{total} = 2.1 \text{ atm} + 2.1 \text{ atm} + 1.0 \text{ atm} = 5.2 \text{ atm}$

% dissociation $= \dfrac{2.1 \text{ atm}}{3.1 \text{ atm}} \cdot 100\% = 69\%$

16.54 $[SO_2Cl_2] = \dfrac{6.70 \text{ g } SO_2Cl_2}{1.00 \text{ L}} \cdot \dfrac{1 \text{ mol } SO_2Cl_2}{135.0 \text{ g}} = 0.0496 \text{ M}$

(a) $K = 0.045 = \dfrac{x^2}{0.0496 - x}$

Solve using the quadratic equation. $x = 0.030$

$[SO_2Cl_2] = 0.0496 - x = 0.020 \text{ M}$

$[SO_2] = [Cl_2] = x = 0.030 \text{ M}$

fraction dissociated $= \dfrac{0.030}{0.0496} = 0.60$

(b) $[Cl_2] = \dfrac{n}{V} = \dfrac{P}{RT} = \dfrac{1.00 \text{ atm}}{(0.082057 \text{ L} \cdot \text{atm/K} \cdot \text{mol})(648 \text{ K})} = 0.0188 \text{ M}$

$K = 0.045 = \dfrac{x(0.0188 + x)}{0.0496 - x}$

Solve using the quadratic equation. $x = 0.025$

$[SO_2Cl_2] = 0.0496 - x = 0.025 \text{ M}$

$[SO_2] = x = 0.025 \text{ M}$

$[Cl_2] = 0.0188 + x = 0.044 \text{ M}$

fraction dissociated $= \dfrac{0.025}{0.0496} = 0.50$

(c) Le Chatelier's principle predicts that the addition of $Cl_2(g)$ would shift the equilibrium to the left,
a prediction that is confirmed by these calculations.

16.55 $K = \dfrac{[HbCO]P_{O_2}}{[HbO_2]P_{CO}}$

$2.0 \times 10^2 = (1)\dfrac{0.20 \text{ atm}}{P_{CO}}$

$P_{CO} = 0.0010 \text{ atm}$

16.56 $K_p = P_{CO_2} = 3.87 \text{ atm}$

$n_{CO_2} = \dfrac{PV}{RT} = \dfrac{(3.87 \text{ atm})(5.00 \text{ L})}{(0.082057 \text{ L} \cdot \text{atm/K} \cdot \text{mol})(1273 \text{ K})} = 0.185 \text{ mol CO}_2$

$0.0185 \text{ mol} \cdot \dfrac{1 \text{ mol CaCO}_3}{1 \text{ mol CO}_2} \cdot \dfrac{100.1 \text{ g}}{1 \text{ mol CaCO}_3} = 18.5 \text{ g CaCO}_3$

16.57   Calculate the more convenient K_c value:

$K_p = K_c(RT)^{\Delta n} = 1.2 \times 10^{-10} = K_c[(0.082057 \text{ L} \cdot \text{atm/K} \cdot \text{mol})(1800 \text{ K})]^1$

$K_c = 8.12 \times 10^{-13}$

Assume that x mol O_2 dissociates and that $2x$ mol O is present at equilibrium:

$K_c = \dfrac{[O]^2}{[O_2]} = 8.12 \times 10^{-13} = \dfrac{(2x)^2}{(1.0 \text{ mol/10. L}) - x}$

K_c is very small, so assume x is very small when compared to $[O_2]_{initial}$

$x = 1.4 \times 10^{-7}$

$[O] = 2x = 2.8 \times 10^{-7} \text{ M}$

$\dfrac{2.8 \times 10^{-7} \text{ mol}}{\text{L}} \cdot 10 \text{ L} \cdot \dfrac{6.02 \times 10^{23} \text{ atoms}}{1 \text{ mol}} = 1.7 \times 10^{18} \text{ O atoms}$

16.58 $190 \text{ mm Hg} \cdot \dfrac{1 \text{ atm}}{760 \text{ mm Hg}} = 0.25 \text{ atm}$

	NOBr	$\rightleftarrows$	NO	+	$^1/_2$ Br$_2$
Initial (atm)	x		0		0
Equilibrium (atm)	0.66x		0.34x		0.17x

$P_{total} = 0.25 \text{ atm} = 0.66x + 0.34x + 0.17x$

$x = 0.21 \text{ atm}$

$P_{NOBr} = 0.66x = 0.14 \text{ atm}$ $P_{NO} = 0.34x = 0.073 \text{ atm}$ $P_{Br_2} = 0.17x = 0.036 \text{ atm}$

$K_p = \dfrac{P_{NO}P_{Br_2}^{1/2}}{P_{NOBr}} = \dfrac{(0.073)(0.036)^{1/2}}{0.14} = 0.098$

16.59 $K = \dfrac{[B(OH)_3 \cdot \text{glycerine}]}{[B(OH)_3][\text{glycerine}]} = 0.90 = \dfrac{(0.60)(0.10)}{(0.40)(0.10)[\text{glycerine}]}$

[glycerine] = 1.7 mol/L

glycerine added to solution = 1.7 mol/L + (0.60)(0.10) mol/L = 1.7 mol/L

16.60   (a) $K_c = \dfrac{K_p}{(RT)^{\Delta n}} = \dfrac{1.16}{[(0.082057 \text{ L} \cdot \text{atm/K} \cdot \text{mol})(1100 \text{ K})]^1} = 0.013$

     (b) $P_{CO_2} = K_p = 1.16$ atm

     (c) $[CO_2] = K_c = 0.013$ mol/L

$$\dfrac{0.013 \text{ mol } CO_2}{1 \text{ L}} \cdot 9.56 \text{ L} \cdot \dfrac{1 \text{ mol } CaCO_3}{1 \text{ mol } CO_2} \cdot \dfrac{100.1 \text{ g}}{1 \text{ mol } CaCO_3} = 12 \text{ g } CaCO_3 \text{ decomposed}$$

$$\dfrac{22.5 \text{ g} - 12 \text{ g}}{22.5 \text{ g}} \cdot 100\% = 45\% \text{ undecomposed}$$

16.61 $N_2O_4(g) \rightleftharpoons 2 NO_2(g)$

     $P_{N_2O_4} = 1.00 \text{ atm} - (0.200)(1.00 \text{ atm}) = 0.80$ atm

     $P_{NO_2} = 2(0.200)(1.00 \text{ atm}) = 0.400$ atm

     (a) $K_p = \dfrac{P_{NO_2}^2}{P_{N_2O_4}} = \dfrac{(0.400)^2}{0.80} = 0.20$

     (b) $K_p = \dfrac{P_{NO_2}^2}{P_{N_2O_4}} = 0.20 = \dfrac{(2x)^2}{010 - x}$

     Solve using the quadratic equation. $x = 0.050$ atm

     $P_{N_2O_4} = 0.10 - x = 0.05$ atm $P_{NO_2} = 2x = 0.10$ atm

$$\dfrac{0.10 \text{ atm} - 0.05 \text{ atm}}{0.10 \text{ atm}} \cdot 100\% = 50\%$$

     This result is in agreement with Le Chatelier's principle: If the initial pressure of the reactant

     decreases, the equilibrium shifts to the right, increasing the fraction of the reactant dissociated.

16.62 $P_{total} = 2.50 \text{ atm} = P_{NO_2} + P_{N_2O_4}$ $P_{N_2O_4} = 2.50 - P_{NO_2}$

     $K_p = 0.15 = \dfrac{P_{NO_2}^2}{2.50 - P_{NO_2}}$

     Solve using the quadratic equation.

     $P_{NO_2} = 0.54$ atm $P_{N_2O_4} = 2.50 - P_{NO_2} = 1.96$ atm

16.63   (a)   False. The magnitude of the equilibrium constant is always dependent on temperature.

     (b)   True

     (c)   False. The equilibrium constant for a reaction is the reciprocal of the value of K for its reverse.

     (d)   True

     (e)   False. $K_p = K_c(RT)^1$

16.64   The dissolution of $PbCl_2$ has a larger K than the dissolution of PbF_2, so solutions of $PbCl_2$ have a greater

     concentration of Pb^{2+}.

16.65   (a) product-favored $K \gg 1$

(b) reactant favored $K \ll 1$

(c) product-favored $K \gg 1$

16.66   This is a dynamic equilibrium. Initially, the rate of evaporation is greater than the rate of condensation. At equilibrium, the two rates are equal.

16.67 $H_2(g) + I_2(g) \rightleftharpoons 2\, HI(g)$

(a) $K_p = K_c(RT)^0 = 56$

(b) Before reaction:

$$P_{H_2} = P_{I_2} = \frac{nRT}{V} = \frac{(0.45\ \text{mol})(0.082057\ \text{L} \cdot \text{atm/K} \cdot \text{mol})(708\ \text{K})}{10.0\ \text{L}} = 2.6\ \text{atm}$$

$P_{total} = 2.6\ \text{atm} + 2.6\ \text{atm} = 5.2\ \text{atm}$

After reaction:

$$K_p = 56 = \frac{P_{HI}^{\,2}}{P_{H_2}\,P_{I_2}} = \frac{(2x)^2}{(2.6 - x)(2.6 - x)}$$

$x = 2.1\ \text{atm}$

$P_{H_2} = P_{I_2} = 0.55\ \text{atm}$ $P_{HI} = 4.1\ \text{atm}$

$P_{total} = 4.1\ \text{atm} + (2)(0.55\ \text{atm}) = 5.2\ \text{atm}$

The total pressure before and after equilibrium is achieved is the same.

(c) see (b)

16.68   The system is not at equilibrium because it continues to gain heat from the surroundings. The temperature of the water/ice mixture will remain at 0 °C until all the ice is melted, then the temperature will rise as more heat is gained. Only if the beaker of water/ice were moved to a perfectly insulated compartment, also at 0 °C, would it attain equilibrium at 0 °C. In this case, it would be a dynamic equilibrium with water molecules moving from the solid to the liquid phase and from the liquid to the solid phase. The quantity of ice would not change. If a D_2O ice cube was added to some $H_2O(\ell)$, an equilibrium would be obtained. The amount of D_2O in the liquid phase would increase due to the continuing molecular exchange. The water could then be sampled for the presence of D_2O.

16.69   The reaction is endothermic. Adding heat shifts an equilibrium in the endothermic direction.

16.70   (a) [B] will immediately increase, and the blue color will become darker.

(b) The reaction equilibrium will shift to the side with fewer molecules (because the flask size has been halved). Thus, it will shift toward the blue molecules, and the blue color will become even more pronounced.

16.71   Any elementary chemical step can occur both in the forward and reverse directions. Solid lead chloride

forms when solutions containing lead ions and chloride ions are mixed, and a solution containing lead ions

and chloride ions forms when pure lead chloride is placed in water and heated.

16.72   (a) $[Fe^{3+}]$ does not go to zero. $K = \dfrac{[FeSCN^{2+}]}{[Fe^{3+}][SCN^-]} = \dfrac{2.060 \times 10^{-3}}{(2.939 \times 10^{-3})(4.939 \times 10^{-3})} = 142$

(b) $[Fe^{3+}] = [SCN^-]$ at equilibrium, and these ions have the largest concentration

(c)   At equilibrium, $[Fe^{3+}] = 2.64 \times 10^{-3}$ M, $[SCN^-] = 3.64 \times 10^{-3}$ M, $[FeSCN^{2+}] = 1.36 \times 10^{-3}$ M

Chapter 17
Principles of Reactivity: Chemistry of Acids and Bases

INSTRUCTOR'S NOTES

Aqueous equilibria have been organized into two chapters, Chapter 17 (The Chemistry of Acids and Bases) and Chapter 18 (Other Aspects of Aqueous Equilibria). Chapter 17 introduces acid-base theories, applies the concepts of equilibria to acids and bases in aqueous solution, and covers acid-base reactions. The common ion effect, buffer solutions, acid-base titrations, and the solubility of salts are topics covered in Chapter 18.

We cover aqueous equilibria in the second semester of our course. We do not give much coverage to polyprotic acids or to equilibria involving complex ions. Lewis acid/base concepts are mentioned briefly.

One aspect of Chapter 17 that we especially emphasize is the concept of conjugate acids and bases and relative acid and base strengths. In lecture we perform some acid-base reactions to build a portion of Table 17.3, the chart of relative strengths of acids and bases.

Students often do have some difficulty with the general topic of aqueous equilibria. The successful student is generally one who takes the time to work through as many examples, exercises, and study questions as possible. Therefore, it is useful to assign a large number of homework problems and point out extra work that may be done. It is a good idea to stress the common features of the problem-solving methods that are used in this material (e.g., ICE table).

The *Study Guide* that accompanies this text is especially useful for the students studying these chapters.

SUGGESTED DEMONSTRATIONS

1. Acids, Bases, and Arrhenius

   *   Acid-base chemistry can be introduced by performing a reaction such as HCO_3^- or CO_3^{2-} plus acid. For example, show the reaction of an Alka-Seltzer tablet with acid in a petri dish on an overhead projector.

   *   Volume 3 of the *Chemical Demonstrations* series by Shakhashiri contains a useful discussion of acid-base chemistry along with 32 demonstrations for this topic. In addition, the videotape, which was prepared by Shakhashiri and which accompanies this text, shows some useful demonstrations.

   *   Another source of acid-base demonstrations is L. R. Summerlin and J. L. Ealy, Jr.: *Chemical Demonstrations: A Sourcebook for Teachers, 2nd Edition*, Volume 1, American Chemical Society, 1988.

2. The Brønsted Concept of Acids and Bases

   *   The concept of strong and weak acids and bases is a topic introduced early in these lectures. Although the demonstration was done for Chapter 5, we like to show again how conductivity differs for aqueous solutions of strong and weak acids and bases.

3. Water and the pH Scale

    - To demonstrate pH in a large classroom we use a variety of solutions in petri dishes on the overhead projector, adding universal indicator to each one. To show acidic pH's we have used the following: dilute HCl; an aqueous Cu^{2+} or Al^{3+} solution; NH_4Cl; dry ice; CO_2 from exhaled breath. For pH's on the basic side: sodium acetate; sodium carbonate; NH_3; dilute NaOH.

4. The Lewis Concept of Acids and Bases

    - The concept of amphoterism is effectively demonstrated by the procedure shown in Figure 17.8. Either $Al(OH)_3$ or $Zn(OH)_2$ works well.

    - We find the reaction depicted in Figure 17.7 to be particularly useful to demonstrate.

    - Many metal ion/Lewis base complexes can be illustrated in lecture. One of the simplest is the formation of $[Cu(NH_3)_4]^{2+}$, but others would include Prussian blue $[Fe(CN)_6^{4-} + Fe^{3+}]$, the deep red iron(III)- thiocyanate complex, or Ni^{2+} and dimethylglyoxime. Conditions for forming these and other complexes may be found in any qualitative analysis book.

5. Acids, Bases, and Indicators:

    - Meyer, L. S.; Schmidt, S.; Nozawa, F.; Panee, D. "Using Demonstrations to Promote Student Comprehension in Chemistry," *Journal of Chemical Education* **2003**, *80*, 430.

SOLUTIONS TO STUDY QUESTIONS

17.1   (a) CN^- cyanide ion

       (b) SO_4^{2-} sulfate ion

       (c) F^- fluoride ion

17.2   (a) NH_4^+ ammonium ion

       (b) H_2CO_3 carbonic acid

       (c) HBr   hydrobromic acid

17.3   (a) HNO_3 + $H_2O \rightarrow$ H_3O^+ + NO_3^-

            acid A   base B   conjugate acid of B   conjugate base of A

       (b) HSO_4^- + $H_2O \rightarrow$ H_3O^+ + SO_4^{2-}

            acid A   base B   conjugate acid of B   conjugate base of A

       (c) H_3O^+ + $F^- \rightarrow$ HF   + H_2O

            acid A   base B   conjugate acid of B   conjugate base of A

17.4   (a) $HClO_4$ + $H_2O \rightarrow$ H_3O^+ + ClO_4^-

            acid A   base B   conjugate acid of B   conjugate base of A

       (b) NH_4^+ + $H_2O \rightarrow$ NH_3 + H_3O^+

            acid A   base B   conjugate base of A   conjugate acid of B

       (c) HCO_3^- + $OH^- \rightarrow$ CO_3^{2-} + H_2O

            acid A   base B   conjugate base of A   conjugate acid of B

17.5   Brønsted acid: $HC_2O_4^-(aq) + H_2O(\ell) \rightleftharpoons H_3O^+(aq) + C_2O_4^{2-}(aq)$

       Brønsted base: $HC_2O_4^-(aq) + H_2O(\ell) \rightleftharpoons H_2C_2O_4(aq) + OH^-(aq)$

17.6   Brønsted acid: $HPO_4^{2-}(aq) + H_2O(\ell) \rightleftharpoons H_3O^+(aq) + PO_4^{3-}(aq)$

       Brønsted base: $HPO_4^{2-}(aq) + H_2O(\ell) \rightleftharpoons OH^-(aq) + H_2PO_4^-(aq)$

17.7

	Brønsted acid	Brønsted base	conjugate base	conjugate acid
(a)	HCO_2H	H_2O	HCO_2^-	H_3O^+
(b)	H_2S	NH_3	HS^-	NH_4^+
(c)	HSO_4^-	OH^-	SO_4^{2-}	H_2O

17.8

	Brønsted acid	Brønsted base	conjugate base	conjugate acid
(a)	CH_3CO_2H	C_5H_5N	$CH_3CO_2^-$	$C_5H_5NH^+$
(b)	HSO_4^-	N_2H_4	SO_4^{2-}	$N_2H_5^+$
(c)	$[Al(H_2O)_6]^{3+}$	OH^-	$[Al(H_2O)_5(OH)]^{2+}$	H_2O

17.9 $[H_3O^+] = 10^{-pH} = 10^{-3.75} = 1.8 \times 10^{-4}$ M

The solution is acidic (pH < 7)

17.10 $[H_3O^+] = 10^{-pH} = 10^{-10.52} = 2.0 \times 10^{-11}$ M

$[OH^-] = \dfrac{K_w}{[H_3O^+]} = \dfrac{1.0 \times 10^{-14}}{3.0 \times 10^{-11}} = 3.3 \times 10^{-4}$ M

The solution is basic (pH > 7)

17.11 HCl is a strong acid so $[H_3O^+] = [HCl] = 0.0075$ M

$pH = -\log[H_3O^+] = -\log(0.0075) = 2.12$

$[OH^-] = \dfrac{K_w}{[H_3O^+]} = \dfrac{1.0 \times 10^{-14}}{0.0075} = 1.3 \times 10^{-12}$ M

17.12 KOH is a strong base so $[OH^-] = [KOH] = 1.2 \times 10^{-4}$

$[H_3O^+] = \dfrac{K_w}{[OH^-]} = \dfrac{1.0 \times 10^{-14}}{1.2 \times 10^{-4}} = 8.3 \times 10^{-11}$ M

$pH = -\log[H_3O^+] = -\log(8.3 \times 10^{-11}) = 10.08$

17.13 $Ba(OH)_2(aq) \rightarrow Ba^{2+}(aq) + 2\,OH^-(aq)$

$[OH^-] = 2 \times [Ba(OH)_2] = 0.0030$ M

$[H_3O^+] = \dfrac{K_w}{[OH^-]} = \dfrac{1.0 \times 10^{-14}}{0.0030} = 3.3 \times 10^{-12}$ M

$pH = -\log[H_3O^+] = -\log(3.3 \times 10^{-12}) = 11.48$

17.14 $pOH = 14.00 - pH = 3.34$

$[OH^-] = 10^{-pOH} = 10^{-3.34} = 4.6 \times 10^{-4}$ M

$\dfrac{4.6 \times 10^{-4} \text{ mol OH}^-}{1 \text{ L}} \cdot 0.125 \text{ L} \cdot \dfrac{1 \text{ mol Ba(OH)}_2}{2 \text{ mol OH}^-} \cdot \dfrac{171.3 \text{ g}}{1 \text{ mol Ba(OH)}_2} = 4.9 \times 10^{-3}$ g

17.15 (a) The strongest acid is HCO_2H (largest K_a) and the weakest acid is C_6H_5OH (smallest K_a).

(b) The strongest acid (HCO_2H) has the weakest conjugate base.

(c) The weakest acid (C_6H_5OH) has the strongest conjugate base.

17.16   (a)   The strongest acid is HF (largest K_a) and the weakest acid is HPO_4^{2-} (smallest K_a).

        (b) F^-

        (c)   The strongest acid (HF) has the weakest conjugate base.

        (d)   The weakest acid (HPO_4^{2-}) has the strongest conjugate base.

17.17   (c)   HClO is the weakest acid of the three, so it has the strongest conjugate base.

17.18   (c) SO_4^{2-} is the weakest base of the three, so it has the strongest conjugate acid.

17.19   Potassium carbonate is soluble in water, producing $K^+(aq)$ and $CO_3^{2-}(aq)$

        $CO_3^{2-}(aq) + H_2O(\ell) \rightleftharpoons HCO_3^-(aq) + OH^-(aq)$

17.20   Ammonium bromide is soluble in water, producing $NH_4^+(aq)$ and $Br^-(aq)$.

        $NH_4^+(aq) + H_2O(\ell) \rightleftharpoons H_3O^+(aq) + NH_3(aq)$

17.21 Na^+, $CH_3CO_2^-$, and Cl^- are neutral ions. S^{2-}, PO_4^{3-}, and F^- are basic ions. $H_2PO_4^-$ and Al^{3+} are acidic ions.
        According to Table 17.3, S^{2-} is most basic. A solution of (a) Na_2S will have the highest pH.
        According to Table 17.3, $Al(H_2O)_6^{3+}$ is most acidic. A solution of (f) $AlCl_3$ will have the lowest pH.

17.22   (a) $NaNO_3$ Neutral. Neither ion affects the pH of the solution.
        (b) $NaC_7H_5O_2$ Basic. Na^+ has no effect on pH, but $C_7H_5O_2^-$, the conjugate base of the weak acid
                                $HC_7H_5O_2$, makes the solution basic.
        (c) Na_2HPO_4 Basic. Na^+ has no effect on pH, but HPO_4^{2-}, the conjugate base of the weak acid
                                $H_2PO_4^-$, makes the solution basic.

17.23 $pK_a = -\log(K_a) = -\log(6.5 \times 10^{-5}) = 4.19$

17.24 $pK_a = -\log(K_a) = -\log(2.4 \times 10^{-11}) = 10.62$

17.25 $K_a = 10^{-pK_a} = 10^{-9.53} = 3.0 \times 10^{-10}$ The acid is weaker than $Fe(H_2O)_6^{2+}$ and stronger than HCO_3^-

17.26 $K_a = 10^{-pK_a} = 10^{-8.95} = 1.1 \times 10^{-9}$ The acid is weaker than $Co(H_2O)_6^{2+}$ and stronger than $B(OH)_3H_2O$

17.27   The acid with the smaller pK_a has the larger K_a. (b) 2-chlorobenzoic acid is the stronger acid

17.28   Acetic acid $pK_a = -\log(1.8 \times 10^{-5}) = 4.74$

        The acid with the smaller pK_a has the larger K_a. (b) chloroacetic acid is the stronger acid

17.29 $K_b = \dfrac{K_w}{K_a} = \dfrac{1.0 \times 10^{-14}}{1.36 \times 10^{-3}} = 7.4 \times 10^{-12}$

17.30 $K_a = \dfrac{K_w}{K_b} = \dfrac{1.0 \times 10^{-14}}{1.5 \times 10^{-9}} = 6.7 \times 10^{-6}$

17.31 $K_a = 10^{-pK_a} = 10^{-9.80} = 1.6 \times 10^{-10}$ $K_b = \dfrac{K_w}{K_a} = \dfrac{1.0 \times 10^{-14}}{1.6 \times 10^{-10}} = 6.3 \times 10^{-5}$

17.32 $K_a = 10^{-pK_a} = 10^{-3.95} = 1.1 \times 10^{-4}$ $K_b = \dfrac{K_w}{K_a} = \dfrac{1.0 \times 10^{-14}}{1.1 \times 10^{-4}} = 8.9 \times 10^{-11}$

17.33 $CH_3CO_2H(aq) + HCO_3^{-}(aq) \rightleftharpoons CH_3CO_2^{-}(aq) + H_2CO_3(aq)$

        $K_a(CH_3CO_2H) > K_a(H_2CO_3)$ The equilibrium will lie predominantly to the right.

17.34 $NH_4^{+}(aq) + H_2PO_4^{-}(aq) \rightleftharpoons NH_3(aq) + H_3PO_4(aq)$

        $K_a(H_3PO_4) > K_a(NH_4^{+})$ The equilibrium will lie predominantly to the left.

17.35   (a) HBr is a stronger acid than NH_4^{+}, so the equilibrium lies predominantly to the left.

       (b) CH_3CO_2H is a stronger acid than HPO_4^{2-}, so the equilibrium lies predominantly to the left.

       (c) $Fe(H_2O)_6^{3+}$ is a stronger acid than H_2CO_3, so the equilibrium lies predominantly to the right.

17.36   (a) H_2S is a stronger acid than HCO_3^{-}, so the equilibrium lies predominantly to the right.

       (b) HSO_4^{-} is a stronger acid than HCN, so the equilibrium lies predominantly to the left.

       (c) HSO_4^{-} is a stronger acid than CH_3CO_2H, so the equilibrium lies predominantly to the left.

17.37   (a) $OH^{-}(aq) + HPO_4^{2-}(aq) \rightleftharpoons H_2O(\ell) + PO_4^{3-}(aq)$

       (b) The resulting solution should be basic because the significant species remaining in solution upon

           completion of the reaction is PO_4^{3-}, the conjugate base of a weak acid.

17.38   (a) $H_3O^{+}(aq) + OCl^{-}(aq) \rightleftharpoons H_2O(\ell) + HOCl(aq)$

       (b) The resulting solution should be acidic because the significant species remaining in solution upon

           completion of the reaction is HOCl, a weak acid.

17.39   (a) $CH_3CO_2H(aq) + HPO_4^{2-}(aq) \rightleftharpoons CH_3CO_2^{-}(aq) + H_2PO_4^{-}(aq)$

       (b) CH_3CO_2H is a stronger acid than $H_2PO_4^{-}$. The equilibrium will lie predominantly to the right.

          $K_a(H_2PO_4^{-}) > K_b(CH_3CO_2^{-})$ The solution will be slightly acidic.

17.40   (a) $NH_3(aq) + H_2PO_4^{-}(aq) \rightleftharpoons NH_4^{+}(aq) + HPO_4^{2-}(aq)$

       (b) $H_2PO_4^{-}$ is a stronger acid than NH_4^{+}. The equilibrium will lie predominantly to the right.

          $K_b(HPO_4^{2-}) > K_a(NH_4^{+})$ The solution will be slightly basic.

17.41   (a) $[H_3O^+] = [OCN^-] = 10^{-pH} = 10^{-2.67} = 0.0021$ M

(b)

	HOCN + H_2O $\rightleftharpoons$	OCN$^-$ +	H_3O$^+$
Initial (M)	0.015	0	0
Change (M)	−0.0021	+0.0021	+0.0021
Equilibrium (M)	0.013	0.0021	0.0021

$$K_a = \frac{[OCN^-][H_3O^+]}{[HOCN]} = \frac{(0.0021)(0.0021)}{0.013} = 3.6 \times 10^{-4}$$

17.42 $[H_3O^+] = [ClCH_2CO_2^-] = 10^{-pH} = 10^{-1.95} = 0.011$ M

	ClCH_2CO_2H + H_2O $\rightleftharpoons$	ClCH_2CO_2$^-$ +	H_3O$^+$
Initial (M)	0.10	0	0
Change (M)	−0.011	+0.011	+0.011
Equilibrium (M)	0.09	0.011	0.011

$$K_a = \frac{[ClCH_2CO_2^-][H_3O^+]}{[ClCH_2CO_2H]} = \frac{(0.011)(0.011)}{0.09} = 1 \times 10^{-3}$$

17.43   pOH = 14.00 − pH = 4.89

$[H_3NOH^+] = [OH^-] = 10^{-pOH} = 10^{-4.89} = 1.3 \times 10^{-5}$ M

$$K_b = \frac{[H_3NOH^+][OH^-]}{[H_2NOH]} = \frac{(1.3 \times 10^{-5})(1.3 \times 10^{-5})}{0.025 - 1.3 \times 10^{-5}} = 6.6 \times 10^{-9}$$

17.44   pOH = 14.00 − pH = 2.30

$[CH_3NH_3^+] = [OH^-] = 10^{-pOH} = 10^{-2.30} = 0.0050$ M

$$K_b = \frac{[CH_3NH_3^+][OH^-]}{[CH_3NH_2]} = \frac{(0.0050)(0.0050)}{0.065 - 0.0050} = 4.2 \times 10^{-4}$$

17.45   (a) $[H_3O^+] = 10^{-pH} = 10^{-3.80} = 1.6 \times 10^{-4}$ M

(b) $K_a = \dfrac{[A^-][H_3O^+]}{[HA]} = \dfrac{(1.6 \times 10^{-4})(1.6 \times 10^{-4})}{2.5 \times 10^{-3} - 1.6 \times 10^{-4}} = 1.1 \times 10^{-5}$ The acid is moderately weak

17.46   (a) $[H_3O^+] = 10^{-pH} = 10^{-10.09} = 8.1 \times 10^{-11}$ M

$[OH^-] = \dfrac{K_w}{[H_3O^+]} = 1.2 \times 10^{-4}$ M

(b) $K_b = \dfrac{(1.2 \times 10^{-4})(1.2 \times 10^{-4})}{0.015 - 1.2 \times 10^{-4}} = 1.0 \times 10^{-6}$ The base is moderately weak.

17.47 $CH_3CO_2H + H_2O \rightleftharpoons CH_3CO_2^- + H_3O^+$

Initial (M)	0.20	0	0
Change (M)	$-x$	$+x$	$+x$
Equilibrium (M)	$0.20 - x$	x	x

$$K_a = 1.8 \times 10^{-5} = \frac{[CH_3CO_2^-][H_3O^+]}{[CH_3CO_2H]} = \frac{x^2}{0.20 - x}$$

Assume that x is much smaller than 0.20

$$1.8 \times 10^{-5} = \frac{x^2}{0.20}$$

$x = [CH_3CO_2^-] = [H_3O^+] = 1.9 \times 10^{-3}$ M $[CH_3CO_2H] = 0.20$ M

17.48 $HA + H_2O \rightleftharpoons A^- + H_3O^+$

Initial (M)	0.040	0	0
Change (M)	$-x$	$+x$	$+x$
Equilibrium (M)	$0.040 - x$	x	x

$$K_a = 4.0 \times 10^{-9} = \frac{[A^-][H_3O^+]}{[HA]} = \frac{x^2}{0.040 - x}$$

Assume that x is much smaller than 0.040

$$4.0 \times 10^{-9} = \frac{x^2}{0.040}$$

$x = [A^-] = [H_3O^+] = 1.3 \times 10^{-5}$ M $[HA] = 0.040$ M

17.49 $HCN + H_2O \rightleftharpoons CN^- + H_3O^+$

Initial (M)	0.025	0	0
Change (M)	$-x$	$+x$	$+x$
Equilibrium (M)	$0.025 - x$	x	x

$$K_a = 4.0 \times 10^{-10} = \frac{[CN^-][H_3O^+]}{[HCN]} = \frac{x^2}{0.025 - x}$$

Assume that x is much smaller than 0.025

$$4.0 \times 10^{-10} = \frac{x^2}{0.025}$$

$x = [CN^-] = [H_3O^+] = 3.2 \times 10^{-6}$ M $[HCN] = 0.025$ M $pH = -\log[H_3O^+] = 5.50$

17.50 $\dfrac{0.195 \text{ g}}{0.125 \text{ L}} \cdot \dfrac{1 \text{ mol } C_6H_5OH}{94.11 \text{ g}} = 0.0166 \text{ M } C_6H_5OH$

$$C_6H_5OH + H_2O \rightleftharpoons C_6H_5O^- + H_3O^+$$

Initial (M)	0.0166	0	0
Change (M)	$-x$	$+x$	$+x$
Equilibrium (M)	$0.0166 - x$	x	x

$K_a = 1.3 \times 10^{-10} = \dfrac{[C_6H_5O^-][H_3O^+]}{[C_6H_5OH]} = \dfrac{x^2}{0.0166 - x}$

Assume x is much smaller than 0.0166

$1.3 \times 10^{-10} = \dfrac{x^2}{0.0166}$

$x = [H_3O^+] = 1.5 \times 10^{-6} \text{ M}$ $pH = -\log[H_3O^+] = 5.83$

17.51 $NH_3(aq) + H_2O(\ell) \rightleftharpoons NH_4^+(aq) + OH^-(aq)$

$K_b = 1.8 \times 10^{-5} = \dfrac{[NH_4^+][OH^-]}{[NH_3]} = \dfrac{x^2}{0.15 - x}$

Assume x is much smaller than 0.15

$1.8 \times 10^{-5} = \dfrac{x^2}{0.15}$

$x = [NH_4^+] = [OH^-] = 0.0016 \text{ M}$ $[NH_3] = 0.15 \text{ M}$

$pOH = -\log[OH^-] = 2.78$ $pH = 14.00 - pOH = 11.22$

17.52 $B(aq) + H_2O(\ell) \rightleftharpoons BH^+(aq) + OH^-(aq)$

$K_b = 5.0 \times 10^{-4} = \dfrac{[BH^+][OH^-]}{[B]} = \dfrac{x^2}{0.15 - x}$

The assumption $x \ll [B]_{initial}$ is not valid. Solve using the quadratic equation.

$x = [BH^+] = [OH^-] = 8.4 \times 10^{-3} \text{ M}$ $[B] = 0.15 - x = 0.14 \text{ M}$

17.53 $K_b = 4.2 \times 10^{-4} = \dfrac{[CH_3NH_3^+][OH^-]}{[CH_3NH_2]} = \dfrac{x^2}{0.25 - x}$

Assume x is much smaller than 0.25

$4.2 \times 10^{-4} = \dfrac{x^2}{0.25}$

$x = [OH^-] = 0.010 \text{ M}$ $pOH = -\log[OH^-] = 1.99$ $pH = 14.00 - pOH = 12.01$

17.54 $K_b = 4.0 \times 10^{-10} = \dfrac{[C_6H_5NH_3^+][OH^-]}{[C_6H_5NH_2]} = \dfrac{x^2}{0.12 - x} \approx \dfrac{x^2}{0.12}$

$x = [OH^-] = 6.9 \times 10^{-6} \text{ M}$ $pOH = -\log[OH^-] = 5.16$ $pH = 14.00 - pOH = 8.84$

17.55 $HF(aq) + H_2O(\ell) \rightleftharpoons H_3O^+(aq) + F^-(aq)$

$$K_a = 7.2 \times 10^{-4} = \frac{[F^-][H_3O^+]}{[HF]} \approx \frac{x^2}{0.0010 - x}$$

The assumption $x \ll [HF]_{initial}$ is not valid. Solve using the quadratic equation.

$x = [H_3O^+] = 5.6 \times 10^{-4}$ M $pH = -\log[H_3O^+] = 3.25$

17.56 $HF(aq) + H_2O(\ell) \rightleftharpoons H_3O^+(aq) + F^-(aq)$

$[F^-] = [H_3O^+] = 10^{-pH} = 10^{-2.30} = 0.0050$ M

$$K_a = 7.2 \times 10^{-4} = \frac{[F^-][H_3O^+]}{[HF]} = \frac{(0.0050)^2}{x}$$

$x = [HF] = 0.035$ M

$[HF]_{initial} = 0.035$ M $+ 0.0050$ M ≈ 0.040 M

17.57 $NH_4^+(aq) + H_2O(\ell) \rightleftharpoons NH_3(aq) + H_3O^+(aq)$

$$K_a = \frac{K_w}{K_b} = \frac{1.0 \times 10^{-14}}{1.8 \times 10^{-5}} = 5.6 \times 10^{-10}$$

$$5.6 \times 10^{-10} = \frac{[NH_3][H_3O^+]}{[NH_4^+]} = \frac{x^2}{0.20 - x} \approx \frac{x^2}{0.20}$$

$x = [H_3O^+] = 1.1 \times 10^{-5}$ M $pH = -\log[H_3O^+] = 4.98$

17.58 $HCO_2^-(aq) + H_2O(\ell) \rightleftharpoons HCO_2H(aq) + OH^-(aq)$

$$K_b = \frac{K_w}{K_a} = \frac{1.0 \times 10^{-14}}{1.8 \times 10^{-4}} = 5.6 \times 10^{-11}$$

$$5.6 \times 10^{-11} = \frac{[HCO_2H][OH^-]}{[HCO_2^-]} = \frac{x^2}{0.015 - x} \approx \frac{x^2}{0.015}$$

$x = [OH^-] = 9.1 \times 10^{-7}$ M $[H_3O^+] = \dfrac{K_w}{[OH^-]} = 1.1 \times 10^{-8}$ M $pH = -\log[H_3O^+] = 7.96$

17.59 $[CN^-]_{initial} = \dfrac{10.8 \text{ g}}{0.500 \text{ L}} \cdot \dfrac{1 \text{ mol NaCN}}{49.01 \text{ g}} \cdot \dfrac{1 \text{ mol CN}^-}{1 \text{ mol NaCN}} = 0.441$ M

$CN^-(aq) + H_2O(\ell) \rightleftharpoons HCN(aq) + OH^-(aq)$

$$K_b = \frac{K_w}{K_a} = \frac{1.0 \times 10^{-14}}{4.0 \times 10^{-10}} = 2.5 \times 10^{-5}$$

$$2.5 \times 10^{-5} = \frac{[HCN][OH^-]}{[CN^-]} = \frac{x^2}{0.441 - x} \approx \frac{x^2}{0.441}$$

$x = [HCN] = [OH^-] = 0.0033$ M $[H_3O^+] = \dfrac{K_w}{[OH^-]} = 3.0 \times 10^{-12}$ $[CN^-] = [Na^+] = 0.441$ M

17.60 $CH_3CH_2CO_2^-(aq) + H_2O(\ell) \rightleftharpoons CH_3CH_2CO_2H(aq) + OH^-(aq)$

$K_b = \dfrac{1.0 \times 10^{-14}}{1.3 \times 10^{-5}} = 7.7 \times 10^{-10}$

$7.7 \times 10^{-10} = \dfrac{[CH_3CH_2CO_2H][OH^-]}{[CH_3CH_2CO_2^-]} = \dfrac{x^2}{0.10 - x} \approx \dfrac{x^2}{0.10}$

$x = [CH_3CH_2CO_2H] = [OH^-] = 8.8 \times 10^{-6}$ M

$pOH = -\log[OH^-] = 5.06$ $pH = 14.00 - pOH = 8.94$ $[H_3O^+] = 10^{-pH} = 1.1 \times 10^{-9}$ M

17.61 $CH_3CO_2H(aq) + OH^-(aq) \rightarrow CH_3CO_2^-(aq) + H_2O(\ell)$

(0.0220 L CH_3CO_2H)(0.15 mol/L) = 0.0033 mol CH_3CO_2H

(0.0220 L NaOH)(0.15 mol/L) = 0.0033 mol NaOH

0.0033 mol $CH_3CO_2H \cdot \dfrac{1 \text{ mol } CH_3CO_2^-}{1 \text{ mol } CH_3CO_2H} = 0.0033$ mol $CH_3CO_2^-$

$[CH_3CO_2^-] = \dfrac{0.0033 \text{ mol}}{(0.0220 + 0.0220) \text{ L}} = 0.075$ M

$CH_3CO_2^-(aq) + H_2O(\ell) \rightleftharpoons CH_3CO_2H(aq) + OH^-(aq)$

$K_b = 5.6 \times 10^{-10} = \dfrac{[CH_3CO_2H][OH^-]}{[CH_3CO_2^-]} = \dfrac{x^2}{0.075 - x} \approx \dfrac{x^2}{0.075}$

$x = [OH^-] = 6.5 \times 10^{-6}$ M $[H_3O^+] = \dfrac{K_w}{[OH^-]} = 1.5 \times 10^{-9}$ $pH = -\log[H_3O^+] = 8.81$

17.62 $NH_3(aq) + H_3O^+(aq) \rightarrow NH_4^+(aq) + H_2O(\ell)$

(0.0500 L NH_3)(0.40 mol/L) = 0.020 mol NH_3

(0.0500 L HCl)(0.40 mol/L) = 0.020 mol HCl

0.020 mol $NH_3 \cdot \dfrac{1 \text{ mol } NH_4^+}{1 \text{ mol } NH_3} = 0.020$ mol NH_4^+

$[NH_4^+] = \dfrac{0.020 \text{ mol}}{(0.0500 + 0.0500) \text{ L}} = 0.20$ M

$NH_4^+(aq) + H_2O(\ell) \rightleftharpoons NH_3(aq) + H_3O^+(aq)$

$K_a = 5.6 \times 10^{-10} = \dfrac{[NH_3][H_3O^+]}{[NH_4^+]} = \dfrac{x^2}{0.20 - x} \approx \dfrac{x^2}{0.20}$

$x = [H_3O^+] = 1.1 \times 10^{-5}$ M $pH = -\log[H_3O^+] = 4.98$

17.63   (a) pH > 7 The predominant ion in solution will be $CH_3CO_2^-$, a weak base.

(b) pH < 7 The predominant ion in solution will be NH_4^+, a weak acid.

(c) pH = 7 Equimolar amounts of strong acid and strong base result in a neutral solution.

17.64   (a) $pH = 7$ Equimolar amounts of strong acid and strong base result in a neutral solution.

       (b) $pH > 7$ The predominant ion in solution will be HCO_2^-, a weak base.

       (c) $pH > 7$ The predominant ion in solution will be $C_2O_4^{2-}$, a weak base.

17.65   The pH of the solution is determined by the first ionization of the acid.

$$H_2SO_3(aq) + H_2O(\ell) \rightleftharpoons HSO_3^-(aq) + H_3O^+(aq) \qquad\qquad K_{a1} = 1.2 \times 10^{-2}$$

       (a) $1.2 \times 10^{-2} = \dfrac{[HSO_3^-][H_3O^+]}{[H_2SO_3]} = \dfrac{x^2}{0.45 - x}$

          The approximation $x \ll 0.45$ is not valid. Solve using the quadratic equation.

          $x = [H_3O^+] = 0.0677$ M $pH = -\log[H_3O^+] = 1.17$

       (b) $[SO_3^{2-}] = K_{a2} = 6.2 \times 10^{-8}$ M

17.66   The pH of the solution is determined by the first ionization of the acid.

$$C_6H_8O_6(aq) + H_2O(\ell) \rightleftharpoons C_6H_7O_6^-(aq) + H_3O^+(aq)$$

       $\dfrac{0.0050 \text{ g}}{0.0010 \text{ L}} \cdot \dfrac{1 \text{ mol } C_6H_8O_6}{176 \text{ g}} = 0.028$ M

       $K_{a1} = 6.8 \times 10^{-5} = \dfrac{[C_6H_7O_6^-][H_3O^+]}{[C_6H_8O_6]} = \dfrac{x^2}{0.028 - x} \approx \dfrac{x^2}{0.028}$

       $x = [H_3O^+] = 1.4 \times 10^{-3}$ M $pH = -\log[H_3O^+] = 2.86$

17.67   The pH of the solution is determined by the first ionization of the base.

$$N_2H_4(aq) + H_2O(\ell) \rightleftharpoons N_2H_5^+(aq) + OH^-(aq)$$

       (a) $K_{b1} = 8.5 \times 10^{-7} = \dfrac{[N_2H_5^+][OH^-]}{[N_2H_4]} = \dfrac{x^2}{0.010 - x} \approx \dfrac{x^2}{0.010}$

          $x = [N_2H_5^+] = [OH^-] = 9.2 \times 10^{-5}$ M $[N_2H_6^{2+}] = K_{b2} = 8.9 \times 10^{-16}$ M

       (b) $pOH = -\log[OH^-] = 4.04$ $pH = 14.00 - pOH = 9.96$

17.68   The pH of the solution is determined by the first ionization.

$$H_2NCH_2CH_2NH_2(aq) + H_2O(\ell) \rightleftharpoons H_2NCH_2CH_2NH_3^+(aq) + OH^-(aq)$$

       $K_{b1} = 8.5 \times 10^{-5} = \dfrac{[H_2NCH_2CH_2NH_3^+][OH^-]}{[H_2NCH_2CH_2NH_2]} = \dfrac{x^2}{0.15 - x} \approx \dfrac{x^2}{0.15}$

       $x = [OH^-] = 3.6 \times 10^{-3}$ M $[H_3NCH_2CH_2NH_3^{2+}] = K_{b2} = 2.7 \times 10^{-8}$ M

17.69   (a) H_2NOH is a Lewis base

       (b) Fe^{2+} is a Lewis acid

       (c) CH_3NH_2 is a Lewis base

17.70   (a) BCl_3 is a Lewis acid.

      (b) H_2NNH_2 is a Lewis base.

      (c) Ag^+ is a Lewis acid, NH_3 is a Lewis base

17.71   CO is a Lewis base in its complexes with Fe, Ni, and other transition metals.

17.72 BH_3 is a Lewis acid.

17.73   HOCN should be a stronger acid than HCN because the H atom in HOCN is attached to a highly electronegative O atom. This induces a positive charge on the H atom, making it more readily removed by an interaction with water.

17.74   The ion with the more highly charged metal ion, $V(H_2O)_6^{3+}$, should be the stronger acid.

17.75   The S atom is surrounded by four highly electronegative O atoms. The inductive effect of these atoms induces a positive charge on the H atom, making it susceptible to removal by water.

17.76   Ethylenediamine can act as a proton acceptor (Brønsted base) and an electron pair donor (Lewis base).

17.77 $$[HC_9H_7O_4] = \frac{2(0.325\ g)}{0.225\ L} \cdot \frac{1\ mol\ HC_9H_7O_4}{180.2\ g} = 0.0160\ M$$

$$K_a = 3.27 \times 10^{-4} = \frac{[C_9H_7O_4^-][H_3O^+]}{[HC_9H_7O_4]} = \frac{x^2}{0.0160 - x}$$

The assumption $x \ll 0.160$ is not valid. Solve using the quadratic equation.

$x = [H_3O^+] = 2.13 \times 10^{-3}\ M$ $pH = -\log[H_3O^+] = 2.671$

17.78   (a) NH_4^+ might lead to an acidic solution, CO_3^{2-} and S^{2-} might lead to a basic solution in water

      (b) Br^- and ClO_4^- have no effect on the pH of a solution.

      (c) S^{2-} is the strongest base.

      (d) $CO_3^{2-}(aq) + H_2O(\ell) \rightleftarrows HCO_3^-(aq) + OH^-(aq)$

           $S^{2-}(aq) + H_2O(\ell) \rightleftarrows HS^-(aq) + OH^-(aq)$

17.79   Benzoic acid is the weaker acid so its solution will have the higher pH.

17.80   (i) $(CH_3)_3NH^+ < ClC_6H_4CO_2H < BrCH_2CO_2H$

           —increasing acid strength$\rightarrow$

      (ii) $BrCH_2CO_2H < ClC_6H_4CO_2H < (CH_3)_3NH^+$

            —increasing pH$\rightarrow$

17.81 $H_2S(aq) + CH_3CO_2^-(aq) \rightleftharpoons HS^-(aq) + CH_3CO_2H(aq)$

CH_3CO_2H is a stronger acid than H_2S so the equilibrium will lie predominantly towards reactants.

17.82   (a) HCO_3^- is a weaker acid than HSO_4^-, so the equilibrium lies predominantly to the left.

(b) HSO_4^- is a stronger acid than CH_3CO_2H, so the equilibrium lies predominantly to the right.

(c) $Co(H_2O)_6^{2+}$ is a weaker acid than CH_3CO_2H, so the equilibrium lies predominantly to the left.

17.83 $K_a = 1.3 \times 10^{-3} = \dfrac{[X^-][H_3O^+]}{[HX]} = \dfrac{x^2}{0.010 - x}$

The assumption $x \ll 0.010$ is not valid. Solve using the quadratic equation.

$x = [H_3O^+] = 3.0 \times 10^{-3}$ M $[HX] = 0.010 - x = 0.007$ M $pH = -\log[H_3O^+] = 2.52$

17.84 $[OH^-] = \dfrac{0.50 \text{ g}}{1.0 \text{ L}} \cdot \dfrac{1 \text{ mol Ca(OH)}_2}{74.1 \text{ g}} \cdot \dfrac{2 \text{ mol OH}^-}{1 \text{ mol Ca(OH)}_2} = 0.013$ M

$pOH = -\log[OH^-] = 1.87$ $pH = 14.00 - pOH = 12.13$

17.85 $[H_3O^+] = 10^{-pH} = 10^{-3.44} = 3.6 \times 10^{-4}$ M

$K_a = \dfrac{[H_3O^+]^2}{[m\text{-nitrophenol}]} = \dfrac{(3.6 \times 10^{-4})^2}{0.010 - 3.6 \times 10^{-4}} = 1.4 \times 10^{-5}$

$pK_a = -\log(K_a) = 4.86$

17.86   (a) $K_b = \dfrac{K_w}{K_a} = \dfrac{1.0 \times 10^{-14}}{2.3 \times 10^{-11}} = 4.3 \times 10^{-4}$

(b) The acid is placed directly below $Ni(H_2O)_6^{2+}$. HPO_4^{2-} is a weaker acid than $C_4H_9NH_3^+$. PO_4^{3-} is a stronger base than $C_4H_9NH_2$.

(c) $K_a = 2.3 \times 10^{-11} = \dfrac{[C_4H_9NH_2][H_3O^+]}{[C_4H_9NH_3^+]} = \dfrac{x^2}{0.015 - x} \approx \dfrac{x^2}{0.015}$

$x = [H_3O^+] = 5.9 \times 10^{-7}$ M $pH = -\log[H_3O^+] = 6.23$

17.87 $K_a = 10^{-pK_a} = 10^{-8.85} = 1.4 \times 10^{-9}$

$HC_{13}H_{20}N_2O_2^+(aq) + H_2O(\ell) \rightleftharpoons H_3O^+(aq) + C_{13}H_{20}N_2O_2(aq)$

$1.4 \times 10^{-9} = \dfrac{[C_{13}H_{20}N_2O_2][H_3O^+]}{[HC_{13}H_{20}N_2O_2^+]} = \dfrac{x^2}{0.0015 - x} \approx \dfrac{x^2}{0.0015}$

$x = [H_3O^+] = 1.4 \times 10^{-6}$ M $pH = -\log[H_3O^+] = 5.84$

17.88 $K_a = 10^{-pK_a} = 10^{-4.60} = 2.5 \times 10^{-5}$

$C_6H_5NH_3^+(aq) + H_2O(\ell) \rightleftharpoons H_3O^+(aq) + C_6H_5NH_2(aq)$

$2.5 \times 10^{-5} = \dfrac{[C_6H_5NH_2][H_3O^+]}{[C_6H_5NH_3^+]} = \dfrac{x^2}{0.080 - x} \approx \dfrac{x^2}{0.080}$

$x = [H_3O^+] = 0.0014$ M $pH = -\log[H_3O^+] = 2.85$

17.89   (a)   Ethylamine is a stronger base (larger K_b value).

         (b) $K_b = 4.3 \times 10^{-4} = \dfrac{[CH_3CH_2NH_3^+][OH^-]}{[CH_3CH_2NH_2]} = \dfrac{x^2}{0.10 - x} \approx \dfrac{x^2}{0.10}$

               $x = [OH^-] = 0.0066 \; M \; pOH = -\log[OH^-] = 2.18$ $pH = 14.00 - pOH = 11.82$

17.90 $ClCH_2CO_2H(aq) + H_2O(\ell) \rightleftharpoons ClCH_2CO_2^-(aq) + H_3O^+(aq)$

         $[ClCH_2CO_2H] = \dfrac{0.0945 \; g}{0.125 \; L} \cdot \dfrac{1 \; mol \; ClCH_2CO_2H}{94.50 \; g} = 0.00800 \; M$

         $K_a = 1.40 \times 10^{-3} = \dfrac{[ClCH_2CO_2^-][H_3O^+]}{[ClCH_2CO_2H]} = \dfrac{x^2}{0.00800 - x}$

         The approximation $x \ll 0.00800$ is not valid. Solve using the quadratic equation.

         $x = [H_3O^+] = 2.72 \times 10^{-3} \; M$ $pH = -\log[H_3O^+] = 2.566$

17.91 $C_5H_5NH^+(aq) + H_2O(\ell) \rightleftharpoons H_3O^+(aq) + C_5H_5N(aq)$

         $K_b(C_5H_5N) = 1.5 \times 10^{-9}$ $K_a(C_5H_5NH^+) = \dfrac{K_w}{K_b} = 6.7 \times 10^{-6}$

         $K_a = 6.7 \times 10^{-6} = \dfrac{[C_5H_5N][H_3O^+]}{[C_5H_5NH^+]} = \dfrac{x^2}{0.025 - x} \approx \dfrac{x^2}{0.025}$

         $x = [H_3O^+] = 4.1 \times 10^{-4} \; M$ $pH = -\log[H_3O^+] = 3.39$

17.92 $C_7H_4NO_3S^-(aq) + H_2O(\ell) \rightleftharpoons HC_7H_4NO_3S(aq) + OH^-(aq)$

         $K_a = 10^{-pK_a} = 10^{-2.32} = 4.8 \times 10^{-3}$ $K_b = \dfrac{K_w}{K_a} = 2.1 \times 10^{-12}$

         $2.1 \times 10^{-12} = \dfrac{[HC_7H_4NO_3S][OH^-]}{[C_7H_4NO_3S^-]} = \dfrac{x^2}{0.10 - x} \approx \dfrac{x^2}{0.10}$

         $x = [OH^-] = 4.6 \times 10^{-7} \; M$ $pOH = -\log[OH^-] = 6.34$ $pH = 14.00 - pOH = 7.66$

17.93   (a) $pH < 7$ HSO_4^- is weak acid   (f) $pH = 7$ Both are neutral ions

         (b) $pH < 7$ NH_4^+ is a weak acid   (g) $pH > 7$ HPO_4^- is a weak base

         (c) $pH = 7$ Both are neutral ions   (h) $pH = 7$ Both are neutral ions

         (d) $pH > 7$ CO_3^{2-} is a weak base   (i) $pH < 7$ $Fe(H_2O)_6^{3+}$ is a weak acid

         (e) $pH > 7$ $K_b(S^{2-}) > K_a(NH_4^+)$

17.94   (i)   (d) 0.1 M CH_3CO_2H and (e) 0.1 M NH_4Cl are acidic solutions

         (ii)   (a) 0.1 M NH_3, (b) 0.1 M Na_2CO_3, and (f) 0.1 M $NaCH_3CO_2$ are basic solutions

         (iii) (d) CH_3CO_2H is a stronger acid than NH_4^+

17.95 $K_{net} = K_{a1}K_{a2} = (5.9 \times 10^{-2})(6.4 \times 10^{-5}) = 3.8 \times 10^{-6}$

17.96 $[C_6H_4NO_2^+] = [H_3O^+] = 10^{-pH} = 10^{-2.70} = 2.0 \times 10^{-3}$ M

$[C_6H_5NO_2] = \dfrac{1.0 \text{ g}}{0.060 \text{ L}} \cdot \dfrac{1 \text{ mol } C_6H_5NO_2}{123.1 \text{ g}} = 0.14$ M

$K_a = \dfrac{[C_6H_4NO_2^+][H_3O^+]}{[C_6H_5NO_2]} = \dfrac{(2.0 \times 10^{-3})^2}{0.14 - 2.0 \times 10^{-3}} = 3.0 \times 10^{-5}$

17.97 $HCO_2H(aq) + H_2O(\ell) \rightleftharpoons HCO_2^-(aq) + H_3O^+(aq)$ $\qquad K_a = 1.8 \times 10^{-4}$

$OH^-(aq) + H_3O^+(aq) \rightleftharpoons 2 H_2O(\ell)$ $\qquad\qquad\qquad K = 1/K_w$

$\overline{HCO_2H(aq) + OH^-(aq) \rightleftharpoons H_2O(\ell) + HCO_2^-(aq) \qquad K = (1.8 \times 10^{-4})/K_w = 1.8 \times 10^{10}}$

17.98 The pH of the solution is determined by the first ionization of the base.

$K_{b1} = 7.0 \times 10^{-7} = \dfrac{[NicH^+][OH^-]}{[Nic]} = \dfrac{x^2}{0.020 - x} \approx \dfrac{x^2}{0.020}$

$x = [OH^-] = 1.2 \times 10^{-4}$ M $\qquad$ pOH $= -\log[OH^-] = 3.93$ $\qquad$ pH $= 14.00 - $ pOH $= 10.07$

17.99 $[A]_1$ = initial concentration of weak acid in original solution

$[A]_2$ = initial concentration of weak acid in diluted solution

$[H_3O^+]_1$ = equilibrium hydronium ion concentration in original solution

$[H_3O^+]_2$ = equilibrium hydronium ion concentration in diluted solution

If the fraction ionized doubles, then $[H_3O^+]_2 = 2 \cdot [H_3O^+]_1$

Because $K \approx \dfrac{[H_3O^+]^2}{[HA]_{initial}}$

$\dfrac{[H_3O^+]_1^{\ 2}}{[A]_1} = \dfrac{[H_3O^+]_2^{\ 2}}{[A]_2}$

$\dfrac{[H_3O^+]_1^{\ 2}}{[A]_1} = \dfrac{(2 \cdot [H_3O^+]_1)^2}{[A]_2}$

$\dfrac{[A]_2}{[A]_1} = 4$

In order to double the percent ionization of the acid, you must dilute 100 mL of solution to 400 mL.

17.100 (a) BF_3 is a Lewis acid, $(CH_3)_2O$ is a Lewis base

(b) $P_{(CH_3)_2OBF_3} = \dfrac{nRT}{V} = \dfrac{\left(0.100 \text{ g} \cdot \dfrac{1 \text{ mol } (CH_3)_2OBF_3}{113.9 \text{ g}}\right)(0.082057 \text{ L} \cdot \text{atm/K} \cdot \text{mol})(298 \text{ K})}{0.565 \text{ L}} = 0.0380$ atm

$K_p = 0.17 = \dfrac{P_{BF_3} P_{(CH_3)_2O}}{P_{(CH_3)_2OBF_3}} = \dfrac{x^2}{0.0380 - x}$

Solve using the quadratic equation

$x = P_{BF_3} = P_{(CH_3)_2O} = 0.032$ atm $\qquad\qquad P_{(CH_3)_2OBF_3} = 0.0380 - x = 0.006$ atm

$P_{total} = 0.032 \text{ atm} + 0.032 \text{ atm} + 0.006 \text{ atm} = 0.0700$ atm

17.101 $H_2NC_6H_4SO_3^-(aq) + H_2O(\ell) \rightleftharpoons H_2NC_6H_4SO_3H(aq) + OH^-(aq)$

$K_a = 10^{-pK_a} = 10^{-3.23} = 5.9 \times 10^{-4}$ $K_b = \dfrac{K_w}{K_a} = 1.7 \times 10^{-11}$

$\dfrac{1.25\text{ g}}{0.125\text{ L}} \cdot \dfrac{1\text{ mol }H_2NC_6H_4SO_3^-}{195.2\text{ g}} = 0.0512\text{ M}$

$1.7 \times 10^{-11} = \dfrac{x^2}{0.0512 - x} \approx \dfrac{x^2}{0.0512}$

$x = [OH^-] = 9.3 \times 10^{-7}\text{ M}$ $pOH = -\log[OH^-] = 6.03$ $pH = 14.00 - pH = 7.97$

17.102 $NH_3(aq) + H_2O(\ell) \rightleftharpoons NH_4^+(aq) + OH^-(aq)$ $K_b = 1.8 \times 10^{-5}$

$OH^-(aq) + H_3O^+(aq) \rightleftharpoons 2\ H_2O(\ell)$ $K = 1/K_w$

_____

$NH_3(aq) + H_3O^+(aq) \rightleftharpoons H_2O(\ell) + NH_4^+(aq)$ $K = (1.8 \times 10^{-5})/K_w = 1.8 \times 10^9$

17.103 $HCl < NH_4Cl < NaCl < NaCH_3CO_2 < KOH$

—increasing pH→

17.104 $HCO_2H(aq) + OH^-(aq) \rightarrow HCO_2^-(aq) + H_2O(\ell)$

$(0.0250\text{ L }HCO_2H)(0.14\text{ mol/L}) = 0.0035\text{ mol }HCO_2H$

$(0.0500\text{ L }NaOH)(0.070\text{ mol/L}) = 0.0035\text{ mol }NaOH$

$0.0035\text{ mol }HCO_2H \cdot \dfrac{1\text{ mol }HCO_2^-}{1\text{ mol }HCO_2H} = 0.0035\text{ mol }HCO_2^-$

$[HCO_2^-] = \dfrac{0.0035\text{ mol}}{(0.0250 + 0.0500)\text{ L}} = 0.047\text{ M}$

$HCO_2^-(aq) + H_2O(\ell) \rightleftharpoons HCO_2H(aq) + OH^-(aq)$

$K_b = 5.6 \times 10^{-11} = \dfrac{[HCO_2H][OH^-]}{[HCO_2^-]} = \dfrac{x^2}{0.047 - x} \approx \dfrac{x^2}{0.047}$

$x = [OH^-] = 1.6 \times 10^{-6}\text{ M}$ $[H_3O^+] = \dfrac{K_w}{[OH^-]} = 6.2 \times 10^{-9}$ $pH = -\log[H_3O^+] = 8.21$

17.105 $[H_3O^+] = \sqrt{(1.12 \times 10^{-3})(3.91 \times 10^{-6})} = 6.62 \times 10^{-5}\text{ M}$

$pH = -\log[H_3O^+] = 4.179$

17.106   (a) $\left[\overset{..}{\underset{..}{:I}} - \overset{..}{\underset{.}{I}} - \overset{..}{\underset{..}{I}} : \right]^-$

(b) $I^-(aq)$ + $I_2(aq)$ → $I_3^-(aq)$

Lewis base   Lewis acid

17.107   Water can both accept a proton (Brønsted base) and donate a lone pair of electrons (Lewis base). Water can donate a proton (Brønsted acid) but it cannot accept a lone pair of electrons (Lewis acid).

17.108   The polar Ni—OH_2 bonds result in polarized O—H bonds, and the H^+ ion can be removed by H_2O in the reaction of $Ni(H_2O)_6^{2+}$ with H_2O..

$$Ni(H_2O)_6^{2+}(aq) + H_2O(\ell) \rightleftharpoons Ni(H_2O)_5(OH)^+(aq) + H_3O^+(aq)$$

17.109   Measure the pH of 0.1 M solutions of the three bases. The solution containing the strongest base will have the largest pH. The solution containing the weakest base will have the lowest pH.

17.110 H_2SeO_4 should be the stronger acid. In oxoacids, the acid with more oxygen atoms leads to a stronger inductive effect. Measure the pH of 0.1 M solutions of the two acids. The solution containing the stronger acid will have the lower pH.

17.111 $H_2O > HCN > CN^- = H_3O^+ > OH^-$

        —decreasing concentration→

17.112 $H_2O > H_2C_2O_4 > HC_2O_4^- = H_3O^+ > C_2O_4^{2-} > OH^-$

        —decreasing concentration→

17.113 $H_2O > CH_3CO_2^- = Na^+ > CH_3CO_2H = OH^- > H_3O^+$

        —decreasing concentration→

17.114   (a) The increasing acidity as Br atoms replace H atoms is due to the inductive effect of the Br atoms.

        (b) The strongest acid (Br_3CCO_2H) will have the lowest pH, and the weakest acid (CH_3CO_2H) will have the highest pH.

17.115   (a) $HClO_4 + H_2SO_4 \rightarrow ClO_4^- + H_3SO_4^+$

        (b)

        Sulfuric acid has lone pairs of electrons on all four oxygen atoms that allow it to act as a proton acceptor (a Brønsted base) or a lone pair donor (a Lewis base).

17.116   Dissolved carbon dioxide gas or dissolved metal ions can cause bottled water to be slightly acidic.

17.117   The possible cation-anion combinations are NaCl (neutral), NaOH (basic), NH_4Cl (acidic), NH_4OH (basic), HCl (acidic), and H_2O (neutral).

        A = H^+ solution; B = NH_4^+ solution, C = Na^+ solution, Y = Cl^- solution, Z = OH^- solution

17.118 (a) The $CH_3C_5H_4NH^+$ solution would have the highest pH (smallest K_a value, weakest conjugate acid).

The $NO_2C_5H_4NH^+$ solution would have the lowest pH (largest K_a value, strongest conjugate acid).

(b) The strongest conjugate acid ($NO_2C_5H_4NH^+$) has the weakest Brønsted base ($NO_2C_5H_4N$). The weakest conjugate acid ($CH_3C_5H_4NH^+$) has the strongest Brønsted base ($CH_3C_5H_4N$).

17.119 (a) $NH_4^+(aq) + H_2O(\ell) \rightleftarrows NH_3(aq) + H_3O^+(aq)$ $K_1 = K_w/K_b$

$CN^-(aq) + H_2O(\ell) \rightleftarrows HCN(aq) + OH^-(aq)$ $K_2 = K_w/K_a$

$H_3O^+(aq) + OH^-(aq) \rightleftarrows 2\ H_2O(\ell)$ $K_3 = 1/K_w$

$NH_4^+(aq) + CN^-(aq) \rightleftarrows NH_3(aq) + HCN(aq)$ $K_{net} = K_1K_2K_3 = \dfrac{K_w}{K_aK_b}$

(b) From the ionization of the ammonium ion we can write the equation

$$[H_3O^+] = \frac{K_a[NH_4^+]}{[NH_3]} = \frac{\dfrac{K_w}{K_b}[NH_4^+]}{[NH_3]}$$

From the ionization of HCN we can write the equation $[H_3O^+] = \dfrac{K_a[HCN]}{[CN^-]}$

Combine these two equations into an expression for $[H_3O^+]^2$:

$$[H_3O^+]^2 = \frac{\dfrac{K_w}{K_b}[NH_4^+]}{[NH_3]} \cdot \frac{K_a[HCN]}{[CN^-]}$$

In any solution of NH_4CN, $[NH_4^+] = [CN^-]$ and $[HCN] = [NH_3]$. The equation for $[H_3O^+]^2$ can be simplified to

$$[H_3O^+]^2 = \frac{K_wK_a}{K_b} \text{ and } [H_3O^+] = \sqrt{\frac{K_wK_a}{K_b}}$$

(c) $[H_3O^+] = \sqrt{\dfrac{K_wK_a}{K_b}} = \sqrt{\dfrac{(1.0 \times 10^{-14})(4.0 \times 10^{-10})}{1.8 \times 10^{-5}}} = 4.7 \times 10^{-10}\ M$

$pH = -\log[H_3O^+] = 9.33$

17.120 (a) Acid strength increases as pK_a decreases, so chloroacetic acid is the strongest acid.

(b) The strongest conjugate base will come from the weakest acid, the benzylammonium ion.

(c) benzylammonium ion < conjugate acid of cocaine < benzoic acid < thioacetic acid < chloroacetic acid

Chapter 18
Principles of Reactivity:
Other Aspects of Aqueous Equilibria

INSTRUCTOR'S NOTES

As described in the previous chapter, this chapter combines the common ion effect, buffers, acid-base titrations, and the solubility of ionic compounds. It is an extension of the concepts introduced in Chapter 17. It should be less intimidating for students if the subject is divided into two chapters, but the commonality of the ideas should be emphasized.

After students work on two chapters of acid-base equilibrium calculations which often permit one to drop the x because it is relatively small, they might erroneously make that assumption in other equilibrium calculations on an exam. A warning about this potential pitfall can be helpful.

SUGGESTED DEMONSTRATIONS

1. The Common Ion Effect

    - See "Effect of Acetate Ion on the Acidity of Acetic Acid: Common Ion Effect" in the third volume of *Chemical Demonstrations* by Shakhashiri.

2. Buffer Solutions

    - "Buffering Action and Capacity" in the third volume of *Chemical Demonstrations* by Shakhashiri.

3. The Solubility Product constant, K_{sp}

    - There are many demonstrations that can be done for this topic. To begin the lectures, we bring some mineral samples to class to show how many common minerals are really insoluble salts whose behavior in water can be treated by the methods of this chapter.

    - Volume 1 of the demonstration books by Shakhashiri contains a number of demonstrations involving insoluble salts. (Many also involve the dissolution of precipitates using complex ion formation.)

    - Ahmad, J. "Crystallization from a Supersaturated Solution of Sodium Acetate," *Journal of Chemical Education* **2000**, *77*, 1446.

4. Solubility and the Common Ion Effect

    - The photograph in Figure 18.13 that illustrates the common ion effect was not difficult to set up. Silver acetate was freshly precipitated. After washing with water, distilled water was added, the mixture was shaken vigorously, and the test tube was allowed to stand for some time. On adding $AgNO_3$, more silver acetate is clearly precipitated.

5. Solubility, Ion Separations, and Qualitative Analysis

    - See Chirpich, T. P. "A simple vivid demonstration of selective precipitation," *Journal of Chemical Education* **1988**, *65*, 359.

SOLUTIONS TO STUDY QUESTIONS

18.1   (a) pH decreases (NH_4^+ is a weak acid)

      (b) pH increases ($CH_3CO_2^-$ is a weak base)

      (c) no change (NaCl is a neutral salt)

18.2   (a) pH increases ($C_2O_4^{2-}$ is a weak base)

      (b) pH decreases slightly (NH_4^+, a weak acid, is being added to a solution containing a strong acid)

      (c) no change (NaCl is a neutral salt)

18.3 $NH_4^+(aq) + H_2O(\ell) \rightleftharpoons H_3O^+(aq) + NH_3(aq)$

$$K_a = 5.6 \times 10^{-10} = \frac{[H_3O^+][NH_3]}{[NH_4^+]} = \frac{(x)(0.20+x)}{(0.20-x)} \approx \frac{(x)(0.20)}{0.20}$$

$x = [H_3O^+] = 5.6 \times 10^{-10}$ M

$pH = -\log[H_3O^+] = 9.25$

18.4 $$[CH_3CO_2^-] = \frac{1.56 \text{ g NaCH}_3CO_2}{0.1000 \text{ L}} \cdot \frac{1 \text{ mol NaCH}_3CO_2}{82.03 \text{ g}} \cdot \frac{1 \text{ mol CH}_3CO_2^-}{1 \text{ mol NaCH}_3CO_2} = 0.190 \text{ M}$$

$$K_a = 1.8 \times 10^{-5} = \frac{[H_3O^+][CH_3CO_2^-]}{[CH_3CO_2H]} = \frac{(x)(0.190+x)}{(0.15-x)} \approx \frac{(x)(0.190)}{0.15}$$

$x = [H_3O^+] = 1.4 \times 10^{-5}$ M

$pH = -\log[H_3O^+] = 4.85$

18.5 $C_6H_5CO_2H(aq) + OH^-(aq) \rightarrow C_6H_5CO_2^-(aq) + H_2O(\ell)$

(0.0300 L KOH)(0.015 mol/L) = 4.5×10^{-4} mol KOH

(0.0500 L $C_6H_5CO_2H$)(0.015 mol/L) = 7.5×10^{-4} mol $C_6H_5CO_2H$

4.5×10^{-4} mol NaOH $\cdot \dfrac{1 \text{ mol } C_6H_5CO_2^-}{1 \text{ mol NaOH}} = 4.5 \times 10^{-4}$ mol $C_6H_5CO_2^-$ produced

4.5×10^{-4} mol NaOH $\cdot \dfrac{1 \text{ mol } C_6H_5CO_2H}{1 \text{ mol NaOH}} = 4.5 \times 10^{-4}$ mol $C_6H_5CO_2H$ consumed

7.5×10^{-4} mol $C_6H_5CO_2H - 4.5 \times 10^{-4}$ mol consumed = 3.0×10^{-4} mol $C_6H_5CO_2H$ remaining

$[C_6H_5CO_2H] = \dfrac{3.0 \times 10^{-4} \text{ mol}}{0.0800 \text{ L}} = 0.0038 \text{ M}$ $[C_6H_5CO_2^-] = \dfrac{4.5 \times 10^{-4} \text{ mol}}{0.0800 \text{ L}} = 0.0056 \text{ M}$

$C_6H_5CO_2H(aq) + H_2O(\ell) \rightleftharpoons H_3O^+(aq) + C_6H_5CO_2^-(aq)$

$$K_a = 6.3 \times 10^{-5} = \frac{[H_3O^+][C_6H_5CO_2^-]}{[C_6H_5CO_2H]} = \frac{(x)(0.0056+x)}{(0.0038-x)} \approx \frac{(x)(0.0056)}{0.0038}$$

$x = [H_3O^+] = 4.2 \times 10^{-5}$ M

$pH = -\log[H_3O^+] = 4.38$

18.6 $NH_3(aq) + H_3O^+(aq) \rightarrow NH_4^+(aq) + H_2O(\ell)$

(0.0250 L HCl)(0.12 mol/L) = 0.0030 mol HCl

(0.0250 L NH$_3$)(0.43 mol/L) = 0.011 mol NH$_3$

$0.0030 \text{ mol HCl} \cdot \dfrac{1 \text{ mol NH}_4^+}{1 \text{ mol HCl}} = 0.0030 \text{ mol NH}_4^+ \text{ produced}$

$0.0030 \text{ mol HCl} \cdot \dfrac{1 \text{ mol NH}_3}{1 \text{ mol HCl}} = 0.0030 \text{ mol NH}_3 \text{ consumed}$

0.011 mol NH$_3$ – 0.0030 mol consumed = 0.008 mol NH$_3$ remaining

$[NH_3] = \dfrac{0.008 \text{ mol}}{0.0500 \text{ L}} = 0.2 \text{ M}$ $[NH_4^+] = \dfrac{0.0030 \text{ mol}}{0.0500 \text{ L}} = 0.060 \text{ M}$

$NH_4^+(aq) + H_2O(\ell) \rightleftharpoons H_3O^+(aq) + NH_3(aq)$

$K_a = 5.6 \times 10^{-10} = \dfrac{[H_3O^+][NH_3]}{[NH_4^+]} = \dfrac{(x)(0.2 + x)}{(0.060 - x)} \approx \dfrac{(x)(0.2)}{0.060}$

$x = [H_3O^+] = 2 \times 10^{-10} \text{ M}$

$pH = -\log[H_3O^+] = 9.7$

18.7 $NH_4^+(aq) + H_2O(\ell) \rightleftharpoons H_3O^+(aq) + NH_3(aq)$

$[NH_4^+] = \dfrac{2.2 \text{ g NH}_4\text{Cl}}{0.25 \text{ L}} \cdot \dfrac{1 \text{ mol NH}_4\text{Cl}}{53.5 \text{ g}} \cdot \dfrac{1 \text{ mol NH}_4^+}{1 \text{ mol NH}_4\text{Cl}} = 0.16 \text{ M}$

$K_a = 5.6 \times 10^{-10} = \dfrac{[H_3O^+][NH_3]}{[NH_4^+]} = \dfrac{(x)(0.12 + x)}{(0.16 - x)} \approx \dfrac{(x)(0.12)}{0.16}$

$x = [H_3O^+] = 7.7 \times 10^{-10} \text{ M}$

$pH = -\log[H_3O^+] = 9.11$

The buffer solution has a lower pH than the original NH$_3$ solution (pH = 11.17) because a weak acid (NH$_4^+$) was added to the ammonia solution.

18.8   (a) $CH_3CHOHCO_2H(aq) + H_2O(\ell) \rightleftharpoons H_3O^+(aq) + CH_3CHOHCO_2^-(aq)$

$\dfrac{2.75 \text{ g NaCH}_3\text{CHOHCO}_2}{0.500 \text{ L}} \cdot \dfrac{1 \text{ mol NaCH}_3\text{CHOHCO}_2}{112.1 \text{ g}} \cdot \dfrac{1 \text{ mol CH}_3\text{CHOHCO}_2^-}{1 \text{ mol NaCH}_3\text{CHOHCO}_2} = 0.0491 \text{ M}$

$K_a = 1.4 \times 10^{-4} = \dfrac{[H_3O^+][CH_3CHOHCO_2^-]}{[CH_3CHOHCO_2H]} = \dfrac{(x)(0.0491 + x)}{(0.100 - x)} \approx \dfrac{(x)(0.0491)}{0.100}$

$x = [H_3O^+] = 2.9 \times 10^{-4} \text{ M}$

$pH = -\log[H_3O^+] = 3.54$

(b) The buffer solution has a higher pH than the original lactic acid solution (pH = 2.43) because a weak base (CH$_3$CHOHCO$_2^-$) was added to the lactic acid solution.

18.9 $[H_3O^+] = 10^{-pH} = 10^{-4.50} = 3.2 \times 10^{-5}$ M

$$K_a = 1.8 \times 10^{-5} = \frac{[H_3O^+][CH_3CO_2^-]}{[CH_3CO_2H]} = \frac{(3.2 \times 10^{-5})(x)}{(0.10)}$$

$x = [CH_3CO_2^-] = 0.057$ M

$$\frac{0.057 \text{ mol}}{1.0 \text{ L}} \cdot \frac{1 \text{ mol NaCH}_3CO_2}{1 \text{ mol CH}_3CO_2^-} \cdot 1.00 \text{ L} \cdot \frac{82.0 \text{ g}}{1 \text{ mol NaCH}_3CO_2} = 4.7 \text{ g}$$

18.10 $[H_3O^+] = 10^{-pH} = 10^{-9.00} = 1.0 \times 10^{-9}$

$$K_a = 5.6 \times 10^{-10} = \frac{[H_3O^+][NH_3]}{[NH_4^+]} = \frac{(1.0 \times 10^{-9})(0.10)}{x}$$

$x = [NH_4^+] = 0.18$ M

$$\frac{0.18 \text{ mol}}{1.0 \text{ L}} \cdot \frac{1 \text{ mol NH}_4Cl}{1 \text{ mol NH}_4^+} \cdot 0.500 \text{ L} \cdot \frac{53.5 \text{ g}}{1 \text{ mol NH}_4Cl} = 4.8 \text{ g NH}_4Cl$$

18.11 $pK_a = -\log(K_a) = -\log(1.8 \times 10^{-5}) = 4.74$

$$pH = pK_a + \log\frac{[CH_3CO_2^-]}{[CH_3CO_2H]} = 4.74 + \log\frac{0.075}{0.050} = 4.92$$

18.12 $pK_a = -\log(K_a) = -\log(5.6 \times 10^{-10}) = 9.25$

$$pH = pK_a + \log\frac{[NH_3]}{[NH_4^+]} = 9.25 + \log\frac{0.045}{0.050} = 9.21$$

18.13   (a) $pK_a = -\log(K_a) = -\log(1.8 \times 10^{-4}) = 3.74$

$$pH = pK_a + \log\frac{[HCO_2^-]}{[HCO_2H]} = 3.74 + \log\frac{0.035}{0.050} = 3.59$$

   (b) $pH = 4.09 = 3.74 + \log\dfrac{[HCO_2^-]}{[HCO_2H]}$

$$0.35 = \log\frac{[HCO_2^-]}{[HCO_2H]}$$

$$-0.35 = \log\frac{[HCO_2H]}{[HCO_2^-]}$$

$$\frac{[HCO_2H]}{[HCO_2^-]} = 10^{-0.35} = 0.45$$

18.14   (a) $pK_a = -\log(6.2 \times 10^{-8}) = 7.21$

$$5.677 \text{ g} \cdot \frac{1 \text{ mol Na}_2HPO_4}{141.96 \text{ g}} = 0.03999 \text{ mol Na}_2HPO_4$$

$$1.360 \text{ g} \cdot \frac{1 \text{ mol KH}_2PO_4}{136.08 \text{ g}} = 0.009994 \text{ mol KH}_2PO_4$$

$$pH = pK_a + \log\frac{[HPO_4^{2-}]}{[H_2PO_4^-]} = 7.21 + \log\left(\frac{0.03999}{0.009994}\right) = 7.81$$

(b) $pH = 7.31 = 7.21 + \log \dfrac{[HPO_4^{2-}]}{[H_2PO_4^-]}$

$0.10 = \log \dfrac{[HPO_4^{2-}]}{[H_2PO_4^-]}$

$\dfrac{[HPO_4^{2-}]}{[H_2PO_4^-]} = 1.3 = \dfrac{0.03999 \text{ mol}}{x}$

$x = 0.032 \text{ mol } H_2PO_4^-$

$0.032 \text{ mol} \cdot \dfrac{1 \text{ mol } KH_2PO_4}{1 \text{ mol } H_2PO_4^-} \cdot \dfrac{136.1 \text{ g}}{1 \text{ mol } KH_2PO_4} = 4.3 \text{ g}$

mass of KH_2PO_4 to add = 4.3 g total − 1.360 g in buffer = 2.9 g

18.15   (a) HCl and NaCl   not a buffer

(b) NH_3 and NH_4Cl $pK_a(NH_4^+) = 9.25$

(c) CH_3CO_2H and $NaCH_3CO_2$ $pK_a(CH_3CO_2H) = 4.74$

The best choice is (b), the NH_3/NH_4Cl buffer

18.16   (a) H_3PO_4/NaH_2PO_4 $pK_a(H_3PO_4) = 2.12$

(b) NaH_2PO_4/Na_2HPO_4 $pK_a(H_2PO_4^-) = 7.21$

(c) Na_2HPO_4/Na_3PO_4 $pK_a(HPO_4^{2-}) = 12.44$

The best choice is (b), the NaH_2PO_4/Na_2HPO_4 buffer.

18.17 $[H_3O^+] = 10^{-pH} = 10^{-7.5} = 3 \times 10^{-8} \text{ M}$

$K_a = 6.2 \times 10^{-8} = \dfrac{[H_3O^+][HPO_4^{2-}]}{[H_2PO_4^-]} = \dfrac{(3 \times 10^{-8})[HPO_4^{2-}]}{[H_2PO_4^-]}$

$\dfrac{[HPO_4^{2-}]}{[H_2PO_4^-]} = 2$

A solution in which the Na_2HPO_4 concentration is twice that of NaH_2PO_4 will have a pH of 7.5. For example, add 2 mol Na_2HPO_4 and 1 mol NaH_2PO_4 to some amount of water.

18.18 $[H_3O^+] = 10^{-pH} = 10^{-9.5} = 3 \times 10^{-10} \text{ M}$

$K_a = 5.6 \times 10^{-10} = \dfrac{[H_3O^+][NH_3]}{[NH_4^+]} = \dfrac{(3 \times 10^{-10})[NH_3]}{[NH_4^+]}$

$\dfrac{[NH_3]}{[NH_4^+]} = 2$

A solution in which the NH_3 concentration is twice that of NH_4Cl will have a pH of 9.5. For example, add 2 mol NH_3 and 1 mol NH_4Cl to some amount of water.

18.19 (a) $[CH_3CO_2^-] = [NaCH_3CO_2] = \dfrac{4.95\ g}{0.250\ L} \cdot \dfrac{1\ mol\ NaCH_3CO_2}{82.03\ g} = 0.241\ M$

$pH = pK_a + \log\dfrac{[CH_3CO_2^-]}{[CH_3CO_2H]} = -\log(1.8 \times 10^{-5}) + \log\left(\dfrac{0.241}{0.150}\right) = 4.95$

(b) $OH^-(aq) + CH_3CO_2H(aq) \rightarrow H_2O(\ell) + CH_3CO_2^-(aq)$

$0.082\ g \cdot \dfrac{1\ mol\ NaOH}{40.0\ g} = 0.0021\ mol\ NaOH$ added to buffer

$\dfrac{0.241\ mol}{1.00\ L} \cdot 0.100\ L = 0.0241\ mol\ CH_3CO_2^-$ before NaOH addition

$\dfrac{0.150\ mol}{1.00\ L} \cdot 0.100\ L = 0.0150\ mol\ CH_3CO_2H$ before NaOH addition

	CH_3CO_2H	$CH_3CO_2^-$
Initial (mol)	0.0150	0.0241
Change (mol)	−0.0021	+0.0021
Equilibrium (mol)	0.0129	0.0262

$[H_3O^+] = \dfrac{[CH_3CO_2H]}{[CH_3CO_2^-]} \cdot K_a \approx \left(\dfrac{0.0129}{0.0262}\right)(1.8 \times 10^{-5}) = 8.9 \times 10^{-6}\ M$

$pH = -\log[H_3O^+] = 5.05$

18.20 $[H_2PO_4^-] = [HPO_4^{2-}]$ so $[H_3O^+] = K_a = 6.2 \times 10^{-8}$

Before adding NaOH: $pH = -\log[H_3O^+] = 7.21$

$[NaOH] = \dfrac{0.425\ g}{2.00\ L} \cdot \dfrac{1\ mol\ NaOH}{40.00\ g} = 0.00531\ M$

$OH^-(aq) + H_2PO_4^-(aq) \rightarrow H_2O(\ell) + HPO_4^{2-}(aq)$

	$H_2PO_4^-$	HPO_4^{2-}
Initial (M)	0.132	0.132
Change (M)	−0.00531	+0.00531
Equilibrium (M)	0.127	0.137

$[H_3O^+] = \dfrac{[H_2PO_4^-]}{[HPO_4^{2-}]} \cdot K_a \approx \left(\dfrac{0.127}{0.137}\right)(6.2 \times 10^{-8}) = 5.7 \times 10^{-8}\ M$

After adding NaOH: $pH = -\log[H_3O^+] = 7.24$

18.21 (a) $[NH_4^+] = \dfrac{0.125\ mol}{0.500\ L} = 0.250\ M$

$pH = pK_a + \log\dfrac{[NH_3]}{[NH_4^+]} = -\log(5.6 \times 10^{-10}) + \log\left(\dfrac{0.500}{0.250}\right) = 9.55$

(b) $[HCl] = \dfrac{0.0100 \text{ mol}}{0.500 \text{ L}} = 0.0200 \text{ M}$

$H_3O^+(aq) + NH_3(aq) \rightarrow H_2O(\ell) + NH_4^+(aq)$

	NH_4^+	NH_3
Initial (M)	0.250	0.500
Change (M)	+0.0200	−0.0200
Equilibrium (M)	0.270	0.480

$pH = pK_a + \log \dfrac{[NH_3]}{[NH_4^+]} = -\log(5.6 \times 10^{-10}) + \log\left(\dfrac{0.480}{0.270}\right) = 9.50$

18.22 $pH = pK_a + \log \dfrac{[NH_3]}{[NH_4^+]} = -\log(5.6 \times 10^{-10}) + \log\left(\dfrac{0.169}{0.183}\right) = 9.22$

(0.0200 L NaOH)(0.100 mol/L) = 0.00200 mol NaOH

(0.0800 L NH_3)(0.169 mol/L) = 0.0135 mol NH_3

(0.0800 L NH_4^+)(0.183 mol/L) = 0.0146 mol NH_4^+

Total volume = 0.0200 L + 0.0800 L = 0.100 L

$OH^-(aq) + NH_4^+(aq) \rightarrow H_2O(\ell) + NH_3(aq)$

	NH_4^+	NH_3
Initial (mol)	0.0146	0.0135
Change (mol)	−0.00200	+0.00200
Equilibrium (mol)	0.0126	0.0155

$pH = pK_a + \log \dfrac{[NH_3]}{[NH_4^+]} = -\log(5.6 \times 10^{-10}) + \log\left(\dfrac{0.0155}{0.0126}\right) = 9.34$

The change in pH is 9.34 − 9.22 = 0.12

18.23   (a) $[C_6H_5OH] = \dfrac{0.515 \text{ g}}{0.125 \text{ L}} \cdot \dfrac{1 \text{ mol } C_6H_5OH}{94.11 \text{ g}} = 0.0438 \text{ M}$

$K_a = 1.3 \times 10^{-10} = \dfrac{[C_6H_5O^-][H_3O^+]}{[C_6H_5OH]} = \dfrac{x^2}{0.0438 - x} \approx \dfrac{x^2}{0.0438}$

$x = [H_3O^+] = 2.4 \times 10^{-6} \text{ M}$

$pH = -\log[H_3O^+] = 5.62$

(b)

	C_6H_5OH	+	OH^-	$\rightarrow$	$C_6H_5O^-$	+ H_2O
Initial (mol)	0.00547		0.00547		0	
Change (mol)	−0.00547		−0.00547		+0.00547	
After reaction (mol)	0		0		0.00547	

Total volume = 0.125 L + (0.00547 mol NaOH)(1 L/0.123 mol) = 0.169 L

$$C_6H_5O^-(aq) + H_2O(\ell) \rightleftharpoons C_6H_6OH(aq) + OH^-(aq)$$

$$[C_6H_5O^-] = \frac{0.00547 \text{ mol}}{0.169 \text{ L}} = 0.0323 \text{ M}$$

$$K_b = \frac{K_w}{K_a} = 7.7 \times 10^{-5} = \frac{[C_6H_5OH][OH^-]}{[C_6H_5O^-]} = \frac{x^2}{0.0323 - x}$$

Solve using the quadratic equation. $x = 0.0015 \text{ M} = [OH^-]$

$$[H_3O^+] = \frac{K_w}{[OH^-]} = 6.5 \times 10^{-12} \text{ M}$$

$$[Na^+] = 0.0323 \text{ M}$$

$$[C_6H_5O^-] = 0.323 - x = 0.0307 \text{ M}$$

(c) $pH = -\log[H_3O^+] = 11.19$

18.24   (a) $[C_6H_5CO_2H] = \dfrac{0.235 \text{ g}}{0.100 \text{ L}} \cdot \dfrac{1 \text{ mol } C_6H_5CO_2H}{122.1 \text{ g}} = 0.0192 \text{ M}$

$$K_a = 6.3 \times 10^{-5} = \frac{[C_6H_5CO_2^-][H_3O^+]}{[C_6H_5CO_2H]} = \frac{x^2}{0.0192 - x} \approx \frac{x^2}{0.0192}$$

$x = [H_3O^+] = 0.0011 \text{ M}$

$pH = -\log[H_3O^+] = 2.96$

(b)

	$C_6H_5CO_2H$	+	OH^-	$\rightarrow$	$C_6H_5CO_2^-$	+ H_2O
Initial (mol)	0.00192		0.00192		0	
Change (mol)	−0.00192		−0.00192		+0.00192	
After reaction (mol)	0		0		0.00192	

Total volume = 0.100 L + (0.00192 mol NaOH)(1 L/0.108 mol) = 0.118 L

$$C_6H_5CO_2^-(aq) + H_2O(\ell) \rightleftharpoons C_6H_5CO_2H(aq) + OH^-(aq)$$

$$[C_6H_5CO_2^-] = \frac{0.00192 \text{ mol}}{0.118 \text{ L}} = 0.0163 \text{ M}$$

$$K_b = \frac{K_w}{K_a} = 1.6 \times 10^{-10} = \frac{[C_6H_5CO_2H][OH^-]}{[C_6H_5CO_2^-]} = \frac{x^2}{0.0163 - x} \approx \frac{x^2}{0.0163}$$

$x = 1.6 \times 10^{-6} \text{ M} = [OH^-]$

$$[H_3O^+] = \frac{K_w}{[OH^-]} = 6.2 \times 10^{-9} \text{ M}$$

$[Na^+] = [C_6H_5CO_2^-] = 0.0163 \text{ M}$

(c) $pH = -\log[H_3O^+] = 8.21$

18.25   (a) $NH_3(aq) + H_3O^+(aq) \rightarrow NH_4^+(aq) + H_2O(\ell)$

$$[NH_3] = \frac{0.0105 \text{ mol HCl}}{1.00 \text{ L}} \cdot 0.03678 \text{ L} \cdot \frac{1 \text{ mol } NH_3}{1 \text{ mol HCl}} \cdot \frac{1}{0.0250 \text{ L}} = 0.0154 \text{ M}$$

(b) $NH_4^+(aq) + H_2O(\ell) \rightleftharpoons H_3O^+(aq) + NH_3(aq)$

Total volume = 0.03678 L + 0.0250 L = 0.0618 L

$$[NH_4^+] = \frac{0.0105 \text{ mol HCl}}{1.00 \text{ L}} \cdot 0.03678 \text{ L} \cdot \frac{1 \text{ mol } NH_4^+}{1 \text{ mol HCl}} \cdot \frac{1}{0.0618 \text{ L}} = 0.00625 \text{ M}$$

$$K_a = 5.6 \times 10^{-10} = \frac{[H_3O^+][NH_3]}{[NH_4^+]} = \frac{x^2}{0.00625 - x} \approx \frac{x^2}{0.00625}$$

$x = 1.9 \times 10^{-6} \text{ M} = [H_3O^+]$

$[OH^-] = \dfrac{K_w}{[H_3O^+]} = 5.3 \times 10^{-9} \text{ M}$

$[NH_4^+] = 0.00625 \text{ M}$

(c) $pH = -\log[H_3O^+] = 5.73$

18.26   (a) $[C_6H_5NH_2] = \dfrac{0.175 \text{ mol HCl}}{1.00 \text{ L}} \cdot 0.02567 \text{ L} \cdot \dfrac{1 \text{ mol } C_6H_5NH_2}{1 \text{ mol HCl}} \cdot \dfrac{1}{0.0250 \text{ L}} = 0.180 \text{ M}$

(b) $C_6H_5NH_3^+(aq) + H_2O(\ell) \rightleftharpoons H_3O^+(aq) + C_6H_5NH_2(aq)$

Total volume = 0.02567 L + 0.0250 L = 0.0507 L

$$[C_6H_5NH_3^+] = \frac{0.175 \text{ mol HCl}}{1.00 \text{ L}} \cdot 0.02567 \text{ L} \cdot \frac{1 \text{ mol } C_6H_5NH_3^+}{1 \text{ mol HCl}} \cdot \frac{1}{0.0507 \text{ L}} = 0.0887 \text{ M}$$

$$K_a = \frac{K_w}{K_b} = 2.5 \times 10^{-5} = \frac{[H_3O^+][C_6H_5NH_2]}{[C_6H_5NH_3^+]} = \frac{x^2}{0.0887 - x} \approx \frac{x^2}{0.0887}$$

$x = 0.0015 \text{ M} = [H_3O^+]$

$[OH^-] = \dfrac{K_w}{[H_3O^+]} = 6.7 \times 10^{-12} \text{ M}$

$[C_6H_5NH_3^+] \approx 0.0887 \text{ M}$

(c) $pH = -\log[H_3O^+] = 2.83$

18.27   Initial pH = 13, pH at equivalence point = 7, total volume at equivalence point = 30 + 30 = 60.0 mL

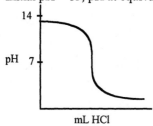

18.28   Initial pH $\approx$ 9, pH at equivalence point $\approx$ 3, total volume at equivalence point = 50 + 25 = 75 mL.

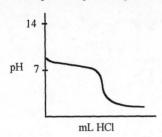

mL HCl

18.29   (a) $K_b = 1.8 \times 10^{-5} = \dfrac{[OH^-][NH_4^+]}{[NH_3]} = \dfrac{x^2}{0.10 - x} \approx \dfrac{x^2}{0.10}$

$x = [OH^-] = 0.0013$ M

$pOH = -\log[OH^-] = 2.87$

$pH = 14.00 - pOH = 11.13$

(b) $NH_3(aq) + H_3O^+(aq) \rightarrow NH_4^+(aq) + H_2O(\ell)$ Total volume = 0.0250 + 0.0250 = 0.0500 L

$[NH_4^+] = \dfrac{0.10 \text{ mol } NH_3}{1.0 \text{ L}} \cdot 0.0250 \text{ L} \cdot \dfrac{1 \text{ mol } NH_4^+}{1 \text{ mol } NH_3} \cdot \dfrac{1}{0.0500 \text{ L}} = 0.050$ M

$NH_4^+(aq) + H_2O(\ell) \rightleftharpoons H_3O^+(aq) + NH_3(aq)$

$K_a = 5.6 \times 10^{-10} = \dfrac{[H_3O^+][NH_3]}{[NH_4^+]} = \dfrac{x^2}{0.050 - x} \approx \dfrac{x^2}{0.050}$

$x = [H_3O^+] = 5.3 \times 10^{-6}$ M

$pH = -\log[H_3O^+] = 5.28$

(c)   At titration midpoint, $[NH_3] = [NH_4^+]$ and $pH = pK_a = -\log(5.6 \times 10^{-10}) = 9.25$

(d)   Methyl red would detect the equivalence point.

(e)

mL HCl added	mol H_3O^+ added	mol NH_4^+ produced	mol NH_3 remaining	pH
5.00	0.00050	0.00050	0.0020	9.85
15.00	0.0015	0.0015	0.0010	9.08
20.00	0.0020	0.0020	0.0005	8.65
22.00	0.0022	0.0022	0.0003	8.39
30.00	0.0030			2.04

When 30.00 mL HCl is added, pH depends only on the excess H_3O^+

$[H_3O^+] = (0.0030\ \text{mol} - 0.0025\ \text{mol})/0.0550\ \text{L} = 0.009\ M$

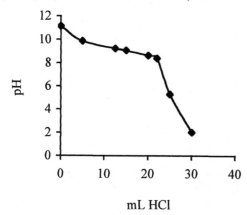

18.30   Rough plot of pH versus volume of base:

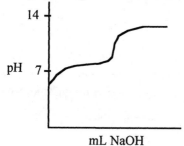

(a) $K_a = 4.0 \times 10^{-10} = \dfrac{[CN^-][H_3O^+]}{[HCN]} = \dfrac{x^2}{0.050 - x} \approx \dfrac{x^2}{0.050}$

$x = [H_3O^+] = 4.5 \times 10^{-6}\ M$

$pH = -\log[H_3O^+] = 5.35$

(b)   At the half-neutralization point, $[HCN] = [CN^-]$, and $pH = pK_a = 9.40$

(c)   When 95% of NaOH has been added

mol $CN^- = 0.95(\text{mol HCN})_{\text{initial}} = 0.95(0.0250\ \text{L})(0.050\ \text{mol/L}) = 0.0012\ \text{mol}\ CN^-$

mol $HCN = 0.05(\text{mol HCN})_{\text{initial}} = 0.05(0.0250\ \text{L})(0.050\ \text{mol/L}) = 6 \times 10^{-5}\ \text{mol}\ HCN$

$pH = pK_a + \log\dfrac{[CN^-]}{[HCN]} = -\log(4.0 \times 10^{-10}) + \log\left(\dfrac{0.0012}{6 \times 10^{-5}}\right) = 10.7$

(d) $\dfrac{0.050\ \text{mol HCN}}{1.0\ \text{L}} \cdot 0.0250\ \text{L} \cdot \dfrac{1\ \text{mol NaOH}}{1\ \text{mol HCN}} \cdot \dfrac{1\ \text{L}}{0.075\ \text{mol NaOH}} = 0.017\ \text{L} = 17\ \text{mL}$

(e) $CN^-(aq) + H_2O(\ell) \rightleftharpoons HCN(aq) + OH^-(aq)$

$$[CN^-] = \frac{0.050 \text{ mol HCN}}{1.0 \text{ L}} \cdot 0.025 \text{ L} \cdot \frac{1 \text{ mol } CN^-}{1 \text{ mol HCN}} \cdot \frac{1}{0.042 \text{ L}} = 0.030 \text{ M}$$

$$K_b = \frac{K_w}{K_a} = 2.5 \times 10^{-5} = \frac{[HCN][OH^-]}{[CN^-]} = \frac{x^2}{0.030 - x} \approx \frac{x^2}{0.030}$$

$$x = [OH^-] = 8.7 \times 10^{-4} \text{ M}$$

$$pOH = -\log[OH^-] = 3.06$$

$$pH = 14.00 - pOH = 10.94$$

(f) Alizarin yellow GG would be a reasonable choice for an indicator.

(g) When 105% of NaOH has been added, pH depends only on the excess OH^-

excess $OH^- = = 0.05(0.017 \text{ L NaOH})(0.075 \text{ mol/L}) = 6 \times 10^{-5}$ mol OH^-

$$[OH^-] = \frac{6 \times 10^{-5} \text{ mol}}{0.042 \text{ L}} = 0.0015 \text{ M}$$

$$pOH = -\log[OH^-] = 2.83$$

$$pH = 14.00 - pOH = 11.17$$

18.31

Titration	pH at Equivalence Point	Possible Indicator
(a) C_5H_5N titrated with HCl	<7 (about 3-4)	thymol blue or bromphenol blue
(b) HCO_2H with NaOH	>7 (about 8-10)	phenolphthalein
(c) $H_2NCH_2CH_2NH_2$ with HCl	<7 (about 5-6)	methyl red
	<7 (about 3-4)	thymol blue or bromphenol blue

18.32

Titration	pH at Equiv. Point	Possible Indicator
(a) HCO_3^- titrated with NaOH	>7 (about 12-13)	alizarin yellow
(b) HClO with NaOH	>7 (about 10-11)	thymolphthalein
(c) $(CH_3)_3N$ with HCl	<7 (about 5-6)	methyl red

18.33   (a) AgCl and $PbCl_2$

(b) $Zn(OH)_2$ and $ZnCO_3$

(c) $Fe(OH)_2$ and FeS

18.34   (a) $BaSO_4$ and $PbSO_4$

(b) $Ni(OH)_2$ and $NiCO_3$

(c) $PbBr_2$ and AgBr

18.35   (a)   soluble (most ammonium salts are soluble)

         (b)   soluble (most sulfate salts are soluble)

         (c)   insoluble (most sulfide salts are insoluble)

         (d)   insoluble (most sulfate salts are soluble, barium sulfate is an exception)

18.36   (a)   soluble (most nitrate salts are soluble).

         (b)   insoluble (most hydroxide salts are insoluble).

         (c)   soluble (most chloride salts are soluble).

         (d)   insoluble (most sulfide salts are insoluble).

18.37   (a) $AgCN(s) \rightleftharpoons Ag^+(aq) + CN^-(aq)$ $K_{sp} = [Ag^+][CN^-]$

         (b) $NiCO_3(s) \rightleftharpoons Ni^{2+}(aq) + CO_3{}^{2-}(aq)$ $K_{sp} = [Ni^{2+}][CO_3{}^{2-}]$

         (c) $AuBr_3(s) \rightleftharpoons Au^{3+}(aq) + 3\ Br^-(aq)$ $K_{sp} = [Au^{3+}][Br^-]^3$

18.38   (a) $PbSO_4(s) \rightleftharpoons Pb^{2+}(aq) + SO_4{}^{2-}(aq)$ $K_{sp} = [Pb^{2+}][SO_4{}^{2-}]$

         (b) $BaF_2(s) \rightleftharpoons Ba^{2+}(aq) + 2\ F^-(aq)$ $K_{sp} = [Ba^{2+}][F^-]^2$

         (c) $Ag_3PO_4(s) \rightleftharpoons 3\ Ag^+(aq) + PO_4{}^{3-}(aq)$ $K_{sp} = [Ag^+]^3[PO_4{}^{2-}]$

18.39 $K_{sp} = [Tl^+][Br^-] = (1.9 \times 10^{-3})(1.9 \times 10^{-3}) = 3.6 \times 10^{-6}$

18.40 $[Ag^+] = [CH_3CO_2{}^-] = \dfrac{1.0\ g}{0.1000\ L} \cdot \dfrac{1\ mol\ AgCH_3CO_2}{167\ g} \cdot \dfrac{1\ mol\ Ag^+}{1\ mol\ AgCH_3CO_2} = 0.060\ M$

         $K_{sp} = [Ag^+][CH_3CO_2{}^-] = (0.060)(0.060) = 0.0036$

18.41 $[F^-] = 2 \times [Sr^{2+}] = 2.06 \times 10^{-3}\ M$

         $K_{sp} = [Sr^{2+}][F^-]^2 = (1.03 \times 10^{-3})(2.06 \times 10^{-3})^2 = 4.37 \times 10^{-9}$

18.42 $[Ca^{2+}] = \dfrac{1.3\ g\ Ca(OH)_2}{1\ L} \cdot \dfrac{1\ mol\ Ca(OH)_2}{74.09\ g} \cdot \dfrac{1\ mol\ Ca^{2+}}{1\ mol\ Ca(OH)_2} = 0.018\ M$

         $K_{sp} = [Ca^{2+}][OH^-]^2 = (0.018)(2 \times 0.018)^2 = 2.2 \times 10^{-5}$

18.43 $pOH = 14.00 - pH = 4.85$

         $[OH^-] = 10^{-pOH} = 1.4 \times 10^{-5}\ M$

         $[Pb^{2+}] = {}^1/_2 \times [OH^-] = 7.1 \times 10^{-6}\ M$

         $K_{sp} = [Pb^{2+}][OH^-]^2 = (7.1 \times 10^{-6})(1.4 \times 10^{-5})^2 = 1.4 \times 10^{-15}$

18.44 $pOH = 14.00 - pH = 1.32$

$[OH^-] = 10^{-pOH} = 0.048$ M

$[Ca^{2+}] = \frac{1}{2} \times [OH^-] = 0.024$

$K_{sp} = [Ca^{2+}][OH^-]^2 = (0.024)(0.048)^2 = 5.5 \times 10^{-5}$

18.45

$$AgI(s) \rightleftharpoons Ag^+(aq) + I^-(aq)$$

Initial (M)	0	0
Change (M)	$+x$	$+x$
Equilibrium (M)	x	x

(a) $K_{sp} = [Ag^+][I^-] = (x)(x) = x^2$

$x = \sqrt{K_{sp}} = \sqrt{8.5 \times 10^{-17}} = 9.2 \times 10^{-9}$ mol/L

(b) $\dfrac{9.2 \times 10^{-9} \text{ mol}}{1 \text{ L}} \cdot \dfrac{235 \text{ g}}{1 \text{ mol AgI}} = 2.2 \times 10^{-6}$ g/L

18.46

$$AuCl(s) \rightleftharpoons Au^+(aq) + Cl^-(aq)$$

Initial (M)	0	0
Change (M)	$+x$	$+x$
Equilibrium (M)	x	x

$K_{sp} = [Au^+][Cl^-] = (x)(x) = x^2$

$x = [Au^+] = \sqrt{K_{sp}} = \sqrt{2.0 \times 10^{-13}} = 4.5 \times 10^{-7}$ mol/L

18.47

$$CaF_2(s) \rightleftharpoons Ca^{2+}(aq) + 2\ F^-(aq)$$

Initial (M)	0	0
Change (M)	$+x$	$+2x$
Equilibrium (M)	x	$2x$

(a) $K_{sp} = [Ca^{2+}][F^-]^2 = (x)(2x)^2 = 4x^3$

$x = \sqrt[3]{\dfrac{K_{sp}}{4}} = \sqrt[3]{\dfrac{5.3 \times 10^{-11}}{4}} = 2.4 \times 10^{-4}$ mol/L

(b) $\dfrac{2.4 \times 10^{-4} \text{ mol Ca}^{2+}}{1 \text{ L}} \cdot \dfrac{1 \text{ mol CaF}_2}{1 \text{ mol Ca}^{2+}} \cdot \dfrac{78.1 \text{ g}}{1 \text{ mol CaF}_2} = 0.018$ g/L

18.48 $PbBr_2(s) \rightleftharpoons Pb^{2+}(aq) + 2\ Br^-(aq)$

Initial (M)	0	0
Change (M)	$+x$	$+2x$
Equilibrium (M)	x	$2x$

(a) $K_{sp} = [Pb^{2+}][Br^-]^2 = (x)(2x)^2 = 4x^3$

$x = \sqrt[3]{\dfrac{K_{sp}}{4}} = \sqrt[3]{\dfrac{6.6 \times 10^{-6}}{4}} = 0.012$ mol/L

(b) $\dfrac{0.012 \text{ mol } Pb^{2+}}{1 \text{ L}} \cdot \dfrac{1 \text{ mol } PbBr_2}{1 \text{ mol } Pb^{2+}} \cdot \dfrac{367 \text{ g}}{1 \text{ mol } PbBr_2} = 4.3$ g/L

18.49 $RaSO_4(s) \rightleftharpoons Ra^{2+}(aq) + SO_4^{2-}(aq)$

Initial (M)	0	0
Change (M)	$+x$	$+x$
Equilibrium (M)	x	x

$K_{sp} = [Ra^{2+}][SO_4^{2-}] = (x)(x) = x^2$

$x = \sqrt{K_{sp}} = \sqrt{3.7 \times 10^{-11}} = 6.1 \times 10^{-6}$ mol/L

$\dfrac{6.1 \times 10^{-6} \text{ mol } Ra^{2+}}{1 \text{ L}} \cdot 0.100 \text{ L} \cdot \dfrac{1 \text{ mol } RaSO_4}{1 \text{ mol } Ra^{2+}} \cdot \dfrac{322 \text{ g}}{1 \text{ mol } RaSO_4} \cdot \dfrac{10^3 \text{ mg}}{1 \text{ g}} = 0.20$ mg $RaSO_4$ dissolves

18.50 $PbSO_4(s) \rightleftharpoons Pb^{2+}(aq) + SO_4^{2-}(aq)$

Initial (M)	0	0
Change (M)	$+x$	$+x$
Equilibrium (M)	x	x

$K_{sp} = [Pb^{2+}][SO_4^{2-}] = (x)(x) = x^2$

$x = \sqrt{K_{sp}} = \sqrt{2.5 \times 10^{-8}} = 1.6 \times 10^{-4}$ mol/L

$\dfrac{1.6 \times 10^{-4} \text{ mol } Pb^{2+}}{1 \text{ L}} \cdot 0.250 \text{ L} \cdot \dfrac{1 \text{ mol } PbSO_4}{1 \text{ mol } Pb^{2+}} \cdot \dfrac{303 \text{ g}}{1 \text{ mol } PbSO_4} \cdot \dfrac{10^3 \text{ mg}}{1 \text{ g}} = 12$ mg $PbSO_4$ dissolves

18.51   (a) $PbCl_2$

(b) FeS

(c) $Fe(OH)_2$

18.52   (a) AgSCN

(b) $SrSO_4$

(c) PbI_2 (Note: Solubility must be calculated.)

(d) CaF_2

18.53 $K_{sp} = 1.0 \times 10^{-12} = [Ag^+][SCN^-] = (x)(x) = x^2$

x = solubility of AgSCN in pure water = 1.0×10^{-6} mol/L

In water containing 0.010 M SCN^-

$K_{sp} = 1.0 \times 10^{-12} = (x)(0.010 + x) \approx x(0.010)$

x = solubility of AgSCN in water containing 0.010 M SCN^- = 1.0×10^{-10} mol/L

18.54 $K_{sp} = 5.4 \times 10^{-13} = [Ag^+][Br^-] = (x)(x) = x^2$

x = solubility of AgBr in pure water = 7.3×10^{-7} mol/L

$$[Br^-] = \frac{0.15 \text{ g NaBr}}{0.225 \text{ L}} \cdot \frac{1 \text{ mol NaBr}}{103 \text{ g}} \cdot \frac{1 \text{ mol Br}^-}{1 \text{ mol NaBr}} = 0.0065 \text{ M}$$

In water containing 0.0065 M Br^-

$K_{sp} = 5.4 \times 10^{-13} = (x)(0.0065 + x) \approx x(0.0065)$

x = solubility of AgBr in water containing 0.0065 M Br^- = 8.3×10^{-11} mol/L

18.55   (a) $K_{sp} = 8.5 \times 10^{-17} = [Ag^+][I^-] = (x)(x) = x^2$

$x = \sqrt{K_{sp}} = \sqrt{8.5 \times 10^{-17}} = 9.2 \times 10^{-9}$ mol/L

$$\frac{9.2 \times 10^{-9} \text{ mol Ag}^+}{1 \text{ L}} \cdot \frac{1 \text{ mol AgI}}{1 \text{ mol Ag}^+} \cdot \frac{235 \text{ g}}{1 \text{ mol AgI}} \cdot \frac{10^3 \text{ mg}}{1 \text{ g}} \cdot \frac{1 \text{ L}}{10^3 \text{ mL}}$$

$$= 2.2 \times 10^{-6} \text{ mg/mL in pure water}$$

(b) $K_{sp} = 8.5 \times 10^{-17} = [Ag^+][I^-] = (x)(0.020 + x) \approx x(0.020)$

$x = 4.3 \times 10^{-15}$ mol/L

$$\frac{4.3 \times 10^{-15} \text{ mol Ag}^+}{1 \text{ L}} \cdot \frac{1 \text{ mol AgI}}{1 \text{ mol Ag}^+} \cdot \frac{235 \text{ g}}{1 \text{ mol AgI}} \cdot \frac{10^3 \text{ mg}}{1 \text{ g}} \cdot \frac{1 \text{ L}}{10^3 \text{ mL}}$$

$$= 1.0 \times 10^{-13} \text{ mg/mL in 0.020 M AgNO}_3$$

18.56   (a) $K_{sp} = 1.8 \times 10^{-7} = [Ba^{2+}][F^-]^2 = (x)(2x)^2 = 4x^3$

$$x = \sqrt[3]{\frac{K_{sp}}{4}} = \sqrt[3]{\frac{1.8 \times 10^{-7}}{4}} = 0.0036 \text{ mol/L}$$

$$\frac{0.0036 \text{ mol Ba}^{2+}}{1 \text{ L}} \cdot \frac{1 \text{ mol BaF}_2}{1 \text{ mol Ba}^{2+}} \cdot \frac{175 \text{ g}}{1 \text{ mol BaF}_2} \cdot \frac{10^3 \text{ mg}}{1 \text{ g}} \cdot \frac{1 \text{ L}}{10^3 \text{ mL}} = 0.62 \text{ mg/mL in pure water}$$

(b) $[F^-] = \dfrac{0.0050 \text{ g KF}}{0.001 \text{ L}} \cdot \dfrac{1 \text{ mol}}{58.1 \text{ g}} = 0.086 \text{ M}$

$K_{sp} = 1.8 \times 10^{-7} = [Ba^{2+}][F^-]^2 = (x)(0.086 + 2x)^2 \approx (x)(0.086)^2$

$x = 2.4 \times 10^{-5} \text{ mol/L}$

$\dfrac{2.4 \times 10^{-5} \text{ mol Ba}^{2+}}{1 \text{ L}} \cdot \dfrac{1 \text{ mol BaF}_2}{1 \text{ mol Ba}^{2+}} \cdot \dfrac{175 \text{ g}}{1 \text{ mol BaF}_2} \cdot \dfrac{10^3 \text{ mg}}{1 \text{ g}} \cdot \dfrac{1 \text{ L}}{10^3 \text{ mL}}$

$= 4.3 \times 10^{-3} \text{ mg/mL in 5.0 mg/mL KF}$

18.57   (a) PbS

(b) Ag_2CO_3

(c) $Al(OH)_3$

18.58   (a) Ag_2CO_3

(b) $PbCO_3$

(c) AgCN

18.59 $Q = [Pb^{2+}][Cl^-]^2 = (0.0012)(0.010)^2 = 1.2 \times 10^{-7}$

$Q < K_{sp}$ $PbCl_2$ will not precipitate

18.60   (a) $Q = [Ni^{2+}][CO_3^{2-}] = (0.0024)(1.0 \times 10^{-6}) = 2.4 \times 10^{-9}$

$Q < K_{sp}$ $NiCO_3$ will not precipitate

(b) $Q = [Ni^{2+}][CO_3^{2-}] = (0.0024)(1.0 \times 10^{-4}) = 2.4 \times 10^{-7}$

$Q > K_{sp}$ $NiCO_3$ will precipitate

18.61 $[OH^-] = \dfrac{0.0040 \text{ g}}{0.010 \text{ L}} \cdot \dfrac{1 \text{ mol NaOH}}{40.0 \text{ g}} \cdot \dfrac{1 \text{ mol OH}^-}{1 \text{ mol NaOH}} = 0.010 \text{ M}$

$Q = [Zn^{2+}][OH^-]^2 = (1.6 \times 10^{-4})(0.010)^2 = 1.6 \times 10^{-8}$

$Q > K_{sp}$ $Zn(OH)_2$ will precipitate

18.62 $[Cl^-] = \dfrac{1.20 \text{ g}}{0.095 \text{ L}} \cdot \dfrac{1 \text{ mol NaCl}}{58.44 \text{ g}} \cdot \dfrac{1 \text{ mol Cl}^-}{1 \text{ mol NaCl}} = 0.216 \text{ M}$

$Q = [Pb^{2+}][Cl^-]^2 = (0.0012)(0.216)^2 = 5.6 \times 10^{-5}$

$Q > K_{sp}$ $PbCl_2$ will precipitate

18.63 $[Mg^+] = \dfrac{1.350 \text{ g Mg}^{2+}}{1 \text{ L}} \cdot \dfrac{1 \text{ mol Mg}^{2+}}{24.305 \text{ g}} = 0.0555 \text{ M}$

For $Mg(OH)_2$ to precipitate, Q must exceed K_{sp} (5.6×10^{-12})

$K_{sp} = [Mg^{2+}][OH^-]^2 = 5.6 \times 10^{-12} = (0.0555)[OH^-]^2$

$[OH^-]$ must be greater than $1.0 \times 10^{-5} \text{ M}$

18.64 $[OH^-] = \dfrac{(0.0250\ L)(0.010\ mol/L)}{0.100\ L} = 0.0025\ M$

$[Mg^{2+}] = \dfrac{(0.0750\ L)(0.10\ mol/L)}{0.100\ L} = 0.075\ M$

$Q = [Mg^{2+}][OH^-]^2 = (0.075)(0.0025)^2 = 4.7 \times 10^{-7}$

$Q > K_{sp}$ $Mg(OH)_2$ will precipitate

18.65 $AuCl(s) \rightleftharpoons Au^+(aq) + Cl^-(aq)$ $K_{sp} = 2.0 \times 10^{-13}$

$Au^+(aq) + 2\ CN^-(aq) \rightleftharpoons Au(CN)_2^-(aq)$ $K_{form} = 2.0 \times 10^{38}$

$AuCl(s) + 2\ CN^-(aq) \rightleftharpoons Au(CN)_2^-(aq) + Cl^-(aq)$ $K_{net} = K_{sp} \cdot K_{form} = 4.0 \times 10^{25}$

18.66 $AgI(s) \rightleftharpoons Ag^+(aq) + I^-(aq)$ $K_{sp} = 8.5 \times 10^{-17}$

$Ag^+(aq) + 2\ CN^-(aq) \rightleftharpoons Ag(CN)_2^-(aq)$ $K_{form} = 5.6 \times 10^{18}$

$AgI(s) + 2\ CN^-(aq) \rightleftharpoons Ag(CN)_2^-(aq) + I^-(aq)$ $K_{net} = K_{sp} \cdot K_{form} = 480$

18.67   (a)   Add H_2SO_4, precipitating $BaSO_4$ and leaving $Na^+(aq)$ in solution.

(b)   Add HCl or another source of chloride ion. $PbCl_2$ will precipitate, but $NiCl_2$ is water-soluble.

18.68   (a)   Add HCl to precipitate the Ag^+ as AgCl and leave $Cu^{2+}(aq)$ in solution.

(b)   Add $(NH_4)_2S$ to precipitate the Fe^{3+} as Fe_2S_3.

18.69   (a) $NaBr(aq) + AgNO_3(aq) \rightarrow AgBr(s) + NaNO_3(aq)$

(b) $2\ KCl(aq) + Pb(NO_3)_2(aq) \rightarrow PbCl_2(s) + 2\ KNO_3(aq)$

18.70   (a)   No precipitate forms.

(b) $K_3PO_4(aq) + FeCl_3(aq) \rightarrow 3\ KCl(aq) + FePO_4(s)$

18.71 $[Ba^{2+}] = \dfrac{(0.048\ L)(0.0.0012\ mol/L)}{0.072\ L} = 8.0 \times 10^{-4}\ M$

$[SO_4^{2-}] = \dfrac{(0.024\ L)(1.0 \times 10^{-6}\ mol/L)}{0.072\ L} = 3.3 \times 10^{-7}\ M$

$Q = [Ba^{2+}][SO_4^{2-}] = (8.0 \times 10^{-4})(3.3 \times 10^{-7}) = 2.6 \times 10^{-10}$

$Q > K_{sp}$ $BaSO_4$ will precipitate

18.72 $CH_3CO_2H(aq) + OH^-(aq) \rightarrow CH_3CO_2^-(aq) + H_2O(\ell)$

(0.0200 L CH_3CO_2H)(0.15 mol/L) = 0.0030 mol CH_3CO_2H

(0.0050 L NaOH)(0.17 mol/L) = 0.00085 mol NaOH = mol CH_3CO_2H consumed

= mol $CH_3CO_2^-$ produced

0.0030 mol CH_3CO_2H – 0.00085 mol consumed = 0.0022 mol CH_3CO_2H remaining

$$pH = pK_a + \log\frac{[CH_3CO_2^-]}{[CH_3CO_2H]} = -\log(1.8 \times 10^{-5}) + \log\left(\frac{0.00085}{0.0022}\right) = 4.33$$

$[H_3O^+] = 10^{-pH} = 4.7 \times 10^{-5}$ M

18.73 $NH_3(aq) + H_3O^+(aq) \rightarrow NH_4^+(aq) + H_2O(\ell)$

(0.0500 L NH_3)(0.40 mol/L) = 0.020 mol NH_3

(0.0250 L HCl)(0.20 mol/L) = 0.0050 mol HCl = mol NH_3 consumed = mol NH_4^+ produced

0.020 mol NH_3 – 0.0050 mol consumed = 0.015 mol NH_3 remaining

$$pH = pK_a + \log\frac{[NH_3]}{[NH_4^+]} = -\log(5.6 \times 10^{-10}) + \log\left(\frac{0.015}{0.0050}\right) = 9.73$$

$[H_3O^+] = 10^{-pH} = 1.9 \times 10^{-10}$ M

18.74   (a) pH > 7 The solution will contain the conjugate base of the weak acid.

(b) pH > 7 The solution will contain the NH_3/NH_4^+ buffer

(c) pH = 7 The solution will contain neutral ions

(d) pH = 7 The solution will contain neutral ions

18.75 $BaCO_3 < Ag_2CO_3 < Na_2CO_3$

18.76   For CaF_2 to precipitate, Q must exceed K_{sp} (5.3×10^{-11})

$K_{sp} = [Ca^{2+}][F^-]^2 = 5.3 \times 10^{-11} = (2.0 \times 10^{-3})[F^-]^2$

$[F^-]$ must be greater than 1.6×10^{-4} M

18.77 $[NH_4^+] = \dfrac{5.15 \text{ g}}{0.10 \text{ L}} \cdot \dfrac{1 \text{ mol } NH_4NO_3}{80.04 \text{ g}} \cdot \dfrac{1 \text{ mol } NH_4^+}{1 \text{ mol } NH_4NO_3} = 0.64$ M

$$pH = pK_a + \log\frac{[NH_3]}{[NH_4^+]} = -\log(5.6 \times 10^{-10}) + \log\left(\frac{0.15}{0.64}\right) = 8.62$$

Diluting a buffer solution will not change the pH.

18.78   (a) $K_b = 3.2 \times 10^{-5} = \dfrac{[OH^-][HOCH_2CH_2NH_3^+]}{[HOCH_2CH_2NH_2]} = \dfrac{x^2}{0.010 - x} \approx \dfrac{x^2}{0.010}$

$x = [OH^-] = 5.7 \times 10^{-4}$ M

pOH = $-\log[OH^-]$ = 3.25

pH = 14.00 – pOH = 10.75

(b) (0.0250 L ethanolamine)(0.010 mol/L) = 2.5×10^{-4} mol ethanolamine

Total volume = 0.025 L + $(2.5 \times 10^{-4}$ mol)(1 L/0.0095 mol) = 0.0513 L

$$[HOCH_2CH_2NH_3^+] = \frac{0.010 \text{ mol}}{1.0 \text{ L}} \cdot 0.0250 \text{ L} \cdot \frac{1}{0.0513 \text{ L}} = 0.0049 \text{ M}$$

$$K_a = \frac{K_w}{K_b} = 3.1 \times 10^{-10} = \frac{[H_3O^+][HOCH_2CH_2NH_2]}{[HOCH_2CH_2NH_3^+]} = \frac{x^2}{0.0049 - x} \approx \frac{x^2}{0.0049}$$

$x = [H_3O^+] = 1.2 \times 10^{-6}$ M

pH = $-\log[H_3O^+]$ = 5.91

(c) At titration midpoint [HOCH_2CH_2NH_2] = [HOCH_2CH_2NH_3^+] and pH = pK_a = $-\log(3.1 \times 10^{-10})$ = 9.51

(d) Methyl red would detect the equivalence point.

(e)

mL HCl added	mol H_3O^+ added	mol conjugate acid produced	mol base remaining	pH
5.00	4.8×10^{-5}	4.8×10^{-5}	2.0×10^{-4}	10.13
10.00	9.5×10^{-5}	9.5×10^{-5}	1.6×10^{-4}	9.72
20.00	1.9×10^{-4}	1.9×10^{-4}	6×10^{-5}	9.00
30.00	2.9×10^{-4}			3.20

When 30.00 mL HCl is added, pH depends only on the excess H_3O^+

$[H_3O^+] = (2.9 \times 10^{-4}$ mol $- 2.5 \times 10^{-4}$ mol)/0.0550 L = 6.4×10^{-4} M

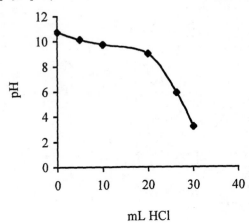

18.79   (a) $K_a = 2.4 \times 10^{-5} = \dfrac{[H_3O^+][C_6H_5NH_3^+]}{[C_6H_5NH_2]} = \dfrac{x^2}{0.100 - x} \approx \dfrac{x^2}{0.100}$

$x = [H_3O^+] = 0.00155$ M

pH = $-\log[H_3O^+]$ = 2.81

(b) $(0.0500 \text{ L } C_6H_5NH_3Cl)(0.100 \text{ mol/L}) = 0.00500 \text{ mol } C_6H_5NH_3^+$

Total volume $= 0.0500 \text{ L} + (0.00500 \text{ mol})(1 \text{ L}/0.185 \text{ mol}) = 0.0770 \text{ L}$

$$[C_6H_5NH_2] = \frac{0.100 \text{ mol}}{1 \text{ L}} \cdot 0.0500 \cdot \frac{1}{0.0770 \text{ L}} = 0.0649 \text{ M}$$

$$K_b = \frac{K_w}{K_a} = 4.2 \times 10^{-10} = \frac{[C_6H_5NH_3^+][OH^-]}{[C_6H_5NH_2]} = \frac{x^2}{0.0649 - x} \approx \frac{x^2}{0.0649}$$

$x = [OH^-] = 5.2 \times 10^{-6} \text{ M}$

$pOH = -\log[OH^-] = 5.28$

$pH = 14.00 - pOH = 8.72$

(c) At the midpoint of the titration, $[C_6H_5NH_3^+] = [C_6H_5NH_2]$, and $pH = pK_a = 4.62$.

(d) o-Cresolphthalein or phenolphthalein would be reasonable choices for an indicator.

(e)

mL NaOH added	mol OH⁻ added	mol conjugate base produced	mol acid remaining	pH
10.00	0.00185	0.00185	0.00315	4.39
20.00	0.00370	0.00370	0.00130	5.07
30.00	0.00555			11.84

When 30.00 mL NaOH is added, pH depends only on the excess OH⁻

$[OH^-] = (0.00555 \text{ mol} - 0.00500 \text{ mol})/0.0800 \text{ L} = 0.00688 \text{ M}$

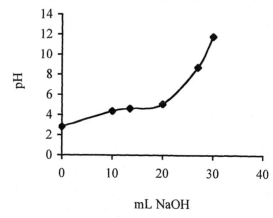

mL NaOH

18.80 $K_{sp} = [Sr^{2+}][CO_3^{2-}] = (x)(x) = x^2$

$x = \sqrt{K_{sp}} = \sqrt{5.6 \times 10^{-10}} = 2.4 \times 10^{-5} \text{ mol/L}$

$$\frac{2.4 \times 10^{-5} \text{ mol Sr}^{2+}}{1 \text{ L}} \cdot 1.0 \text{ L} \cdot \frac{1 \text{ mol SrCO}_3}{1 \text{ mol Sr}^{2+}} \cdot \frac{148 \text{ g}}{1 \text{ mol SrCO}_3} \cdot \frac{10^3 \text{ mg}}{1 \text{ g}} = 3.5 \text{ mg SrCO}_3 \text{ dissolves}$$

18.81 $pH = 2.50 = -\log(7.5 \times 10^{-3}) + \log \dfrac{[H_2PO_4^-]}{[H_3PO_4]}$

$\dfrac{[H_2PO_4^-]}{[H_3PO_4]} = \dfrac{mol\ H_2PO_4^-}{mol\ H_3PO_4} = 2.4$

$(0.100\ L\ H_3PO_4)(0.230\ mol/L) = 0.0230\ mol\ H_3PO_4$

One mole of $H_2PO_4^-$ is formed for each mole of H_3PO_4 consumed by reaction with NaOH

$\dfrac{x}{0.0230 - x} = 2.4$

$x = mol\ H_2PO_4^- = mol\ OH^- = 0.016\ mol$

$(0.016\ mol\ OH^-)(1\ L/0.150\ mol) = 0.11\ L$

18.82 $pH = 7.75 = -\log(6.2 \times 10^{-8}) + \log \dfrac{[HPO_4^{2-}]}{[H_2PO_4^-]}$

$\dfrac{[HPO_4^{2-}]}{[H_2PO_4^-]} = \dfrac{mol\ HPO_4^{2-}}{mol\ H_2PO_4^-} = 3.5$

$(0.0800\ L\ HCl)(0.200\ mol/L) = 0.0160\ mol\ H_3O^+$

The total H_3O^+ available can be used to produce HPO_4^- (1 H_3O^+/PO_4^{3-}) and $H_2PO_4^-$ (2 H_3O^+/PO_4^{3-})

$0.0160\ mol\ H_3O^+ = (mol\ HPO_4^{2-}) + 2 \times (mol\ H_2PO_4^-) = (mol\ H_2PO_4^-)(3.5) + 2 \times (mol\ H_2PO_4^-)$

total mol PO_4^{3-} needed $= mol\ HPO_4^{2-} + mol\ H_2PO_4^- = 0.0029\ mol + 0.010\ mol = 0.013\ mol\ PO_4^{3-}$

$0.013\ mol\ Na_3PO_4 \cdot \dfrac{164\ g}{1\ mol\ Na_3PO_4} = 2.1\ g\ Na_3PO_4$

18.83   (a) $K_b = 4.27 \times 10^{-4} = \dfrac{[OH^-][C_2H_5NH_3^+]}{[C_2H_5NH_2]} = \dfrac{x^2}{0.150 - x}$

The approximation $x \ll 0.150$ is not valid. Solve using the quadratic equation.

$x = [OH^-] = 0.00779\ M$

$pOH = -\log[OH^-] = 2.11$

$pH = 14.00 - pOH = 11.89$

(b)   At the halfway point $[C_2H_5NH_2] = [C_2H_5NH_3^+]$ and $pH = pK_a = -\log(2.3 \times 10^{-11}) = 10.63$

(c) $(0.0500\ L\ C_2H_5NH_2)(0.150\ mol/L) = 0.00750\ mol\ C_2H_5NH_2$

When 75% of required acid has been added

$(0.75)(0.00750\ mol\ C_2H_5NH_2) = 0.00563\ mol\ C_2H_5NH_2$ consumed $= mol\ C_2H_5NH_3^+$ produced

$(0.25)(0.00750\ mol\ C_2H_5NH_2) = 0.00188\ mol\ C_2H_5NH_2$ remains

$pH = pK_a + \log \dfrac{[C_2H_5NH_2]}{[C_2H_5NH_3^+]} = 10.63 + \log\left(\dfrac{0.00188}{0.00563}\right) = 10.15$

(d) Total volume = 0.0500 L + (0.00750 mol)(1 L/0.100 mol) = 0.125 L

$$[C_2H_5NH_3^+] = \frac{0.00750 \text{ mol}}{0.125 \text{ L}} = 0.0600 \text{ M}$$

$$K_a = 2.3 \times 10^{-11} = \frac{[H_3O^+][C_2H_5NH_2]}{[C_2H_5NH_3^+]} = \frac{x^2}{0.0600 - x} \approx \frac{x^2}{0.0600}$$

$$x = [H_3O^+] = 1.2 \times 10^{-6} \text{ M}$$

$$pH = -\log[H_3O^+] = 5.93$$

(e) pH depends only on the excess H_3O^+

$$[H_3O^+] = \frac{(0.0100 \text{ L})(0.100 \text{ mol/L})}{0.135 \text{ L}} = 0.00741 \text{ M}$$

$$pH = -\log[H_3O^+] = 2.13$$

(f)

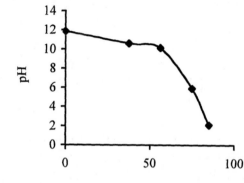

(g) Alizarin or bromcresol purple would detect the equivalence point.

18.84 $$pH = 4.70 = -\log(6.4 \times 10^{-5}) + \log\frac{[C_2O_4^{2-}]}{[HC_2O_4^-]}$$

$$\frac{[C_2O_4^{2-}]}{[HC_2O_4^-]} = \frac{\text{mol } C_2O_4^{2-}}{\text{mol } HC_2O_4^-} = 3.2$$

(0.100 L $HC_2O_4^-$)(0.100 mol/L) = 0.0100 mol $HC_2O_4^-$

One mole of $C_2O_4^{2-}$ is formed for each mole of $HC_2O_4^-$ consumed by reaction with NaOH

$$\frac{x}{0.0100 - x} = 3.2$$

$$x = \text{mol } C_2O_4^{2-} = \text{mol } OH^- = 0.0076 \text{ mol}$$

(0.0076 mol OH^-)(1 L/0.120 mol) = 0.064 L

18.85   (a) pH will increase

(b) pH will not change

(c) In (a), pH increases because a weak base is added to the solution. In (b), both ions in $NaNO_3$ are neutral and do not affect the pH of a solution.

18.86 $1.50 \text{ g} \cdot \dfrac{1 \text{ mol } C_6H_5CO_2H}{122.1 \text{ g}} = 0.0123 \text{ mol}$

$1.50 \text{ g} \cdot \dfrac{1 \text{ mol } NaC_6H_5CO_2}{144.1 \text{ g}} = 0.0104 \text{ mol}$

(a) $pH = pK_a + \log \dfrac{[C_6H_5CO_2^-]}{[C_6H_5CO_2H]} = -\log(6.3 \times 10^{-5}) + \log\left(\dfrac{0.0104}{0.0123}\right) = 4.13$

(b)   Additional acid $(C_6H_5CO_2H)$ must be added to lower the pH to 4.00

$4.00 = -\log(6.3 \times 10^{-5}) + \log \dfrac{0.0104 \text{ mol}}{x}$

$x = 0.017 \text{ mol } C_6H_5CO_2H$

$(0.017 \text{ mol} - 0.0123 \text{ mol}) \cdot \dfrac{122.1 \text{ g}}{1 \text{ mol } C_6H_5CO_2H} = 0.5 \text{ g } C_6H_5CO_2H$ should be added

(c) $4.00 = -\log(6.3 \times 10^{-5}) + \log \dfrac{[C_6H_5CO_2^-]}{[C_6H_5CO_2H]}$

$\dfrac{[C_6H_5CO_2^-]}{[C_6H_5CO_2H]} = \dfrac{\text{mol } C_6H_5CO_2^-}{\text{mol } C_6H_5CO_2H} = 0.63 = \dfrac{0.0104 - x}{0.0123 + x}$

$x = 0.0016 \text{ mol } H_3O^+$

$(0.0016 \text{ mol})(1 \text{ L}/2.0 \text{ mol}) = 8.2 \times 10^{-4} \text{ L}$ or 8.2 mL of 2.0 M HCl should be added

18.87   (a) $pH = 12.00 = -\log(3.6 \times 10^{-13}) + \log \dfrac{[PO_4^{3-}]}{[HPO_4^{2-}]}$

$\dfrac{[PO_4^{3-}]}{[HPO_4^{2-}]} = 0.36$ HPO_4^{2-} is present in a larger amount

(b) $\dfrac{0.400}{[HPO_4^{2-}]} = 0.36$ $[HPO_4^{2-}] = 1.1 \text{ mol/L}$

$\dfrac{1.1 \text{ mol } HPO_4^{2-}}{1 \text{ L}} \cdot 0.2000 \text{ L} \cdot \dfrac{1 \text{ mol } Na_2HPO_4}{1 \text{ mol } HPO_4^{2-}} \cdot \dfrac{142.0 \text{ g}}{1 \text{ mol } Na_2HPO_4} = 32 \text{ g } Na_2HPO_4$

(c)   Additional base (PO_4^{3-}) must be added to raise the pH to 12.25.

$12.25 = -\log(3.6 \times 10^{-13}) + \log \dfrac{x}{1.1}$

$x = [PO_4^{3-}] = 0.70 \text{ mol/L}$

$(0.70 \text{ mol/L})(0.2000 \text{ L}) - (0.400 \text{ mol/L})(0.2000 \text{ L}) = 0.061 \text{ mol } Na_3PO_4$

$0.061 \text{ mol } Na_3PO_4 \cdot \dfrac{163.9 \text{ g}}{1 \text{ mol } Na_3PO_4} = 10. \text{ g } Na_3PO_4$ should be added

18.88 $pH = 9.00 = -\log(5.6 \times 10^{-10}) + \log\dfrac{[NH_3]}{[NH_4^+]}$

$\dfrac{[NH_3]}{[NH_4^+]} = 0.56$

$(0.5000 \text{ L } NH_3)(0.250 \text{ mol/L}) = 0.125 \text{ mol } NH_3$

$\dfrac{[NH_3]}{[NH_4^+]} = \dfrac{0.125 - x}{x} = 0.56$

$x = 0.080 \text{ mol } H_3O^+$ to be added

$(0.080 \text{ mol } H_3O^+)(1 \text{ L}/0.200 \text{ mol}) = 0.40 \text{ L of } 0.200 \text{ M HCl should be added}$

18.89   (a) $K_{sp}(BaSO_4) < K_{sp}(SrSO_4)$ $BaSO_4$ will precipitate first

     (b) $K_{sp}(SrSO_4) = 3.4 \times 10^{-7} = [Sr^{2+}][SO_4^{2-}] = (x)(x) = x^2$

        $x = [SO_4^{2-}]$ when $SrSO_4$ begins to precipitate $= 5.8 \times 10^{-4}$ M

        $K_{sp}(BaSO_4) = 1.1 \times 10^{-10} = [Ba^{2+}][SO_4^{2-}] = [Ba^{2+}](5.8 \times 10^{-4})$

        $[Ba^{2+}]$ when $SrSO_4$ begins to precipitate $= 1.8 \times 10^{-7}$ M

18.90 $K_{sp} = 4.9 \times 10^{-17} = [Fe^{2+}][OH^-]^2 = (0.1)[OH^-]^2$ $[OH^-]$ required to precipitate $Fe(OH)_2 = 2.2 \times 10^{-8}$ M

     $K_{sp} = 1.4 \times 10^{-15} = [Pb^{2+}][OH^-]^2 = (0.1)[OH^-]^2$ $[OH^-]$ required to precipitate $Pb(OH)_2 = 1.2 \times 10^{-7}$ M

     $K_{sp} = 1.3 \times 10^{-33} = [Al^{3+}][OH^-]^3 = (0.1)[OH^-]^3$ $[OH^-]$ required to precipitate $Al(OH)_3 = 2.4 \times 10^{-11}$ M

     $Al(OH)_3$ will precipitate first, followed by $Fe(OH)_2$ and then $Pb(OH)_2$

18.91 $AgCl(s) \rightleftarrows Ag^+(aq) + Cl^-(aq)$ $K_{sp} = 1.8 \times 10^{-10}$

     $Ag^+(aq) + I^-(aq) \rightleftarrows AgI(s)$ $K = 1/K_{sp} = 1.2 \times 10^{16}$

     $AgCl(s) + I^-(aq) \rightleftarrows AgI(s) + Cl^-(aq)$ $K_{net} = (1.8 \times 10^{-10})(1.2 \times 10^{16}) = 2.1 \times 10^6$

The equilibrium lies predominantly to the right. AgI will form if I^- is added to a saturated solution of AgCl.

18.92 $Zn(OH)_2(s) \rightleftarrows Zn^{2+}(aq) + 2 OH^-(aq)$ $K_{sp} = 3 \times 10^{-17}$

     $Zn^{2+}(aq) + 2 CN^-(aq) \rightleftarrows Zn(CN)_2(s)$ $K = 1/K_{sp} = 1.3 \times 10^{11}$

     $Zn(OH)_2(s) + 2 CN^-(aq) \rightleftarrows Zn(CN)_2(s) + 2 OH^-(aq)$ $K_{net} = (3 \times 10^{-17})(1.3 \times 10^{11}) = 4 \times 10^{-6}$

The equilibrium lies predominantly to the left. The transformation of zinc hydroxide into zinc cyanide will not occur to a large extent because of the unfavorable equilibrium constant.

18.93   (a) $K_{sp} = 1.8 \times 10^{-7} = [Ba^{2+}][F^-]^2 = (0.10)[F^-]^2$

        $[F^-] = 1.3 \times 10^{-3}$ M

        When $[F^-]$ reaches this concentration, the maximum amount of CaF_2 will have precipitated without precipitating BaF_2.

(b) $K_{sp} = 5.3 \times 10^{-11} = [Ca^{2+}][F^-]^2 = [Ca^{2+}](1.3 \times 10^{-3})^2$

$[Ca^{2+}] = 2.9 \times 10^{-5}$ M

18.94 (a) $K_{sp} = 9.8 \times 10^{-9} = [Pb^{2+}][I^-]^2 = [Pb^{2+}](0.10)^2$

$[Pb^{2+}] = 9.8 \times 10^{-7}$ mol/L

$K_{sp} = 7.4 \times 10^{-14} = [Pb^{2+}][CO_3^{2-}] = [Pb^{2+}](0.10)$

$[Pb^{2+}] = 7.4 \times 10^{-13}$ mol/L

$PbCO_3$ will precipitate first

(b) $K_{sp} = 7.4 \times 10^{-14} = [Pb^{2+}][CO_3^{2-}] = (9.8 \times 10^{-7})[CO_3^{2-}]$

$[CO_3^{2-}] = 7.6 \times 10^{-8}$ mol/L

18.95 (a) $K_{sp} = 4.9 \times 10^{-5} = [Ca^{2+}][SO_4^{2-}] = (0.010)[SO_4^{2-}]$

$[SO_4^{2-}] = 4.9 \times 10^{-3}$ mol/L

$K_{sp} = 2.5 \times 10^{-8} = [Pb^{2+}][SO_4^{2-}] = (0.010)[SO_4^{2-}]$

$[SO_4^{2-}] = 2.5 \times 10^{-8}$ mol/L

$PbSO_4$ will precipitate first

(b) $K_{sp} = 2.5 \times 10^{-8} = [Pb^{2+}][SO_4^{2-}] = [Pb^{2+}](4.9 \times 10^{-3})$

$[Pb^{2+}] = 5.1 \times 10^{-6}$ mol/L

18.96 The initial pH is 4.74

$$5.74 = pK_a + \log\frac{[CH_3CO_2^-]}{[CH_3CO_2H]} = 4.74 + \log\frac{[CH_3CO_2^-]}{[CH_3CO_2H]}$$

$$\frac{[CH_3CO_2^-]}{[CH_3CO_2H]} = 10$$

The ratio must change from 1:1 to 10:1 for the pH to change by one unit.

$$10 = \frac{0.10 + x}{0.10 - x}$$

$x = 0.082$ mol/L

The buffer capacity is therefore 0.082 mol.

18.97 CuS has a K_{spa} value of 6×10^{-37} (see Appendix), so it is not expected to be readily soluble in strong acid.

Addition of strong acid to the mixture of CuS and $Cu(OH)_2$ will dissolve the hydroxide salt but not CuS.

18.98 $Ba(OH)_2$ and $BaCO_3$

18.99 The strong base (OH^-) is consumed completely in a reaction with the weak acid present in the buffer.

$OH^-(aq) + CH_3CO_2H(aq) \rightarrow CH_3CO_2^-(aq) + H_2O(\ell)$

18.100 $pH = pK_a + \log \dfrac{[\text{conjugate base}]}{[\text{acid}]}$

   (a) If K_a increases, pK_a decreases. Therefore, the pH should decrease.

   (b) If [acid] decreases, the ratio [conjugate base]/[acid] will increase. The log term will increase, so the

   pH should increase. (In order words, as the conjugate base concentration increases, the solution will

       become more basic, and the pH increases.)

18.101   When Ag_3PO_4 dissolves slightly, it produces a small concentration of PO_4^{3-} ion. The phosphate ion is a

   strong base and readily hydrolyzes to HPO_4^{2-}. As this removes PO_4^{3-} from the equilibrium with Ag_3PO_4,

   the equilibrium shifts to the right, $Ag_3PO_4(s) \rightleftharpoons 3\ Ag^+(aq) + PO_4^{3-}(aq)$ and Ag_3PO_4 dissolves to a greater

   extent than expected from the K_{sp} value.

18.102   (a) HB is a stronger acid than HA.

   (b) A^- is a stronger base than B^-.

18.103   (a) To increase the pH, base must be added. The added base reacts with acetic acid to form more acetate

       ion in the mixture. As acid is converted to conjugate base, the ratio $[CH_3CO_2H]/[CH_3CO_2^-]$ changes

       and the pH rises.

   (b) At pH = 4 the acid predominates (85% acid to 15% acetate ion); at pH = 6 the acetate ion

       predominates (95% acetate ion to 5% acid).

   (c) At the point where the lines cross $[CH_3CO_2H] = [CH_3CO_2^-]$. At this point $pH = pK_a$; pK_a for acetic

       acid is 4.74.

18.104   (a) As the pH increases (H_3O^+ concentration decreases), the first ionization equilibrium

       $H_2CO_3(aq) + H_2O(\ell) \rightleftharpoons HCO_3^-(aq) + H_3O^+(aq)$

       is shifted to the right and more HCO_3^- is produced. As the pH rises further, the second ionization

       occurs and is shifted to the right with increasing pH.

       $HCO_3^-(aq) + H_2O(\ell) \rightleftharpoons CO_3^{2-}(aq) + H_3O^+(aq)$

       and is shifted to the right with increasing pH, decreasing the amount of HCO_3^- present in the solution.

   (b) At pH = 6.0, the solution is 72% H_2CO_3 and 28% HCO_3^-.

       At pH = 10.0, the solution is 66% HCO_3^- and 34% CO_3^{2-}.

   (c) A solution buffered at pH = 11.0 should have a HCO_3^- to CO_3^{2-} ratio of 0.2 to 1.

18.105   (a) (i)   120°

            (ii) 120°

            (iii) 109°

            (iv) 120°

   (b) All C atoms in salicylic acid are sp^2 hybridized.

(c) $[C_6H_4(OH)CO_2H] = \dfrac{1.00 \text{ g}}{0.460 \text{ L}} \cdot \dfrac{1 \text{ mol } C_6H_4(OH)CO_2H}{138.1 \text{ g}} = 0.0157$ M

$[H_3O^+] = 10^{-pH} = 10^{-2.4} = 0.004$ M

$K_a = \dfrac{[H_3O^+][C_6H_4(OH)CO_2^-]}{[C_6H_4(OH)CO_2H]} = \dfrac{(0.004)^2}{0.0157 - 0.004} = 1 \times 10^{-3}$

(d) $[H_3O^+] = 10^{-pH} = 10^{-2.0} = 0.01$ M

$K_a = 1 \times 10^{-3} = \dfrac{[H_3O^+][C_6H_4(OH)CO_2^-]}{[C_6H_4(OH)CO_2H]} = \dfrac{(0.01)[C_6H_4(OH)CO_2^-]}{[C_6H_4(OH)CO_2H]}$

$\dfrac{[C_6H_4(OH)CO_2^-]}{[C_6H_4(OH)CO_2H]} = 0.1$

percent ionization = 10%

(e) At the halfway point, pH = pK_a = 3

$0.0250 \text{ L} \cdot \dfrac{0.014 \text{ mol } C_6H_4(OH)CO_2H}{1 \text{ L}} = 3.5 \times 10^{-4} \text{ mol } C_6H_4(OH)CO_2H$

$3.5 \times 10^{-4} \text{ mol } C_6H_4(OH)CO_2H \cdot \dfrac{1 \text{ mol NaOH}}{1 \text{ mol } C_6H_4(OH)CO_2H} \cdot \dfrac{1 \text{ L}}{0.010 \text{ mol NaOH}} = 0.035 \text{ L NaOH}$

$[C_6H_4(OH)CO_2^-] = \dfrac{3.5 \times 10^{-4} \text{ mol } C_6H_4(OH)CO_2^-}{(0.0250 \text{ L} + 0.035 \text{ L})} = 5.8 \times 10^{-3}$ M

$C_6H_4(OH)CO_2^-(aq) + H_2O(\ell) \rightarrow C_6H_4(OH)CO_2H(aq) + OH^-(aq)$

$K_b = \dfrac{K_w}{K_a} = \dfrac{[C_6H_4(OH)CO_2H][OH^-]}{[C_6H_4(OH)CO_2^-]} = \dfrac{(x)(x)}{5.8 \times 10^{-3} - x}$

$x = [OH^-] = 2 \times 10^{-7}$

$pOH = -\log[OH^-] = 6.7$

$pH = 14.0 - pH = 7.3$

18.106 (a) 15.0 mL

(b) pH = 9.01 The principle species in solution is the weak base, $CH_3CO_2^-$

(c) either phenolphthalein or thymolphthalein

18.107 Adding Cl^- to the test tube shifts the equilibrium to the left, forming more $PbCl_2$ and decreasing $[Pb^{2+}]$

18.108 If the lead chloride equilibrium were static, only a small amount of lead chromate would precipitate and the lead chloride would not dissolve in a solution containing $CrO_4^{2-}(aq)$.

18.109 Decreasing pH by 1.0 is equivalent to increasing $[H_3O^+]$ by a factor of 10, which decreases $[OH^-]$ by a factor of 10. The hydroxide ion concentration is squared in the equilibrium constant expression, so decreasing $[OH^-]$ by factor of 10 results in the solubility increasing by a factor of 10^2, or 100.

18.110 See the description of floor wax application and removal on the sidebar to Screen 18.17.

Chapter 19
Principles of Reactivity: Entropy and Free Energy

INSTRUCTOR'S NOTES

At the introductory level our goal for this chapter is relatively limited: to convey the idea of reaction spontaneity and to differentiate this from reaction speed.

Although we usually cover thermodynamics following our discussion of equilibria, we have sometimes reversed these topics and find no particular problems in doing so. When thermodynamics is discussed before equilibrium we make the connection between ΔG and K very early in the lectures on general equilibria.

This chapter has been modified over the past two editions to expand the discussion of entropy to include an introduction to probability as it relates to S. Energy dispersal is treated explicitly in Figures 19.4 and 19.6 and matter dispersal in Figure 19.5.

The discussion of entropy is further developed to include considerations and calculations of the entropy of the surroundings. This then allows a natural lead-in to Gibb's Free Energy . Figure 19.12 is used to visually clarify the sign of ΔG as a function of temperature for the four possible sign combinations of ΔH and ΔS.

SUGGESTED DEMONSTRATIONS

1. Spontaneous Reactions and Speed: Thermodynamics versus Kinetics
    *   We usually begin these lectures with a series of reactions designed to show that some product-favored reactions ($Na + H_2O$, $Mg + O_2$) proceed with the evolution of heat, while others proceed while requiring heat (the melting of ice, the evaporation of liquid nitrogen, or the dissolution of some solids).
    *   There are many suitable demonstrations in Volume 1 of Shakhashiri's *Chemical Demonstrations*.
    *   Alexander, M. D. "The Ammonia Smoke Fountain: An Interesting Thermodynamic Adventure," *Journal of Chemical Education* **1999**, *76*, 210.
    *   Muiño, P. L. "Illustrating Thermodynamic Concepts Using a Hero's Engine," *Journal of Chemical Education* **2000**, *77*, 615.
    *   Erné, B. H. "Thermodynamics of Water Superheated in the Microwave," *Journal of Chemical Education* **2000**, *77*, 1309.

SOLUTIONS TO STUDY QUESTIONS

19.1   (a) The CO_2 vapor at 0 °C has a higher entropy than the sample of solid CO_2

(b) Liquid water at the higher temperature (50 °C) has a higher entropy

(c) Ruby has a higher entropy than pure alumina

(d) The sample of $N_2(g)$ at the lower pressure (1 bar) has a higher entropy

19.2   (a) The sample of silicon containing trace impurities has a higher entropy

(b) The sample of $O_2(g)$ at the higher temperature (0 °C) has a higher entropy

(c) $I_2(g)$ has a higher entropy than $I_2(s)$

(d) The sample of $O_2(g)$ at the lower pressure (0.01 bar) has a higher entropy

19.3   (a) $CH_3OH(g)$ has a higher entropy than $O_2(g)$

(b) $HBr(g)$ has a higher entropy than $HCl(g)$ or $HF(g)$

(c) $NH_4Cl(aq)$ has a higher entropy than $NH_4Cl(s)$

(d) $HNO_3(g)$ has a higher entropy than $HNO_3(\ell)$ or $HNO_3(aq)$

19.4   (a) $NaCl(g)$ has a higher entropy than $NaCl(s)$ or $NaCl(aq)$

(b) $H_2S(g)$ has a higher entropy than $H_2O(g)$

(c) $C_2H_4(g)$ has a higher entropy than $N_2(g)$

(d) $H_2SO_4(aq)$ has a higher entropy than $H_2SO_4(\ell)$

19.5   (a) $\Delta S° = S°[KOH(aq)] – S°[KOH(s)]$

$\Delta S° = 1$ mol (91.6 J/K·mol) – 1 mol (78.9 J/K·mol) = 12.7 J/K

A positive $\Delta S°$ indicates an increase in entropy

(b) $\Delta S° = S°[Na(s)] – S°[Na(g)]$

$\Delta S° = 1$ mol (51.21 J/K·mol) – 1 mol (153.765 J/K·mol) = –102.56 J/K

A negative $\Delta S°$ indicates a decrease in entropy

(c) $\Delta S° = S°[Br_2(g)] – S°[Br_2(\ell)]$

$\Delta S° = 1$ mol (245.42 J/K·mol) – 1 mol (152.2 J/K·mol) = 93.2 J/K

A positive $\Delta S°$ indicates an increase in entropy

(d) $\Delta S° = S°[HCl(aq)] – S°[HCl(g)]$

$\Delta S° = 1$ mol (56.5 J/K·mol) – 1 mol (186.2 J/K·mol) = –129.7 J/K

A negative $\Delta S°$ indicates a decrease in entropy

19.6   (a) $\Delta S° = S°[NH_4Cl(aq)] - S°[NH_4Cl(s)]$

$\Delta S° = 1 \text{ mol } (169.9 \text{ J/K·mol}) - 1 \text{ mol } (94.85 \text{ J/K·mol}) = 75.1 \text{ J/K}$

A positive $\Delta S°$ indicates an increase in entropy

(b) $\Delta S° = S°[C_2H_5OH(g)] - S°[C_2H_5OH(\ell)]$

$\Delta S° = 1 \text{ mol } (282.70 \text{ J/K·mol}) - 1 \text{ mol } (160.7 \text{ J/K·mol}) = 122.0 \text{ J/K}$

A positive $\Delta S°$ indicates an increase in entropy

(c) $\Delta S° = S°[CCl_4(\ell)] - S°[CCl_4(g)]$

$\Delta S° = 1 \text{ mol } (214.39 \text{ J/K·mol}) - 1 \text{ mol } (309.65 \text{ J/K·mol}) = -95.26 \text{ J/K}$

A negative $\Delta S°$ indicates a decrease in entropy

(d) $\Delta S° = S°[NaCl(g)] - S°[NaCl(s)]$

$\Delta S° = 1 \text{ mol } (229.79 \text{ J/K·mol}) - 1 \text{ mol } (72.11 \text{ J/K·mol}) = 157.68 \text{ J/K}$

A positive $\Delta S°$ indicates an increase in entropy

19.7 $\Delta S° = S°[C_2H_6(g)] - \{2 \, S°[C(graphite)] + 3 \, S°[H_2(g)]\}$

$\Delta S° = 1 \text{ mol } (229.2 \text{ J/K·mol}) - [2 \text{ mol } (5.6 \text{ J/K·mol}) + 3 \text{ mol } (130.7 \text{ J/K·mol})]$

$\Delta S° = -174.1 \text{ J/K}$

19.8 $\Delta S° = S°[NH_3(g)] - \{^1/_2 \, S°[N_2(g)] + {}^3/_2 \, S°[H_2(g)]\}$

$\Delta S° = 1 \text{ mol } (192.77 \text{ J/K·mol}) - [^1/_2 \text{ mol } (191.56 \text{ J/K·mol}) + {}^3/_2 \text{ mol } (130.7 \text{ J/K·mol})]$

$\Delta S° = -99.1 \text{ J/K}$

19.9   (a) $^1/_2 \text{ H}_2(g) + {}^1/_2 \text{ Cl}_2(g) \rightarrow HCl(g)$

$\Delta S° = S°[HCl(g)] - \{^1/_2 \, S°[H_2(g)] + {}^1/_2 \, S°[Cl_2(g)]\}$

$\Delta S° = 1 \text{ mol } (186.2 \text{ J/K·mol}) - [^1/_2 \text{ mol } (130.7 \text{ J/K·mol}) + {}^1/_2 \text{ mol } (223.08 \text{ J/K·mol})]$

$\Delta S° = 9.3 \text{ J/K}$

(b) $Ca(s) + O_2(g) + H_2(g) \rightarrow Ca(OH)_2(s)$

$\Delta S° = S°[Ca(OH)_2(s)] - \{S°[Ca(s)] + S°[O_2(g)] + S°[H_2(g)]\}$

$\Delta S° = 1 \text{ mol } (83.39 \text{ J/K·mol}) - [1 \text{ mol } (41.59 \text{ J/K·mol}) + 1 \text{ mol } (205.07 \text{ J/K·mol})$

$+ 1 \text{ mol } (130.7 \text{ J/K·mol}]$

$\Delta S° = -294.0 \text{ J/K}$

19.10   (a) $H_2(g) + S(s) \rightarrow H_2S(g)$

$\Delta S° = S°[H_2S(g)] - \{S°[H_2(g)] + S°[S(s)]\}$

$\Delta S° = 1 \text{ mol } (205.79 \text{ J/K·mol}) - [1 \text{ mol } (130.7 \text{ J/K·mol}) + 1 \text{ mol } (32.1 \text{ J/K·mol})]$

$\Delta S° = 43.0 \text{ J/K}$

(b) $Mg(s) + C(graphite) + \frac{3}{2} O_2(g) \rightarrow MgCO_3(s)$

$\Delta S° = S°[MgCO_3(s)] - \{S°[Mg(s)] + S°[C(graphite)] + \frac{3}{2} S°[O_2(g)]\}$

$\Delta S° = 1 \text{ mol } (65.84 \text{ J/K·mol}) - [1 \text{ mol } (32.67 \text{ J/K·mol}) + 1 \text{ mol } (5.6 \text{ J/K·mol})$

$+ \frac{3}{2} \text{ mol } (205.07 \text{ J/K·mol})]$

$\Delta S° = -280.0 \text{ J/K}$

19.11   (a) $\Delta S° = 2 S°[AlCl_3(s)] - \{2 S°[Al(s)] + 3 S°[Cl_2(g)]\}$

$\Delta S° = 2 \text{ mol } (109.29 \text{ J/K·mol}) - [2 \text{ mol } (28.3 \text{ J/K·mol}) + 3 \text{ mol } (223.08 \text{ J/K·mol})]$

$\Delta S° = -507.3 \text{ J/K}$ A negative $\Delta S°$ indicates a decrease in entropy

(b) $\Delta S° = 2 S°[CO_2(g)] + 4 S°[H_2O(g)] - \{2 S°[CH_3OH(\ell)] + 3 S°[O_2(g)]\}$

$\Delta S° = 2 \text{ mol } (213.74 \text{ J/K·mol}) + 4 \text{ mol } (188.84 \text{ J/K·mol}) - [2 \text{ mol } (127.19 \text{ J/K·mol})$

$+ 3 \text{ mol } (205.07 \text{ J/K·mol})]$

$\Delta S° = 313.25 \text{ J/K}$ A positive $\Delta S°$ indicates an increase in entropy

19.12   (a) $\Delta S° = 2 S°[NaOH(aq)] + S°[H_2(g)] - \{2 S°[Na(s)] + 2 S°[H_2O(\ell)]\}$

$\Delta S° = 2 \text{ mol } (48.1 \text{ J/K·mol}) + 1 \text{ mol } (130.7 \text{ J/K·mol}) - [2 \text{ mol } (51.21 \text{ J/K·mol})$

$+ 2 \text{ mol } (69.96 \text{ J/K·mol})]$

$\Delta S° = -15.4 \text{ J/K}$ A negative $\Delta S°$ indicates a decrease in entropy

(b) $\Delta S° = 2 S°[NaCl(aq)] + S°[H_2O(\ell)] + S°[CO_2(g)] - \{S°[Na_2CO_3(s)] + 2 S°[HCl(aq)]\}$

$\Delta S° = 2 \text{ mol } (115.5 \text{ J/K·mol}) + 1 \text{ mol } (69.95 \text{ J/K·mol}) + 1 \text{ mol } (213.74 \text{ J/K·mol})$

$- [1 \text{ mol } (134.79 \text{ J/K·mol}) + 2 \text{ mol } (56.5 \text{ J/K·mol})]$

$\Delta S° = 266.9 \text{ J/K}$ A positive $\Delta S°$ indicates an increase in entropy

19.13 $\Delta S°_{sys} = S°[SiCl_4(g)] - \{S°[Si(s)] + 2 S°[Cl_2(g)]\}$

$\Delta S°_{sys} = 1 \text{ mol } (330.86 \text{ J/K·mol}) - [1 \text{ mol } (18.82 \text{ J/K·mol}) + 2 \text{ mol } (223.08 \text{ J/K·mol})]$

$\Delta S°_{sys} = -134.12 \text{ J/K}$

$\Delta S°_{surr} = -\Delta H°_{sys}/T = -\Delta H_f°[SiCl_4(g)]/(298.15 \text{ K}) = -[1 \text{ mol } (-662.75 \text{ kJ/mol})/(298.15 \text{ K})] = 2.2229 \text{ kJ/K}$

$\Delta S°_{univ} = \Delta S°_{sys} + \Delta S°_{surr} = -134.12 \text{ J/K} + (2.2229 \text{ kJ/K})(10^3 \text{ J/1 kJ}) = 2088.8 \text{ J/K}$

The reaction is spontaneous

19.14 $\Delta S°_{sys} = S°[SiH_4(g)] - \{S°[Si(s)] + 2 S°[H_2(g)]\}$

$\Delta S°_{sys} = 1 \text{ mol } (204.65 \text{ J/K·mol}) - [1 \text{ mol } (18.82 \text{ J/K·mol}) + 2 \text{ mol } (130.7 \text{ J/K·mol})]$

$\Delta S°_{sys} = -75.6 \text{ J/K}$

$\Delta S°_{surr} = -\Delta H°_{sys}/T = -\Delta H_f°[SiH_4(g)]/(298.15 \text{ K}) = -[1 \text{ mol } (34.31 \text{ kJ/mol})/(298.15 \text{ K})] = -0.1151 \text{ kJ/K}$

$\Delta S°_{univ} = \Delta S°_{sys} + \Delta S°_{surr} = -75.6 \text{ J/K} + (-0.01151 \text{ kJ/K})(10^3 \text{ J/1 kJ}) = -190.7 \text{ J/K}$

The reaction is not spontaneous

19.15 $H_2O(\ell) \rightarrow H_2(g) + {}^1\!/_2\ O_2(g)$

$\Delta H^\circ = -\Delta H_f^\circ[H_2O(\ell)] = -[1\ mol\ (-285.83\ kJ/mol)] = 285.83\ kJ$

$\Delta S^\circ = S^\circ[H_2(g)] + {}^1\!/_2\ S^\circ[O_2(g)] - S^\circ[H_2O(\ell)]$

$\Delta S^\circ = 1\ mol\ (130.7\ J/K\cdot mol) + {}^1\!/_2\ mol\ (205.07\ J/K\cdot mol) - 1\ mol\ (69.95\ J/K\cdot mol) = 163.3\ J/K$

$\Delta S^\circ_{univ} = \Delta S^\circ_{sys} + \Delta S^\circ_{surr} = (163.3\ J/K) + -[(285.83\ kJ)(10^3\ J/1\ kJ)/298.15\ K)] = -795.4\ J/K$

The reaction is not spontaneous as ΔS°_{univ} is negative. The reaction is disfavored by energy dispersal.

19.16 ${}^1\!/_2\ H_2(g) + {}^1\!/_2\ Cl_2(g) \rightarrow HCl(g)$

$\Delta H^\circ = \Delta H_f^\circ[HCl(g)] = 1\ mol\ (-92.31\ kJ/mol) = -92.31\ kJ$

$\Delta S^\circ = S^\circ[HCl(g)] - \{{}^1\!/_2\ S^\circ[H_2(g)] + {}^1\!/_2\ S^\circ[Cl_2(g)]\}$

$\Delta S^\circ = 1\ mol\ (186.2\ J/K\cdot mol) - [{}^1\!/_2\ mol\ (130.7\ J/K\cdot mol) + {}^1\!/_2\ mol\ (223.08\ J/K\cdot mol)] = 9.3\ J/K$

$\Delta S^\circ_{univ} = \Delta S^\circ_{sys} + \Delta S^\circ_{surr} = (9.3\ J/K) + -[(-92.31\ kJ)(10^3\ J/1\ kJ)/298.15\ K)] = 318.9\ J/K$

The reaction is spontaneous as ΔS°_{univ} is positive.

19.17   (a) $\Delta H^\circ < 0,\ \Delta S^\circ < 0$; depends on T and relative magnitudes of ΔH and ΔS, more favorable at lower T.

(b) $\Delta H^\circ > 0,\ \Delta S^\circ < 0$; not spontaneous under all conditions

19.18   (a) $\Delta H^\circ < 0,\ \Delta S^\circ > 0$; spontaneous under all conditions

(b) $\Delta H^\circ > 0,\ \Delta S^\circ > 0$; depends on T and relative magnitudes of ΔH and ΔS, more favorable at higher T.

19.19   (a) $\Delta H^\circ = \Delta H_f^\circ[MgO(s)] + \Delta H_f^\circ[CO_2(g)] - \Delta H_f^\circ[MgCO_3(s)]$

$\Delta H^\circ = 1\ mol\ (-601.24\ kJ/mol) + 1\ mol\ (-393.509\ kJ/mol) - 1\ mol\ (-1111.69\ kJ/mol)$

$\Delta H^\circ = 116.94\ kJ$

$\Delta S^\circ = S^\circ[MgO(s)] + S^\circ[CO_2(g)] - S^\circ[MgCO_3(s)]$

$\Delta S^\circ = 1\ mol\ (26.85\ J/K\cdot mol) + 1\ mol\ (213.74\ J/K\cdot mol) - 1\ mol\ (65.84\ J/K\cdot mol)$

$\Delta S^\circ = 174.75\ J/K$

(b) $\Delta G^\circ = \Delta H^\circ - T\Delta S^\circ = 116.94\ kJ - (298\ K)(174.75\ J/K)(1\ kJ/10^3\ J) = 64.9\ kJ$

The reaction is predicted to be non-spontaneous at 298 K ($\Delta G^\circ > 0$)

(c) The reaction is predicted to be spontaneous at higher temperatures.

19.20 $\Delta H^\circ = \Delta H_f^\circ[CO_2(g)] - \Delta H_f^\circ[SnO_2(s)]$

$\Delta H^\circ = 1\ mol\ (-393.509\ kJ/mol) - 1\ mol\ (-577.63\ kJ/mol) = 184.12\ kJ$

$\Delta S^\circ = S^\circ[Sn(s,\ white)] + S^\circ[CO_2(g)] - \{S^\circ[SnO_2(s)] + S^\circ[C(graphite)]\}$

$\Delta S^\circ = 1\ mol\ (51.08\ J/K\cdot mol) + 1\ mol\ (213.74\ J/K\cdot mol) - [1\ mol\ (49.04\ J/K\cdot mol) - 1\ mol\ (5.6\ J/K\cdot mol)]$

$\Delta S^\circ = 210.2\ J/K$

(a) $\Delta G° = \Delta H° - T\Delta S° = 184.12$ kJ $- (298$ K$)(210.2$ J/K$)(1$ kJ$/10^3$ J$) = 121.5$ kJ

The reaction is predicted to be non-spontaneous at 298 K ($\Delta G° > 0$)

(b) The reaction is predicted to be spontaneous at higher temperatures.

19.21 (a) $\Delta H° = 2\ \Delta H_f°[PbO(s)] = 2$ mol $(-219$ kJ/mol$) = -438$ kJ

$\Delta S° = 2\ S°[(PbO(s)] - \{2\ S°[Pb(s)] + S°[O_2(g)]\}$

$\Delta S° = 2$ mol $(66.5$ J/K·mol$) - [2$ mol $(64.81$ J/K·mol$) + 1$ mol $(205.07$ J/K·mol$)] = -201.7$ J/K

$\Delta G° = \Delta H° - T\Delta S° = -438$ kJ $- (298$ K$)(-201.7$ J/K$)(1$ kJ$/10^3$ J$) = -378$ kJ

(b) $\Delta H° = \Delta H_f°[NH_4NO_3(aq)] - \{\Delta H_f°[NH_3(g)] + \Delta H_f°[HNO_3(aq)]\}$

$\Delta H° = 1$ mol $(-339.87$ kJ/mol$) - [1$ mol $(-45.90$ kJ/mol$) + 1$ mol $(-207.36$ kJ/mol$)] = -86.61$ kJ

$\Delta S° = S°[NH_4NO_3(aq)] - \{S°[NH_3(g)] + S°[HNO_3(aq)]\}$

$\Delta S° = 1$ mol $(259.8$ J/K·mol$) - [1$ mol $(192.77$ J/K·mol$) + 1$ mol $(146.4$ J/K·mol$)] = -79.4$ J/K

$\Delta G° = \Delta H° - T\Delta S° = -86.61$ kJ $- (298$ K$)(-79.4$ J/K$)(1$ kJ$/10^3$ J$) = -62.9$ kJ

Reaction (a) is product-favored and enthalpy-driven.

Reaction (b) is product-favored and enthalpy-driven.

19.22 (a) $\Delta H° = \Delta H_f°[Ca(OH)_2(aq)] - 2\ \Delta H_f°[H_2O(\ell)]$

$\Delta H° = 1$ mol $(-1002.82$ kJ/mol$) - 2$ mol $(-285.83$ kJ/mol$) = -431.16$ kJ

$\Delta S° = S°[Ca(OH)_2(aq)] + 2\ S°[H_2(g)] - \{S°[Ca(s)] + 2\ S°[H_2O(\ell)]\}$

$\Delta S° = 1$ mol $(-74.5$ J/K·mol$) + 2$ mol $(130.7$ J/K·mol$) - [1$ mol $(41.59$ J/K·mol$)$

$+ 2$ mol $(69.95$ J/K·mol$)]$

$\Delta S° = 5.41$ J/K

$\Delta G° = \Delta H° - T\Delta S° = -431.16$ kJ $- (298$ K$)(5.41$ J/K$)(1$ kJ$/10^3$ J$) = -432.8$ kJ

(b) $\Delta H° = \Delta H_f°[C_6H_6(\ell)] = 1$ mol $(49.03$ kJ/mol$) = 49.03$ kJ

$\Delta S° = S°[C_6H_6(\ell)] - \{6\ S°[C(graphite)] + 3\ S°[H_2(g)]\}$

$\Delta S° = 1$ mol $(173.26$ J/K·mol$) - [6$ mol $(5.6$ J/K·mol$) + 3$ mol $(130.7$ J/K·mol$)] = -252.4$ J/K

$\Delta G° = \Delta H° - T\Delta S° = 49.03$ kJ $- (298$ K$)(-252.4$ J/K$)(1$ kJ$/10^3$ J$) = 124.3$ kJ

Reaction (a) is product-favored and enthalpy-driven.

Reaction (b) is enthalpy-driven.

19.23 (a) $C(graphite) + 2\ S(s) \rightarrow CS_2(g)$

$\Delta H° = \Delta H_f°[CS_2(g)] = 1$ mol $(116.7$ kJ/mol$) = 116.7$ kJ

$\Delta S° = S°[CS_2(g)] - \{S°[C(graphite)] + 2\ S°[S(s)]\}$

$\Delta S° = 1$ mol $(237.8$ J/K·mol$) - [1$ mol $(5.6$ J/K·mol$) + 2$ mol $(32.1$ J/K·mol$)] = 168.0$ J/K

$\Delta G_f° = \Delta H° - T\Delta S° = 116.7$ kJ $- (298$ K$)(168.0$ J/K$)(1$ kJ$/10^3$ J$) = 66.6$ kJ

Appendix L value 66.61 kJ

(b) $Na(s) + \frac{1}{2} O_2(g) + \frac{1}{2} H_2(g) \rightarrow NaOH(s)$

$\Delta H° = \Delta H_f°[NaOH(s)] = 1 \text{ mol } (-425.93 \text{ kJ/mol}) = -425.93 \text{ kJ}$

$\Delta S° = S°[NaOH(s)] - \{S°[Na(s)] + \frac{1}{2} S°[O_2(g)] + \frac{1}{2} S°[H_2(g)]\}$

$\Delta S° = 1 \text{ mol } (64.46 \text{ J/K·mol}) - [1 \text{ mol } (51.21 \text{ J/K·mol}) + \frac{1}{2} \text{ mol } (205.087 \text{ J/K·mol})$

$+ \frac{1}{2} \text{ mol } (130.7 \text{ J/K·mol})]$

$\Delta S° = -154.6 \text{ J/K}$

$\Delta G_f° = \Delta H° - T\Delta S° = -425.93 \text{ kJ} - (298 \text{ K})(-154.6 \text{ J/K})(1 \text{ kJ}/10^3 \text{ J}) = -379.9 \text{ kJ}$

Appendix L value −379.75 kJ

(c) $\frac{1}{2} I_2(s) + \frac{1}{2} Cl_2(g) \rightarrow ICl(g)$

$\Delta H° = \Delta H_f°[ICl(g)] = 1 \text{ mol } (17.51 \text{ kJ/mol}) = 17.51 \text{ kJ}$

$\Delta S° = S°[ICl(g)] - \{\frac{1}{2} S°[I_2(s)] + \frac{1}{2} S°[Cl_2(g)]\}$

$\Delta S° = 1 \text{ mol } (247.56 \text{ J/K·mol}) - [\frac{1}{2} \text{ mol } (116.135 \text{ J/K·mol}) + \frac{1}{2} \text{ mol } (223.08 \text{ J/K·mol})] = 77.95 \text{ J/K}$

$\Delta G_f° = \Delta H° - T\Delta S° = 17.51 \text{ kJ} - (298 \text{ K})(77.95 \text{ J/K})(1 \text{ kJ}/10^3 \text{ J}) = -5.72 \text{ kJ}$

Appendix L value −5.73 kJ

Reactions (b) and (c) are product-favored.

19.24   (a) $Ca(s) + O_2(g) + H_2(g) \rightarrow Ca(OH)_2(s)$

$\Delta H° = \Delta H_f°[Ca(OH)_2(s)] = 1 \text{ mol } (-986.09 \text{ kJ/mol}) = -986.09 \text{ kJ}$

$\Delta S° = S°[Ca(OH)_2(s)] - \{S°[Ca(s)] + S°[O_2(g)] + S°[H_2(g)]\}$

$\Delta S° = 1 \text{ mol } (83.39 \text{ J/K·mol}) - [1 \text{ mol } (41.59 \text{ J/K·mol}) + 1 \text{ mol } (205.07 \text{ J/K·mol})$

$+ 1 \text{ mol } (130.7 \text{ J/K·mol})]$

$\Delta S° = -294.0 \text{ J/K}$

$\Delta G_f° = \Delta H° - T\Delta S° = -986.09 \text{ kJ} - (298 \text{ K})(-294.0 \text{ J/K})(1 \text{ kJ}/10^3 \text{ J}) = -898.5 \text{ kJ}$

Appendix L value −898.43 kJ

(b) $\frac{1}{2} Cl_2(g) \rightarrow Cl(g)$

$\Delta H° = \Delta H_f°[Cl(g)] = 1 \text{ mol } (121.3 \text{ kJ/mol}) = 121.3 \text{ kJ}$

$\Delta S° = S°[Cl(g)] - \frac{1}{2} S°[Cl_2(g)]$

$\Delta S° = 1 \text{ mol } (165.19 \text{ J/K·mol}) - \frac{1}{2} \text{ mol } (223.08 \text{ J/K·mol}) = 53.65 \text{ J/K}$

$\Delta G_f° = \Delta H° - T\Delta S° = 121.3 \text{ kJ} - (298 \text{ K})(53.65 \text{ J/K})(1 \text{ kJ}/10^3 \text{ J}) = 105.3 \text{ kJ}$

Appendix L value 105.3 kJ

(c) $2\ Na(s) + C(graphite) + {}^3/_2\ O_2(g) \rightarrow Na_2CO_3(s)$

$\Delta H° = \Delta H_f°[Na_2CO_3(s)] = 1\ mol\ (-1130.77\ kJ/mol) = -1130.77\ kJ$

$\Delta S° = S°[Na_2CO_3(s)] - \{2\ S°[Na(s)] + S°[C(graphite)] + {}^3/_2\ S°[O_2(g)]\}$

$\Delta S° = 1\ mol\ (134.79\ J/K\cdot mol) - [2\ mol\ (51.21\ J/K\cdot mol) + 1\ mol\ (5.6\ J/K\cdot mol)$

$+ {}^3/_2\ mol\ (205.07\ J/K\cdot mol)]$

$\Delta S° = -280.84\ J/K$

$\Delta G_f° = \Delta H° - T\Delta S° = -1130.77\ kJ - (298\ K)(-280.84\ J/K)(1\ kJ/10^3\ J) = -1047.08\ kJ$

Appendix L value $-1048.08\ kJ$

Reactions (a) and (c) are product-favored.

19.25 (a) $\Delta G°_{rxn} = 2\ \Delta G_f°[KCl(s)] = 2\ mol\ (-408.77\ kJ/mol) = -817.54\ kJ$

product-favored

(b) $\Delta G°_{rxn} = -(2\ \Delta G_f°[CuO(s)]) = -[2\ mol\ (-128.3\ kJ/mol)] = 256.6\ kJ$

reactant-favored

(c) $\Delta G°_{rxn} = 4\ \Delta G_f°[NO_2(g)] + 6\ \Delta G_f°[H_2O(g)] - 4\ \Delta G_f°[NH_3(g)]$

$\Delta G°_{rxn} = 4\ mol\ (51.23\ kJ/mol) + 6\ mol\ (-228.59\ kJ/mol) - 4\ mol\ (-16.37\ kJ/mol) = -1101.14\ kJ$

product-favored

19.26 (a) $\Delta G°_{rxn} = \Delta G_f°[SO_2(g)] - \Delta G_f°[HgS(s)]$

$\Delta G°_{rxn} = 1\ mol\ (-300.13\ kJ/mol) - 1\ mol\ (-50.6\ kJ/mol) = -249.5\ kJ$

product-favored

(b) $\Delta G°_{rxn} = 2\ \Delta G_f°[H_2O(g)] + 2\ \Delta G_f°[SO_2(g)] - 2\ \Delta G_f°[H_2S(g)]$

$\Delta G°_{rxn} = 2\ mol\ (-228.59\ kJ/mol) + 2\ mol\ (-300.13\ kJ/mol) - 2\ mol\ (-33.56\ kJ/mol) = -990.32\ kJ$

product-favored

(c) $\Delta G°_{rxn} = 2\ \Delta G_f°[MgCl_2(s)] - \Delta G_f°[SiCl_4(g)]$

$\Delta G°_{rxn} = 2\ mol\ (-592.09\ kJ/mol) - 1\ mol\ (-622.76\ kJ/mol) = -561.42\ kJ$

product favored

19.27 $\Delta G°_{rxn} = \Delta G_f°[BaO(s)] + \Delta G_f°[CO_2(g)] - \Delta G_f°[BaCO_3(s)]$

$219.7\ kJ = 1\ mol\ (-520.38\ kJ/mol) + 1\ mol\ (-394.359\ kJ/mol) - 1\ mol\ \Delta G_f°[BaCO_3(s)]$

$\Delta G_f°[BaCO_3(s)] = -1134.4\ kJ/mol$

19.28 $\Delta G°_{rxn} = \Delta G_f°[TiCl_4(\ell)] - \Delta G_f°[TiCl_2(s)]$

$-272.8\ kJ = 1\ mol\ (-737.2\ kJ/mol) - 1\ mol\ \Delta G_f°[TiCl_2(s)]$

$\Delta G_f°[TiCl_2(s)] = -464.4\ kJ/mol$

19.29   (a) $\Delta S° = 2 S°[NO_2(g)] - \{S°[N_2(g)] + 2 S°[O_2(g)]\}$

$\Delta S° = 2$ mol (240.04 J/K·mol) – [1 mol (191.56 J/K·mol) + 2 mol (205.07 J/K·mol)] = –121.62 J/K

Entropy-disfavored. Increasing the temperature will make the reaction more reactant-favored

(b) $\Delta S° = 2 S°[CO(g)] - \{2 S°[C(graphite)] + S°[O_2(g)]\}$

$\Delta S° = 2$ mol (197.674 J/K·mol) – [2 mol (5.6 J/K·mol) + 1 mol (205.07 J/K·mol)] = 179.1 J/K

Entropy-favored. Increasing the temperature will make the reaction more product-favored

(c) $\Delta S° = S°[CaCO_3(s)] - \{S°[CaO(s)] + S°[CO_2(g)]\}$

$\Delta S° = 1$ mol (91.7 J/K·mol) – [1 mol (38.2 J/K·mol) + 1 mol (213.74 J/K·mol)] = –160.2 J/K

Entropy-disfavored. Increasing the temperature will make the reaction more reactant-favored

(d) $\Delta S° = 2 S°[Na(s)] + S°[Cl_2(g)] - 2 S°[NaCl(s)]$

$\Delta S° = 2$ mol (51.21 J/K·mol) + 1 mol (223.08 J/K·mol) – 2 mol (72.11 J/K·mol) = 181.28 J/K

Entropy-favored. Increasing the temperature will make the reaction more product-favored

19.30   (a) $\Delta S° = 2 S°[I(g)] - S°[I_2(g)]$

$\Delta S° = 2$ mol (180.791 J/K·mol) – 1 mol (260.69 J/K·mol) = 100.89 J/K

Entropy-favored. Increasing the temperature will make the reaction more product-favored

(b) $\Delta S° = 2 S°[SO_3(g)] - \{2 S°[SO_2(g)] + S°[O_2(g)]\}$

$\Delta S° = 2$ mol (256.77 J/K·mol) – [2 mol (248.21 J/K·mol) + 1 mol (205.07 J/K·mol)] = –187.95 J/K

Entropy-disfavored. Increasing the temperature will make the reaction more reactant-favored

(c) $\Delta S° = S°[SiO_2(s)] + 4 S°[HCl(g)] - \{S°[SiCl_4(g)] + 2 S°[H_2O(\ell)]\}$

$\Delta S° = 1$ mol (41.46 J/K·mol) + 4 mol (186.2 J/K·mol) – [1 mol (330.86 J/K·mol)

+ 2 mol (69.95 J/K·mol)]

$\Delta S° = 315.5$ J/K

Entropy-favored. Increasing the temperature will make the reaction more product-favored

(d) $\Delta S° = 4 S°[PH_3(g)] - \{S°[P_4(s, white)] + 6 S°[H_2(g)]\}$

$\Delta S° = 4$ mol (210.24 J/K·mol) – [1 mol (41.1 J/K·mol) + 6 mol (130.7 J/K·mol)] = 15.7 J/K

Entropy-favored. Increasing the temperature will make the reaction more product-favored

19.31 $HgS(s) \rightarrow Hg(\ell) + S(g)$

$\Delta H° = \Delta H_f°[S(g)] - \Delta H_f°[HgS(s)] = 1$ mol (278.98 kJ/mol) – 1 mol (–58.2 kJ/mol) = 337.2 kJ

$\Delta S° = S°[Hg(\ell)] + S°[S(g)] - S°[HgS(s)]$

$\Delta S° = 1$ mol (76.02 J/K·mol) + 1 mol (167.83 J/K·mol) – 1 mol (82.4 J/K·mol) = 161.5 J/K

$\Delta G° = 0 = \Delta H° - T\Delta S° = 337.2$ kJ – T(161.5 J/K)(1 kJ/10^3 J)

$T = 2088$ K or greater

19.32 $CaSO_4(s) \rightarrow CaO(s) + SO_3(g)$

$\Delta H^\circ = \Delta H_f^\circ[CaO(s)] + \Delta H_f^\circ[SO_3(g)] - \Delta H_f^\circ[CaSO_4(s)]$

$\Delta H^\circ = 1$ mol $(-635.09$ kJ/mol$) + 1$ mol $(-395.77$ kJ/mol$) - 1$ mol $(-1434.52$ kJ/mol$) = 403.66$ kJ

$\Delta S^\circ = S^\circ[CaO(s)] + S^\circ[SO_3(g)] - S^\circ[CaSO_4(s)]$

$\Delta S^\circ = 1$ mol $(38.2$ J/K·mol$) + 1$ mol $(256.77$ J/K·mol$) - 1$ mol $(106.5$ J/K·mol$) = 188.5$ J/K

$\Delta G^\circ = 0 = \Delta H^\circ - T\Delta S^\circ = 403.66$ kJ $- T(188.5$ J/K$)(1$ kJ/10^3 J$)$

$T = 2141$ K or greater

19.33 $\Delta G^\circ = -RT \ln K_p$

86.58 kJ/mol $= -(8.3145 \times 10^{-3}$ kJ/K·mol$)(298$ K$) \ln K_p$

$\ln K_p = -34.94$

$K_p = 6.7 \times 10^{-16}$

The large, positive ΔG° value results in a K_p value much less than 1

19.34 $\Delta G^\circ = -RT \ln K_p$

163.2 kJ/mol $= -(8.3145 \times 10^{-3}$ kJ/K·mol$)(298$ K$) \ln K_p$

$\ln K_p = -65.87$

$K_p = 2.5 \times 10^{-29}$

The large, positive ΔG° value results in a K_p value much less than 1

19.35 $\Delta G^\circ = \Delta G_f^\circ[C_2H_6(g)] - \Delta G_f^\circ[C_2H_4(g)]$

$\Delta G^\circ = 1$ mol $(-31.89$ kJ/mol$) - 1$ mol $(68.35$ kJ/mol$) = -100.24$ kJ

$\Delta G^\circ = -RT \ln K_p$

-100.24 kJ/mol $= -(8.3145 \times 10^{-3}$ kJ/K·mol$)(298$ K$) \ln K_p$

$\ln K_p = 40.46$

$K_p = 3.7 \times 10^{17}$

Both the negative ΔG° value and the large K value indicate a product-favored reaction

19.36 $\Delta G^\circ = 2 \Delta G_f^\circ[HCl(g)] - 2 \Delta G_f^\circ[HBr(g)]$

$\Delta G^\circ = 2$ mol $(-95.09$ kJ/mol$) - 2$ mol $(-53.45$ kJ/mol$) = -83.28$ kJ

$\Delta G^\circ = -RT \ln K_p$

-83.28 kJ/mol $= -(8.3145 \times 10^{-3}$ kJ/K·mol$)(298$ K$) \ln K_p$

$\ln K_p = 33.61$

$K_p = 4.0 \times 10^{14}$

Both the negative ΔG° value and the large K value indicate a product-favored reaction

19.37 $\Delta S°(1) = S°[CH_4(g)] - \{S°[C(graphite)] + 2\ S°[H_2(g)]\}$

$\Delta S°(1) = 1\ mol\ (186.26\ J/K \cdot mol) - [1\ mol\ (5.6\ J/K \cdot mol) + 2\ mol\ (130.7\ J/K \cdot mol)]$

$\Delta S°(1) = -80.74\ J/K$

$\Delta S°(2) = S°[CH_3OH(\ell)] - \{S°[CH_4(g)] + {}^1/_2\ S°[O_2(g)]\}$

$\Delta S°(2) = 1\ mol\ (127.19\ J/K \cdot mol) - [1\ mol\ (186.26\ J/K \cdot mol) + {}^1/_2\ mol\ (205.07\ J/K \cdot mol)]$

$\Delta S°(2) = -161.61\ J/K$

$\Delta S°(3) = S°[CH_3OH(\ell) - \{S°[C(graphite)] + 2\ S°[H_2(g)] + {}^1/_2\ S°[O_2(g)]\}$

$\Delta S°(3) = 1\ mol\ (127.19\ J/K \cdot mol) - [1\ mol\ (5.6\ J/K \cdot mol) + 2\ mol\ (130.7\ J/K \cdot mol)$

$+ {}^1/_2\ mol\ (205.07\ J/K \cdot mol)]$

$\Delta S°(3) = -242.35\ J/K$

$\Delta S°(3) = \Delta S°(1) + \Delta S°(2)$ Entropy is a state function

19.38 $\Delta H° = \Delta H_f°[C_8H_{18}(g)] - \Delta H_f°[C_8H_{16}(g)] = 1\ mol\ (-208.45\ kJ/mol) - 1\ mol\ (-82.93\ kJ/mol) = -125.52\ kJ$

$\Delta S° = S°[C_8H_{18}(g)] - \{S°[C_8H_{16}(g)] + S°[H_2(g)]\}$

$\Delta S° = 1\ mol\ (463.639\ J/K \cdot mol) - [1\ mol\ (462.8\ J/K \cdot mol) + 1\ mol\ (130.7\ J/K \cdot mol)] = -129.9\ J/K$

$\Delta G° = \Delta H° - T\Delta S° = -125.52\ kJ - (298\ K)(-129.9\ J/K)(1\ kJ/10^3\ J) = -86.81\ kJ$

The reaction is product-favored under standard conditions

19.39 $\Delta H° = 2\ \Delta H_f°[CO_2(g)] + 3\ \Delta H_f°[H_2O(g)] - \Delta H_f°[C_2H_6(g)]$

$\Delta H° = 2\ mol\ (-393.509\ kJ/mol) + 3\ mol\ (-241.83\ kJ/mol) - 1\ mol\ (-83.85\ kJ/mol) = -1428.66\ kJ$

$\Delta S°_{sys} = 2\ S°[CO_2(g)] + 3\ S°[H_2O(g)] - \{S°[C_2H_6(g)] + {}^7/_2\ S°[O_2(g)]\}$

$\Delta S°_{sys} = 2\ mol\ (213.74\ J/K \cdot mol) + 3\ mol\ (188.84\ J/K \cdot mol) - [1\ mol\ (229.2\ J/K \cdot mol)$

$+ {}^7/_2\ mol\ (205.07\ J/K \cdot mol)]$

$\Delta S°_{sys} = 47.1\ J/K$

$\Delta S°_{univ} = \Delta S°_{sys} + \Delta S°_{surr} = 47.1\ J/K + [-(-1428.66\ kJ)(10^3\ J/1\ kJ)/298\ K] = 4840\ J/K$

The reaction is spontaneous

19.40 $2\ Fe(s) + {}^3/_2\ O_2(g) \rightarrow Fe_2O_3(s)$

from Appendix L, $\Delta G_f°[Fe_2O_3(s)] = -742.2\ kJ/mol$

$454\ g\ Fe_2O_3 \cdot \dfrac{1\ mol\ Fe_2O_3}{159.7\ g} \cdot \dfrac{-742.2\ kJ}{1\ mol\ Fe_2O_3} = -2110\ kJ$

19.41   (a)   The reaction occurs spontaneously and is product-favored. Therefore $\Delta S^\circ_{univ} > 0$ and $\Delta G^\circ_{rxn} < 0$. The

reaction is likely to be exothermic, so $\Delta H^\circ_{rxn} < 0$ and $\Delta S^\circ_{surr} > 0$. $\Delta S^\circ_{sys} < 0$ because two moles of gas

form one mole of solid.

$\Delta S^\circ_{sys} = S^\circ[NH_4Cl(s)] - \{S^\circ[HCl(g)] + S^\circ[NH_3(g)]\}$

$\Delta S^\circ_{sys} = 1 \text{ mol } (94.85 \text{ J/K·mol}) - [1 \text{ mol } (186.2 \text{ J/K·mol}) + 1 \text{ mol } (192.77 \text{ J/K·mol})] = -284.1 \text{ J/K}$

$\Delta H^\circ = \Delta H_f^\circ[NH_4Cl(s)] - \{\Delta H_f^\circ[HCl(g)] + \Delta H_f^\circ[NH_3(g)]\}$

$\Delta H^\circ = 1 \text{ mol } (-314.55 \text{ kJ/mol}) - [1 \text{ mol } (-92.31 \text{ kJ/mol}) + 1 \text{ mol } (-45.90 \text{ kJ/mol})] = -176.34 \text{ kJ}$

$\Delta S^\circ_{surr} = -\Delta H^\circ/T = -[(-176.34 \text{ kJ})(10^3 \text{ J/1 kJ})/298 \text{ K}] = 591.7 \text{ J/K}$

$\Delta S_{univ} = \Delta S^\circ_{sys} + \Delta S^\circ_{surr} = -284.1 \text{ J/K} + 591.7 \text{ J/K} = 307.6 \text{ J/K}$

$\Delta G^\circ = \Delta H^\circ - T\Delta S^\circ = -176.34 \text{ kJ} - (298 \text{ K})(-284.1 \text{ J/K})(1 \text{ kJ}/10^3 \text{ J}) = -91.68 \text{ kJ}$

(b) $\Delta G^\circ = -RT \ln K_p$

$-91.68 \text{ kJ/mol} = -(8.3145 \times 10^{-3} \text{ kJ/K·mol})(298 \text{ K}) \ln K_p$

$\ln K_p = 37.00$

$K_p = 1.2 \times 10^{16}$

19.42   (a) $\Delta S^\circ_{sys} = S^\circ[NaCl(aq)] - S^\circ[NaCl(s)]$

$\Delta S^\circ_{sys} = 1 \text{ mol } (115.5 \text{ J/K·mol}) - 1 \text{ mol } (72.11 \text{ J/K·mol}) = 43.4 \text{ J/K}$

$\Delta H^\circ = \Delta H_f^\circ[NaCl(aq)] - \Delta H_f^\circ[NaCl(s)]$

$\Delta H^\circ = 1 \text{ mol } (-407.27 \text{ kJ/mol}) - 1 \text{ mol } (-411.12 \text{ kJ/mol}) = 3.85 \text{ kJ}$

$\Delta S^\circ_{surr} = -\Delta H^\circ/T = -[(3.85 \text{ kJ})(10^3 \text{ J/1 kJ})/298 \text{ K}] = -12.9 \text{ J/K}$

$\Delta S_{univ} = \Delta S^\circ_{sys} + \Delta S^\circ_{surr} = 43.4 \text{ J/K} + (-12.9 \text{ J/K}) = 30.5 \text{ J/K}$

(b) $\Delta S^\circ_{sys} = S^\circ[NaOH(aq)] - S^\circ[NaOH(s)]$

$\Delta S^\circ_{sys} = 1 \text{ mol } (48.1 \text{ J/K·mol}) - 1 \text{ mol } (64.46 \text{ J/K·mol}) = -16.4 \text{ J/K}$

$\Delta H^\circ = \Delta H_f^\circ[NaOH(aq)] - \Delta H_f^\circ[NaOH(s)]$

$\Delta H^\circ = 1 \text{ mol } (-469.15 \text{ kJ/mol}) - 1 \text{ mol } (-425.93 \text{ kJ/mol}) = -43.22 \text{ kJ}$

$\Delta S^\circ_{surr} = -\Delta H^\circ/T = -[(-43.22 \text{ kJ})(10^3 \text{ J/1 kJ})/298 \text{ K}] = 145.0 \text{ J/K}$

$\Delta S_{univ} = \Delta S^\circ_{sys} + \Delta S^\circ_{surr} = -16.4 \text{ J/K} + 145.0 \text{ J/K} = 128.6 \text{ J/K}$

Both systems are product-favored, but the NaCl system is entropy-driven while the NaOH system is

enthalpy-driven.

19.43 $\Delta G° = \Delta G_f°[CH_3OH(\ell)] = -166.27$ kJ

-166.27 kJ $= -RT \ln K_p = -(8.3145 \times 10^{-3}$ kJ/K·mol$)(298$ K$) \ln K_p$

$\ln K_p = 67.1$

$K_p = 1.3 \times 10^{29}$

The large, negative $\Delta G°$ value results in a K_p value much greater than 1. The reaction has a negative $\Delta S°$ value (-242.3 J/K) so a higher temperature would make the reaction less product-favored but a lower temperature would make the reaction more product-favored, increasing K_p.

19.44   (a) $(C_2H_5)_2O(\ell) \rightleftharpoons (C_2H_5)_2O(g)$ At equilibrium, $\Delta G° = 0$

$$\Delta S° = \frac{\Delta H°_{vap}}{T} = \frac{26.0 \times 10^3 \text{ J/mol}}{308.2 \text{ K}} = 84.4 \text{ J/K} \cdot \text{mol}$$

(b) $(C_2H_5)_2O(g) \rightleftharpoons (C_2H_5)_2O(\ell)$ $\Delta S° = -84.4$ J/K·mol

19.45 $C_2H_5OH(\ell) \rightleftharpoons C_2H_5OH(g)$ At equilibrium, $\Delta G° = 0$

$$\Delta S° = \frac{\Delta H°_{vap}}{T} = \frac{39.3 \times 10^3 \text{ J/mol}}{351.2 \text{ K}} = 112 \text{ J/K} \cdot \text{mol}$$

19.46 $\Delta S° = S°[CH_4(g)] + S°[H_2O(g)] - \{3\ S°[H_2(g)] + S°[CO(g)]\}$

$\Delta S° = 1$ mol $(186.26$ J/K·mol$) + 1$ mol $(188.84$ J/K·mol$) - [3$ mol $(130.7$ J/K·mol$)$

$+ 1$ mol $(197.674$ J/K·mol$)]$

$\Delta S° = -214.7$ J/K

$\Delta H° = \Delta H_f°[CH_4(g)] + \Delta H_f°[H_2O(g)] - \Delta H_f°[CO(g)]$

$\Delta H° = 1$ mol $(-74.87$ kJ/mol$) + 1$ mol $(-241.83$ kJ/mol$) - 1$ mol $(-110.525$ kJ/mol$) = -206.18$ kJ

$\Delta G° = \Delta H° - T\Delta H° = -206.18$ kJ $- (298$ K$)(-214.7$ J/K$)(1$ kJ/10^3 J$) = -142.2$ kJ

The reaction is predicted to be product-favored.

19.47 $C_2H_5OH(\ell) \rightleftharpoons C_2H_5OH(g)$

$\Delta S° = S°[C_2H_5OH(g)] - S°[C_2H_5OH(\ell)] = 1$ mol $(282.70$ J/K·mol$) - 1$ mol $(160.7$ J/K·mol$) = 122.0$ J/K

$\Delta H° = \Delta H_f°[C_2H_5OH(g)] - \Delta H_f°[C_2H_5OH(\ell)] = 1$ mol $(-235.3$ kJ/mol$) - 1$ mol $(-277.0$ J/K·mol$)$

$\Delta H° = 41.7$ kJ

At equilibrium, $\Delta G° = 0$ and $\Delta S° = \dfrac{\Delta H°}{T}$

$$T = \frac{\Delta H°}{\Delta S°} = \frac{41.7 \times 10^3 \text{ J/mol}}{122.0 \text{ J/K} \cdot \text{mol}} = 342 \text{ K} = 69 \text{ °C}$$

The calculated value is somewhat lower than the actual value (78 °C).

19.48   At the normal boiling point of ethanol, 78 °C, the vapor pressure of ethanol is 1.0 atm. From Study

Question 19.45, ΔH_{vap} = 39.3 kJ/mol

$$\ln\left(\frac{P_2}{P_1}\right) = \frac{\Delta H_{vap}}{R}\left(\frac{1}{T_1} - \frac{1}{T_2}\right)$$

$$\ln\left(\frac{P_2}{760 \text{ mm Hg}}\right) = \frac{39.3 \text{ kJ/mol}}{0.0083145 \text{ kJ/K} \cdot \text{mol}}\left(\frac{1}{351 \text{ K}} - \frac{1}{310. \text{ K}}\right)$$

P_2 = 128 mm Hg

19.49 $\Delta S°$ for this reaction is positive (+137.2 J/K, one mole of gaseous reactant forms two moles of gaseous

products). This means that raising the temperature will increase the product-favorability of the reaction

(because $T\Delta S°$ will become more negative).

19.50   At 897 °C the system is at equilibrium

$\Delta G° = -RT \ln K_p = -RT \ln (1.00) = 0$

Assuming $\Delta H°$ values are relatively constant as the temperature changes,

$$\Delta S° = \frac{\Delta H°}{T} = \frac{179.1 \times 10^3 \text{ J/mol}}{1170 \text{ K}} = 153.1 \text{ J/K} \cdot \text{mol}$$

19.51   (a) The reaction is endothermic and reactant-favored. Therefore, $\Delta H° > 0$, $\Delta S°_{surr} < 0$, $\Delta S°_{univ} < 0$, and

$\Delta G > 0$. $\Delta S°_{sys} > 0$ because one mol of gas and two mol of liquid are produced from two mol solid

$\Delta S°_{sys} = 2 \ S°[Hg(\ell)] + S°[O_2(g)] - 2 \ S°[HgO(s)]$

$\Delta S°_{sys} = 2 \text{ mol } (76.02 \text{ J/K·mol}) + 1 \text{ mol } (205.07 \text{ J/K·mol}) - 2 \text{ mol } (70.29 \text{ J/K·mol}) = 216.53 \text{ J/K}$

$\Delta H° = -(2 \ \Delta H_f°[HgO(s)]) = -[2 \text{ mol } (-90.83 \text{ kJ/mol})] = 181.66 \text{ kJ}$

$\Delta S°_{surr} = -\Delta H°/T = -[(181.66 \text{ kJ})(10^3 \text{ J/1 kJ})/298 \text{ K}] = -609.6 \text{ J/K}$

$\Delta S_{univ} = \Delta S°_{sys} + \Delta S°_{surr} = 216.53 \text{ J/K} + (-609.6 \text{ J/K}) = -393.1 \text{ J/K}$

$\Delta G° = \Delta H° - T\Delta S° = 181.66 \text{ kJ} - (298 \text{ K})(216.53 \text{ J/K})(1 \text{ kJ}/10^3 \text{ J}) = 117 \text{ kJ}$

(b) $\Delta G° = -RT \ln K_p$

$117 \text{ kJ/mol} = -(8.3145 \times 10^{-3} \text{ kJ/K·mol})(298 \text{ K}) \ln K_p$

$\ln K_p = -47.22$

$K_p = 3.1 \times 10^{-21}$

The reaction is reactant-favored

19.52 $H_2O(\ell) \rightleftharpoons H_2O(g)$

$\Delta H° = \Delta H_f°[H_2O(g)] - \Delta H_f°[H_2O(\ell)] = 1 \text{ mol } (-241.83 \text{ kJ/mol}) - 1 \text{ mol } (-285.83 \text{ kJ/mol}) = 44.00 \text{ kJ}$

$$\ln\left(\frac{P_2}{P_1}\right) = \frac{\Delta H_{vap}}{R}\left(\frac{1}{T_1} - \frac{1}{T_2}\right)$$

$$\ln\left(\frac{630 \text{ mm Hg}}{760 \text{ mm Hg}}\right) = \frac{44.00 \text{ kJ/mol}}{0.0083145 \text{ kJ/K} \cdot \text{mol}}\left(\frac{1}{373 \text{ K}} - \frac{1}{T_2}\right)$$

T_2 = 368 K = 95 °C

19.53 ΔH° is negative (exothermic) and ΔS° is positive (solid and liquid converted to aqueous solution and gas)

$\Delta H^\circ = \Delta H_f^\circ[\text{NaOH(aq)}] - \Delta H_f^\circ[\text{H}_2\text{O}(\ell)] = 1 \text{ mol } (-469.15 \text{ kJ/mol}) - 1 \text{ mol } (-285.83 \text{ kJ/mol}) = -183.32 \text{ kJ}$

$\Delta S^\circ = S^\circ[\text{NaOH(aq)}] + {}^1\!/_2 \, S^\circ[\text{H}_2(\text{g})] - \{S^\circ[\text{Na(s)}] + S^\circ[\text{H}_2\text{O}(\ell)]\}$

$\Delta S^\circ = 1 \text{ mol } (48.1 \text{ J/K·mol}) + {}^1\!/_2 \text{ mol } (130.7 \text{ J/K·mol}) - [1 \text{ mol } (51.21 \text{ J/K·mol}) + 1 \text{ mol } (69.95 \text{ J/K·mol})]$

$\Delta S^\circ = -7.7 \text{ J/K}$

The entropy change is slightly negative, not positive as predicted. The reason for this is the negative entropy change for dissolving NaOH.

19.54 $\Delta H^\circ = 2 \, \Delta H_f^\circ[\text{C}_2\text{H}_5\text{OH}(\ell)] + 2 \, \Delta H_f^\circ[\text{CO}_2(\text{g})] - \Delta H_f^\circ[\text{C}_6\text{H}_{12}\text{O}_6(\text{aq})]$

$\Delta H^\circ = 2 \text{ mol } (-277.0 \text{ kJ/mol}) + 2 \text{ mol } (-393.509 \text{ kJ/mol}) - 1 \text{ mol } (-1260.0 \text{ kJ/mol}) = -81.2 \text{ kJ}$

$\Delta S^\circ = 2 \, S^\circ[\text{C}_2\text{H}_5\text{OH}(\ell)] + 2 \, S^\circ[\text{CO}_2(\text{g})] - S^\circ[\text{C}_6\text{H}_{12}\text{O}_6(\text{aq})]$

$\Delta S^\circ = 2 \text{ mol } (160.7 \text{ J/K·mol}) + 2 \text{ mol } (213.74 \text{ J/K·mol}) - 1 \text{ mol } (289 \text{ J/K·mol}) = 460. \text{ J/K}$

$\Delta G^\circ = \Delta H^\circ - T\Delta S^\circ = -81.2 \text{ kJ} - (298 \text{ K})(460. \text{ J/K})(1 \text{ kJ}/10^3 \text{ J}) = -218.1 \text{ kJ}$

The reaction is product-favored.

19.55 $\Delta H^\circ = 3 \, \Delta H_f^\circ[\text{HCl(g)}] - \Delta H_f^\circ[\text{BCl}_3(\text{g})] = 3 \text{ mol } (-92.31 \text{ kJ/mol}) - 1 \text{ mol } (-402.96 \text{ kJ/mol}) = 126.03 \text{ kJ}$

$\Delta S^\circ = S^\circ[\text{B(s)}] + 3 \, S^\circ[\text{HCl(g)}] - \{S^\circ[\text{BCl}_3(\text{g})] + {}^3\!/_2 \, S^\circ[\text{H}_2(\text{g})]\}$

$\Delta S^\circ = 1 \text{ mol } (5.86 \text{ J/K·mol}) + 3 \text{ mol } (186.2 \text{ J/K·mol}) - [1 \text{ mol } (290.17 \text{ J/K·mol})$

$+ {}^3\!/_2 \text{ mol } (130.7 \text{ J/K·mol})]$

$\Delta S^\circ = 78.2 \text{ J/K}$

$\Delta G^\circ = \Delta H^\circ - T\Delta S^\circ = 126.03 \text{ kJ} - (298 \text{ K})(78.2 \text{ J/K})(1 \text{ kJ}/10^3 \text{ J}) = 103 \text{ kJ}$

The reaction is not predicted to be product-favored under standard conditions.

19.56 $\Delta G^\circ = -RT \ln K_p = -(8.3145 \times 10^{-3} \text{ kJ/K·mol})(298 \text{ K}) \ln(0.14) = 4.87 \text{ kJ/mol}$

$\Delta G^\circ = 2 \, \Delta G_f^\circ[\text{NO}_2(\text{g})] - \Delta G_f^\circ[\text{N}_2\text{O}_4(\text{g})] = 2 \text{ mol } (51.23 \text{ kJ/mol}) - 1 \text{ mol } (97.73 \text{ kJ/mol}) = 4.73 \text{ kJ}$

19.57 $\Delta G^\circ_{\text{rxn}} = -RT \ln K = -(8.3145 \times 10^{-3} \text{ kJ/K·mol})(973 \text{ K}) \ln(0.422) = 6.98 \text{ kJ/mol}$

19.58 $\Delta G^\circ_{\text{rxn}} = -RT \ln K = -(8.3145 \times 10^{-3} \text{ kJ/K·mol})(298 \text{ K}) \ln(2.5) = -2.27 \text{ kJ/mol}$

19.59 $\Delta G^\circ = \Delta H^\circ - T\Delta S^\circ = -206.7 \text{ kJ} - (298 \text{ K})(-361.5 \text{ J/K})(1 \text{ kJ}/10^3 \text{ J}) = -99.0 \text{ kJ}$

The reaction is spontaneous under standard conditions and is enthalpy-driven.

19.60   (a) $\Delta G^\circ_{\text{rxn}} = \Delta G_f^\circ[\text{CO(g)}] - \Delta G_f^\circ[\text{H}_2\text{O(g)}] = 1 \text{ mol } (-137.168 \text{ kJ/mol}) - 1 \text{ mol } (-228.59 \text{ kJ/mol})$

$\Delta G^\circ_{\text{rxn}} = 91.42 \text{ kJ}$

(b) $91.4 \text{ kJ} = -RT \ln K_p = -(8.3145 \times 10^{-3} \text{ kJ/K·mol})(298 \text{ K}) \ln K_p$

$\ln K_p = -36.9$

$K_p = 9.5 \times 10^{-17}$

(c) The reaction is not spontaneous at 25 °C

$\Delta H^\circ_{rxn} = \Delta H_f^\circ[CO(g)] - \Delta H_f^\circ[H_2O(g)] = 1\ mol\ (-110.525\ kJ/mol) - 1\ mol\ (-241.83\ kJ/mol)$

$\Delta H^\circ_{rxn} = 131.31\ kJ$

$\Delta S^\circ_{rxn} = S^\circ[CO(g)] + S^\circ[H_2(g)] - \{S^\circ[C(s)] + S^\circ[H_2O(g)]\}$

$\Delta S^\circ = 1\ mol\ (197.674\ J/K \cdot mol) + 1\ mol\ (130.7\ J/K \cdot mol) - [1\ mol\ (5.6\ J/K \cdot mol)$

$+ 1\ mol\ (188.84\ J/K \cdot mol)]$

$\Delta S^\circ = 133.9\ J/K$

$T = \dfrac{\Delta H^\circ}{\Delta S^\circ} = \dfrac{131.31 \times 10^3\ J/mol}{133.9\ J/K} = 980.4\ K = 707.3\ °C$

19.61 $\Delta G^\circ_{rxn} = 2\ \Delta G_f^\circ[SO_2(g)] - 2\ \Delta G_f^\circ[SO_3(g)] = 2\ mol\ (-300.13\ kJ/mol) - 2\ mol\ (-371.04\ kJ/mol) = 141.82\ kJ$

(a) The reaction is not spontaneous under standard conditions.

(b) $\Delta H^\circ_{rxn} = 2\ \Delta H_f^\circ[SO_2(g)] - 2\ \Delta H_f^\circ[SO_3(g)] = 2\ mol\ (-296.84\ kJ/mol) - 2\ mol\ (-395.77\ kJ/mol)$

$\Delta H^\circ_{rxn} = 197.86\ kJ$

$\Delta S^\circ = 2\ S^\circ[SO_2(g)] + S^\circ[O_2(g)] - 2\ S^\circ[SO_3(g)]$

$\Delta S^\circ = 2\ mol\ (248.21\ J/K \cdot mol) + 1\ mol\ (205.07\ J/K \cdot mol) - 2\ mol\ (256.77\ J/K \cdot mol) = 187.95\ J/K$

$T = \dfrac{\Delta H^\circ}{\Delta S^\circ} = \dfrac{197.86 \times 10^3\ J/mol}{187.95\ J/K} = 1052.7\ K = 779.6\ °C$

(c) $\Delta G^\circ_{rxn} = \Delta H^\circ_{rxn} - T\Delta S^\circ_{rxn} = 197.86\ kJ - (1773\ K)(187.95\ J/K)(1\ kJ/10^3\ J) = -135\ kJ$

$-135\ kJ = -RT \ln K = -(8.3145 \times 10^{-3}\ kJ/K \cdot mol)(1773\ K) \ln K$

$\ln K = 9.2$

$K = 1 \times 10^4$

19.62   (a) $\Delta S^\circ = S^\circ[CH_4(g)] + \frac{1}{2}\ S^\circ[O_2(g)] - S^\circ[CH_3OH(\ell)]$

$\Delta S^\circ = 1\ mol\ (186.26\ J/K \cdot mol) + \frac{1}{2}\ mol\ (205.07\ J/K \cdot mol) - 1\ mol\ (127.19\ J/K \cdot mol) = 161.61\ J/K$

The sign of ΔS° agrees with the predicted sign because a liquid is being converted to two gases.

(b) $\Delta H^\circ = \Delta H_f^\circ[CH_4(g)] - \Delta H_f^\circ[CH_3OH(\ell)] = 1\ mol\ (-74.87\ kJ/mol) - 1\ mol\ (-238.4\ kJ/mol) = 163.5\ kJ$

$\Delta G^\circ = \Delta H^\circ - T\Delta S^\circ = 163.5\ kJ - (298\ K)(161.61\ J/K)(1\ kJ/10^3\ J) = 115.3\ kJ$

The reaction is not spontaneous at 25 °C

(c) $T = \dfrac{\Delta H^\circ}{\Delta S^\circ} = \dfrac{163.5 \times 10^3\ J/mol}{161.61\ J/K} = 1012\ K = 739\ °C$

19.63 $\Delta H^\circ = \Delta H_f^\circ[H_2SO_4(\ell)] - \Delta H_f^\circ[H_2S(g)] = 1\ mol\ (-814\ kJ/mol) - 1\ mol\ (-20.63\ kJ/mol) = -793\ kJ$

$\Delta S^\circ = S^\circ[H_2SO_4(\ell)] - \{S^\circ[H_2S(g)] + 2\ S^\circ[O_2(g)]\}$

$\Delta S^\circ = 1\ mol\ (156.9\ J/K \cdot mol) - [1\ mol\ (205.79\ J/K \cdot mol) + 2\ mol\ (205.07\ J/K \cdot mol)] = -459.0\ J/K$

$\Delta G^\circ = \Delta H^\circ - T\Delta S^\circ = -793\ kJ - (298\ K)(-459.0\ J/K)(1\ kJ/10^3\ J) = -657\ kJ$

The reaction is spontaneous and enthalpy-driven.

19.64 $CaCO_3(s) + SO_2(g) + {}^1/_2 H_2O(\ell) \rightarrow CaSO_3 \cdot {}^1/_2 H_2O(s) + CO_2(g)$

$\Delta H^{\circ} = \Delta H_f^{\circ}[CaSO_3 \cdot {}^1/_2 H_2O(s)] + \Delta H_f^{\circ}[CO_2(g)] - \{\Delta H_f^{\circ}[CaCO_3(s)] + \Delta H_f^{\circ}[SO_2(g)] + {}^1/_2 \Delta H_f^{\circ}[H_2O(\ell)]\}$

$\Delta H^{\circ} = 1 \text{ mol } (-1311.7 \text{ kJ/mol}) + 1 \text{ mol } (-393.509 \text{ kJ/mol})$

$$- [1 \text{ mol } (-1207.6 \text{ kJ/mol}) + 1 \text{ mol } (-296.84 \text{ kJ/mol}) + {}^1/_2 \text{ mol } (-285.83 \text{ kJ/mol})]$$

$\Delta H^{\circ} = -57.9 \text{ kJ}$

$\Delta S^{\circ} = S^{\circ}[CaSO_3 \cdot {}^1/_2 H_2O(s)] + S^{\circ}[CO_2(g)] - \{S^{\circ}[CaCO_3(s)] + S^{\circ}[SO_2(g)] + {}^1/_2 S^{\circ}[H_2O(\ell)]\}$

$\Delta S^{\circ} = 1 \text{ mol } (121.3 \text{ J/K·mol}) + 1 \text{ mol } (213.74 \text{ J/K·mol})$

$$- [1 \text{ mol } (91.7 \text{ J/K·mol}) + 1 \text{ mol } (248.21 \text{ J/K·mol}) + {}^1/_2 \text{ mol } (69.95 \text{ J/K·mol})]$$

$\Delta S^{\circ} = -39.8 \text{ J/K}$

$\Delta G^{\circ} = \Delta H^{\circ} - T\Delta S^{\circ} = -57.9 \text{ kJ} - (298 \text{ K})(-39.8 \text{ J/K})(1 \text{ kJ}/10^3 \text{ J}) = -46.0 \text{ kJ}$

$CaCO_3(s) + SO_2(g) + {}^1/_2 H_2O(\ell) + {}^1/_2 O_2(g) \rightarrow CaSO_4 \cdot {}^1/_2 H_2O(s) + CO_2(g)$

$\Delta H^{\circ} = \Delta H_f^{\circ}[CaSO_4 \cdot {}^1/_2 H_2O(s)] + \Delta H_f^{\circ}[CO_2(g)] - \{\Delta H_f^{\circ}[CaCO_3(s)] + \Delta H_f^{\circ}[SO_2(g)] + {}^1/_2 \Delta H_f^{\circ}[H_2O(\ell)]\}$

$\Delta H^{\circ} = 1 \text{ mol } (-1574.65 \text{ kJ/mol}) + 1 \text{ mol } (-393.509 \text{ kJ/mol})$

$$- [1 \text{ mol } (-1207.6 \text{ kJ/mol}) + 1 \text{ mol } (-296.84 \text{ kJ/mol}) + {}^1/_2 \text{ mol } (-285.83 \text{ kJ/mol})]$$

$\Delta H^{\circ} = -320.8 \text{ kJ}$

$\Delta S^{\circ} = S^{\circ}[CaSO_4 \cdot {}^1/_2 H_2O(s)] + S^{\circ}[CO_2(g)] - \{S^{\circ}[CaCO_3(s)] + S^{\circ}[SO_2(g)] + {}^1/_2 S^{\circ}[H_2O(\ell)] + {}^1/_2 S^{\circ}[O_2(g)]\}$

$\Delta S^{\circ} = 1 \text{ mol } (134.8 \text{ J/K·mol}) + 1 \text{ mol } (213.74 \text{ J/K·mol}) - [1 \text{ mol } (91.7 \text{ J/K·mol})$

$$+ 1 \text{ mol } (248.21 \text{ J/K·mol}) + {}^1/_2 \text{ mol } (69.95 \text{ J/K·mol}) + {}^1/_2 \text{ mol } (205.07 \text{ J/K·mol})]$$

$\Delta S^{\circ} = -128.9 \text{ J/K}$

$\Delta G^{\circ} = \Delta H^{\circ} - T\Delta S^{\circ} = -320.8 \text{ kJ} - (298 \text{ K})(-128.9 \text{ J/K})(1 \text{ kJ}/10^3 \text{ J}) = -282.4 \text{ kJ}$

The second reaction is more product-favored.

19.65   (a) $\Delta G^{\circ}(80.0 \text{ °C}) = 3.213 \text{ kJ} - (353.2 \text{ K})(8.7 \text{ J/K})(1 \text{ kJ}/10^3 \text{ J}) = 0.14 \text{ kJ}$

           $\Delta G^{\circ}(110.0 \text{ °C}) = 3.213 \text{ kJ} - (383.2 \text{ K})(8.7 \text{ J/K})(1 \text{ kJ}/10^3 \text{ J}) = -0.12 \text{ kJ}$

           Rhombic sulfur is more stable than monoclinic sulfur at 80 °C, but the reverse is true at 110 °C.

        (b) $T = \dfrac{\Delta H^{\circ}}{\Delta S^{\circ}} = \dfrac{3.213 \times 10^3 \text{ J/mol}}{8.7 \text{ J/K}} = 370 \text{ K} = 96 \text{ °C}$

           This is the temperature at which the phase transition takes place.

19.66 $\Delta G^{\circ} = \Delta G_f^{\circ}[H_2O(g)] - \Delta G_f^{\circ}[CuO(s)] = 1 \text{ mol } (-228.59 \text{ kJ/mol}) - 1 \text{ mol } (-128.3 \text{ kJ/mol}) = -100.3 \text{ kJ}$

The reaction is product-favored

19.67   (a) $\Delta H^\circ = 2 \, \Delta H_f^\circ[NO(g)] = 2$ mol (90.29 kJ/mol) = 180.58 kJ

$\Delta S^\circ = 2 \, S^\circ[NO(g)] - \{S^\circ[N_2(g)] + S^\circ[O_2(g)]\}$

$\Delta S^\circ = 2$ mol (210.76 J/K·mol) − [1 mol (191.56 J/K·mol) + 1 mol (205.07 J/K·mol)] = 24.89 J/K

$\Delta G^\circ = \Delta H^\circ - T\Delta S^\circ = 180.58$ kJ − (298 K)(24.89 J/K)(1 kJ/10^3 J) = 173.16 kJ

173.16 kJ = −(8.3145 × 10^{-3} kJ/K·mol)(298 K) ln K_p

$K_p = 4.4 \times 10^{-31}$ The reaction is not product-favored at this temperature

(b) $\Delta G^\circ = 180.58$ kJ − (973 K)(24.89 J/K)(1 kJ/10^3 J) = 156.4 kJ

156.4 kJ = −(8.3145 × 10^{-3} kJ/K·mol)(973 K) ln K_p

$K_p = 4 \times 10^{-9}$ The reaction is not product-favored at this temperature

(c) $K_p = 4 \times 10^{-9} = \dfrac{P_{NO}^{\,2}}{P_{N_2} P_{O_2}} = \dfrac{(2x)^2}{(1.00 - x)(1.00 - x)} \approx \dfrac{(2x)^2}{(1.00)^2}$

$x = 3 \times 10^{-5}$ bar

$P_{NO} = 2x = 6 \times 10^{-5}$ bar

$P_{N_2} = P_{O_2} = 1.00$ bar

19.68   (a) $\Delta H^\circ_{rxn} = 2 \, \Delta H_f^\circ[Ag_2O(s)] = 2$ mol (−31.1 kJ/mol) = −62.2 kJ/mol

$\Delta S^\circ_{rxn} = 2 \, S^\circ[Ag_2O(s)] - \{4 \, S^\circ[Ag(s)] + S^\circ[O_2(g)]\}$

$\Delta S^\circ_{rxn} = 2$ mol (121.3 J/K·mol) − [4 mol (42.55 J/K·mol) + 1 mol (205.07 J/K·mol)] = −132.7 J/K

$\Delta G^\circ_{rxn} = 2 \, \Delta G_f^\circ[Ag_2O(s)] = 2$ mol (−11.32 kJ/mol) = −22.64 kJ/mol

(b)   −22.64 = −(8.3145 × 10^{-3} kJ/K·mol)(298 K) ln K_p

$K_p = 9.3 \times 10^3 = 1/P_{O_2}$

$P_{O_2} = 1.1 \times 10^4$ atm

(c) $T = \dfrac{\Delta H^\circ}{\Delta S^\circ} = \dfrac{-62.2 \times 10^3 \text{ J/mol}}{-132.7 \text{ J/K}} = 469 \text{ K} = 196 \text{ °C}$

19.69 $K_p = \dfrac{P_{HI}}{P_{H_2}^{1/2} P_{I_2}^{1/2}} = \dfrac{1.61}{(0.132)^{1/2}(0.295)^{1/2}} = 8.16$

$\Delta G^\circ = -RT \ln K_p = -(8.3145 \times 10^{-3}$ kJ/K·mol)(623 K) ln(8.16) = −10.9 kJ/mol

19.70   HCl(g) → HCl(aq)

$\Delta S^\circ = S^\circ[HCl(aq)] - S^\circ[HCl(g)] = 1$ mol (56.5 J/K·mol) − 1 mol (186.2 J/K·mol) = −129.7 J/K

Yes, the negative value indicates a decrease in entropy, which is expected when going from a gaseous phase to a solvated phase.

19.71   First, calculate ΔS°_{rxn}, ΔH°_{rxn}, and ΔG°_{rxn}

$\Delta S^\circ_{rxn} = S^\circ[Hg(g)] - S^\circ[Hg(\ell)] = 1$ mol (174.97 J/K·mol) − 1 mol (76.02 J/K·mol) = 98.95 J/K

$\Delta H^\circ_{rxn} = \Delta H_f^\circ[Hg(g)] = 61.38$ kJ

$\Delta G^\circ_{rxn} = \Delta G_f^\circ[Hg(g)] = 31.88$ kJ

(a) $K_p = P_{Hg(g)}$

When $K_p = 1$, $\Delta G^\circ_{rxn} = 0$ and $T = \Delta H^\circ/\Delta S^\circ$. Therefore,

$$T = \frac{61.38 \times 10^3 \text{ J}}{98.95 \text{ J/K}} = 620.3 \text{ K} = 347.2 \text{ °C}$$

(b) Use the Clausius-Clapeyron equation and the temperature for $P = 1.00$ atm to calculate the temperature at which $P_{Hg(g)} = 1$ mm Hg:

$$\ln\left(\frac{P_2}{P_1}\right) = \frac{\Delta H_{vap}}{R}\left(\frac{1}{T_1} - \frac{1}{T_2}\right)$$

$$\ln\left(\frac{1 \text{ mm Hg}}{760 \text{ mm Hg}}\right) = \frac{61.38 \text{ kJ/mol}}{0.0083145 \text{ kJ/K} \cdot \text{mol}}\left(\frac{1}{620.3 \text{ K}} - \frac{1}{T_2}\right)$$

$T_2 = 398.3$ K = 125.2 °C

Since $K_p = P_{Hg(g)}$

347.2 °C: $P_{Hg(g)} = 1$ bar = 0.987 atm   125.2 °C: $P_{Hg(g)} = (1/760)$ bar = 0.987 mm Hg

19.72 $\Delta H^\circ = -(2 \Delta H_f^\circ[Ag_2O(s)]) = -[2 \text{ mol } (-31.1 \text{ kJ/mol})] = 62.2$ kJ/mol

$\Delta S^\circ = 4 S^\circ[Ag(s)] + S^\circ[O_2(g)] - 2 S^\circ[Ag_2O(s)]$

$\Delta S^\circ = 4 \text{ mol } (42.55 \text{ J/K} \cdot \text{mol}) + 1 \text{ mol } (205.07 \text{ J/K} \cdot \text{mol}) - 2 \text{ mol } (121.3 \text{ J/K} \cdot \text{mol}) = 132.7$ J/K

$\Delta G^\circ = -(2 \Delta G_f^\circ[Ag_2O(s)]) = -[2 \text{ mol } (-11.32 \text{ kJ/mol})] = 22.64$ kJ/mol

The decomposition is not product-favored at 25 °C

$$T = \frac{\Delta H^\circ}{\Delta S^\circ} = \frac{62.2 \times 10^3 \text{ J/mol}}{132.7 \text{ J/K}} = 469 \text{ K} = 196 \text{ °C}$$

19.73   (a) Reactant-favored (mercury is a liquid under standard conditions)

(b) Product-favored (water vapor will condense to liquid)

(c) Reactant-favored (a continuous supply of energy is required)

(d) Product-favored (carbon will burn)

(e) Product-favored (salt will dissolve in water

(f) Reactant-favored (calcium carbonate is insoluble)

19.74   (a) The entropy of the universe increases in all product-favored reactions.

(b) Product-favored reactions can occur at any rate, not necessarily a fast rate.

(c) While many spontaneous processes are exothermic, endothermic processes can be spontaneous at high temperatures.

(d) Endothermic processes can be spontaneous at high temperatures.

19.75   (a) True

   (b) False Whether an exothermic reaction is product- or reactant- favored depends on both the enthalpy
        and the entropy change of the system.

   (c) False Reactions with $+\Delta H^\circ_{rxn}$ and $+\Delta S^\circ_{rxn}$ are product-favored at higher temperatures.

   (d) True

19.76   The entropy of a pure crystal is zero at 0 K. A substance cannot have $S = 0$ J/K·mol at standard conditions
        (25 °C, 1 bar). All substances have positive entropy values at temperatures above 0 K. Based on the third
        law of thermodynamics, negative values of entropy cannot occur. The only exception to this is the entropy
        of the solvation process. When water molecules are constrained to a more ordered arrangement in a
        solution than in pure water, a higher degree of order results and entropy is negative.

19.77   Dissolving a solid such as NaCl in water is a spontaneous process. Thus, $\Delta G^\circ < 0$. If ΔH° is zero, then the
        only way the free energy change can be negative is if ΔS° is positive. Generally the entropy change is the
        driving force in forming a solution.

19.78

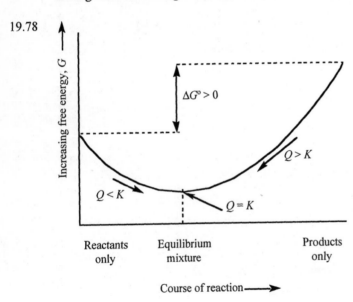

19.79 $2\,C_2H_6(g) + 7\,O_2(g) \rightarrow 4\,CO_2(g) + 6\,H_2O(g)$

   (a) The reaction is exothermic and product-favored. Therefore, $\Delta S^\circ_{surr} > 0$ and $\Delta S^\circ_{univ} > 0$. $\Delta S^\circ_{sys} > 0$
        because 10 mol of gas are produced from 9 mol gaseous reactants.

   (b) The exothermic reaction has $\Delta H^\circ_{rxn} < 0$. Combined with a positive ΔS°_{sys}, the value of ΔG°_{rxn} is
        negative.

   (c) The value of K_p is likely to be much greater than 1. Further, because ΔS°_{sys} is positive, the value of K_p
        will be even larger at a higher temperature.,

19.80   (a) positive (endothermic process)

        (b) positive (solid → liquid)

        (c) zero (equilibrium)

        (d) positive (reactant-favored)

        (e) negative (product-favored)

19.81   In a solid the particles have fixed positions in the solid lattice. When a solid is dissolved in water the ions are dispersed throughout the solution.

19.82 $\quad \Delta H°\quad\quad \Delta S°\quad\quad \Delta G°$

        (a) +   +   +

        (b) –   +   –

        (c) –   +   –

19.83   Iodine dissolves readily so the process is favorable and $\Delta G°_{rxn}$ must be less than zero. Because $\Delta H° = 0$, the process is entropy-driven.

19.84   Abba's refrigerator has liquid water on the cloth covering the pots and moistened sand in between the pots. The evaporation process is spontaneous at "room temperature," so $\Delta G < 0$. But we also know that $\Delta H° > 0$ (evaporation absorbs heat), and $\Delta S° > 0$ (evaporation increases disorder). This means at "room temperature" the process is entropy driven. Eventually, however, as the system approaches equilibrium ($\Delta G = 0$), the temperature must drop in order that $\Delta H° = T\Delta S°$.

19.85   (a) $\Delta H° = \Delta H_f°[Mg(OH)_2(s)] - 2\,\Delta H_f°[H_2O(\ell)]$

             $\Delta H° = 1\text{ mol }(-924.54\text{ kJ/mol}) - 2\text{ mol }(-285.83\text{ kJ/mol})$

             $\Delta H° = -352.88\text{ kJ}$

             $\Delta S°_{sys} = S°[Mg(OH)_2(s)] + S°[H_2(g)] - \{S°[Mg(s)] + 2\,S°[H_2O(\ell)]\}$

             $\Delta S°_{sys} = 1\text{ mol }(63.18\text{ J/K·mol}) + 1\text{ mol }(130.7\text{ J/K·mol}) - [1\text{ mol }(32.67\text{ J/K·mol})$

                                                                          $+ 2\text{ mol }(69.95\text{ J/K·mol})]$

             $\Delta S°_{sys} = 21.31\text{ J/K}$

             $\Delta S_{univ} = \Delta S°_{sys} + \Delta S°_{surr} = 21.31\text{ J/K} + [-(-352.88\text{ kJ})(10^3\text{ J/1 kJ})/298\text{ K}] = 1205\text{ J/K}$

             The reaction is spontaneous

        (b) $q_{water} + q_{Mg} = 0$

             $(225\text{ mL})(0.996\text{ g/mL})(4.184\text{ J/g·K})(373.2\text{ K} - 298.2\text{ K})(1\text{ kJ/}10^3\text{ J}) + q_{Mg} = 0$

             $q_{Mg} = -70.3\text{ kJ}$

             $70.3\text{ kJ} \cdot \dfrac{1\text{ mol Mg}}{352.88\text{ kJ}} \cdot \dfrac{24.31\text{ g}}{1\text{ mol Mg}} = 4.84\text{ g Mg}$

19.86   C(graphite) → C(diamond)

(a) $\Delta S°_{sys} = S°[C(diamond)] - S°[C(graphite)]$

$\Delta S°_{sys} = 1 \text{ mol } (2.377 \text{ J/K·mol}) - 1 \text{ mol } (5.6 \text{ J/K·mol}) = -3.2 \text{ J/K}$

$\Delta H° = \Delta H_f°[C(diamond)] = 1 \text{ mol } (1.8 \text{ kJ/mol}) = 1.8 \text{ kJ}$

$\Delta S°_{surr} = -\Delta H°/T = -[(1.8 \text{ kJ})(10^3 \text{ J/1 kJ})/298 \text{ K}] = -6.0 \text{ J/K}$

$\Delta S_{univ} = \Delta S°_{sys} + \Delta S°_{surr} = -3.2 \text{ J/K} + (-6.0 \text{ J/K}) = -9.2 \text{ J/K}$

$\Delta G° = \Delta H° - T\Delta S° = 1.8 \text{ kJ} - (298 \text{ K})(-3.2 \text{ J/K})(1 \text{ kJ}/10^3 \text{ J}) = 2.8 \text{ kJ}$

(b) Nonstandard conditions of extremely high pressure and temperature must be used to "force" the carbon atoms are close to one another, overcoming the unfavorable thermodynamics and allowing the conversion of graphite to diamond.

19.87   (a) $N_2H_4(\ell) + O_2(g) \rightarrow 2 H_2O(\ell) + N_2(g)$

O_2 is the oxidizing agent and N_2H_4 is the reducing agent

(b) $\Delta H° = 2 \Delta H_f°[H_2O(\ell)] - \Delta H_f°[N_2H_4(\ell)] = 2 \text{ mol } (-285.83 \text{ kJ/mol}) - 1 \text{ mol } (50.63 \text{ kJ/mol})$

$\Delta H° = -622.29 \text{ kJ}$

$\Delta S° = 2 S°[H_2O(\ell)] + S°[N_2(g)] - \{S°[N_2H_4(\ell)] + S°[O_2(g)]\}$

$\Delta S° = 2 \text{ mol } (69.95 \text{ J/K·mol}) + 1 \text{ mol } (191.56 \text{ J/K·mol}) - [1 \text{ mol } (121.52 \text{ J/K·mol})$

$+ 1 \text{ mol } (205.07 \text{ J/K·mol})]$

$\Delta S° = 4.87 \text{ J/K}$

$\Delta G° = -622.29 \text{ kJ} - (298 \text{ K})(4.87 \text{ J/K})(1 \text{ kJ}/10^3 \text{ J}) = -623.77 \text{ kJ}$

(c) $\Delta T = \dfrac{q}{(m)(c)} = \dfrac{(622.29 \text{ kJ})(10^3 \text{ J/1 kJ})}{(5.5 \times 10^4 \text{ kg})(10^3 \text{ g/1 kg})(4.184 \text{ J/g·K})} = 0.0027 \text{ K}$

(d) $5.5 \times 10^4 \text{ kg} \cdot \dfrac{10^3 \text{ g}}{1 \text{ kg}} \cdot \dfrac{0.000434 \text{ g O}_2}{100 \text{ g H}_2\text{O}} \cdot \dfrac{1 \text{ mol O}_2}{32.00 \text{ g}} = 7.5 \text{ mol O}_2$

(e) $7.5 \text{ mol O}_2 \cdot \dfrac{1 \text{ mol N}_2\text{H}_4}{1 \text{ mol O}_2} \cdot \dfrac{32.05 \text{ g}}{1 \text{ mol N}_2\text{H}_4} \cdot \dfrac{100 \text{ g solution}}{5.0 \text{ g N}_2\text{H}_4} = 4800 \text{ g solution}$

(f) Assume standard conditions are 1.00 atm, 0 K

$7.5 \text{ mol O}_2 \cdot \dfrac{1 \text{ mol N}_2}{1 \text{ mol O}_2} = 7.5 \text{ mol N}_2$

$V = \dfrac{nRT}{P} = \dfrac{(7.5 \text{ mol N}_2)(0.082057 \text{ L·atm/K·mol})(273 \text{ K})}{1.00 \text{ atm}} = 170 \text{ L}$

19.88   Kinetics

19.89   (a) -60.49 J/K

       (b)   no

       (c)   yes

       (d)   yes

       (e)   No. ΔS°_{sys} is equal to ΔS°_{rxn}; it is not related to ΔH°_{rxn}.

       (f)   The reaction is spontaneous at 400 K but not at 700 K.

19.90   (a)   The spontaneity decreases as temperature increases.

       (b)   There is no temperature between 400 K and 1000 K at which the decomposition is spontaneous.

19.91   (a) ΔG° decreases as temperature increases. The reaction is spontaneous above 835 K.

       (b)   No, this reaction is always spontaneous.

       (c)   The spontaneity of a reaction is dependent on temperature, and it is related to the sign of ΔH°_{rxn}.

19.92   (a)   There will not be an appreciable concentration of B. Species C will predominate because the activation energies are relatively small and the overall free energy change is negative.

       (b)   There is not an appreciable concentration of B. Species A and C are present in equal amounts. The activation energies remain relatively small, but now the overall free energy change is zero.

Chapter 20
Principles of Reactivity: Electron Transfer Reactions

INSTRUCTOR'S NOTES

About 4-5 lecture hours are reserved for a discussion of oxidation-reduction reactions. These lectures are usually placed after those on equilibrium and thermodynamics. However, it is possible to place electrochemistry before these other subjects. If this chapter is moved, the material in 20.6 Electrochemistry and Thermodynamics will either require more explanation or be omitted. Electrochemistry does provide excellent applications for thermodynamic and equilibrium principles as seen in that section. For example, the measurement of the electrochemical potential is a very good method for determining equilibrium constants. Electrochemistry should be covered before beginning any systematic descriptive chemistry.

SUGGESTED DEMONSTRATIONS

1. Oxidation–Reduction Reactions

- This subject lends itself well to demonstrations, particularly to show the practical importance of redox reactions. A variety of redox reactions were described as demonstrations for Chapters 4 and 5, and the *Periodic Table Videodisc* and the *Redox Videodisc* contain many examples of such reactions and demonstrations.

- Volume 4 of Shakhashiri's *Chemical Demonstrations* contains many useful electrochemistry demonstrations.

- To illustrate redox reactions in general we suggest the following possibilities:

    (a) The reaction of Al foil with concentrated $CuCl_2$ solution:

    $$3 \ Cu^{2+}(aq) + 2 \ Al(s) \rightarrow 2 \ Al^{3+}(aq) + 3 \ Cu(s) + heat$$

    This reaction is interesting because it does not occur with other copper salts such as $Cu(NO_3)_2$ or $CuSO_4$. Apparently the reason is that the Cl^- ion is able to diffuse through the layer of Al_2O_3 on the foil and open a pathway for electron transfer between Cu^{2+} and Al. This is, in itself, a very useful point to make, since this shows the importance of Cl^- in corroding systems; for example, one can note that aluminum objects are particularly sensitive to corrosion near the ocean.

    (b) A copper screen is placed in a silver nitrate solution in a petri dish on an overhead projector.

    $$2 \ Ag^+(aq) + Cu(s) \rightarrow 2 \ Ag(s) + Cu^{2+}(aq)$$

    In a short time silver needles are clearly seen growing off of the copper wire, and the solution visibly takes on a blue color from aqueous copper(II) ion.

- Wellman, W. E.; Noble, M. E. "Greening the Blue Bottle," *Journal of Chemical Education* **2003**, *80*, 537.

- Eliason, R.; Lee, E. J.; Wakefield, D.; Bergren, A. "Improvement of Sugar-Chlorate Rocket Demonstration," *Journal of Chemical Education* **2000**, *77*, 1580.

2. Chemical Change Leading to Electric Current

-   Contrast the reaction of zinc foil in a copper solution with a true electrochemical cell setup, where current is obtained.

-   Contrast the reactivity of Zn metal in 1 M HCl with that of Cu metal in the same acid.

-   See Scharlin, P. "The Human Salt Bridge," *Journal of Chemical Education* **1990**, *67*, 156; and Schearer, E. C. "The Construction and Use of Commercial Cell Displays in Freshman Chemistry," *ibid.* **1990**, *67*, 158.

3. Corrosion: Redox Reactions in the Environment

-   See Ward, C. R.; Greenbowe, T. J. "Cathodic Protection: An Overhead Projector Demonstration," *Journal of Chemical Education* **1981**, *58*, 505.

4. Electrolysis: Chemical Change from Electrical Energy

-   The electrolytic process in Figure 20.19 can be done in a cell such as that shown there or in a petri dish on the overhead projector. Fill the dish with dilute NaI and place platinum electrodes in the dish; add a few drops of phenolphthalein. When the cell is attached to a battery, I_2 is clearly seen at the anode and H_2 gas (as well as a red color from OH^- ions) at the cathode.

-   H_2 and O_2 can be obtained by the electrolysis of aqueous sulfuric acid (see Heidemen, S. "Electrolysis of Water," *Journal of Chemical Education* **1986**, *63*, 809).

-   Manjkow, J.; Levine, D. "Electrodeposition of Ni on Cu," *Journal of Chemical Education* **1986**, *63*, 809 5.

5. Additional suggestions:

-   Cortel, A. "Fast Ionic Migration of Copper Chromate," *Journal of Chemical Education* **2001**, *78*, 207.

-   There are *ChemMatters* issues about electrochemistry (February 1990) and batteries (April 1993).

SOLUTIONS TO STUDY QUESTIONS

20.1   (a) $Cr(s) \rightarrow Cr^{3+}(aq) + 3\ e^-$ oxidation

         (b) $AsH_3(g) \rightarrow As(s) + 3\ H^+(aq) + 3\ e^-$ oxidation

         (c) $VO_3^-(aq) + 6\ H^+(aq) + 3\ e^- \rightarrow V^{2+}(aq) + 3\ H_2O(\ell)$ reduction

         (d) $2\ Ag(s) + 2\ OH^-(aq) \rightarrow Ag_2O(s) + H_2O(\ell) + 2\ e^-$ oxidation

20.2   (a) $H_2O_2(aq) \rightarrow O_2(g) + 2\ H^+(aq) + 2\ e^-$ oxidation

         (b) $H_2C_2O_4(aq) \rightarrow 2\ CO_2(g) + 2\ H^+(aq) + 2\ e^-$ oxidation

         (c) $NO_3^-(aq) + 4\ H^+(aq) + 3\ e^- \rightarrow NO(g) + 2\ H_2O(\ell)$ reduction

         (d) $MnO_4^-(aq) + 2\ H_2O(\ell) + 3\ e^- \rightarrow MnO_2(s) + 4\ OH^-(aq)$ reduction

20.3   (a) $Ag(s) \rightarrow Ag^+(aq) + e^-$

              $NO_3^-(aq) + 2\ H^+(aq) + e^- \rightarrow NO_2(g) + H_2O(\ell)$
              _____
              $Ag(s) + NO_3^-(aq) + 2\ H^+(aq) \rightarrow Ag^+(aq) + NO_2(g) + H_2O(\ell)$

         (b) $2[MnO_4^-(aq) + 8\ H^+(aq) + 5\ e^- \rightarrow Mn^{2+}(aq) + 4\ H_2O(\ell)]$

              $5[HSO_3^-(aq) + H_2O(\ell) \rightarrow SO_4^{2-}(aq) + 3\ H^+(aq) + 2\ e^-]$
              _____
              $2\ MnO_4^-(aq) + H^+(aq) + 5\ HSO_3^-(aq) \rightarrow 2\ Mn^{2+}(aq) + 3\ H_2O(\ell) + 5\ SO_4^{2-}(aq)$

         (c) $4[Zn(s) \rightarrow Zn^{2+}(aq) + 2\ e^-]$

              $2\ NO_3^-(aq) + 8\ e^- + 10\ H^+(aq) \rightarrow 5\ H_2O(\ell) + N_2O(g)$
              _____
              $4\ Zn(s) + 2\ NO_3^-(aq) + 10\ H^+(aq) \rightarrow 5\ H_2O(\ell) + 4\ Zn^{2+}(aq) + N_2O(g)$

         (d) $Cr(s) \rightarrow Cr^{3+}(aq) + 3\ e^-$

              $NO_3^-(aq) + 4\ H^+(aq) + 3\ e^- \rightarrow NO(g) + 2\ H_2O(\ell)$
              _____
              $Cr(s) + NO_3^-(aq) + 4\ H^+(aq) \rightarrow Cr^{3+}(aq) + NO(g) + 2\ H_2O(\ell)$

20.4   (a) $Sn(s) \rightarrow Sn^{2+}(aq) + 2\ e^-$

              $2\ H^+(aq) + 2\ e^- \rightarrow H_2(g)$
              _____
              $Sn(s) + 2\ H^+(aq) \rightarrow Sn^{2+}(aq) + H_2(g)$

         (b) $Cr_2O_7^{2-}(aq) + 14\ H^+(aq) + 6\ e^- \rightarrow 2\ Cr^{3+}(aq) + 7\ H_2O(\ell)$

              $6[Fe^{2+}(aq) \rightarrow Fe^{3+}(aq) + e^-]$
              _____
              $Cr_2O_7^{2-}(aq) + 14\ H^+(aq) + 6\ Fe^{2+}(aq) \rightarrow 2\ Cr^{3+}(aq) + 7\ H_2O(\ell) + 6\ Fe^{3+}(aq)$

         (c) $MnO_2(s) + 4\ H^+(aq) + 2\ e^- \rightarrow Mn^{2+}(aq) + 2\ H_2O(\ell)$

              $2\ Cl^-(aq) \rightarrow Cl_2(g) + 2\ e^-$
              _____
              $MnO_2(s) + 4\ H^+(aq) + 2\ Cl^-(aq) \rightarrow Mn^{2+}(aq) + 2\ H_2O(\ell) + Cl_2(g)$

(d) $H_2CO(aq) + H_2O(\ell) \rightarrow HCO_2H(aq) + 2\ H^+(aq) + 2\ e^-$

   $2[Ag^+(aq) + e^- \rightarrow Ag(s)]$
   _____

   $H_2CO(aq) + H_2O(\ell) + 2\ Ag^+(aq) \rightarrow HCO_2H(aq) + 2\ H^+(aq) + 2\ Ag(s)$

20.5   (a) $2[Al(s) + 4\ OH^-(aq) \rightarrow 3\ e^- + Al(OH)_4^-(aq)]$

   $3[2\ H_2O(\ell) + 2\ e^- \rightarrow 2\ OH^-(aq) + H_2(g)]$
   _____

   $2\ Al(s) + 6\ H_2O(\ell) + 2\ OH^-(aq) \rightarrow 2\ Al(OH)_4^-(aq) + 3$

   $H_2(g)$

   (b) $2[CrO_4^-(aq) + 4\ H_2O(\ell) + 3\ e^- \rightarrow Cr(OH)_3(s) + 5\ OH^-(aq)]$

   $3[SO_3^{2-}(aq) + 2\ OH^-(aq) \rightarrow SO_4^{2-}(aq) + H_2O(\ell) + 2\ e^-]$
   _____

   $2\ CrO_4^-(aq) + 5\ H_2O(\ell) + 3\ SO_3^{2-}(aq) \rightarrow 2\ Cr(OH)_3(s) + 4\ OH^-(aq) + 3\ SO_4^{2-}(aq)$

   (c) $Zn(s) + 4\ OH^-(aq) \rightarrow Zn(OH)_4^{2-}(aq) + 2\ e^-$

   $Cu(OH)_2(s) + 2\ e^- \rightarrow Cu(s) + 2\ OH^-(aq)$
   _____

   $Zn(s) + 2\ OH^-(aq) + Cu(OH)_2(s) \rightarrow Zn(OH)_4^{2-}(aq) + Cu(s)$

   (d) $3[HS^-(aq) + OH^-(aq) \rightarrow S(s) + H_2O(\ell) + 2\ e^-]$

   $ClO_3^-(aq) + 3\ H_2O(\ell) + 6\ e^- \rightarrow Cl^-(aq) + 6\ OH^-(aq)$
   _____

   $3\ HS^-(aq) + ClO_3^-(aq) \rightarrow 3\ S(s) + Cl^-(aq) + 3\ OH^-(aq)$

20.6   (a) $3[Fe(OH)_3(s) + e^- \rightarrow Fe(OH)_2(s) + OH^-(aq)]$

   $Cr(s) + 3\ OH^-(aq) \rightarrow Cr(OH)_3(s) + 3\ e^-$
   _____

   $3\ Fe(OH)_3(s) + Cr(s) \rightarrow 3\ Fe(OH)_2(s) + Cr(OH)_3(s)$

   (b) $NiO_2(s) + 2\ H_2O(\ell) + 2\ e^- \rightarrow Ni(OH)_2(s) + 2\ OH^-(aq)$

   $Zn(s) + 2\ OH^-(aq) \rightarrow Zn(OH)_2(s) + 2\ e^-$
   _____

   $NiO_2(s) + 2\ H_2O(\ell) + Zn(s) \rightarrow Ni(OH)_2(s) + Zn(OH)_2(s)$

   (c) $3[Fe(OH)_2(s) + OH^-(aq) \rightarrow Fe(OH)_3(s) + e^-]$

   $CrO_4^{2-}(aq) + 3\ e^- + 4\ H_2O(\ell) \rightarrow Cr(OH)_4^-(aq) + 4\ OH^-(aq)$
   _____

   $3\ Fe(OH)_2(s) + CrO_4^{2-}(aq) + 4\ H_2O(\ell) \rightarrow 3\ Fe(OH)_3(s) + Cr(OH)_4^-(aq) + OH^-(aq)$

   (d) $N_2H_4(aq) + 4\ OH^-(aq) \rightarrow N_2(g) + 4\ H_2O(\ell) + 4\ e^-$

   $2[Ag_2O(s) + H_2O(\ell) + 2\ e^- \rightarrow 2\ Ag(s) + 2\ OH^-(aq)]$
   _____

   $N_2H_4(aq) + 2\ Ag_2O(s) \rightarrow N_2(g) + 2\ H_2O(\ell) + 4\ Ag(s)$

20.7   Electrons in the external circuit flow from the Cr electrode to the Fe electrode. Negative ions move in the salt bridge from the Fe/Fe^{2+} half-cell to the Cr/Cr^{3+} half-cell. The half-reaction at the anode is $Cr(s) \rightarrow Cr^{3+}(aq) + 3\ e^-$ and that at the cathode is $Fe^{2+}(aq) + 2\ e^- \rightarrow Fe(s)$.

20.8   (a) Oxidation (anode): $Mg(s) \rightarrow Mg^{2+}(aq) + 2\ e^-$

        Reduction (cathode): $2\ H^+(aq) + 2\ e^- \rightarrow H_2(g)$

        (b) Oxidation occurs in the Mg/Mg^{2+} compartment and reduction occurs in the H^+/H_2 compartment.

        (c) Electrons in the external circuit flow from the Mg electrode to the positive (site of H^+ reduction) electrode. Negative ions move in the salt bridge from the H^+/H_2 half-cell to the Mg/Mg^{2+} half-cell. The half-reaction at the anode and the cathode are shown in (a).

20.9   (a) Oxidation: $Fe(s) \rightarrow Fe^{2+}(aq) + 2\ e^-$

        Reduction: $O_2(g) + 4\ H^+(aq) + 4\ e^- \rightarrow 2\ H_2O(\ell)$

        Overall: $2\ Fe(s) + O_2(g) + 4\ H^+(aq) \rightarrow 2\ H_2O(\ell) + 2\ Fe^{2+}(aq)$

        (b) Oxidation occurs in the anode compartment and reduction occurs in the cathode compartment.

        (c) Electrons in the external circuit flow from the Fe electrode to the positive (site of O_2 reduction) electrode. Negative ions move in the salt bridge from the O_2/H_2O half-cell to the Fe/Fe^{2+} half-cell.

20.10   (a) Oxidation: $Ag(s) \rightarrow Ag^+(aq) + e^-$

        Reduction: $Cl_2(g) + 2\ e^- \rightarrow 2\ Cl^-(aq)$

        Overall: $2\ Ag(s) + Cl_2(g) \rightarrow 2\ Ag^+(aq) + 2\ Cl^-(aq)$

        (b) Oxidation occurs in the anode compartment and reduction occurs in the cathode compartment.

        (c) Electrons in the external circuit flow from the Ag electrode to the positive (site of Cl_2 reduction) electrode. Negative ions move in the salt bridge from the Cl_2/Cl^- half-cell to the Ag/Ag^+ half-cell.

20.11   See section 20.3

        Dry cells and alkaline batteries are primary batteries (not rechargeable), and ni-cad batteries are rechargeable.

        Dry cells and alkaline batteries have Zn as the anode, ni-cad batteries have a Cd anode.

        Dry cells have an acidic environment, whereas the environment is alkaline for alkaline and ni-cad batteries.

20.12   Lead(II) sulfate is oxidized to lead(IV) oxide and reduced to elemental lead.

20.13   (a) $E^\circ_{cell} = E^\circ_{cathode} - E^\circ_{anode} = (-0.763\ V) - (+0.535\ V) = -1.298\ V$ not product-favored

        (b) $E^\circ_{cell} = E^\circ_{cathode} - E^\circ_{anode} = (-0.763\ V) - (-0.25\ V) = -0.51\ V$ not product-favored

        (c) $E^\circ_{cell} = E^\circ_{cathode} - E^\circ_{anode} = (+0.337\ V) - (+1.360\ V) = -1.023\ V$ not product-favored

        (d) $E^\circ_{cell} = E^\circ_{cathode} - E^\circ_{anode} = (+0.80\ V) - (+0.771\ V) = +0.03\ V$ product-favored

20.14   (a) $E°_{cell} = E°_{cathode} - E°_{anode} = (+1.08 \text{ V}) - (-2.37 \text{ V}) = +3.45 \text{ V}$ product-favored

     (b) $E°_{cell} = E°_{cathode} - E°_{anode} = (-0.763 \text{ V}) - (-2.37 \text{ V}) = +1.61 \text{ V}$ product-favored

     (c) $E°_{cell} = E°_{cathode} - E°_{anode} = (+0.80 \text{ V}) - (+0.15 \text{ V}) = +0.65 \text{ V}$ product-favored

     (d) $E°_{cell} = E°_{cathode} - E°_{anode} = (+0.40 \text{ V}) - (-1.22 \text{ V}) = +1.62 \text{ V}$ product-favored

20.15   (a) $Sn^{2+}(aq) + 2 \text{ e}^- \rightarrow Sn(s)$

          $2[Ag(s) \rightarrow Ag^+(aq) + \text{e}^-]$
_____

          $Sn^{2+}(aq) + 2 \text{ Ag}(s) \rightarrow Sn(s) + 2 \text{ Ag}^+(aq)$

          $E°_{cell} = E°_{cathode} - E°_{anode} = (-0.14 \text{ V}) - (+0.80 \text{ V}) = -0.94 \text{ V}$ not product-favored

     (b) $2[Al(s) \rightarrow Al^{3+}(aq) + 3 \text{ e}^-]$

          $3[Sn^{4+}(aq) + 2 \text{ e}^- \rightarrow Sn^{2+}(aq)]$
_____

          $2 \text{ Al}(s) + 3 \text{ Sn}^{4+}(aq) \rightarrow 2 \text{ Al}^{3+}(aq) + 3 \text{ Sn}^{2+}(aq)$

          $E°_{cell} = E°_{cathode} - E°_{anode} = (+0.15 \text{ V}) - (-1.66 \text{ V}) = +1.81 \text{ V}$ product-favored

     (c) $ClO_3^-(aq) + 6 \text{ H}^+(aq) + 6 \text{ e}^- \rightarrow Cl^-(aq) + 3 \text{ H}_2O(\ell)$

          $6[Ce^{3+}(aq) \rightarrow Ce^{4+}(aq) + \text{e}^-]$
_____

          $ClO_3^-(aq) + 6 \text{ H}^+(aq) + 6 \text{ Ce}^{3+}(aq) \rightarrow Cl^-(aq) + 3 \text{ H}_2O(\ell) +$

          $Ce^{4+}(aq)$

          $E°_{cell} = E°_{cathode} - E°_{anode} = (+0.62 \text{ V}) - (+1.61 \text{ V}) = -0.99 \text{ V}$ not product-favored

     (d) $3[Cu(s) \rightarrow Cu^{2+}(aq) + 2 \text{ e}^-]$

          $2[NO_3^-(aq) + 4 \text{ H}^+(aq) + 3 \text{ e}^- \rightarrow NO(g) + 2 \text{ H}_2O(\ell)]$
_____

          $3 \text{ Cu}(s) + 2 \text{ NO}_3^-(aq) + 8 \text{ H}^+(aq) \rightarrow 2 \text{ NO}(g) + 3 \text{ Cu}^{2+}(aq) + 4 \text{ H}_2O(\ell)$

          $E°_{cell} = E°_{cathode} - E°_{anode} = (+0.96 \text{ V}) - (+0.337 \text{ V}) = +0.62 \text{ V}$ product-favored

20.16   (a) $I_2(s) + 2 \text{ e}^- \rightarrow 2 \text{ I}^-(aq)$

          $2 \text{ Br}^-(aq) \rightarrow Br_2(\ell) + 2 \text{ e}^-$
_____

          $I_2(s) + 2 \text{ Br}^-(aq) \rightarrow 2 \text{ I}^-(aq) + Br_2(\ell)$

          $E°_{cell} = E°_{cathode} - E°_{anode} = (+0.535 \text{ V}) - (+1.08 \text{ V}) = -0.55 \text{ V}$ not product-favored

     (b) $2[Fe^{2+}(aq) \rightarrow Fe^{3+}(aq) + \text{e}^-]$

          $Cu^{2+}(aq) + 2 \text{ e}^- \rightarrow Cu(s)$
_____

          $2 \text{ Fe}^{2+}(aq) + Cu^{2+}(aq) \rightarrow Fe^{3+}(aq) +$

          $Cu(s)$

          $E°_{cell} = E°_{cathode} - E°_{anode} = (+0.337 \text{ V}) - (+0.771 \text{ V}) = -0.434 \text{ V}$ not product-favored

     (c) $6[Fe^{2+}(aq) \rightarrow Fe^{3+}(aq) + \text{e}^-]$

          $Cr_2O_7^{2-}(aq) + 14 \text{ H}^+(aq) + 6 \text{ e}^- \rightarrow 2 \text{ Cr}^{3+}(aq) + 7 \text{ H}_2O(\ell)$

$6 \, Fe^{2+}(aq) + Cr_2O_7^{2-}(aq) + 14 \, H^+(aq) \rightarrow 6 \, Fe^{3+}(aq) + 7 \, H_2O(\ell) + 2 \, Cr^{3+}(aq)$

$E^\circ{}_{cell} = E^\circ{}_{cathode} - E^\circ{}_{anode} = (+1.33 \, V) - (+.0771 \, V) = +0.56 \, V$ \qquad product-favored

(d) $2[MnO_4^-(aq) + 8 \, H^+(aq) + 5 \, e^- \rightarrow Mn^{2+}(aq) + 4 \, H_2O(\ell)]$

$5[HNO_2(aq) + H_2O(\ell) \rightarrow NO_3^-(aq) + 3 \, H^+(aq) + 2 \, e^-]$

$2 \, MnO_4^-(aq) + H^+(aq) + 5 \, HNO_2(aq) \rightarrow 2 \, Mn^{2+}(aq) + 5 \, NO_3^-(aq) + 3 \, H_2O(\ell)$

$E^\circ{}_{cell} = E^\circ{}_{cathode} - E^\circ{}_{anode} = (+1.52 \, V) - (+0.94 \, V) = +0.58 \, V$ \qquad product-favored

20.17 (a) Al(s)

(b) Zn(s) and Al(s)

(c) $Fe^{2+}(aq) + Sn(s) \rightarrow Fe(s) + Sn^{2+}(aq)$

$E^\circ{}_{cell} = E^\circ{}_{cathode} - E^\circ{}_{anode} = (-0.44 \, V) - (-0.14 \, V) = -0.30 \, V$ \qquad reactant-favored

(d) $Zn^{2+}(aq) + Sn(s) \rightarrow Zn(s) + Sn^{2+}(aq)$

$E^\circ{}_{cell} = E^\circ{}_{cathode} - E^\circ{}_{anode} = (-0.76 \, V) - (-0.14 \, V) = -0.62 \, V$ \qquad reactant-favored

20.18 (a) MnO_4^- is the strongest oxidizing agent and SO_4^{2-} is the weakest oxidizing agent

(b) MnO_4^-

(c) $Cr_2O_7^{2-}(aq) + 14 \, H^+(aq) + 6 \, e^- \rightarrow 2 \, Cr^{3+}(aq) + 7 \, H_2O(\ell)$

$3[SO_2(g) + 2 \, H_2O(\ell) \rightarrow SO_4^{2-}(aq) + 4 \, H^+(aq) + 2 \, e^-]$

$Cr_2O_7^{2-}(aq) + 2 \, H^+(aq) + 3 \, SO_2(g) \rightarrow 2 \, Cr^{3+}(aq) + H_2O(\ell) + 3 \, SO_4^{2-}(aq)$

$E^\circ{}_{cell} = E^\circ{}_{cathode} - E^\circ{}_{anode} = (+1.33 \, V) - (+0.20 \, V) = +1.13 \, V$ \qquad reactant-favored

(d) $5[Cr_2O_7^{2-}(aq) + 14 \, H^+(aq) + 6 \, e^- \rightarrow 2 \, Cr^{3+}(aq) + 7 \, H_2O(\ell)]$

$6[Mn^{2+}(aq) + 4 \, H_2O(\ell) \rightarrow MnO_4^-(aq) + 8 \, H^+(aq) + 5 \, e^-]$

$5 \, Cr_2O_7^{2-}(aq) + 22 \, H^+(aq) + 6 \, Mn^{2+}(aq) \rightarrow 10 \, Cr^{3+}(aq) + 11 \, H_2O(\ell) + 6 \, MnO_4^-$
(aq)

$E^\circ{}_{cell} = E^\circ{}_{cathode} - E^\circ{}_{anode} = (+1.33 \, V) - (+1.51 \, V) = -0.18 \, V$ \qquad reactant-favored

20.19 (b) Zn

20.20 (b) Zn, (c) Fe, and (e) Cr

20.21 (d) $Ag^+(aq)$

20.22 (a) $Cu^{2+}(aq)$ and (d) $Ag^+(aq)$

20.23 (a) F_2

(b) Cl_2 and F_2

20.24   (a) I^-(aq)

(b) Br^-(aq) and I^-(aq)

20.25 $Zn(s) + 4\ OH^-(aq) \rightarrow Zn(OH)_4^{2-}(aq) + 2\ e^-$

$2\ H_2O(\ell) + 2\ e^- \rightarrow H_2(g) + 2\ OH^-(aq)$

$E^{\circ}_{cell} = E^{\circ}_{cathode} - E^{\circ}_{anode} = (-0.8277\ V) - (-1.22\ V) = +0.39\ V$

$E_{cell} = E^{\circ}_{cell} - \dfrac{0.0257}{n}\ \ln\dfrac{[Zn(OH)_4^{2-}]P_{H_2}}{[OH^-]^2} = +0.39\ V - \dfrac{0.0257}{2}\ \ln\dfrac{(0.025)(1.0)}{(0.025)^2} = 0.34\ V$

20.26 $2[Fe^{2+}(aq) \rightarrow Fe^{3+}(aq) + e^-]$

$H_2O_2(aq) + 2\ H^+(aq) + 2\ e^- \rightarrow 2\ H_2O(\ell)$

$E^{\circ}_{cell} = E^{\circ}_{cathode} - E^{\circ}_{anode} = (1.77\ V) - (0.771\ V) = +1.00\ V$

$E_{cell} = E^{\circ}_{cell} - \dfrac{0.0257}{n}\ \ln\dfrac{[Fe^{3+}]^2}{[Fe^{2+}]^2[H_2O_2][H^+]^2} = +1.00\ V - \dfrac{0.0257}{2}\ \ln\dfrac{(0.015)^2}{(0.015)^2(0.015)(0.015)^2}$

$E_{cell} = 0.84\ V$

20.27 $Zn(s) \rightarrow Zn^{2+}(aq) + 2\ e^-$

$2[Ag^+(aq) + e^- \rightarrow Ag(s)]$

$\overline{Zn(s) + 2\ Ag^+(aq) \rightarrow Zn^{2+}(aq) + 2\ Ag(s)}$

$E^{\circ}_{cell} = E^{\circ}_{cathode} - E^{\circ}_{anode} = (0.80\ V) - (-0.763\ V) = +1.56\ V$

$E_{cell} = E^{\circ}_{cell} - \dfrac{0.0257}{n}\ \ln\dfrac{[Zn^{2+}]}{[Ag^+]^2} = +1.56\ V - \dfrac{0.0257}{2}\ \ln\dfrac{0.010}{(0.25)^2} = 1.59\ V$

20.28 $Zn(s) + Cu^{2+}(aq) \rightarrow Zn^{2+}(aq) + Cu(s)$

$E^{\circ}_{cell} = E^{\circ}_{cathode} - E^{\circ}_{anode} = (0.337\ V) - (-0.763\ V) = +1.100\ V$

$E_{cell} = E^{\circ}_{cell} - \dfrac{0.0257}{n}\ \ln\dfrac{[Zn^{2+}]}{[Cu^{2+}]} = +1.100\ V - \dfrac{0.0257}{2}\ \ln\dfrac{0.40}{4.8 \times 10^{-3}} = 1.043\ V$

20.29 $Zn(s) + 2\ Ag^+(aq) \rightarrow Zn^{2+}(aq) + 2\ Ag(s)$

$E^{\circ}_{cell} = E^{\circ}_{cathode} - E^{\circ}_{anode} = (0.80\ V) - (-0.763\ V) = +1.56\ V$

$E_{cell} = 1.48\ V = 1.56\ V - \dfrac{0.0257}{2}\ \ln\dfrac{1.0}{[Ag^+]^2}$

$[Ag^+] = 0.040\ M$

20.30 $Fe(s) + 2\ H^+(aq) \rightarrow Fe^{2+}(aq) + H_2(g)$

$E^{\circ}_{cell} = E^{\circ}_{cathode} - E^{\circ}_{anode} = (0.00\ V) - (-0.44\ V) = +0.44\ V$

$E_{cell} = 0.49\ V = 0.44\ V - \dfrac{0.0257}{2}\ \ln\dfrac{[Fe^{2+}]1.0}{(1.0)^2}$

$[Fe^{2+}] = 0.020\ M$

20.31   (a) $2[Fe^{3+}(aq) + e^- \rightarrow Fe^{2+}(aq)]$

$2\,I^-(aq) \rightarrow I_2(s) + 2\,e^-$

$E^\circ_{cell} = E^\circ_{cathode} - E^\circ_{anode} = (0.771\ V) - (0.535\ V) = +0.236\ V$

$\Delta G^\circ = -nFE^\circ = -(2\ mol\ e^-)(96,500\ C/mol\ e^-)(0.236\ V)(1\ J/1\ C\cdot V)(1\ kJ/10^3\ J) = -45.5\ kJ$

$\ln K = \dfrac{nE^\circ}{0.0257\ V} = \dfrac{(2)(0.236\ V)}{0.0257\ V} = 18.4$

$K = 9 \times 10^7$

(b) $I_2(s) + 2\,e^- \rightarrow 2\,I^-(aq)$

$2\,Br^-(aq) \rightarrow Br_2(\ell) + 2\,e^-$

$E^\circ_{cell} = E^\circ_{cathode} - E^\circ_{anode} = (0.535\ V) - (1.08\ V) = -0.55\ V$

$\Delta G^\circ = -nFE^\circ = -(2\ mol\ e^-)(96,500\ C/mol\ e^-)(-0.55\ V)(1\ J/1\ C\cdot V)(1\ kJ/10^3\ J) = 110\ kJ$

$\ln K = \dfrac{nE^\circ}{0.0257\ V} = \dfrac{(2)(-0.55\ V)}{0.0257\ V} = -42$

$K = 4 \times 10^{-19}$

20.32   (a) $Zn^{2+}(aq) + 2\,e^- \rightarrow Zn(s)$

$Ni(s) \rightarrow Ni^{2+}(aq) + 2\,e^-$

$E^\circ_{cell} = E^\circ_{cathode} - E^\circ_{anode} = (-0.763\ V) - (-0.25\ V) = -0.51\ V$

$\Delta G^\circ = -nFE^\circ = -(2\ mol\ e^-)(96,500\ C/mol\ e^-)(-0.51\ V)(1\ J/1\ C\cdot V)(1\ kJ/10^3\ J) = 99\ kJ$

$\ln K = \dfrac{nE^\circ}{0.0257\ V} = \dfrac{(2)(-0.51\ V)}{0.0257\ V} = -40.$

$K = 5 \times 10^{-18}$

(b) $Cu(s) \rightarrow Cu^{2+}(aq) + 2\,e^-$

$2[Ag^+(aq) + e^- \rightarrow Ag(s)]$

$E^\circ_{cell} = E^\circ_{cathode} - E^\circ_{anode} = (0.80\ V) - (0.337\ V) = 0.46\ V$

$\Delta G^\circ = -nFE^\circ = -(2\ mol\ e^-)(96,500\ C/mol\ e^-)(0.46\ V)(1\ J/1\ C\cdot V)(1\ kJ/10^3\ J) = -89\ kJ$

$\ln K = \dfrac{nE^\circ}{0.0257\ V} = \dfrac{(2)(0.46\ V)}{0.0257\ V} = 36$

$K = 4 \times 10^{15}$

20.33 $AgBr(s) + e^- \rightarrow Ag(s) + Br^-(aq)$

$Ag(s) \rightarrow Ag^+(aq) + e^-$

$AgBr(s) \rightarrow Ag^+(aq) + Br^-(aq)$

$E^\circ_{cell} = E^\circ_{cathode} - E^\circ_{anode} = (0.0713\ V) - (0.7994\ V) = -0.7281\ V$

$\ln K = \dfrac{nE^\circ}{0.0257\ V} = \dfrac{(1)(-0.7281\ V)}{0.0257\ V} = -28.33$

$K = 5.0 \times 10^{-13}$

20.34 $Hg_2Cl_2(s) + 2\ e^- \rightarrow 2\ Hg(\ell) + 2\ Cl^-(aq)$

$2\ Hg(\ell) \rightarrow Hg_2^{2+}(aq) + 2\ e^-$

$Hg_2Cl_2(s) \rightarrow Hg_2^{2+}(aq) + 2\ Cl^-(aq)$

$E°_{cell} = E°_{cathode} - E°_{anode} = (0.27\ V) - (0.789\ V) = -0.52\ V$

$\ln K = \dfrac{nE°}{0.0257\ V} = \dfrac{(2)(-0.52\ V)}{0.0257\ V} = -40.$

$K = 3 \times 10^{-18}$

20.35 $Au(s) + 4\ Cl^-(aq) \rightarrow AuCl_4^-(aq) + 3\ e^-$

$Au^{3+}(aq) + 3\ e^- \rightarrow Au(s)$

$Au^{3+}(aq) + 4\ Cl^-(aq) \rightarrow AuCl_4^-(aq)$

$E°_{cell} = E°_{cathode} - E°_{anode} = (1.50\ V) - (1.00\ V) = 0.50\ V$

$\ln K = \dfrac{nE°}{0.0257\ V} = \dfrac{(3)(0.50\ V)}{0.0257\ V} = 58$

$K = 2 \times 10^{25}$

20.36 $Zn(s) + 4\ OH^-(aq) \rightarrow Zn(OH)_4^{2-}(aq) + 2\ e^-$

$Zn^{2+}(aq) + 2\ e^- \rightarrow Zn(s)$

$Zn^{2+}(aq) + 4\ OH^-(aq) \rightarrow Zn(OH)_4^{2-}(aq)$

$E°_{cell} = E°_{cathode} - E°_{anode} = (-0.763\ V) - (-1.22\ V) = 0.46\ V$

$\ln K = \dfrac{nE°}{0.0257\ V} = \dfrac{(2)(0.46\ V)}{0.0257\ V} = 36$

$K = 3 \times 10^{15}$

20.37   (a) $Fe^{2+}(aq) + 2\ e^- \rightarrow Fe(s)$

$2[Fe^{2+}(aq) \rightarrow Fe^{3+}(aq) + e^-]$

(b) $E°_{cell} = E°_{cathode} - E°_{anode} = (-0.44\ V) - (0.771\ V) = -1.21\ V$ not product-favored

(c) $\ln K = \dfrac{nE°}{0.0257\ V} = \dfrac{(2)(-1.21\ V)}{0.0257\ V} = -94.2$

$K = 1 \times 10^{-41}$

20.38   (a) $Cu^+(aq) + e^- \rightarrow Cu(s)$

$Cu^+(aq) \rightarrow Cu^{2+}(aq) + e^-$

(b) $E°_{cell} = E°_{cathode} - E°_{anode} = (0.521\ V) - (0.153\ V) = 0.368\ V$ product-favored

(c) $\ln K = \dfrac{nE°}{0.0257\ V} = \dfrac{(1)(0.368\ V)}{0.0257\ V} = 14.3$

$K = 2 \times 10^6$

20.39

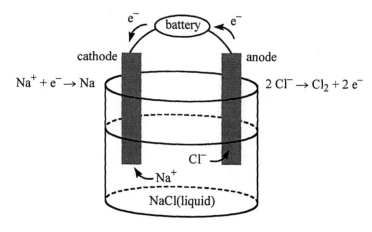

$Na^+ + e^- \rightarrow Na$ $2\,Cl^- \rightarrow Cl_2 + 2\,e^-$

20.40

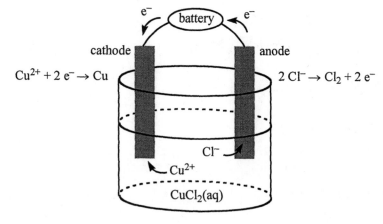

$Cu^{2+} + 2\,e^- \rightarrow Cu$ $2\,Cl^- \rightarrow Cl_2 + 2\,e^-$

20.41 F^- is much more difficult to oxidize than water, so O_2 is more likely to be formed at the anode.

20.42 Ca^{2+} is much more difficult to reduce than water, so H_2 is more likely to be formed at the cathode.

20.43   (a) $2\,H_2O(\ell) + 2\,e^- \rightarrow H_2(g) + 2\,OH^-(aq)$

            (b) $2\,Br^-(aq) \rightarrow Br_2(\ell) + 2\,e^-$

20.44   (a) $2\,H_2O(\ell) + 2\,e^- \rightarrow H_2(g) + 2\,OH^-(aq)$

            (b) $S^{2-}(aq) \rightarrow S(s) + 2\,e^-$

20.45   Charge = current × time = (0.150 A)(12.2 min)(60.0 s/min) = 110. C

$$mol\ e^- = (110.\ C)\left(\frac{1\ mol\ e^-}{96{,}500\ C}\right) = 0.00114\ mol\ e^-$$

$$mass\ of\ Ni = (0.00114\ mol\ e^-)\left(\frac{1\ mol\ Ni}{2\ mol\ e^-}\right)\left(\frac{58.69\ g}{1\ mol\ Ni}\right) = 0.0334\ g\ Ni$$

20.46   Charge = current × time = (1.12 A)(2.40 h)(60.0 min/h)(60.0 s/min) = 9.68×10^3 C

mol e⁻ = $(9.68 \times 10^3 \text{ C})\left(\dfrac{1 \text{ mol e}^-}{96,500 \text{ C}}\right)$ = 0.100 mol e⁻

mass of Ag = $(0.100 \text{ mol e}^-)\left(\dfrac{1 \text{ mol Ag}}{1 \text{ mol e}^-}\right)\left(\dfrac{107.9 \text{ g}}{1 \text{ mol Ag}}\right)$ = 10.8 g Ag

20.47   mol e⁻ = $(0.50 \text{ g Cu})\left(\dfrac{1 \text{ mol Cu}}{63.55 \text{ g}}\right)\left(\dfrac{2 \text{ mol e}^-}{1 \text{ mol Cu}}\right)$ = 0.016 mol e⁻

Charge = $(0.016 \text{ mol e}^-)\left(\dfrac{96,500 \text{ C}}{1 \text{ mol e}^-}\right)$ = 1.5×10^3 C

Time = 1.5×10^3 C/0.66 A = 2300 s (or 38 min)

20.48   mol e⁻ = $(2.5 \text{ g Zn})\left(\dfrac{1 \text{ mol Zn}}{65.39 \text{ g}}\right)\left(\dfrac{2 \text{ mol e}^-}{1 \text{ mol Zn}}\right)$ = 0.076 mol e⁻

Charge = $(0.076 \text{ mol e}^-)\left(\dfrac{96,500 \text{ C}}{1 \text{ mol e}^-}\right)$ = 7.4×10^3 C

Time = 7.4×10^3 C/2.12 A = 3500 s (or 58 min)

20.49 $Al(s) \rightarrow Al^{3+}(aq) + 3 \text{ e}^-$

$(84 \text{ g Al})\left(\dfrac{1 \text{ mol Al}}{27.0 \text{ g}}\right)\left(\dfrac{3 \text{ mol e}^-}{1 \text{ mol Al}}\right)\left(\dfrac{96,500 \text{ C}}{1 \text{ mol e}^-}\right)$ = 9.0×10^5 C

$(9.0 \times 10^5 \text{ C}/1.0 \text{ A})(1 \text{ min}/60.0 \text{ s})(1 \text{ h}/60.0 \text{ min})$ = 250 h

20.50   Charge = current × time = (0.25 A)(1.00 h)(60.0 min/h)(60.0 s/min) = 9.0×10^2 C

mass of Cd = $(9.0 \times 10^2 \text{ C})\left(\dfrac{1 \text{ mol e}^-}{96,500 \text{ C}}\right)\left(\dfrac{1 \text{ mol Cd}}{2 \text{ mol e}^-}\right)\left(\dfrac{112.4 \text{ g}}{1 \text{ mol Cd}}\right)$ = 0.52 g Cd

20.51   (a) $UO_2^+(aq) + 4 H^+(aq) + e^- \rightarrow U^{4+}(aq) + 2 H_2O(\ell)$

(b) $ClO_3^-(aq) + 6 H^+(aq) + 6 e^- \rightarrow Cl^-(aq) + 3 H_2O(\ell)$

(c) $N_2H_4(aq) + 4 OH^-(aq) \rightarrow N_2(g) + 4 H_2O(\ell) + 4 e^-$

(d) $OCl^-(aq) + H_2O(\ell) + 2 e^- \rightarrow Cl^-(aq) + 2 OH^-(aq)$

20.52   (a) $Zn(s) \rightarrow Zn^{2+}(aq) + 2 e^-$

$2[VO^{2+}(aq) + 2 H^+(aq) + e^- \rightarrow V^{3+}(aq) + H_2O(\ell)]$

$\overline{\qquad\qquad\qquad\qquad\qquad\qquad\qquad\qquad\qquad\qquad\qquad\qquad}$

$Zn(s) + 2 VO^{2+}(aq) + 4 H^+(aq) \rightarrow Zn^{2+}(aq) + 2 V^{3+}(aq) + 2 H_2O(\ell)$

(b) $3[Zn(s) \rightarrow Zn^{2+}(aq) + 2 e^-]$

$2[VO_3^-(aq) + 6 H^+(aq) + 3 e^- \rightarrow V^{2+}(aq) + 3 H_2O(\ell)]$

$\overline{\qquad\qquad\qquad\qquad\qquad\qquad\qquad\qquad\qquad\qquad\qquad\qquad}$

$3 Zn(s) + 2 VO_3^-(aq) + 12 H^+(aq) \rightarrow 3 Zn^{2+}(aq) + 2 V^{3+}(aq) + 6 H_2O(\ell)$

(c) $Zn(s) + 2 OH^-(aq) \rightarrow Zn(OH)_2(s) + 2 e^-$

$ClO^-(aq) + H_2O(\ell) + 2 e^- \rightarrow Cl^-(aq) + 2 OH^-(aq)$

$Zn(s) + OCl^-(aq) + H_2O(\ell) \rightarrow Zn(OH)_2(s) + Cl^-$

(aq)

(d) $3[ClO^-(aq) + H_2O(\ell) + 2 e^- \rightarrow Cl^-(aq) + 2 OH^-(aq)]$

$2[Cr(OH)_4^-(aq) + 4 OH^-(aq) \rightarrow CrO_4^{2-}(aq) + 4 H_2O(\ell) + 3 e^-]$

$3 ClO^-(aq) + 2 Cr(OH)_4^-(aq) + 2 OH^-(aq) \rightarrow 3 Cl^-(aq) + 2 CrO_4^{2-}(aq) + 5 H_2O(\ell)$

20.53   (a) The electrode at the right is a magnesium anode; magnesium metal supplies electrons and is oxidized to Mg^{2+} ions. Electrons pass through the wire to the silver cathode where Ag^+ ions are reduced to silver. Nitrate ions in the salt bridge move from the $AgNO_3$ solution to the $Mg(NO_3)_2$ solution (and Na^+ ions move in the opposite direction).

(b) Anode: $Mg(s) \rightarrow Mg^{2+}(aq) + 2 e^-$

Cathode: $Ag^+(aq) + e^- \rightarrow Ag(s)$

Net reaction: $Mg(s) + 2 Ag^+(aq) \rightarrow Mg^{2+}(aq) + 2 Ag(s)$

(c) See (a). The salt bridge is necessary to maintain charge balance in the cell.

20.54 $Zn^{2+}(aq) + 2 e^- \rightarrow Zn(s)$ $E^\circ_{cathode} = -0.763$ V

$Zn(s) \rightarrow Zn^{2+}(aq) + 2 e^-$ $E^\circ_{anode} = -0.763$ V

(a) $E^\circ_{anode} = E^\circ_{cathode} - E^\circ_{cell} = -0.763$ V $- (1.1$ V$) = -1.86$ V

Aluminum (-1.66 V) would be an appropriate choice

$E^\circ_{cathode} = E^\circ_{cell} + E^\circ_{anode} = 1.1$ V $+ (-0.763$ V$) = 0.34$ V

Copper (0.337 V) would be an appropriate choice

(b) $E^\circ_{anode} = E^\circ_{cathode} - E^\circ_{cell} = -0.763$ V $- (0.5$ V$) = -1.26$ V

Vanadium (-1.18 V) or manganese (-1.18 V) would be appropriate choices

$E^\circ_{cathode} = E^\circ_{cell} + E^\circ_{anode} = 0.5$ V $+ (-0.763$ V$) = -0.26$ V

Nickel (-0.25 V) or cobalt (-0.28 V) would be appropriate choices

20.55 $Ag^+(aq) + e^- \rightarrow Ag(s)$ $E^\circ_{cathode} = 0.7994$ V

$Ag(s) \rightarrow Ag^+(aq) + e^-$ $E^\circ_{anode} = 0.7994$ V

(a) $E^\circ_{anode} = E^\circ_{cathode} - E^\circ_{cell} = 0.7994$ V $- (1.7$ V$) = -0.90$ V

Chromium (-0.91 V) would be an appropriate choice

$E^\circ_{cathode} = E^\circ_{cell} + E^\circ_{anode} = 1.7$ V $+ (0.7994$ V$) = 2.5$ V

Fluorine (2.87 V) would be an appropriate choice

(b) $E^{\circ}_{anode} = E^{\circ}_{cathode} - E^{\circ}_{cell} = 0.7994 \text{ V} - (0.5 \text{ V}) = 0.30 \text{ V}$

Copper (0.337 V) would be an appropriate choice

$E^{\circ}_{cathode} = E^{\circ}_{cell} + E^{\circ}_{anode} = 0.5 \text{ V} + (0.7994 \text{ V}) = 1.3 \text{ V}$

Chlorine (1.36 V) would be an appropriate choice

20.56 (a) product-favored (I_2 is a stronger oxidizing agent than Zn^{2+})

(b) reactant-favored (Cl_2 is a stronger oxidizing agent than I_2)

(c) reactant-favored (Cl_2 is a stronger oxidizing agent than Na^+)

(d) product-favored (H_2O is a stronger oxidizing agent than K^+)

20.57 (a) $Zn^{2+}(aq)$ (e) Yes

(b) $Au^+(aq)$ (f) No

(c) $Zn(s)$ (g) $Cu^{2+}(aq)$, $Ag^+(aq)$, $Au^+(aq)$

(d) $Au(s)$ (h) $Cu(s)$, $Sn(s)$, $Co(s)$, $Zn(s)$

20.58 (a) $Se(s)$ (e) Yes

(b) $F^-(aq)$ (f) No

(c) $Cl_2(g)$, $F_2(g)$ (g) No

(d) $F_2(g)$, $Cl_2(g)$, $O_2(g)$, $Br_2(\ell)$, $I_2(s)$ (h) Yes

20.59 (a) The combination of a negative E°_{anode} half-cell with a SHE cathode (0 V) will result in a positive E°_{cell}

$Cr^{3+}(aq) + 3 \text{ e}^- \rightarrow Cr(s)$ $E^{\circ}_{anode} = -0.74 \text{ V}$

$Fe^{2+}(aq) + 2 \text{ e}^- \rightarrow Fe(s)$ $E^{\circ}_{anode} = -0.44 \text{ V}$

$Mg^{2+}(aq) + 2 \text{ e}^- \rightarrow Mg(s)$ $E^{\circ}_{anode} = -2.37 \text{ V}$

(b) Highest voltage (Mg): $E^{\circ}_{cell} = (0.00 \text{ V}) - (-2.37 \text{ V}) = 2.37 \text{ V}$

Lowest voltage (Cu): $E^{\circ}_{cell} = (0.337 \text{ V}) - (0.00 \text{ V}) = 0.337 \text{ V}$

20.60 (a) Cu-Zn and Cu-Co

Cu-Co and Ag-Co

(b) Ag-Zn: $E^{\circ}_{cell} = (0.7994 \text{ V}) - (-0.763 \text{ V}) = 1.562 \text{ V}$

Ag-Cu: $E^{\circ}_{cell} = (0.7994 \text{ V}) - (0.337 \text{ V}) = 0.462 \text{ V}$

20.61 $(24 \text{ h})(60 \text{ min}/1 \text{ h})(60 \text{ s}/1 \text{ min})(1.0 \times 10^5 \text{ A}) = 8.6 \times 10^9 \text{ C}$

$(8.6 \times 10^9 \text{ C})\left(\dfrac{1 \text{ mol e}^-}{96,500 \text{ C}}\right)\left(\dfrac{1 \text{ mol Al}}{3 \text{ mol e}^-}\right)\left(\dfrac{27.0 \text{ g}}{1 \text{ mol Al}}\right) = 8.1 \times 10^5 \text{ g Al}$

20.62 (a) $E°_{cathode} = E°_{cell} + E°_{anode} = -0.146$ V $+ (0.7994$ V$) = 0.653$ V

(b) $\ln K = \dfrac{nE°}{0.0257 \text{ V}} = \dfrac{(2)(-0.146 \text{ V})}{0.0257 \text{ V}} = -11.4$

$K = 1 \times 10^{-5}$

20.63 (a) $E°_{anode} = E°_{cathode} - E°_{cell} = -0.126$ V $- (0.142$ V$) = -0.268$ V

(b) $\ln K = \dfrac{nE°}{0.0257 \text{ V}} = \dfrac{(2)(0.142 \text{ V})}{0.0257 \text{ V}} = 11.1$

$K = 6 \times 10^4$

$K_{sp} = 1/K = 2 \times 10^{-5}$

20.64 $Cl_2(g) + Zn(s) \rightarrow Zn^{2+}(aq) + 2 Cl^-(aq)$

$\Delta G° = nFE° = -(2 \text{ mol e}^-)(96,500 \text{ C/mol e}^-)(2.12 \text{ V})(1 \text{ J}/1 \text{ C·V})(1 \text{ kJ}/10^3 \text{ J}) = -409$ kJ

20.65 $Mg(s) + I_2(s) \rightarrow 2 I^-(aq) + Mg^{2+}(aq)$

$\Delta G° = nFE° = -(2 \text{ mol e}^-)(96,500 \text{ C/mol e}^-)(2.91 \text{ V})(1 \text{ J}/1 \text{ C·V})(1 \text{ kJ}/10^3 \text{ J}) = -562$ kJ

20.66 $(1.0 \times 10^3 \text{ kg})\left(\dfrac{10^3 \text{ g}}{1 \text{ kg}}\right)\left(\dfrac{1 \text{ mol Al}}{27.0 \text{ g}}\right)\left(\dfrac{3 \text{ mol e}^-}{1 \text{mol Al}}\right)\left(\dfrac{96,500 \text{ C}}{1 \text{ mol e}^-}\right)(5.0 \text{ V})\left(\dfrac{1 \text{ J}}{1 \text{ C·V}}\right)\left(\dfrac{1 \text{ kwh}}{3.6 \times 10^6 \text{ J}}\right)$

$= 1.5 \times 10^4$ kwh

20.67 $2 NaCl(\ell) \rightarrow 2 Na(s) + Cl_2(g)$

$(24 \text{ h})(60 \text{ min}/1 \text{ h})(60 \text{ s}/1 \text{ min})(4.0 \times 10^4 \text{ A}) = 3.5 \times 10^9$ C

$(3.5 \times 10^9 \text{ C})\left(\dfrac{1 \text{ mol e}^-}{96,500 \text{ C}}\right)\left(\dfrac{2 \text{ mol Na}}{2 \text{ mol e}^-}\right)\left(\dfrac{23.0 \text{ g}}{1 \text{ mol Na}}\right) = 8.2 \times 10^5$ g Na

$(3.5 \times 10^9 \text{ C})\left(\dfrac{1 \text{ mol e}^-}{96,500 \text{ C}}\right)\left(\dfrac{1 \text{ mol Cl}_2}{2 \text{ mol e}^-}\right)\left(\dfrac{70.9 \text{ g}}{1 \text{ mol Cl}_2}\right) = 1.3 \times 10^6$ g Cl$_2$

$(3.5 \times 10^9 \text{ C})(7.0 \text{ V})(1 \text{ J}/1 \text{ C·V})(1 \text{ kwh}/3.6 \times 10^6 \text{ J}) = 6700$ kwh

20.68 $0.038 \text{ g} \cdot \dfrac{1 \text{ mol Rh}}{102.9 \text{ g}} = 3.7 \times 10^{-4}$ mol Rh

$(3.00 \text{ h})(60.0 \text{ min}/1 \text{ h})(60.0 \text{ s}/1 \text{ min})(0.0100 \text{ A}) = 108$ C

$(108 \text{ C})\left(\dfrac{1 \text{ mol e}^-}{96,500 \text{ C}}\right) = 0.00112$ mol e$^-$

$\dfrac{0.00112 \text{ mol e}^-}{3.7 \times 10^{-4} \text{ mol Rh}} = 3 \text{ mol e}^-/\text{mol Rh} \qquad\qquad Rh^{3+} \qquad\qquad Rh_2(SO_4)_3$

20.69 $0.345 \text{ g} \cdot \dfrac{1 \text{ mol Ru}}{101.1 \text{ g}} = 0.00341 \text{ mol Ru}$

$(25.0 \text{ min})(60.0 \text{ s}/1 \text{ min})(0.44 \text{ A}) = 660 \text{ C}$

$(660 \text{ C})\left(\dfrac{1 \text{ mol e}^-}{96,500 \text{ C}}\right) = 0.0068 \text{ mol e}^-$

$\dfrac{0.0068 \text{ mol e}^-}{0.00341 \text{ mol Ru}} = 2 \text{ mol e}^-/\text{mol Ru}$ Ru^{2+} $Ru(NO_3)_2$

20.70 $(35 \text{ A-h})\left(\dfrac{1 \text{ C/s}}{1 \text{ A}}\right)\left(\dfrac{3600 \text{ sec}}{1 \text{ h}}\right)\left(\dfrac{1 \text{ mol e}^-}{96,500 \text{ C}}\right)\left(\dfrac{1 \text{ mol Zn}}{2 \text{ mol e}^-}\right)\left(\dfrac{65.39 \text{ g}}{1 \text{ mol Zn}}\right) = 43 \text{ g Zn}$

20.71 $(24 \text{ h})(60.0 \text{ min}/1 \text{ h})(60.0 \text{ s}/1 \text{ min})(3.0 \times 10^5 \text{ A}) = 2.4 \times 10^{11} \text{ C}$

$(2.4 \times 10^{11} \text{ C})\left(\dfrac{1 \text{ mol e}^-}{96,500 \text{ C}}\right)\left(\dfrac{1 \text{ mol Cl}_2}{2 \text{ mol e}^-}\right)\left(\dfrac{70.9 \text{ g}}{1 \text{ mol Cl}_2}\right) = 8.9 \times 10^7 \text{ g Cl}_2$

20.72 $0.052 \text{ g Ag}\left(\dfrac{1 \text{ mol Ag}}{107.9 \text{ g}}\right)\left(\dfrac{1 \text{ mol e}^-}{1 \text{ mol Ag}}\right)\left(\dfrac{96,500 \text{ C}}{1 \text{ mol e}^-}\right) = 47 \text{ C}$

Current = charge/time = $(46 \text{ C})/(450 \text{ s}) = 0.10 \text{ A}$

20.73 $0.089 \text{ g}\left(\dfrac{1 \text{ mol Ag}}{107.9 \text{ g}}\right)\left(\dfrac{1 \text{ mol e}^-}{1 \text{ mol Ag}}\right)\left(\dfrac{1 \text{ mol Au}}{3 \text{ mol e}^-}\right)\left(\dfrac{197.0 \text{ g}}{1 \text{ mol Au}}\right) = 0.054 \text{ g Au}$

20.74   (a) $HCO_2H + 2 H^+ + 2 e^- \rightarrow HCHO + H_2O$

(b) $C_6H_5CO_2H + 6 H^+ + 6 e^- \rightarrow C_6H_5CH_3 + 2 H_2O$

(c) $CH_3CH_2CHO + 2 H^+ + 2 e^- \rightarrow CH_3CH_2CH_2OH$

(d) $CH_3OH + 2 H^+ + 2 e^- \rightarrow CH_4 + H_2O$

20.75   (a) $2[Ag^+(aq) + e^- \rightarrow Ag(s)]$

$\underline{C_6H_5CHO(aq) + H_2O(\ell) \rightarrow C_6H_5CO_2H(aq) + 2 H^+(aq) + 2 e^-}$

$2 Ag^+(aq) + C_6H_5CHO(aq) + H_2O(\ell) \rightarrow C_6H_5CO_2H(aq) + 2 H^+(aq) + Ag(s)$

(b) $3[CH_3CH_2OH(aq) + H_2O(\ell) \rightarrow CH_3CO_2H(aq) + 4 H^+(aq) + 4 e^-]$

$\underline{2[Cr_2O_7{}^{2-}(aq) + 14 H^+(aq) + 6 e^- \rightarrow 2 Cr^{3+}(aq) + 7 H_2O(\ell)]}$

$3 CH_3CH_2OH(aq) + 2 Cr_2O_7{}^{2-}(aq) + 16 H^+(aq) \rightarrow 3 CH_3CO_2H(aq) + 4 Cr^{3+}(aq) + 11 H_2O(\ell)$

20.76   (a) $E°_{cell} = E°_{cathode} - E°_{anode} = (0.7994 \text{ V}) - (0.771 \text{ V}) = 0.028 \text{ V}$

       (b) $Ag^+(aq) + Fe^{2+}(aq) \rightarrow Ag(s) + Fe^{3+}(aq)$

       (c) Reduction takes place at the silver cathode and oxidation occurs at the platinum electrode in the Fe^{2+}/Fe^{3+} solution.

       (d) $E_{cell} = E°_{cell} - \dfrac{0.0257}{n} \ln \dfrac{[Fe^{3+}]}{[Ag^+][Fe^{2+}]} = 0.028 \text{ V} - \dfrac{0.0257}{1} \ln \dfrac{1.0}{(0.10)(1.0)} = -0.031 \text{ V}$

          The net cell reaction is now the reverse: $Ag(s) + Fe^{3+}(aq) \rightarrow Ag^+(aq) + Fe^{2+}(aq)$

20.77   (a) $\left(\dfrac{1 \text{ mol reactants}}{231.7 \text{ g} + 65.39 \text{ g} + 18.02 \text{ g}}\right)\left(\dfrac{2 \text{ mol e}^-}{1 \text{ mol reactants}}\right)\left(\dfrac{96{,}500 \text{ C}}{1 \text{ mol e}^-}\right)(1.59 \text{ V})\left(\dfrac{1 \text{ J}}{1 \text{ C·V}}\right)\left(\dfrac{1 \text{ kJ}}{10^3 \text{ J}}\right) = 0.974 \text{ kJ/g}$

       (b) $Pb(s) + PbO_2(s) + 2 H_2SO_4(aq) \rightarrow 2 PbSO_4(s) + 2 H_2O(\ell)$

          $\left(\dfrac{1 \text{ mol reactants}}{207.2 \text{ g} + 239.2 \text{ g} + 2(98.08 \text{ g})}\right)\left(\dfrac{2 \text{ mol e}^-}{1 \text{ mol reactants}}\right)\left(\dfrac{96{,}500 \text{ C}}{1 \text{ mol e}^-}\right)(2.0 \text{ V})\left(\dfrac{1 \text{ J}}{1 \text{ C·V}}\right)\left(\dfrac{1 \text{ kJ}}{10^3 \text{ J}}\right) = 0.60 \text{ kJ/g}$

       (c) The silver-zinc battery produces more energy per gram of reactants

20.78   (a) $(15 \text{ h})(60.0 \text{ min}/1 \text{ h})(60.0 \text{ s}/1 \text{ min})(1.5 \text{ A}) = 8.1 \times 10^4 \text{ C}$

          $(8.1 \times 10^4 \text{ C})\left(\dfrac{1 \text{ mol e}^-}{96{,}500 \text{ C}}\right)\left(\dfrac{1 \text{ mol Pb}}{2 \text{ mol e}^-}\right)\left(\dfrac{207.2 \text{ g}}{1 \text{ mol Pb}}\right) = 87 \text{ g Pb}$

       (b) $(8.1 \times 10^4 \text{ C})\left(\dfrac{1 \text{ mol e}^-}{96{,}500 \text{ C}}\right)\left(\dfrac{1 \text{ mol PbO}_2}{2 \text{ mol e}^-}\right)\left(\dfrac{239.2 \text{ g}}{1 \text{ mol PbO}_2}\right) = 100. \text{ g PbO}_2$

       (c) $(8.1 \times 10^4 \text{ C})\left(\dfrac{1 \text{ mol e}^-}{96{,}500 \text{ C}}\right)\left(\dfrac{2 \text{ mol H}_2SO_4}{2 \text{ mol e}^-}\right)\left(\dfrac{1}{0.50 \text{ L}}\right) = 1.7 \text{ M}$

20.79   (a) $150 \text{ g} \cdot \dfrac{1 \text{ mol CH}_3SO_2F}{98.1 \text{ g}} \cdot \dfrac{3 \text{ mol HF}}{1 \text{ mol CH}_3SO_2F} \cdot \dfrac{20.0 \text{ g}}{1 \text{ mol HF}} = 92 \text{ g HF}$

          $150 \text{ g} \cdot \dfrac{1 \text{ mol CH}_3SO_2F}{98.1 \text{ g}} \cdot \dfrac{1 \text{ mol CF}_3SO_2F}{1 \text{ mol CH}_3SO_2F} \cdot \dfrac{152 \text{ g}}{1 \text{ mol CF}_3SO_2F} = 230 \text{ g CF}_3SO_2F$

          $150 \text{ g} \cdot \dfrac{1 \text{ mol CH}_3SO_2F}{98.1 \text{ g}} \cdot \dfrac{3 \text{ mol H}_2}{1 \text{ mol CH}_3SO_2F} \cdot \dfrac{2.02 \text{ g}}{1 \text{ mol H}_2} = 9.3 \text{ g H}_2$

       (b) H_2 is produced at the cathode.

       (c) $(24 \text{ h})\left(\dfrac{3600 \text{ sec}}{1 \text{ h}}\right)\left(\dfrac{250 \text{ C}}{1 \text{ sec}}\right)(8.0 \text{ V})\left(\dfrac{1 \text{ J}}{1 \text{ V·C}}\right)\left(\dfrac{1 \text{ kwh}}{3.6 \times 10^6 \text{ J}}\right) = 48 \text{ kwh}$

20.80   (a) Efficiency $= \dfrac{\Delta G_f°[H_2O(\ell)]}{\Delta H_f°[H_2O(\ell)]} \cdot 100\% = \dfrac{-237.15 \text{ kJ/mol}}{-285.83 \text{ kJ/mol}} \cdot 100\% = 82.969\%$

       (b) Efficiency $= \dfrac{\Delta G_f°[H_2O(g)]}{\Delta H_f°[H_2O(g)]} \cdot 100\% = \dfrac{-228.59 \text{ kJ/mol}}{-241.83 \text{ kJ/mol}} \cdot 100\% = 94.525\%$

       (c) The efficiency is greater for the gaseous product, possibly due to energy loss when converting gaseous water to the liquid phase.

20.81 (a)

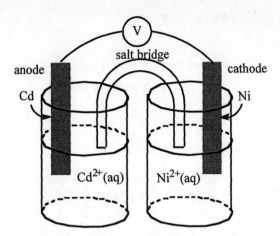

(b) $Ni^{2+}(aq) + Cd(s) \rightarrow Ni(s) + Cd^{2+}(aq)$

(c) The anode is negative and the cathode is positive

(d) $E^\circ_{cell} = (-0.25 \text{ V}) - (-0.40\text{V}) = 0.15 \text{ V}$

(e) Electrons flow from the anode to the cathode

(f) Na^+ ions move from the cathode compartment to the anode compartment. NO_3^- ions move in the opposite direction.

(g) $\ln K = \dfrac{nE^\circ}{0.0257 \text{ V}} = \dfrac{(2)(0.15 \text{ V})}{0.0257 \text{ V}} = 12 \qquad K = 1 \times 10^5$

(h) $E_{cell} = E^\circ_{cell} - \dfrac{0.0257}{n} \ln \dfrac{[Cd^{2+}]}{[Ni^{2+}]} = 0.15 \text{ V} - \dfrac{0.0257}{2} \ln\left(\dfrac{0.010}{1.0}\right) = 0.21 \text{ V}$

The reaction is still the one written in part (b).

(i) Determine which reactant is consumed first:

$(1.0 \text{ L Ni}^{2+})(1.0 \text{ mol/L}) = 1.0 \text{ mol Ni}^2$

$50.0 \text{ g Cd} \cdot \dfrac{1 \text{mol Cd}}{112.4 \text{ g}} = 0.445 \text{ mol Cd (limiting reactant)}$

$(0.445 \text{ mol Cd})\left(\dfrac{2 \text{ mol } e^-}{1 \text{ mol Cd}}\right)\left(\dfrac{96{,}500 \text{ C}}{1 \text{ mol } e^-}\right) = 8.59 \times 10^4 \text{ C}$

$(8.59 \times 10^4 \text{ C}/0.050 \text{ A}) = 1.7 \times 10^6 \text{ s (or 480 h)}$

20.82 pH = 7: $E_{cell} = E^\circ_{cell} - \dfrac{0.0257}{n} \ln [OH^-]^2 P_{H_2} = -0.83 \text{ V} - \dfrac{0.0257}{2} \ln(1.0 \times 10^{-7})^2 (1) = -0.42 \text{ V}$

pH = 0: $E_{cell} = -0.83 \text{ V} - \dfrac{0.0257}{2} \ln(1.0 \times 10^{-14})^2 (1) = 0 \text{ V}$

pH = 1: $E_{cell} = -0.83 \text{ V} - \dfrac{0.0257}{2} \ln(1.0 \times 10^{-13})^2 (1) = -0.06 \text{ V}$

It is much more advantageous to reduce water in an acidic solution.

20.83 I^- is the strongest reducing agent of the three halide ions. It reduces Cu^{2+} to Cu^+, forming insoluble $CuI(s)$.

$2 \text{ Cu}^{2+}(aq) + 4 \text{ I}^-(aq) \rightarrow 2 \text{ CuI}(s) + I_2(aq)$

20.84   (a) Reducing agent strength: $H_2 < A$ and C

(b) C is stronger than B, D, and A

(c) D is stronger than B

$B < D < H_2 < A < C$

20.85 $n_{H_2} = \dfrac{PV}{RT} = \dfrac{(200.\ atm)(1.0\ L)}{(0.082057\ L \cdot atm/K \cdot mol)(298\ K)} = 8.2\ mol\ H_2$

$(8.2\ mol\ H_2)\left(\dfrac{2\ mol\ e^-}{1\ mol\ H_2}\right)\left(\dfrac{96{,}500\ C}{1\ mol\ e^-}\right) = 1.6 \times 10^6\ C$

Time = $(1.6 \times 10^6\ C)/(1.5\ A) = 1.1 \times 10^6$ s (or 290 h)

20.86   (a) $2.4 \times 10^3\ kcal \cdot \dfrac{4.184\ kJ}{1\ kcal} \cdot \dfrac{1\ mol\ glucose}{2800\ kJ} = 3.6\ mol\ glucose$

$3.6\ mol\ glucose \cdot \dfrac{6\ mol\ O_2}{1\ mol\ glucose} = 22\ mol\ O_2$

(b) $O_2(g) + 4\ H^+(aq) + 4\ e^- \rightarrow 2\ H_2O(\ell)$

$22\ mol\ O_2 \cdot \dfrac{4\ mol\ e^-}{1\ mol\ O_2} = 86\ mol\ e^-$

(c) $\left(\dfrac{3.6\ mol\ glucose}{24\ h}\right)\left(\dfrac{1\ h}{3600\ sec}\right)\left(\dfrac{86\ mol\ e^-}{3.6\ mol\ glucose}\right)\left(\dfrac{96{,}500\ C}{1\ mol\ e^-}\right) = 96$ amps

(d) $\left(\dfrac{96\ C}{1\ sec}\right)(1.0\ V)\left(\dfrac{1\ J}{1\ V \cdot C}\right)\left(\dfrac{1\ watt}{1\ J/s}\right) = 96$ watts

20.87   (a) Au^{3+}, Br_2, Hg^{2+}, Ag^+, Hg_2^{2+}

(b) Al, Mg, Li

Chapter 21
The Chemistry of the Main Group Elements

INSTRUCTOR'S NOTES

Because main group elements and their compounds are of such great economic importance, and have an interesting chemistry, this chapter is a brief introduction to these elements. Beginning with this chapter, the material in the remainder of the book is covered to the extent that time is available at the end of the course. We have, regrettably, too little time for a thorough discussion of descriptive chemistry. Indeed, this was one motivating factor in placing as much descriptive chemistry as possible early in the text.

Normally we hope to have at least six to nine lectures on descriptive chemistry at the end of the second term. This enables us to discuss a few aspects of the chemistry of the following elements: H; Li and Na; Mg and Ca; B and Al; C and Si; N and P; O and S; and F and Cl.

This edition has been expanded to include some general coverage of elements in each group instead of just one or two examples (e.g. addition of boron chemistry to that of aluminum in Group 3A; other halogens with chlorine in Group 7A).

The diverse chemistry of these elements provides a perfect opportunity for demos, both live and on video. In addition to the media found on *General ChemistryNow CD-ROM* there is a video clip of the Hindenburg on the National Geographic's website: http://www.nationalgeographic.com/tv/explorer/exp101099.html

SUGGESTED DEMONSTRATIONS

1. The Periodic Table—A Guide to the Elements
    *   *The Periodic Table Videodisc* and the *Periodic Table Live!* CD-ROM have excellent images of the reactions of the elements with air, water, and acids and bases. The advantage in using the videodisc is that one can quickly scan through the various types of reactions and illustrate the periodic trends of the elements. In addition, the videodisc contains images of the uses of the elements. Many of the demonstrations described in this chapter can also be found on the *Redox Videodisc*.

2. Hydrogen
    *   An excellent demonstration to use at the beginning of the discussion of hydrogen chemistry is to blow up a hydrogen-filled balloon. This can be made more interesting by filling a balloon with He and contrasting their behavior. The students can readily figure out which balloon contains H_2 gas.
    *   One can demonstrate the various ways of making H_2, such as electrolysis, a metal + acid, Al + base, or a metal hydride + water. For more information on hydrogen, you will find it interesting and useful to read the book *Hydrogen Power* by L. O. Williams, Pergamon, 1980. Also useful are chapters in *The Modern Inorganic Chemicals Industry* (R. Thompson, ed., Royal Society, 1977) and *Industrial Inorganic Chemistry*

by W. Büchner, R. Schliebs, G. Winter, and K. H. Büchel (VCH, 1989). A very interesting article on the "hydrogen economy" was done by G. Graff in *High Technology* magazine, May, 1983.

- *ChemMatters* for October, 1985 was devoted to hydrogen and helium chemistry.

3. Sodium and Potassium

- Demonstrate the flame colors of Na- and K-containing salts. (Sanger, M. J.; Phelps, A. J. "Simple Flame Test Techniques Using Cotton Swabs," *Journal of Chemical Education* **2004**, *81*, 969; Johnson, K. A.; Schreiner, R. "A Dramatic Flame Test Demonstration," *Journal of Chemical Education* **2001**, *78*, 640; Dragojlovik, V. "Flame Tests Using Improvised Alcohol Burners," *Journal of Chemical Education* **1999**, *76*, 929.)

- Show the reactions of the alkali metals with water. *Caution!* The reaction of K with water should be done behind a shield. In both cases, place an indicator in the water to show the formation of metal hydroxide.

- Show the ease with which Na and K can be cut with a knife.

- Herman, Z. S. "Ionic Crystals: A Simple and Safe Lecture Demonstration of the Preparation of NaI from its Elements," *Journal of Chemical Education* **2000**, *77*, 619.

4. Calcium and Magnesium

- Minerals containing alkaline earth metals are readily available: calcite, marble, shells, and fluorite, among others.

- Show the flame colors of the alkaline earth elements. (Sanger, M. J.; Phelps, A. J. "Simple Flame Test Techniques Using Cotton Swabs," *Journal of Chemical Education* **2004**, *81*, 969; Johnson, K. A.; Schreiner, R. "A Dramatic Flame Test Demonstration," *Journal of Chemical Education* **2001**, *78*, 640; Dragojlovik, V. "Flame Tests Using Improvised Alcohol Burners," *Journal of Chemical Education* **1999**, *76*, 929.)

- The reactions of Mg and Ca can be compared with Group 1 A elements. Magnesium will not react with water at room temperature, whereas Ca will react readily.

- Calcium carbide is an important chemical. Its hydrolysis to give acetylene is readily illustrated.

5. Aluminum

- Demonstrate the formation of $Al(OH)_3$ and its amphoterism.

- Illustrate the absorption of dyes by aluminum hydroxide and alumina.

- Show the non reactivity of aluminum with an oxidizing acid. This can be contrasted with the reaction of Al with $CuCl_2$.

- The thermite reaction is an impressive classroom demonstration. Directions for this reaction are given in Shakhashiri, Volume 1. We do the reaction by piling a small quantity of the reactants on a bed of sand on the demonstration table. The students are kept back about 20 feet.

- Aluminum chloride is a very important industrial chemical; almost 25000 tons are produced annually in the United States. It is very useful to show that this halide is unstable toward water, in contrast with Group 1A and 2A halides. Use $AlCl_3$ from a newly opened bottle of $AlCl_3$ and add a spatula-full to 10-20 mL of water.

- The reaction of Al with Br_2 is spectacular. However, it can only be done in a lecture room that has an excellent hood.

6. Silicon

- Silicon and silicon-based minerals are extremely important in our economy. It would be well to exhibit as many examples as possible. These include quartz, amethyst, various clays (including "kitty litter), zeolites, mica, talc, vermiculite, and (with proper precautions) asbestos.

- Other silicon-containing materials are silicon carbide, glass, and cement.

7. Nitrogen and Phosphorus

- Demonstrations involving nitrogen and phosphorus that can be found in B. Z. Shakhashiri's *Chemical Demonstrations: A Handbook for Teachers of Chemistry*:

   Reaction of Zn with NH_4NO_3 and NH_4Cl

   Reaction of white P_4 and Cl_2

   Reaction of red P_4 and Br_2

   Combustion of white P_4

   Decomposition of $(NH_4)_2Cr_2O_7$

   Preparation and properties of NO NO_2/N_2O_4 equilibrium

8. Oxygen and Sulfur

- Demonstrations involving sulfur and oxygen that can be found in B. Z. Shakhashiri's *Chemical Demonstrations: A Handbook for Teachers of Chemistry*:

   Heat of Dilution of H_2SO_4

   Reaction of Zn and S_8

   Reaction of Fe and S_8

   Dehydration of sugar by H_2SO_4

   Preparation and properties of O_2

   Preparation and properties of liquid O_2

9. Chlorine

- Demonstrations involving chlorine that can be found in B. Z. Shakhashiri's *Chemical Demonstrations: A Handbook for Teachers of Chemistry*:

   Reaction of Na and Cl_2

   Reaction of Fe and Cl_2

SOLUTIONS TO STUDY QUESTIONS

21.1 $4 \, Li(s) + O_2(g) \rightarrow 2 \, Li_2O(s)$ $Li_2O(s) + H_2O(\ell) \rightarrow 2 \, LiOH(aq)$

   $2 \, Ca(s) + O_2(g) \rightarrow 2 \, CaO(s)$ $CaO(s) + H_2O(\ell) \rightarrow Ca(OH)_2(aq)$

21.2 $N_2(g) + 2 \, O_2(g) \rightarrow 2 \, NO_2(g)$ $2 \, NO_2(g) + H_2O(\ell) \rightarrow HNO_3(aq) + HNO_2(aq)$

   $2 \, S(s) + 3 \, O_2(g) \rightarrow 2 \, SO_3(g)$ $SO_3(g) + H_2O(\ell) \rightarrow H_2SO_4(aq)$

21.3   These are the elements of Group 3A: Boron, B; Aluminum, Al; Gallium, Ga; Indium, In; Thallium, Tl

21.4 S^{2-}, sulfide ion; Cl^-, chloride ion; K^+, potassium ion; Ca^{2+}, calcium ion

21.5 $2 \, Na(s) + Cl_2(g) \rightarrow 2 \, NaCl(s)$

   The reaction is likely to be exothermic and the product is ionic.

21.6 $2 \, Mg(s) + O_2(g) \rightarrow 2 \, MgO(s)$

   The reaction is likely to be exothermic and the product is ionic.

21.7   NaCl is colorless, a solid, and soluble in water.

21.8   MgO is white, a solid, and insoluble in water.

21.9   No, calcium is a reactive metal and would not be found as a free element.

21.10   Only C is found as the free element in Earth's crust. H, Li, Be, B, N, O, and F are found in compounds.

21.11 $CO_2 < SiO_2 < SnO_2$

   —increasing basicity→

21.12 $SO_3 < SiO_2 < Al_2O_3 < Na_2O$

   —increasing basicity→

21.13   (a) $2 \, Na(s) + Br_2(\ell) \rightarrow 2 \, NaBr(s)$

   (b) $2 \, Mg(s) + O_2(g) \rightarrow 2 \, MgO(s)$

   (c) $2 \, Al(s) + 3 \, F_2(g) \rightarrow 2 \, AlF_3(g)$

   (d) $C(s) + O_2(g) \rightarrow CO_2(g)$

21.14   (a) $2\ K(s) + I_2(s) \rightarrow 2\ KI(s)$

(b) $2\ Ba(s) + O_2(g) \rightarrow 2\ BaO(s)$

(c) $16\ Al(s) + 3\ S_8(s) \rightarrow 8\ Al_2S_3(s)$

(d) $Si(s) + 2\ Cl_2(g) \rightarrow SiCl_4(\ell)$

21.15 $2\ H_2(g) + O_2(g) \rightarrow 2\ H_2O(g)$

$H_2(g) + Cl_2(g) \rightarrow 2\ HCl(g)$

$3\ H_2(g) + N_2(g) \rightarrow 2\ NH_3(g)$

21.16 $2\ K(s) + H_2(g) \rightarrow 2\ KH(s)$ potassium hydride

The compound is ionic, a solid, and has a high melting point, and reacts vigorously with water.

21.17 $CH_4(g) + H_2O(g) \rightarrow 3\ H_2(g) + CO(g)$

$\Delta H° = \Delta H_f°[CO(g)] - \{\Delta H_f°[CH_4(g)] + \Delta H_f°[H_2O(g)]\}$

$\Delta H° = 1\ mol\ (-110.525\ kJ/mol) - [1\ mol\ (-74.87\ kJ/mol) + 1\ mol\ (-241.83\ kJ/mol)] = 206.18\ kJ$

$\Delta S° = 3\ S°[H_2(g)] + S°[CO(g)] - \{S°[CH_4(g)] + S°[H_2O(g)]\}$

$\Delta S° = 3\ mol\ (130.7\ J/K{\cdot}mol) + 1\ mol\ (197.674\ J/K{\cdot}mol) - [1\ mol\ (186.26\ J/K{\cdot}mol)$

$+ 1\ mol\ (188.84\ J/K{\cdot}mol)]$

$\Delta S° = 214.7\ J/K$

$\Delta G° = \Delta H° - T\Delta S° = 206.18\ kJ - (298\ K)(214.7\ J/K)(1\ kJ/10^3\ J) = 142.2\ kJ$

21.18 $C(s) + H_2O(g) \rightarrow CO(g) + H_2(g)$

$\Delta H° = \Delta H_f°[CO(g)] - \Delta H_f°[H_2O(g)] = 1\ mol\ (-110.525\ kJ/mol) - 1\ mol\ (-241.83\ kJ/mol) = 131.31\ kJ$

$\Delta S° = S°[CO(g)] + S°[H_2(g)] - \{S°[C(s)] + S°[H_2O(g)]\}$

$\Delta S° = 1\ mol\ (197.674\ J/K{\cdot}mol) + 1\ mol\ (130.7\ J/K{\cdot}mol) - [1\ mol\ (5.6\ J/K{\cdot}mol)$

$+ 1\ mol\ (188.84\ J/K{\cdot}mol)]$

$\Delta S° = 133.9\ J/K$

$\Delta G° = \Delta H° - T\Delta S° = 131.31\ kJ - (298\ K)(133.9\ J/K)(1\ kJ/10^3\ J) = 91.4\ kJ$

21.19   (a) $2\ SO_2(g) + 4\ H_2O(\ell) + 2\ I_2(s) \rightarrow 2\ H_2SO_4(\ell) + 4\ HI(g)$

(b) $2\ H_2SO_4(\ell) \rightarrow 2\ H_2O(\ell) + 2\ SO_2(g) + O_2(g)$

(c) $4\ HI(g) \rightarrow 2\ H_2(g) + 2\ I_2(g)$

$\overline{}$

$2\ H_2O(\ell) \rightarrow 2\ H_2(g) + O_2(g)$

21.20   Methane: $CH_4(g) + 3\ H_2O(g) \rightarrow H_2(g) + CO(g)$

$1\ mol\ CH_4 \cdot \dfrac{1\ mol\ H_2}{1\ mol\ CH_4} \cdot \dfrac{2.02\ g}{1\ mol\ H_2} = 2.0\ g\ H_2$

Petroleum: $CH_2(\ell) + H_2O(g) \rightarrow 2\ H_2(g) + CO(g)$

$1\ mol\ CH_2 \cdot \dfrac{2\ mol\ H_2}{1\ mol\ CH_2} \cdot \dfrac{2.02\ g}{1\ mol\ H_2} = 4.0\ g\ H_2$

Coal: $2\ CH(s) + 2\ H_2O(g) \rightarrow 3\ H_2(g) + 2\ CO(g)$

$1\ mol\ CH \cdot \dfrac{3\ mol\ H_2}{2\ mol\ CH} \cdot \dfrac{2.02\ g}{1\ mol\ H_2} = 3.0\ g\ H_2$

21.21 $Na(s) + F_2(g) \rightarrow 2\ NaF(s)$

$Na(s) + Cl_2(g) \rightarrow 2\ NaCl(s)$

$Na(s) + Br_2(\ell) \rightarrow 2\ NaBr(s)$

$Na(s) + I_2(s) \rightarrow 2\ NaI(s)$

The alkali metal halides are white, crystalline solids. They have high melting and boiling points, and are soluble in water.

21.22 $4\ Li(s) + O_2(g) \rightarrow 2\ Li_2O(s)$ lithium oxide

$2\ Na(s) + O_2(g) \rightarrow 2\ Na_2O_2(s)$ sodium peroxide

$K(s) + O_2(g) \rightarrow KO_2(s)$ potassium superoxide

21.23   (a) $2\ NaCl(aq) + 2\ H_2O(\ell) \rightarrow Cl_2(g) + H_2(g) + 2\ NaOH(aq)$

(b) $\dfrac{2\ mol\ NaOH}{1\ mol\ Cl_2} \cdot \dfrac{1\ mol\ Cl_2}{70.91\ g} \cdot \dfrac{40.00\ g}{1\ mol\ NaOH} = \dfrac{1.13\ g\ NaOH}{1\ g\ Cl_2}$

$\dfrac{1.19 \times 10^{10}\ kg\ NaOH}{1.14 \times 10^{10}\ kg\ Cl_2} = \dfrac{1.04\ kg\ NaOH}{1\ kg\ Cl_2}$

More chlorine is produced than can be accounted for by the electrolysis of aqueous sodium chloride. Chlorine is most likely produced by additional methods industrially.

21.24   (a) Anode: $2\ Cl^-(aq) \rightarrow Cl_2(g) + 2\ e^-$

Cathode: $2\ H_2O(\ell) + 2\ e^- \rightarrow 2\ OH^-(aq) + H_2(g)$

Chloride ion is oxidized and water is reduced.

(b) Anode: $2\ I^-(aq) \rightarrow I_2(s) + 2\ e^-$

Cathode: $2\ H_2O(\ell) + 2\ e^- \rightarrow 2\ OH^-(aq) + H_2(g)$

21.25 $2\ Mg(s) + O_2(g) \rightarrow 2\ MgO(s)$

$3\ Mg(s) + N_2(g) \rightarrow Mg_3N_2(s)$

21.26   (a) $Ca(s) + H_2(g) \rightarrow CaH_2(s)$

(b) $CaH_2(s) + 2\ H_2O(\ell) \rightarrow Ca(OH)_2(s) + 2\ H_2(g)$

21.27 $CaCO_3$ is used in agriculture to neutralize acidic soil, to prepare CaO for use in mortar, and in steel production. $CaCO_3(s) + H_2O(\ell) + CO_2(g) \rightarrow Ca^{2+}(aq) + 2\ HCO_3^-(aq)$

21.28   Hard water contains metal ions such as Ca^{2+} and Mg^{2+}. Hard water occurs as ground water flows through mineral beds having slightly soluble salts such as carbonates. Hard water ions react with soap to form insoluble soap scum. The ions decrease the lathering ability of the soap. Hard water leads to deposits of boiler scale in hot water heaters.

21.29 $CaO(s) + SO_2(g) \rightarrow CaSO_3(s)$

$$1.2 \times 10^3\ kg \cdot \frac{10^3\ g}{1\ kg} \cdot \frac{1\ mol\ CaO}{56.1\ g} \cdot \frac{1\ mol\ SO_2}{1\ mol\ CaO} \cdot \frac{64.1\ g}{1\ mol\ SO_2} = 1.4 \times 10^6\ g\ SO_2$$

21.30 $Ca(OH)_2(s) \rightleftharpoons Ca^{2+}(aq) + 2\ OH^-(aq)$ $K_{sp} = 5.5 \times 10^{-5}$

$Mg^{2+}(aq) + 2\ OH^-(aq) \rightleftharpoons Mg(OH)_2(s)$ $1/K_{sp} = 1/(5.6 \times 10^{-12})$

$Ca(OH)_2(s) + Mg^{2+}(aq) \rightleftharpoons Mg(OH)_2(s) + Ca^{2+}(aq)$ $K = 9.8 \times 10^6$

Adding $Ca(OH)_2$ to sea water will lead to the precipitation of $Mg(OH)_2$ which can then be further processed to ultimately yield Mg metal.

21.31 $B_3O_6{}^{3-}$ $B_2O_5{}^{4-}$

21.32   (a) $BCl_3(g) + 3\ H_2O(\ell) \rightarrow B(OH)_3(s) + 3\ HCl(aq)$

(b) $\Delta H^\circ = \Delta H_f^\circ[B(OH)_3(s)] + 3\ \Delta H_f^\circ[HCl(aq)] - \{\Delta H_f^\circ[BCl_3(g)] + 3\ \Delta H_f^\circ[H_2O(\ell)]\}$

$\Delta H^\circ = 1\ mol\ (-1094\ kJ/mol) + 1\ mol\ (-92.31\ kJ/mol)$

$- [1\ mol\ (-403\ kJ/mol) + 3\ mol\ (-285.83\ kJ/mol)]$

$\Delta H^\circ = 74\ kJ$

21.33 (a) $2\ B_5H_9(g) + 12\ O_2(g) \rightarrow 5\ B_2O_3(s) + 9\ H_2O(g)$

(b) $\Delta H° = 5\ \Delta H_f°[B_2O_3(s)] + 9\ \Delta H_f°[H_2O(g)] - 2\ \Delta H_f°[B_5H_9(g)]$

$\Delta H° = 5\ mol\ (-1271.9\ kJ/mol) + 9\ mol\ (-241.83\ kJ/mol) - 2\ mol\ (73.2\ kJ/mol)$

$\Delta H° = -8682.4\ kJ$

$\Delta H°_{comb} = -8682.4\ kJ/2\ mol\ B_5H_9 = -4341.2\ kJ/mol\ B_5H_9$

The heat of combustion is more than twice the heat of combustion of $B_2H_6(g)$.

(c) $2\ C_2H_6(g) + 7\ O_2(g) \rightarrow 4\ CO_2(g) + 6\ H_2O(g)$

$\Delta H° = 4\ \Delta H_f°[CO_2(g)] + 6\ \Delta H_f°[H_2O(g)] - 2\ \Delta H_f°[C_2H_6(g)]$

$\Delta H°_{rxn} = 4\ mol\ (-393.509\ kJ/mol) + 6\ mol\ (-241.83\ kJ/mol) - 2\ mol\ (-83.85\ kJ/mol)$

$\Delta H°_{rxn} = -2857.32\ kJ$

$$\frac{-2857.32\ kJ}{2\ mol\ C_2H_6} \cdot \frac{1\ mol\ C_2H_6}{30.0694\ g} = -47.5121\ kJ/g$$

$$\frac{-2038\ kJ}{1\ mol\ B_2H_6} \cdot \frac{1\ mol\ B_2H_6}{27.669\ g} = -73.66\ kJ/g$$

21.34 $NaBH_4$ is oxidized and I_2 is reduced.

21.35 $2\ Al(s) + 6\ HCl(aq) \rightarrow 2\ Al^{3+}(aq) + 6\ Cl^-(aq) + 3\ H_2(g)$

$2\ Al(s) + 3\ Cl_2(g) \rightarrow 2\ AlCl_3(s)$

$4\ Al(s) + 3\ O_2(g) \rightarrow 2\ Al_2O_3(s)$

21.36 (a) $2\ Al(s) + 3\ H_2O(\ell) \rightarrow 3\ H_2(g) + Al_2O_3(s)$

(b) $\Delta H° = \Delta H_f°[Al_2O_3(s)] - 3\ \Delta H_f°[H_2O(\ell)] = 1\ mol\ (-1675.7\ kJ/mol) - 3\ mol\ (-285.83\ kJ/mol)$

$\Delta H° = -818.2\ kJ$

$\Delta S° = S°[Al_2O_3(s)] + 3\ S°[H_2(g)] - \{2\ S°[Al(s)] + 3\ S°[H_2O(\ell)]\}$

$\Delta S° = 1\ mol\ (50.92\ J/K·mol) + 3\ mol\ (130.7\ J/K·mol)$

$- [2\ mol\ (28.3\ J/K·mol) + 3\ mol\ (69.95\ J/K·mol)]$

$\Delta S° = 176.6\ J/K$

$\Delta G° = \Delta G_f°[Al_2O_3(s)] - 3\ \Delta G_f°[H_2O(\ell)] = 1\ mol\ (-1582.3\ kJ/mol) - 3\ mol\ (-237.15\ kJ/mol)$

$\Delta G° = -870.9\ kJ$

The data suggest the reaction is product-favored.

(c) A thin film of Al_2O_3 on the surface of the metal is slow to react with water and other substances, preventing further reaction.

21.37 $2 \text{ Al(s)} + 2 \text{ NaOH(aq)} + 6 \text{ H}_2\text{O}(\ell) \rightarrow 2 \text{ Na}^+(\text{aq}) + 2 \text{ Al(OH)}_4^-(\text{aq}) + 3 \text{ H}_2(\text{g})$

$$n_{\text{H}_2} = 13.2 \text{ g Al} \cdot \frac{1 \text{ mol Al}}{26.98 \text{ g}} \cdot \frac{3 \text{ mol H}_2}{2 \text{ mol Al}} = 0.734 \text{ mol H}_2$$

$$V = \frac{nRT}{P} = \frac{(0.734 \text{ mol})(0.082057 \text{ L} \cdot \text{atm/ K} \cdot \text{mol})(295.7 \text{ K})}{735 \text{ mm Hg} \cdot \dfrac{1 \text{ atm}}{760 \text{ mm Hg}}} = 18.4 \text{ L (or } 1.84 \times 10^4 \text{ mL)}$$

21.38   (a) $\text{Al}_2\text{O}_3(\text{s}) + 3 \text{ SiO}_2(\text{s}) \rightarrow \text{Al}_2(\text{SiO}_3)_3(\text{s})$

(b) $\text{Al}_2\text{O}_3(\text{s}) + \text{CaO(s)} \rightarrow \text{Ca(AlO}_2)_2(\text{s})$

21.39 $\text{Al}_2\text{O}_3(\text{s}) + 3 \text{ H}_2\text{SO}_4(\text{aq}) \rightarrow \text{Al}_2(\text{SO}_4)_3(\text{aq}) + 3 \text{ H}_2\text{O}(\ell)$

$$1.00 \times 10^3 \text{ g} \cdot \frac{1 \text{ mol Al}_2(\text{SO}_4)_3}{342.15 \text{ g}} \cdot \frac{1 \text{ mol Al}_2\text{O}_3}{1 \text{ mol Al}_2(\text{SO}_4)_3} \cdot \frac{101.96 \text{ g}}{1 \text{ mol Al}_2\text{O}_3} \cdot \frac{1 \text{ kg}}{10^3 \text{ g}} = 0.298 \text{ kg Al}_2\text{O}_3$$

$$1.00 \times 10^3 \text{ g} \cdot \frac{1 \text{ mol Al}_2(\text{SO}_4)_3}{342.15 \text{ g}} \cdot \frac{3 \text{ mol H}_2\text{SO}_4}{1 \text{ mol Al}_2(\text{SO}_4)_3} \cdot \frac{98.08 \text{ g}}{1 \text{ mol H}_2\text{SO}_4} \cdot \frac{1 \text{ kg}}{10^3 \text{ g}} = 0.860 \text{ kg H}_2\text{SO}_4$$

21.40   (a) $\text{Ga(OH)}_3(\text{s}) + 3 \text{ HCl(aq)} \rightarrow \text{GaCl}_3(\text{aq}) + 3 \text{ H}_2\text{O}(\ell)$

$\text{Ga(OH)}_3(\text{s}) + \text{NaOH(aq)} \rightarrow \text{Ga(OH)}_4^-(\text{aq}) + \text{Na}^+(\text{aq})$

(b) $1.25 \text{ g} \cdot \dfrac{1 \text{ mol Ga(OH)}_3}{120.7 \text{ g}} \cdot \dfrac{3 \text{ mol HCl}}{1 \text{ mol Ga(OH)}_3} \cdot \dfrac{1 \text{ L}}{0.0112 \text{ mol HCl}} = 2.77 \text{ L}$

21.41   The ion has a tetrahedral geometry. The Al atom is sp^3 hybridized.

21.42 $0.56 \text{ g Al} \cdot \dfrac{1 \text{ mol Al}}{27.0 \text{ g}} \cdot \dfrac{3 \text{ mol H}_2}{2 \text{ mol Al}} = 0.031 \text{ mol H}_2$

$$V = \frac{nRT}{P} = \frac{(0.031 \text{ mol H}_2)(0.082057 \text{ L} \cdot \text{atm/K} \cdot \text{mol})(299 \text{ K})}{745 \text{ mm Hg} \cdot \dfrac{1 \text{ atm}}{760 \text{ mm Hg}}} = 0.78 \text{ L}$$

21.43 SiO_2 is a network solid, with tetrahedral silicon atoms covalently bonded to four oxygens in an infinite array; CO_2 consists of individual molecules, with oxygen atoms double bonded to carbon. Melting SiO_2 requires breaking very stable Si—O bonds. Weak intermolecular forces of attraction between CO_2 molecules result in this substance being a gas at ambient conditions.

21.44   Sand (SiO_2) is reduced to Si by reaction with coke (C) in an electric furnace at 3000 °C. The Si obtained this way is reacted with chlorine to form $SiCl_4(\ell)$, which is purified by distillation. The $SiCl_4(\ell)$ is reduced to Si by reaction with very pure magnesium or zinc. This "pure" silicon is made ultrapure by a process known as zone refining.

21.45   (a) $Si(s) + 2 CH_3Cl(g) \rightarrow (CH_3)_2SiCl_2(\ell)$

(b) $n_{CH_3Cl} = 2.65 \text{ g} \cdot \dfrac{1 \text{ mol Si}}{28.09 \text{ g}} \cdot \dfrac{2 \text{ mol CH}_3\text{Cl}}{1 \text{ mol Si}} = 0.189 \text{ mol CH}_3\text{Cl}$

$P = \dfrac{nRT}{V} = \dfrac{(0.189 \text{ mol})(0.082057 \text{ L} \cdot \text{atm/K} \cdot \text{mol})(297.7 \text{ K})}{5.60 \text{ L}} = 0.823 \text{ atm}$

(c) $2.65 \text{ g} \cdot \dfrac{1 \text{ mol Si}}{28.09 \text{ g}} \cdot \dfrac{1 \text{ mol (CH}_3)_2\text{SiCl}_2}{1 \text{ mol Si}} \cdot \dfrac{129.1 \text{ g}}{1 \text{ mol (CH}_3)_2\text{SiCl}_2} = 12.2 \text{ (CH}_3)_2\text{SiCl}_2$

21.46   Pyroxenes have as their basic structural unit an extended chain of linked SiO_4 tetrahedra. The ratio of Si to O is 1:3.

21.47   None of the nitrogen oxides are stable with respect to decomposition to the elements. All have negative ΔG_f° values, so the general reaction $N_xO_y(g) \rightarrow {}^x/_2 N_2(g) + {}^y/_2 O_2(g)$ will have a positive ΔG° value.

21.48 $\Delta H^\circ = \Delta H_f^\circ[N_2O_4(g)] - 2 \Delta H_f^\circ[NO_2(g)] = 1 \text{ mol } (9.08 \text{ kJ/mol}) - 2 \text{ mol } (33.1 \text{ kJ/mol}) = -57.1 \text{ kJ}$

$\Delta G^\circ = \Delta G_f^\circ[N_2O_4(g)] - 2 \Delta G_f^\circ[NO_2(g)] = 1 \text{ mol } (97.73 \text{ kJ/mol}) - 2 \text{ mol } (51.23 \text{ kJ/mol}) = -4.73 \text{ kJ}$

The reaction is exothermic and product-favored.

21.49 $\Delta H^\circ = 2 \Delta H_f^\circ[NO_2(g)] - 2 \Delta H_f^\circ[NO(g)] = 2 \text{ mol } (33.1 \text{ kJ/mol}) - 2 \text{ mol } (90.29 \text{ kJ/mol}) = -114.4 \text{ kJ}$

$\Delta G^\circ = 2 \Delta G_f^\circ[NO_2(g)] - 2 \Delta G_f^\circ[NO(g)] = 2 \text{ mol } (51.23 \text{ kJ/mol}) - 2 \text{ mol } (86.58 \text{ kJ/mol}) = -70.7 \text{ kJ}$

The reaction is exothermic and product-favored.

21.50   (a) $\Delta G^\circ = \Delta G_f^\circ[HNO_3(aq)] + \Delta G_f^\circ[H_2O(\ell)] - \Delta G_f^\circ[NH_3(g)]$

$\Delta G^\circ = 1 \text{ mol } (-111.25 \text{ kJ/mol}) + 1 \text{ mol } (-237.15 \text{ kJ/mol}) - 1 \text{ mol } (-16.37 \text{ kJ/mol}) = -332.03 \text{ kJ}$

$\Delta G^\circ = -332.03 \text{ kJ}$

(b) $\Delta G^\circ = -332.03 \text{ kJ} = -RT \ln K = -(8.3145 \times 10^{-3} \text{ kJ/K·mol})(298 \text{ K}) \ln K$

$K = 2 \times 10^{58}$

21.51   (a) $N_2H_4(aq) + O_2(g) \rightarrow N_2(g) + 2 H_2O(\ell)$

(b) $3.00 \times 10^4 \text{ L H}_2\text{O} \cdot \dfrac{3.08 \text{ mL O}_2}{100. \text{ mL H}_2\text{O}} \cdot \dfrac{1 \text{ mol O}_2}{22.414 \text{ L}} \cdot \dfrac{1 \text{ mol N}_2\text{H}_4}{1 \text{ mol O}_2} \cdot \dfrac{32.05 \text{ g}}{1 \text{ mol N}_2\text{H}_4} = 1320 \text{ g N}_2\text{H}_4$

21.52 $3.00 \times 10^4 \text{ L H}_2\text{O} \cdot \dfrac{3.08 \text{ mL O}_2}{100. \text{ mL H}_2\text{O}} \cdot \dfrac{1 \text{ mol O}_2}{22.414 \text{ L}} \cdot \dfrac{2 \text{ mol Na}_2\text{SO}_3}{1 \text{ mol O}_2} \cdot \dfrac{126.0 \text{ g}}{1 \text{ mol Na}_2\text{SO}_3} = 1.04 \times 10^4 \text{ g Na}_2\text{SO}_3$

21.53 $5[N_2H_5^+(aq) \rightarrow N_2(g) + 5\ H^+(aq) + 4\ e^-]$

$4[IO_3^-(aq) + 6\ H^+(aq) + 5\ e^- \rightarrow {}^1/_2\ I_2(aq) + 3\ H_2O(\ell)]$

$5\ N_2H_5^+(aq) + 4\ IO_3^-(aq) \rightarrow 5\ N_2(g) + H^+(aq) + 2\ I_2(aq) + 12\ H_2O(\ell)$

$E^\circ = E^\circ_{cathode} - E^\circ_{anode} = (1.195\ V) - (-0.23\ V) = 1.43\ V$

21.54   The azide ion has three resonance structures:

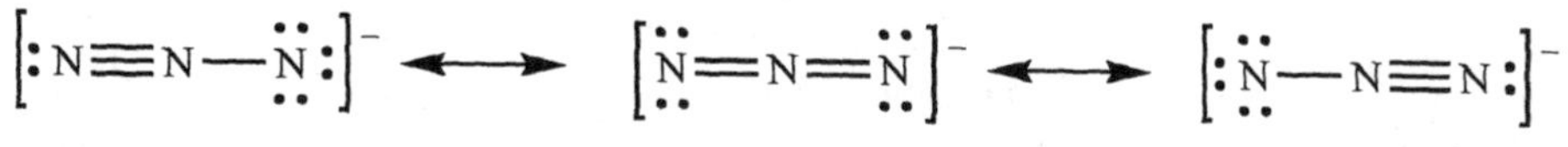

21.55   (a) +3

(b) The two —OH protons can dissociate in water (a diprotic acid).

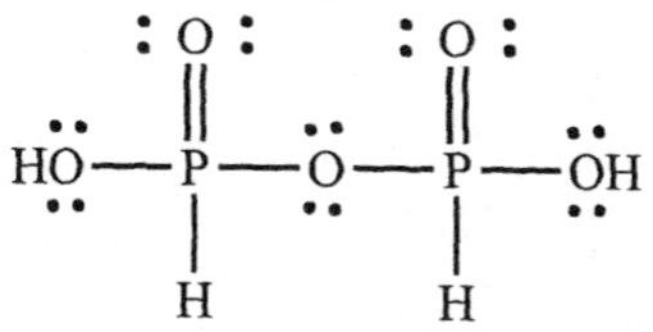

21.56 $CaO(s) + H_3PO_4(aq) \rightarrow CaHPO_4(s) + H_2O(\ell)$

21.57   (a) $1.80 \times 10^6\ kg \cdot \dfrac{1\ mol\ H_2SO_4}{98.08\ g} \cdot \dfrac{1\ mol\ SO_2}{1\ mol\ H_2SO_4} \cdot \dfrac{64.06\ g}{1\ mol\ SO_2} \cdot \dfrac{0.0030\ kg\ SO_2\ released}{1.00\ kg\ SO_2\ produced}$

$= 3.5 \times 10^3\ kg\ SO_2$

(b) $3.5 \times 10^3\ kg \cdot \dfrac{1\ mol\ SO_2}{64.06\ g} \cdot \dfrac{1\ mol\ Ca(OH)_2}{1\ mol\ SO_2} \cdot \dfrac{74.09\ g}{1\ mol\ Ca(OH)_2} = 4.1 \times 10^3\ kg\ Ca(OH)_2$

21.58   (1) $S + O_2 \rightarrow SO_2$ $\Delta H^\circ = \Delta H_f^\circ[SO_2] = -296.84\ kJ$

(2) $SO_2 + {}^1/_2\ O_2 \rightarrow SO_3$ $\Delta H^\circ = \Delta H_f^\circ[SO_3] - \Delta H_f^\circ[SO_2] = -98.93\ kJ$

(3) $SO_3 + H_2O \rightarrow H_2SO_4$ $\Delta H^\circ = -130\ kJ$

$S + {}^3/_2\ O_2 + H_2O \rightarrow H_2SO_4$ $\Delta H^\circ_{rxn} = \Delta H^\circ(1) + \Delta H^\circ(2) + \Delta H^\circ(3) = -530\ kJ$

$1000\ kg \cdot \dfrac{10^3\ g}{1\ kg} \cdot \dfrac{1\ mol\ H_2SO_4}{98.08\ g} \cdot \dfrac{530\ kJ}{1\ mol\ H_2SO_4} = 5.4 \times 10^6\ kJ$

21.59

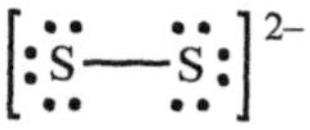

21.60 S_2F_2 :$\ddot{F}$-$\ddot{S}$-$\ddot{S}$-$\ddot{F}$:   S oxidation number is +1.

         SF_2 :$\ddot{F}$-$\ddot{S}$-$\ddot{F}$:   S oxidation number is +2

         SF_4 S oxidation number is +4 (lone pairs on F not shown)

         SF_6 S oxidation number is +6 (lone pairs on F not shown)

         S_2F_{10} S oxidation number is +5 (lone pairs on F not shown)

21.61 $2[Mn^{2+}(aq) + 4\ H_2O(\ell) \rightarrow MnO_4^-(aq) + 8\ H^+(aq) + 5\ e^-]$

         $2\ BrO_3^-(aq) + 12\ H^+(aq) + 10\ e^- \rightarrow Br_2(aq) + 6\ H_2O(\ell)$

         $2\ Mn^{2+}(aq) + 2\ H_2O(\ell) + 2\ BrO_3^-(aq) \rightarrow 2\ MnO_4^-(aq) + 4\ H^+(aq) + Br_2(aq)$

         $E^\circ_{cell} = E^\circ_{cathode} - E^\circ_{anode} = (1.44\ V) - (1.51\ V) = -0.07\ V$

         The reaction is not product-favored

21.62 $OCl^-(aq) + H_2O(\ell) \rightleftharpoons HClO(aq) + OH^-(aq)$

         $K_b = \dfrac{K_w}{K_a} = 2.9 \times 10^{-7} = \dfrac{[HClO][OH^-]}{[OCl^-]} = \dfrac{(x)(x)}{0.10 - x} \approx \dfrac{x^2}{0.10}$

         $x = [HClO] = [OH^-] = 1.7 \times 10^{-4}\ M$

         $pOH = -\log[OH^-] = 3.77$

         $pH = 14.00 - pOH = 10.23$

21.63 $Cl_2(g) + 2\ Br^-(aq) \rightarrow 2\ Cl^-(aq) + Br_2(\ell)$

         Cl_2 is the oxidizing agent and Br^- is the reducing agent

         $E^\circ_{cell} = E^\circ_{cathode} - E^\circ_{anode} = (1.36\ V) - (1.08\ V) = 0.28\ V$

         The reaction is product-favored

21.64 BrO_3^-: $BrO_3^-(aq) + 6\ H^+(aq) + 6\ Cl^-(aq) \rightarrow Br^-(aq) + 3\ H_2O(\ell) + 3\ Cl_2(g)$

         MnO_4^-: $2\ MnO_4^-(aq) + 10\ Cl^-(aq) + 16\ H^+(aq) \rightarrow 2\ Mn^{2+}(aq) + 5\ Cl_2(g) + 8\ H_2O(\ell)$

         Ce^{4+}: $2\ Ce^{4+}(aq) + 2\ Cl^-(aq) \rightarrow 2\ Ce^{3+}(aq) + Cl_2(g)$

21.65   Charge = current × time = $(5.00 \times 10^3 \text{ A})(24 \text{ hr})(3600 \text{ s/1 hr}) = 4.32 \times 10^8 \text{ C}$

mol e$^-$ = $(4.32 \times 10^8 \text{ C})\left(\dfrac{1 \text{ mol e}^-}{96,500 \text{ C}}\right) = 4.48 \times 10^3 \text{ mol e}^-$

mass of F$_2$ = $(4.48 \times 10^3 \text{ mol e}^-)\left(\dfrac{1 \text{ mol F}_2}{2 \text{ mol e}^-}\right)\left(\dfrac{38.00 \text{ g}}{1 \text{ mol F}_2}\right) = 8.51 \times 10^4 \text{ g F}_2$

21.66   The bond angles in BrF$_3$ will be less than the ideal 90°.

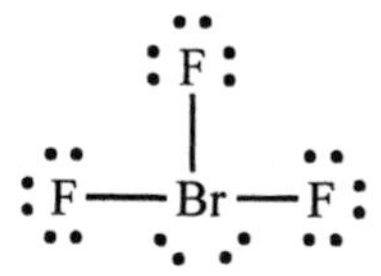

21.67

Element	(a)	(b)	(c)
Na	metal	silvery gray	solid
Mg	metal	silvery gray	solid
Al	metal	silvery gray	solid
Si	metalloid	black, shiny	solid
P	nonmetal	white or red	solid
S	nonmetal	yellow	solid
Cl	nonmetal	pale yellow-green	gas
Ar	nonmetal	colorless	gas

21.68

Element	(a)	(b)	(c)
Li	metal	silvery gray	solid
Be	metal	silvery gray	solid
B	metalloid	gray	solid
C	nonmetal	gray/black	solid
N	nonmetal	colorless	gas
O	nonmetal	colorless	gas
F	nonmetal	pale yellow/green	gas
Ne	nonmetal	colorless	gas

21.69   Element   (a)   (b)

        Na $2\,Na(s) + Cl_2(g) \rightarrow 2\,NaCl(s)$ ionic

        Mg $Mg(s) + Cl_2(g) \rightarrow MgCl_2(s)$ ionic

        Al $2\,Al(s) + 3\,Cl_2(g) \rightarrow 2\,AlCl_3(s)$ covalent

        Si $Si(s) + 2\,Cl_2(g) \rightarrow SiCl_4(\ell)$ covalent

        P $P_4(s) + 10\,Cl_2(g) \rightarrow 4\,PCl_5(s)$ covalent

        S $S_8(s) + 8\,Cl_2(g) \rightarrow 8\,SCl_2(s)$ covalent

    (c)

	tetrahedral	trigonal bipyramidal
electron pair geometry	tetrahedral	trigonal bipyramidal
molecular geometry	tetrahedral	trigonal bipyramidal

21.70   Element   (a)   (b)

        C $C(s) + 2\,Cl_2(g) \rightarrow CCl_4(\ell)$ covalent

        Si $Si(s) + 2\,Cl_2(g) \rightarrow SiCl_4(\ell)$ covalent

        Ge $Ge(s) + 2\,Cl_2(g) \rightarrow GeCl_4(s)$ covalent

        Sn $Sn(s) + Cl_2(g) \rightarrow SnCl_2(s)$ ionic

                         $Sn(s) + 2\,Cl_2(g) \rightarrow SnCl_4(s)$ covalent

        Pb $Pb(s) + Cl_2(g) \rightarrow PbCl_2(s)$ ionic

21.71   (a) $2\,KClO_3(s) \rightarrow 2\,KCl(s) + 3\,O_2(g)$

      (b) $2\,H_2S(g) + 3\,O_2(g) \rightarrow 2\,H_2O(g) + 2\,SO_2(g)$

      (c) $2\,Na(s) + O_2(g) \rightarrow Na_2O_2(s)$

      (d) $P_4(s) + 3\,KOH(aq) + 3\,H_2O(\ell) \rightarrow PH_3(g) + 3\,KH_2PO_4(aq)$

      (e) $NH_4NO_3(s) \rightarrow N_2O(g) + 2\,H_2O(g)$

      (f) $2\,In(s) + 3\,Br_2(\ell) \rightarrow 2\,InBr_3(s)$

      (g) $SnCl_4(\ell) + 2\,H_2O(\ell) \rightarrow SnO_2(s) + 4\,HCl(aq)$

21.72   (a) $2\,NaBH_4(s) + 2\,AgNO_3(aq) \rightarrow 2\,Ag(s) + H_2(g) + 2\,B(OH)_3(aq) + 2\,NaNO_3(aq)$

      (b) $0.575\ L \cdot \dfrac{0.011\ mol\ AgNO_3}{1\ L} \cdot \dfrac{2\ mol\ Ag}{2\ mol\ AgNO_3} \cdot \dfrac{107.9\ g}{1\ mol\ Ag} = 0.68\ g\ Ag$

             $13.0\ g \cdot \dfrac{1\ mol\ NaBH_4}{37.83\ g} \cdot \dfrac{2\ mol\ Ag}{2\ mol\ NaBH_4} \cdot \dfrac{107.9\ g}{1\ mol\ Ag} = 37.1\ g\ Ag$

      0.68 g Ag is produced

21.73 (a)

(b) Each B atom is surrounded in a planar trigonal arrangement by another B atom and two Cl atoms. Each B atom is sp^2 hybridized.

21.74 (a) $4 BCl_3(g) + 6 H_2(g) + C(s) \rightarrow B_4C(s) + 12 HCl(g)$

(b) $n_{BCl_3} = \dfrac{PV}{RT} = \dfrac{\left(456 \text{ mm Hg} \cdot \dfrac{1 \text{ atm}}{760 \text{ mm Hg}}\right)(5.45 \text{ L})}{(0.082057 \text{ L} \cdot \text{atm/K} \cdot \text{mol})(299.7 \text{ K})} = 0.133 \text{ mol } BCl_3$

$0.133 \text{ mol } BCl_3 \cdot \dfrac{1 \text{ mol } B_4C}{4 \text{ mol } BCl_3} \cdot \dfrac{55.26 \text{ g}}{1 \text{ mol } B_4C} = 1.84 \text{ g } B_4C$

21.75 (a) $2 BaO(s) + O_2(g) \rightarrow 2 BaO_2(s)$

(b) $3 BaO_2(s) + 2 Fe(s) \rightarrow Fe_2O_3(s) + 3 BaO(s)$

21.76 $1.0 \times 10^5 \text{ metric tons SiC} \cdot \dfrac{100 \text{ g sand}}{70 \text{ g SiC}} = 1.4 \times 10^5 \text{ metric tons sand}$

21.77 Cathode: $Li^+ + e^- \rightarrow Li$

Anode: $2 H^- \rightarrow H_2 + 2 e^-$

21.78 $1.0 \times 10^3 \text{ g H}_2 \cdot \dfrac{1 \text{ mol H}_2}{2.02 \text{ g}} = 5.0 \times 10^2 \text{ mol H}_2$

$V = \dfrac{nRT}{P} = \dfrac{(5.0 \times 10^2 \text{ mol})(0.082057 \text{ L} \cdot \text{atm/K} \cdot \text{mol})(298 \text{ K})}{1.0 \text{ atm}} = 1.2 \times 10^4 \text{ L}$

21.79 $MCO_3(s) \rightarrow MO(s) + CO_2(g)$ $\Delta G° = \Delta G_f°[MO(s)] + \Delta G_f°[CO_2(g)] - \Delta G_f°[MCO_3(s)]$

Mg: $\Delta G° = 1 \text{ mol } (-568.93 \text{ kJ/mol}) + 1 \text{ mol } (-394.359 \text{ kJ/mol}) - 1 \text{ mol } (-1028.2 \text{ kJ/mol}) = 64.9 \text{ kJ}$

Ca: $\Delta G° = 1 \text{ mol } (-603.42 \text{ kJ/mol}) + 1 \text{ mol } (-394.359 \text{ kJ/mol}) - 1 \text{ mol } (-1129.16 \text{ kJ/mol}) = 131.38 \text{ kJ}$

Ba: $\Delta G° = 1 \text{ mol } (-520.38 \text{ kJ/mol}) + 1 \text{ mol } (-394.359 \text{ kJ/mol}) - 1 \text{ mol } (-1134.41 \text{ kJ/mol}) = 219.67 \text{ kJ}$

Relative tendency to decompose: $MgCO_3 > CaCO_3 > BaCO_3$

21.80 $2 NH_4ClO_4(s) \rightarrow N_2(g) + Cl_2(g) + 2 O_2(g) + 4 H_2O(g)$

(a) $6.35 \times 10^5 \text{ kg} \cdot \dfrac{1 \text{ mol } NH_4ClO_4}{117.5 \text{ g}} \cdot \dfrac{4 \text{ mol } H_2O}{2 \text{ mol } NH_4ClO_4} \cdot \dfrac{18.02 \text{ g}}{1 \text{ mol } H_2O} = 1.95 \times 10^5 \text{ kg } H_2O$

$6.35 \times 10^5 \text{ kg} \cdot \dfrac{1 \text{ mol } NH_4ClO_4}{117.5 \text{ g}} \cdot \dfrac{2 \text{ mol } O_2}{2 \text{ mol } NH_4ClO_4} \cdot \dfrac{32.00 \text{ g}}{1 \text{ mol } O_2} = 1.73 \times 10^5 \text{ kg } O_2$

(b) $4 Al(s) + 3 O_2(g) \rightarrow 2 Al_2O_3(s)$

$1.73 \times 10^5 \text{ kg} \cdot \dfrac{1 \text{ mol } O_2}{32.00 \text{ g}} \cdot \dfrac{4 \text{ mol } Al}{3 \text{ mol } O_2} \cdot \dfrac{26.98 \text{ g}}{1 \text{ mol } Al} = 1.94 \times 10^5 \text{ kg } Al$

(c) $1.73 \times 10^5 \text{ kg} \cdot \dfrac{1 \text{ mol } O_2}{32.00 \text{ g}} \cdot \dfrac{2 \text{ mol } Al_2O_3}{3 \text{ mol } O_2} \cdot \dfrac{102.0 \text{ g}}{1 \text{ mol } Al_2O_3} = 3.67 \times 10^5 \text{ kg } Al_2O_3$

21.81   (a) $\Delta G°$ must be < 0 for the reaction to be product-favored. Calculate $\Delta G_f°[MX_n]$ when $\Delta G° = 0$

$\Delta G_f°[MX_n(s)] = n\Delta G_f°[HCl(g)] = n(-95.1 \text{ kJ/mol})$ when $\Delta G° = 0$

If $\Delta G_f° [MX_n(s)] < n(-95.1 \text{ kJ/mol})$ then $\Delta G°$ will be negative

(b)

Metal	Ba	Pb	Hg	Ti
$\Delta G_f°[MX_n(s)]$	–810.4	–310.10	–178.6	–737.2
n	2	2	2	4
$n(-95.1$ kJ/mol)	–190.2	–190.2	–190.2	–380.4

Ba, Pb, and Ti will react with HCl

21.82   (a) $\left[:\!\overset{\displaystyle ..}{\underset{\displaystyle ..}{I}}\!-\!\overset{\displaystyle ..}{\underset{\displaystyle ..}{I}}\!-\!\overset{\displaystyle ..}{\underset{\displaystyle ..}{I}}\!: \right]^-$ linear

(b) $\left[:\!\overset{\displaystyle ..}{\underset{\displaystyle ..}{Cl}}\!-\!\overset{\displaystyle ..}{\underset{\displaystyle ..}{Br}}\!-\!\overset{\displaystyle ..}{\underset{\displaystyle ..}{Cl}}\!: \right]^-$ linear

(c) $\left[:\!\overset{\displaystyle ..}{\underset{\displaystyle ..}{F}}\!-\!\overset{\displaystyle ..}{Cl}\!-\!\overset{\displaystyle ..}{\underset{\displaystyle ..}{F}}\!: \right]^+$ bent

21.83 $^1\!/_2 O_2(g) + F_2(g) \rightarrow OF_2(g)$

$\Delta H°_{rxn} = {}^1\!/_2 \text{ mol} \cdot D_{O=O} + 1 \text{ mol} \cdot D_{F-F} - 2 \text{ mol} \cdot D_{O-F}$

$24.5 \text{ kJ} = {}^1\!/_2 \text{ mol} (498 \text{ kJ/mol}) + 1 \text{ mol} (155 \text{ kJ/mol}) - 2 \text{ mol} (D_{O-F})$

$D_{O-F} = 190. \text{ kJ/mol}$

21.84 $1.0 \times 10^6 \text{ L} \cdot \dfrac{2.0 \times 10^{-5} \text{ mol } F^-}{1 \text{ L}} \cdot \dfrac{1 \text{ mol } CaF_2}{2 \text{ mol } F^-} \cdot \dfrac{78.1 \text{ g}}{1 \text{ mol } CaF_2} = 780 \text{ g } CaF_2$

21.85   (a) N_2O_4 is the oxidizing agent and $H_2NN(CH_3)_2$ is the reducing agent.

(b) $4100 \text{ kg} \cdot \dfrac{1 \text{ mol } H_2NN(CH_3)_2}{60.1 \text{ g}} \cdot \dfrac{2 \text{ mol } N_2O_4}{1 \text{ mol } H_2NN(CH_3)_2} \cdot \dfrac{92.0 \text{ g}}{1 \text{ mol } N_2O_4} = 13000 \text{ kg } N_2O_4$

$4100 \text{ kg} \cdot \dfrac{1 \text{ mol } H_2NN(CH_3)_2}{60.1 \text{ g}} \cdot \dfrac{3 \text{ mol } N_2}{1 \text{ mol } H_2NN(CH_3)_2} \cdot \dfrac{28.0 \text{ g}}{1 \text{ mol } N_2} = 5700 \text{ kg } N_2$

$4100 \text{ kg} \cdot \dfrac{1 \text{ mol } H_2NN(CH_3)_2}{60.1 \text{ g}} \cdot \dfrac{4 \text{ mol } H_2O}{1 \text{ mol } H_2NN(CH_3)_2} \cdot \dfrac{18.0 \text{ g}}{1 \text{ mol } H_2O} = 4900 \text{ kg } H_2O$

$4100 \text{ kg} \cdot \dfrac{1 \text{ mol } H_2NN(CH_3)_2}{60.1 \text{ g}} \cdot \dfrac{2 \text{ mol } CO_2}{1 \text{ mol } H_2NN(CH_3)_2} \cdot \dfrac{44.0 \text{ g}}{1 \text{ mol } CO_2} = 6.0 \times 10^3 \text{ kg } CO_2$

21.86   Unit cell volume:

$\dfrac{4 \text{ Pb atoms}}{\text{unit cell}} \cdot \dfrac{207.2 \text{ g}}{1 \text{ mol Pb}} \cdot \dfrac{1 \text{ cm}^3}{11.350 \text{ g}} \cdot \dfrac{1 \text{ mol Pb}}{6.0221 \times 10^{23} \text{ atoms}} = 1.213 \times 10^{-22} \text{ cm}^3$

Unit cell edge length:

$V = 1.213 \times 10^{-22} \text{ cm}^3 = (\text{edge length})^3$

$\text{edge length} = \sqrt[3]{1.213 \times 10^{-22} \text{ cm}^3} = 4.950 \times 10^{-8} \text{ cm}$

$\text{face diagonal} = 4 \cdot \text{radius} = \sqrt{2} \cdot \text{edge length}$

$\text{radius} = \dfrac{\sqrt{2} \cdot (4.950 \times 10^{-8} \text{ cm})}{4} = 1.750 \times 10^{-8} \text{ cm} = 175.0 \text{ pm}$

21.87   (a) The NO bond with a length of 114.2 pm is a double bond. The other two NO bonds (with a length of 121 pm) have a bond order of 1.5 (as there are two resonance structures involving these bonds).

(b) $\Delta G° = \Delta H° - T\Delta S°$

$-1.59 \text{ kJ/mol} = 40.5 \text{ kJ/mol} - (298 \text{ K})\Delta S°$

$\Delta S° = 0.141 \text{ kJ/K·mol}$

$\Delta G° = -RT \ln K_p$

$-1.59 \text{ kJ/mol} = -(8.3145 \times 10^{-3} \text{ kJ/K·mol})(298 \text{ K}) \ln K$

$\ln K = 0.642$

$K = 1.900$

(c) $\Delta H°_{rxn} = \Delta H_f°[NO(g)] + \Delta H_f°[NO_2(g)] - \Delta H_f°[N_2O_3(g)]$

$40.5 \text{ kJ} = 1 \text{ mol} (90.29 \text{ kJ/mol}) + 1 \text{ mol} (33.1 \text{ kJ/mol}) - \Delta H_f°[N_2O_3(g)]$

$\Delta H_f°[N_2O_3(g)] = 82.9 \text{ kJ/mol}$

21.88   (a)

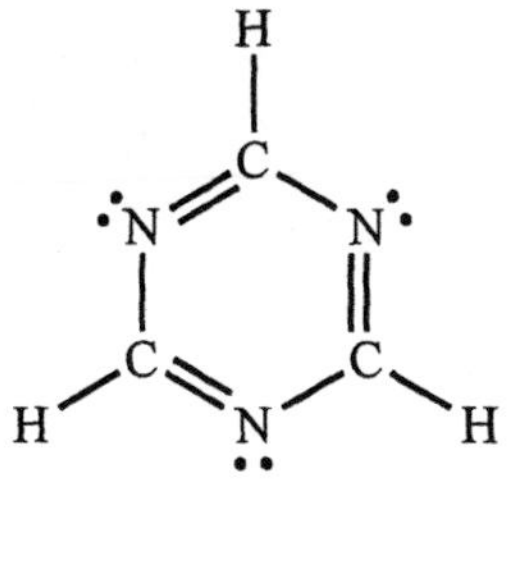

(b) $3 \, HCN(\ell) \rightarrow (HCN)_3(\ell)$

Three C—H bonds do not change during the reaction

$\Delta H^{\circ}_{rxn} = 3 \, mol \cdot D_{C\equiv N} - (3 \, mol \cdot D_{C-N} + 3 \, mol \cdot D_{C=N})$

$\Delta H^{\circ}_{rxn} = 3 \, mol \, (887 \, kJ/mol) - [3 \, mol \, (305 \, kJ/mol) + 3 \, mol \, (615 \, kJ/mol)]$

$\Delta H^{\circ}_{rxn} = -99 \, kJ$

21.89 $\Delta H^{\circ} = 4 \, \Delta H_f^{\circ}[HNO_3(aq)] - 2 \, \Delta H_f^{\circ}[H_2O(\ell)] = 4 \, mol \, (-207.36 \, kJ/mol) - 2 \, mol \, (-285.83 \, kJ/mol)$

$\Delta H^{\circ} = -257.78 \, kJ$

This reaction is entropy-disfavored, however, with $\Delta S^{\circ} = -963 \, J/K$ because of the decrease in the number of moles of gases. Combining these values gives $\Delta G^{\circ} = 29.34 \, kJ$, indicating that under standard conditions at 298 K the reaction is not favorable. (The reaction has a favorable ΔG° below 268 K, indicating that further research on this system might be worthwhile. Note, however, that at that temperature water is a solid.)

21.90   (a) $1.00 \times 10^3 \, g \cdot \dfrac{1 \, mol \, Mg}{24.31 \, g} \cdot \dfrac{1 \, L}{0.050 \, mol \, Mg^{2+}} = 820 \, L \, seawater$

$CaO(s) + H_2O(\ell) + Mg^{2+}(aq) \rightarrow Mg(OH)_2(s) + Ca^{2+}(aq)$

$1.00 \times 10^3 \, g \cdot \dfrac{1 \, mol \, Mg}{24.31 \, g} \cdot \dfrac{1 \, mol \, CaO}{1 \, mol \, Mg^{2+}} \cdot \dfrac{56.08 \, g}{1 \, mol \, CaO} \cdot \dfrac{1 \, kg}{10^3 \, g} = 2.31 \, kg \, CaO$

(b) $MgCl_2(\ell) \rightarrow Mg(s) + Cl_2(g)$

$1.2 \times 10^3 \, kg \cdot \dfrac{1 \, mol \, MgCl_2}{95.2 \, g} \cdot \dfrac{1 \, mol \, Mg}{1 \, mol \, MgCl_2} \cdot \dfrac{24.3 \, g}{1 \, mol \, Mg} = 310 \, kg \, Mg$

Cl_2 gas is produced at the anode

$1.2 \times 10^3 \, kg \cdot \dfrac{1 \, mol \, MgCl_2}{95.2 \, g} \cdot \dfrac{1 \, mol \, Cl_2}{1 \, mol \, MgCl_2} \cdot \dfrac{70.9 \, g}{1 \, mol \, Cl_2} = 890 \, kg \, Cl_2$

$1.2 \times 10^3 \, kg \cdot \dfrac{10^3 \, g}{1 \, kg} \cdot \dfrac{1 \, mol \, MgCl_2}{95.2 \, g} \cdot \dfrac{2 \, mol \, e^-}{1 \, mol \, MgCl_2} \cdot \dfrac{1 \, F}{1 \, mol \, e^-} = 2.5 \times 10^4 \, F$

(c) $\dfrac{18.5 \, kwh}{1 \times 10^3 \, g \, Mg} \cdot \dfrac{3.6 \times 10^6 \, J}{1 \, kwh} \cdot \dfrac{24.31 \, g}{1 \, mol \, Mg} \cdot \dfrac{1 \, kJ}{10^3 \, J} = 1600 \, kJ/mol$

$-(\Delta H_f^{\circ}[MgCl_2(s)]) = -(641.62 \, kJ/mol) = 641.62 \, kJ/mol$

The electrolysis process requires more energy because the $MgCl_2$ must be melted.

21.91 $2 \, Cl^-(aq) \rightarrow Cl_2(g) + 2 \, e^-$

$1.00 \times 10^3 \, g \cdot \dfrac{1 \, mol \, Cl_2}{70.91 \, g} \cdot \dfrac{2 \, mol \, e^-}{1 \, mol \, Cl_2} \cdot \dfrac{96,500 \, C}{1 \, mol \, e^-} = 2.72 \times 10^6 \, C$

$(2.72 \times 10^6 \, C)(4.6 \, V)\left(\dfrac{1 \, J}{1 \, C \cdot V}\right)\left(\dfrac{1 \, kwh}{3.6 \times 10^6 \, J}\right) = 3.5 \, kwh$

21.92 $2 NaCl(\ell) \rightarrow 2 Na(s) + Cl_2(g)$

(a) $\left(\dfrac{23 \text{ g Na}}{1 \text{ mol Na}}\right)\left(\dfrac{2 \text{ mol Na}}{2 \text{ mole } e^-}\right)\left(\dfrac{1 \text{ mole } e^-}{96,500 \text{ C}}\right)\left(\dfrac{1 \text{ C}}{1 \text{ A} \cdot 1s}\right)(25 \times 10^3 \text{ A})\left(\dfrac{3600 \text{ s}}{1 \text{ h}}\right)\left(\dfrac{1 \text{ kg}}{1000 \text{ g}}\right) = 2.1 \text{ kg/h}$

(b) $\left(\dfrac{1 \text{ kwh}}{3.6 \times 10^6 \text{ J}}\right)\left(\dfrac{1 \text{ J}}{1 \text{ V} \cdot \text{C}}\right)(7.0 \text{ V})\left(\dfrac{96,500 \text{ C}}{1 \text{ mol } e^-}\right)\left(\dfrac{1 \text{ mol } e^-}{1 \text{ mol Na}}\right)\left(\dfrac{1 \text{ mol Na}}{23.0 \text{ g Na}}\right)(1.00 \times 10^3 \text{ g Na}) = 8.2 \text{ kwh}$

21.93   Since the flask contains a fixed number of moles of gas at the given pressure and temperature, one could determine the total mass of gas present and solve for the mass of H_2 in the mixture.

21.94   (a)

(b) B is sp^2 hybridized.

(c)

(d) Reaction is possible because boron has an empty, unhybridized p orbital that can accept a pair of electrons from a Lewis base such as water. Boric acid acts as a Lewis acid in this reaction.

21.95   Use an inert dry chemical fire extinguisher if available. The worst thing would be to throw water on this fire (sodium reacts with water to produce hydrogen, a flammable gas).

21.96   (a) 8 corner Ti $\times \frac{1}{8}$ = 1 Ti   4 face O $\times \frac{1}{2}$ = 2 O

1 internal Ti   = 1 Ti   2 internal O   = 2 O

= 2 Ti total   = 4 O total

(b) $SnO_2(s) + 4 HCl(g) \rightarrow SnCl_4(\ell) + 2 H_2O(g)$

$\Delta G° = \Delta G_f°[SnCl_4(\ell)] + 2 \Delta G_f°[H_2O(g)] - \{\Delta G_f°[SnO_2(s)] + 4 \Delta G_f°[HCl(g)]\}$

$\Delta G° = 1 \text{ mol } (-511.3 \text{ kJ/mol}) + 2 \text{ mol } (-241.83 \text{ kJ/mol})$

$- [1 \text{ mol } (-577.63 \text{ kJ/mol}) + 4 \text{ mol } (-92.31 \text{ kJ/mol})]$

$\Delta G° = -48.1 \text{ kJ}$

$-48.1 \text{ kJ} = -RT \ln K_p = -(8.3145 \times 10^{-3} \text{ kJ/K·mol})(298 \text{ K}) \ln K$

$\ln K = 19.4$

$K = 3 \times 10^8$

The reaction is product-favored.

21.97   Insert a glowing splint in to the gas. Hydrogen will ignite (burning in air). If the gas is oxygen, the splint will burst into flame. If it is nitrogen, the splint will cease to glow.

21.98   (a)   We rationalize the equivalence of the two N—O bond lengths by writing two resonance structures for this molecule. The greater bond order (1.5) explains the shorter bond length when compared to a NO single bond.

         (b)   The central atom, nitrogen, has three sets of bonding electrons in its valence shell; VSEPR predicts that this atom is trigonal-planar. Oxygen, in the —OH group, has four electron pairs in its valence shell, arranged tetrahedrally. Two are bonding pairs, defining the bent molecular geometry.

         (c) sp^2. There is an empty p orbital on N that is perpendicular to the plane of the molecule; this can overlap with p orbitals on the two terminal oxygens to form a delocalized π bond.

21.99   The reducing ability of the Group 3A metals declines considerably on descending the group, with the largest drop occurring on going from Al to Ga. The reducing ability of gallium and indium are similar, but another large change is observed on going to thallium. In fact, thallium is most stable in the +1 oxidation state. (This same tendency for elements to be more stable with lower oxidation numbers is seen in Groups 4A (Ge and Pb) and 5A (Bi).

21.100   Starting materials:

         Produce $H_2(g)$ by the electrolysis of water.

         Liquefy air and separate $N_2(\ell)$.

         Use the Haber process to produce $NH_3(g)$ from $H_2(g)$ and $N_2(g)$.

         React ammonia with water to produce $NH_4OH(aq)$.

         Use Ostwald process to produce $HNO_3(aq)$ from $NH_3(g)$, $O_2(g)$, and $H_2O(\ell)$.

         Combine $NH_4OH(aq)$ and $HNO_3(aq)$ to produce $NH_4NO_3(aq)$ and $H_2O(\ell)$.

         Evaporate the water to isolate $NH_4NO_3(s)$.

21.101   A is $BaCO_3$; B is BaO; C is $CaCO_3$; D is $BaCl_2$; E is $BaSO_4$

Chapter 22
The Chemistry of the Transition Elements

INSTRUCTOR'S NOTES

As this material is usually covered at the end of the course, there is not usually enough time to cover the entire chapter. However, enough of the basic ideas of crystal field theory can be introduced so that the color of complexes may be understood. Because several of these elements and compounds are commonly seen in student's lives (e.g., iron, copper, gold, colored complexes) their interest in the material could be stimulated.

SUGGESTED DEMONSTRATIONS

1. Properties of the Transition Elements

    *   Flame test for copper: Johnson, K. A.; Schreiner, R. "A Dramatic Flame Test Demonstration," *Journal of Chemical Education* **2001**, *78*, 640.

    *   The photographs in this chapter suggest many demonstrations, particularly of colored complexes. One that we have used to show the different colors of chromium in its different oxidation states is Figure 22.4. (Also see Cornelius, R. *Journal of Chemical Education* **1980**, *57*, 316 for an experiment involving vanadium oxidation states.)

    *   The chemistry of nickel and iron can be illustrated using demonstrations outlined in Shakhashiri, Volume 1. In addition, there are several other demonstrations in Shakhashiri and in L. R. Summerlin, J. L. Ealy, Jr. *Chemical Demonstrations: A Sourcebook for Teachers, 2nd Edition*, Volumes 1 and 2 involving transition metal compounds and chemical equilibria.

    *   The *Periodic Table Videodisc* and the *Periodic Table Live!* CD-ROM have images of almost all of the transition elements, the uses of these elements, and their reactions with air, water, acids, and bases. The *Redox Videodisc* is also a video source of transition metals, their chemistry, and their industrial uses.

    *   Demonstrations of magnetism involving transition metals: Malerich, C.; Ruff, P. K. "Demonstrating and Measuring Relative Molar Magnetic Susceptibility Using a Neodymium Magnet," *Journal of Chemical Education* **2004**, *81*, 1155; Walker, N. "Paramagnetic Properties of Fe(II) and Fe(III)," *Journal of Chemical Education* **1977**, *54*, 431; Knox, K.; Strothkamp, R. "Ferrimagnetism," *Journal of Chemical Education* **1989**, *66*, 337.

2. Coordination Compounds

    *   For demonstrations of coordination complexes, see Volume 1 of Shakhashiri's *Chemical Demonstrations*.

    *   Zingales, R. "Chemical Equilibria Involving Copper(II) Ethylenediamine Complexes," *Journal of Chemical Education* **2003**, *80*, 535.

    *   Schäffer, C. E.; Steenberg, P. "Cobalt Alums," *Journal of Chemical Education* **2002**, *78*, 958.

    *   Hughes, J. G. "Thermochromic Solids," *Journal of Chemical Education* **1998**, *75*, 57.

SOLUTIONS TO STUDY QUESTIONS

22.1   (a) Cr^{3+} $[Ar]3d^3$ paramagnetic

         (b) V^{2+} $[Ar]3d^3$ paramagnetic

         (c) Ni^{2+} $[Ar]3d^8$ paramagnetic

         (d) Cu^+ $[Ar]3d^{10}$ diamagnetic

22.2   (a) Fe^{2+}, Co^{3+} (c) Mn^{2+}, Fe^{3+}

         (b) Cu^+, Zn^{2+} (d) Ni^{2+}, Co^+

22.3   (a) Mn^{2+} is isoelectronic with Fe^{3+}

         (b) Cu^+ is isoelectronic with Zn^{2+}

         (c) Co^{3+} is isoelectronic with Fe^{2+}

         (d) V^{2+} is isoelectronic with Cr^{3+}

22.4 Cu^+ and Zn^{2+}; Mn^{2+} and Fe^{3+}; Fe^{2+} and Co^{3+}; Ti^{2+} and V^{3+}

22.5   (a) $Cr_2O_3(s) + 2\,Al(s) \rightarrow Al_2O_3(s) + 2\,Cr(s)$

         (b) $TiCl_4(\ell) + 2\,Mg(s) \rightarrow Ti(s) + 2\,MgCl_2(s)$

         (c) $2\,[Ag(CN)_2]^-(aq) + Zn(s) \rightarrow 2\,Ag(s) + [Zn(CN)_4]^{2-}(aq)$

         (d) $3\,Mn_3O_4(s) + 8\,Al(s) \rightarrow 9\,Mn(s) + 4\,Al_2O_3(s)$

22.6   (a) $CuSO_4(aq) + Zn(s) \rightarrow Cu(s) + ZnSO_4(aq)$

         (b) $Zn(s) + 2\,HCl(aq) \rightarrow ZnCl_2(aq) + H_2(g)$

         (c) $2\,Fe(s) + 3\,Cl_2(g) \rightarrow 2\,FeCl_3(s)$

         (d) $4\,V(s) + 5\,O_2(g) \rightarrow 2\,V_2O_5(s)$

22.7   (a)   monodentate   (d)   bidentate

         (b)   monodentate   (e)   monodentate

         (c)   monodentate   (f)   bidentate

22.8 NH_4^+ is incapable of serving as a ligand because it does not have any unshared electron pairs.

22.9   (a) Mn^{2+} (c) Co^{3+}

         (b) Co^{3+} (d) Cr^{2+}

22.10   (a) Fe^{2+} (c) Co^{2+}

         (b) Zn^{2+} (d) Cu^{2+}

22.11 $[Ni(NH_3)_3(H_2O)(en)]^{2+}$ The complex has a +2 charge.

22.12 $[Cr(en)_2(NH_3)_2]^{3+}$ The complex has a +3 charge.

22.13   (a) $[NiCl_2(en)_2]$

       (b) $K_2[PtCl_4]$

       (c) $K[Cu(CN)_2]$

       (d) $[Fe(NH_3)_4(H_2O)_2]^{2+}$

22.14   (a) $[Cr(NH_3)_2(H_2O)_3(OH)]NO_3$

       (b) $[Fe(NH_3)_6](NO_3)_3$

       (c) $[Fe(CO)_5]$

       (d) $(NH_4)_2[CuCl_4]$

22.15   (a) diaquabis(oxalato)nickelate(II) ion

       (b) dibromobis(ethylenediamine)cobalt(II) ion

       (c) amminechlorobis(ethylenediamine)cobalt(III) ion

       (d) diammineoxalatoplatinum(II)

22.16   (a) tetraaquadichlorocobalt(III) ion

       (b) triaquatrifluorocobalt(III)

       (c) amminetribromoplatinate(II) ion

       (d) triamminechloroethylenediaminecobalt(III) ion

22.17   (a) $[Fe(H_2O)_5OH]^{2+}$

       (b) potassium tetracyanonickelate(II)

       (c) potassium diaquabis(oxalato)chromate(III)

       (d) $(NH_4)_2[PtCl_4]$

22.18   (a) $[CrCl_2(H_2O)_4]Cl$

       (b) pentaamminesulfatochromium(III) chloride

       (c) $Na_2[CoCl_4]$

       (d) tris(oxalato)ferrate(III) ion

22.19   (a)

$$\begin{array}{c}
Cl \\
H_3N\cdots\underset{|}{\overset{|}{Fe}}\cdots NH_3 \\
H_3N \diagdown \quad \diagup NH_3 \\
Cl
\end{array}$$

$$\begin{array}{c}
NH_3 \\
H_3N\cdots\underset{|}{\overset{|}{Fe}}\cdots NH_3 \\
H_3N \diagdown \quad \diagup Cl \\
Cl
\end{array}$$

(b)

$$\begin{array}{c}
H_3N\cdots\underset{}{Pt}\cdots Br \\
H_3N \diagdown \quad \diagup SCN
\end{array}$$

$$\begin{array}{c}
Br\cdots\underset{}{Pt}\cdots NH_3 \\
H_3N \diagdown \quad \diagup SCN
\end{array}$$

(c)

$$\begin{array}{c}
NO_2 \\
H_3N\cdots\underset{|}{\overset{|}{Co}}\cdots NH_3 \\
H_3N \diagdown \quad \diagup NO_2 \\
NO_2
\end{array}$$

$$\begin{array}{c}
NH_3 \\
H_3N\cdots\underset{|}{\overset{|}{Co}}\cdots NH_3 \\
O_2N \diagdown \quad \diagup NO_2 \\
NO_2
\end{array}$$

(d)

$$\left[\begin{array}{c}
\quad\quad Cl \\
H_2C-\underset{H_2}{\overset{H_2}{N}}\cdots\underset{|}{\overset{|}{Co}}\cdots Cl \\
H_2C-\underset{H_2}{N}\diagdown \quad \diagup Cl \\
\quad\quad Cl
\end{array} \right]^{-}$$

22.20   (a)

$$\left[\begin{array}{c}
Cl \\
H_2O\cdots\underset{|}{\overset{|}{Co}}\cdots OH_2 \\
H_2O \diagdown \quad \diagup OH_2 \\
Cl
\end{array} \right]^{+}$$

$$\left[\begin{array}{c}
H_2O \\
H_2O\cdots\underset{|}{\overset{|}{Co}}\cdots OH_2 \\
H_2O \diagdown \quad \diagup Cl \\
Cl
\end{array} \right]^{+}$$

trans   *cis*

(b)

$$\begin{array}{c}
F \\
H_3N\cdots\underset{|}{\overset{|}{Co}}\cdots NH_3 \\
H_3N \diagdown \quad \diagup F \\
F
\end{array}$$

$$\begin{array}{c}
NH_3 \\
H_3N\cdots\underset{|}{\overset{|}{Co}}\cdots NH_3 \\
F \diagdown \quad \diagup F \\
F
\end{array}$$

mer   *fac*

(c) No geometrical isomers possible.

(d)

$$\left[\begin{array}{c}
\quad NH_3 \\
\underset{H_2}{\overset{H_2}{N}}\cdots\underset{|}{\overset{|}{Co}}\cdots\underset{H_2}{\overset{H_2}{N}} \\
\underset{H_2}{N}\diagdown \quad \diagup \underset{H_2}{N} \\
\quad Cl
\end{array} \right]^{2+}$$

$$\left[\begin{array}{c}
\underset{H_2}{\overset{H_2N}{N}}\cdots\underset{|}{\overset{|}{Co}}\cdots NH_2 \\
\underset{H_2}{N}\diagdown \quad \diagup NH_3 \\
\quad Cl
\end{array} \right]^{2+}$$

trans   *cis*

22.21   (a) Yes. Mirror images of complexes of the stoichiometry $[M(bidentate)_3]^{n+}$ do not superimpose

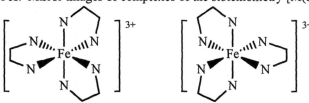

(b) Optical isomers are not possible. The mirror images are superimposable.

(c) Optical isomers are not possible. The mirror images are superimposable.

(d) Optical isomers are not possible. The mirror images are superimposable.

22.22

$$\left[\begin{array}{c} NH_3 \\ N/\!\!/\!\!/\!\!/_{\cdots}\,\overset{|}{\underset{|}{Co}}\cdots\!\!\backslash\!\!\backslash OH_2 \\ N\!\!\blacktriangledown \overset{|}{\underset{NH_3}{}} \!\!\blacktriangledown Cl \end{array}\right]^+$$ $$\left[\begin{array}{c} H_2O \\ N/\!\!/\!\!/\!\!/_{\cdots}\,\overset{|}{\underset{|}{Co}}\cdots\!\!\backslash\!\!\backslash NH_3 \\ N\!\!\blacktriangledown \overset{|}{\underset{Cl}{}} \!\!\blacktriangledown NH_3 \end{array}\right]^+$$ $$\left[\begin{array}{c} NH_3 \\ N/\!\!/\!\!/\!\!/_{\cdots}\,\overset{|}{\underset{|}{Co}}\cdots\!\!\backslash\!\!\backslash NH_3 \\ N\!\!\blacktriangledown \overset{|}{\underset{Cl}{}} \!\!\blacktriangledown OH_2 \end{array}\right]^+$$ $$\left[\begin{array}{c} NH_3 \\ N/\!\!/\!\!/\!\!/_{\cdots}\,\overset{|}{\underset{|}{Co}}\cdots\!\!\backslash\!\!\backslash NH_3 \\ N\!\!\blacktriangledown \overset{|}{\underset{H_2O}{}} \!\!\blacktriangledown Cl \end{array}\right]^+$$

   trans   *cis*   *cis* (chiral)   *cis* (chiral)

22.23   (a) Mn^{2+}, d^5 paramagnetic, 1 unpaired electron $\underline{\uparrow\downarrow}$ $\underline{\uparrow\downarrow}$ $\underline{\uparrow}$

        (b) Co^{3+}, d^6 diamagnetic $\underline{\uparrow\downarrow}$ $\underline{\uparrow\downarrow}$ $\underline{\uparrow\downarrow}$

        (c) Fe^{3+}, d^5 paramagnetic, 1 unpaired electron $\underline{\uparrow\downarrow}$ $\underline{\uparrow\downarrow}$ $\underline{\uparrow}$

        (d) Cr^{2+}, d^4 paramagnetic, 2 unpaired electrons $\underline{\uparrow\downarrow}$ $\underline{\uparrow}$ $\underline{\uparrow}$

22.24   (a) Fe^{2+}, d^6 4 unpaired electrons $\underline{\uparrow}$ $\underline{\uparrow}$ / $\underline{\uparrow\downarrow}$ $\underline{\uparrow}$ $\underline{\uparrow}$

        (b) Mn^{2+}, d^5 5 unpaired electrons $\underline{\uparrow}$ $\underline{\uparrow}$ / $\underline{\uparrow}$ $\underline{\uparrow}$ $\underline{\uparrow}$

        (c) Cr^{2+}, d^4 4 unpaired electrons $\underline{\uparrow}$ / $\underline{\uparrow}$ $\underline{\uparrow}$ $\underline{\uparrow}$

        (d) Fe^{3+}, d^5 5 unpaired electrons $\underline{\uparrow}$ $\underline{\uparrow}$ / $\underline{\uparrow}$ $\underline{\uparrow}$ $\underline{\uparrow}$

22.25   (a) Fe^{2+}, d^6 4 unpaired electrons

↑   ↑   ↑

↑↓ ↑

(b) Co^{2+}, d^7 3 unpaired electrons

↑   ↑   ↑

↑↓ ↑↓

(c) Mn^{2+}, d^5 5 unpaired electrons

↑   ↑   ↑

↑   ↑

(d) Zn^{2+}, d^{10} No unpaired electrons

↑↓ ↑↓ ↑↓

↑↓ ↑↓

22.26   (a) Zn^{2+}, d^{10} No unpaired electrons

↑↓ ↑↓ ↑↓

↑↓ ↑↓

(b) V^{5+}, d^0 No d electrons, no unpaired electrons

(c) Mn^{2+}, d^5 5 unpaired electrons

↑   ↑   ↑

↑   ↑

(d) Cu^{2+}, d^9 1 unpaired electron

↑↓ ↑↓ ↑

↑↓ ↑↓

22.27   (a) The coordination number of iron is 6

(b) The coordination geometry is octahedral

(c) Fe^{2+}

(d) 4 unpaired electrons ([Ar]$3d^6$, high spin)

(e) paramagnetic

22.28   (a)   The coordination number of cobalt is 6

        (b)   The coordination geometry is octahedral

        (c) Co^{3+}

        (d)   No unpaired electrons ($[Ar]3d^6$, low spin)

        (e)   diamagnetic

        (f)

22.29   When $Co_2(SO_4)_3$ dissolves in water it forms $[Co(H_2O)_6]^{3+}$; addition of fluoride converts this to $[CoF_6]^{3-}$.
        The hexaaqua complex is low spin (d^6, diamagnetic, no unpaired electrons), and the fluoride complex is
        high spin (paramagnetic, 4 unpaired electrons). Fluoride is a weaker field ligand than water.

22.30   When $FeSO_4$ dissolves in water it forms $[Fe(H_2O)_6]^{2+}$; addition of ammonia converts this to $[Fe(NH_3)_6]^{2+}$.
        The hexaaqua complex is high spin (d^6, paramagnetic, 4 unpaired electrons), and the ammonia complex is
        low spin (diamagnetic, no unpaired electrons). Ammonia is a stronger field ligand than water.

22.31   The light absorbed is in the blue region of the spectrum. Therefore, the light transmitted (the color of the
        solution) is yellow.

22.32   The light absorbed is in the red region of the spectrum. Therefore, the light transmitted (the color of the
        solution) is blue-green.

22.33   Determine the magnetic properties of the complex. Square planar (Ni^{2+}, d^8) complexes are diamagnetic,
        whereas tetrahedral complexes are paramagnetic.

22.34   (a) Cr^{3+}, d^3 3 unpaired electrons   (c) Fe^{2+}, d^6 No unpaired electrons
        (b) Mn^{2+}, d^5 1 unpaired electron   (d) Ni^{2+}, d^8 2 unpaired electrons

22.35   high spin

        4 unpaired electrons   low spin   No unpaired electrons

22.36   Only one chloride is not coordinated directly to the metal, so one mole of AgCl will precipitate.

22.37 d^8 complexes are commonly square planar. (b) $Ni(CN)_4^{2-}$ and (d) $Pt(CN)_4^{2-}$

22.38   Only (b) cis-$[Fe(C_2O_4)_2Cl_2]^{2-}$ has a nonsuperimposable mirror image.

22.39   Two geometric isomers are possible, with *cis* and *trans* chloride ligands.

22.40   (c) The d_{xz}, d_{yz}, and d_{xy} orbitals are higher in energy than the $d_{x^2-y^2}$ and d_{z^2} orbitals.

22.41   The light absorbed is in the blue region of the spectrum. Therefore, the light transmitted (the color of the solution) is yellow.

22.42   (a) Fe^{3+}

(b) The coordination number for iron is 6

(c) The coordination geometry is octahedral

(d) 1 unpaired electron ($[Ar]3d^5$, low spin)

(e) Paramagnetic

(f) Two possible geometric isomers, *cis* and *trans*

22.43   (a) Mn^{2+}

(b) The coordination number for manganese is 6

(c) The coordination geometry is octahedral

(d) 5 unpaired electrons ($[Ar]3d^5$, high spin)

(e) Paramagnetic

(f) Two possible geometric isomers, *cis* and *trans*

22.44 $[Pt(NH_3)_4]^{2+}$ tetraammineplatinum(II) ion $[PtCl_4]^{2-}$ tetrachloroplatinate(II) ion

22.45 $[Co(NH_3)_4Cl_2]Cl$ tetraamminedichlorocobalt(III) chloride

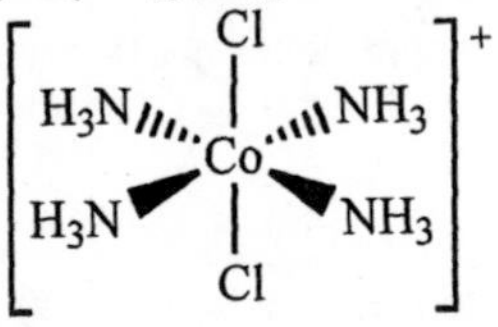

    trans 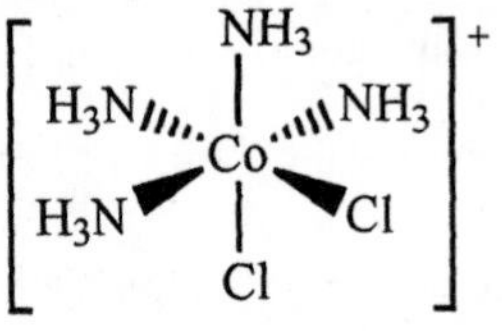   *cis*

22.46 $[Pt(NO_2)Cl(NH_3)_2]$ diamminechloronitroplatinum(II)

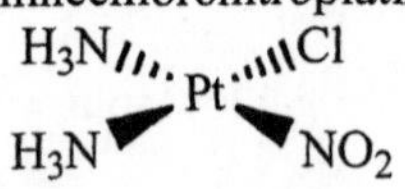

Two geometric isomers   *cis*   *trans*

22.47 $[Co(en)_2(H_2O)Cl]^+$ aquachlorobis(ethylenediamine)cobalt(III) ion   The complex has a +1 charge

22.48   Two geometric isomers of [Cr(dmen)₃]³⁺ can exist

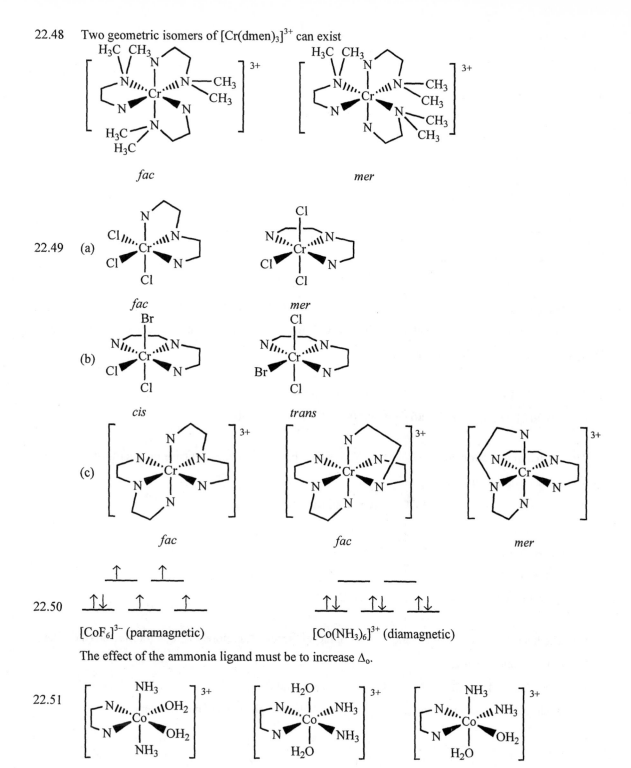

22.50   The effect of the ammonia ligand must be to increase Δ₀.

22.52   The bond angles and bond lengths are such that the nitrogen atoms cannot span the diagonal of the Pt complex and accomplish reasonable overlap with the Pt orbitals to form the bonds.

22.53   In $[Mn(H_2O)_6]^{2+}$ and $[Mn(CN)_6]^{4-}$, Mn has an oxidation number of +2 ($[Ar]3d^5$).

$[Mn(H_2O)_6]^{2+}$ $[Mn(CN)_6]^{4-}$

paramagnetic, 5 unpaired e^- paramagnetic, 1 unpaired e^-

The CN^- ligand results in an increased Δ_o

22.54   In $K_4[Cr(CN)_6]$ and $K_4[Cr(SCN)_6]$, Cr has an oxidation number of +2 ($[Ar]3d^4$).

Cr^{2+} Cr^{2+}

paramagnetic, 2 unpaired e^- paramagnetic, 4 unpaired e^-

The SCN^- ligand is a weaker field ligand than the CN^- ligand. The SCN^- ligand occurs to the left (lower)

in the spectrochemical series relative to CN^-.

22.55   A: $[Co(NH_3)_5Br]SO_4$ B: $[Co(NH_3)_5SO_4]Br$

$[Co(NH_3)_5Br]SO_4(aq) + BaCl_2(aq) \rightarrow BaSO_4(s) + [Co(NH_3)_5Br]Cl_2(aq)$

22.56   Titrate each of the four compounds with $AgNO_3$. Only the "free" chloride outside the coordination sphere
        of the metal will precipitate.

Compound	mol Cl^- precipitated with $AgNO_3$
$[Cr(H_2O)_6]Cl_3$	3
$[Cr(H_2O)_5Cl]Cl_2$	2
$[Cr(H_2O)_4Cl_2]Cl$	1
$[[Cr(H_2O)_3Cl_3]$	0

22.57   (a)   The light absorbed is in the orange region of the spectrum. Therefore, the light transmitted (the color
              of the solution) is blue or cyan.

        (b)   According to Table 22.3, CO_3^{2-} belongs between F^- and $C_2O_4^{2-}$.

        (c) Δ_o should be small and therefore the complex should be high spin and paramagnetic.

22.58   (a) Cu^{2+}

        (b)   The coordination number of copper is 6

        (c) $[Ar]3d^9$ 1 unpaired electron

        (d)   Paramagnetic

22.59   O ⌢ N   = $\begin{bmatrix} O \\ \parallel \\ C-CH_2 \\ \vert \qquad \vert \\ O \qquad NH_2 \end{bmatrix}^-$

not chiral   not chiral

chiral   chiral   chiral

22.60   Determine the empirical formula:

$19.51 \text{ g} \cdot \dfrac{1 \text{ mol Cr}}{51.996 \text{ g}} = 0.3752 \text{ mol Cr} = 1 \text{ mol Cr}$

$39.92 \text{ g} \cdot \dfrac{1 \text{ mol Cl}}{35.453 \text{ g}} = 1.126 \text{ mol Cl} = 3 \text{ mol Cl}$

$40.57 \text{ g} \cdot \dfrac{1 \text{ mol H}_2\text{O}}{18.015 \text{ g}} = 2.252 \text{ mol H}_2\text{O} = 6 \text{ mol H}_2\text{O}$

$[Cr(H_2O)_6]Cl_3$ hexaaquachromium(III) chloride

$Cl^-(aq) + Ag^+(aq) \rightarrow AgCl(s)$

22.61 $1.00 \times 10^3 \text{ g} \cdot \dfrac{1 \text{ mol FeTiO}_3}{151.7 \text{ g}} \cdot \dfrac{3 \text{ mol H}_2\text{SO}_4}{1 \text{ mol FeTiO}_3} \cdot \dfrac{1 \text{ L}}{18.0 \text{ mol H}_2\text{SO}_4} = 1.10 \text{ L}$

$1.00 \times 10^3 \text{ g} \cdot \dfrac{1 \text{ mol FeTiO}_3}{151.7 \text{ g}} \cdot \dfrac{1 \text{ mol TiO}_2}{1 \text{ mol FeTiO}_3} \cdot \dfrac{79.87 \text{ g}}{1 \text{ mol TiO}_2} = 526 \text{ g TiO}_2$

22.62   (a) $FeTiO_3(s) + 2\ HCl(aq) \rightarrow FeCl_2(aq) + TiO_2(s) + H_2O(\ell)$

(b) $2\ FeTiO_3(s) + 4\ HCl(aq) \rightarrow 2\ FeCl_2(aq) + 2\ TiO_2(s) + 2\ H_2O(\ell)$

$2\ FeCl_2(aq) + 2\ H_2O(\ell) + {}^1\!/_2\ O_2(g) \rightarrow Fe_2O_3(s) + 4\ HCl(aq)$

$2\ FeTiO_3(s) + {}^1\!/_2\ O_2(g) \rightarrow Fe_2O_3(s) + 2\ TiO_2(s)$

Yes, the HCl used in the first step is recovered in the second step.

(c) $908 \times 10^3 \text{ g} \cdot \dfrac{1 \text{ mol FeTiO}_3}{151.7 \text{ g}} \cdot \dfrac{1 \text{ mol Fe}_2\text{O}_3}{2 \text{ mol FeTiO}_3} \cdot \dfrac{159.7 \text{ g}}{1 \text{ mol Fe}_2\text{O}_3} = 4.78 \times 10^5 \text{ g Fe}_2\text{O}_3$

22.63   (a) $0.213 \text{ g} \cdot \dfrac{1 \text{ mol } UO_2(NO_3)_2}{394.0 \text{ g}} \cdot \dfrac{1 \text{ mol } U^{n+}}{1 \text{ mol } UO_2(NO_3)_2} = 5.41 \times 10^{-4} \text{ mol } U^{n+}$

$0.01247 \text{ L} \cdot \dfrac{0.0173 \text{ mol } MnO_4^-}{1 \text{ L}} = 2.16 \times 10^{-4} \text{ mol } MnO_4^-$

$\dfrac{5.41 \times 10^{-4} \text{ mol } U^{n+}}{2.16 \times 10^{-4} \text{ mol } MnO_4^-} = \dfrac{2.5 \text{ mol } U^{n+}}{1 \text{ mol } MnO_4^-} = \dfrac{5 \text{ mol } U^{n+}}{2 \text{ mol } MnO_4^-}$

The reduction of 2 mol MnO_4^- (oxidation number +7) to 2 mol Mn^{2+} requires 10 mol e^-, so 10 mol e^- are required to oxidize 5 mol U^{n+} to UO_2^{2+} (oxidation number 6+). The charge on the ion is 4+.

   (b) $UO_2^{2+}(aq) + 4 H^+(aq) + 2 e^- \rightarrow U^{4+}(aq) + 2 H_2O(\ell)$

$Zn(s) \rightarrow Zn^{2+}(aq) + 2 e^-$

$\overline{\phantom{UO_2^{2+}(aq) + 4 H^+(aq) + Zn(s) \rightarrow U^{4+}(aq) + 2 H_2O(\ell) + Zn^{2+}(aq)}}$

$UO_2^{2+}(aq) + 4 H^+(aq) + Zn(s) \rightarrow U^{4+}(aq) + 2 H_2O(\ell) + Zn^{2+}(aq)$

   (c) $5[U^{4+}(aq) + 2 H_2O(\ell) \rightarrow UO_2^{2+}(aq) + 4 H^+(aq) + 2 e^-]$

$2[MnO_4^-(aq) + 8 H^+(aq) + 5 e^- \rightarrow Mn^{2+}(aq) + 4 H_2O(\ell)]$

$\overline{\phantom{5 U^{4+}(aq) + 2 H_2O(\ell) + 2 MnO_4^-(aq) \rightarrow 5 UO_2^{2+}(aq) + 4 H^+(aq) + 2 Mn^{2+}(aq)}}$

$5 U^{4+}(aq) + 2 H_2O(\ell) + 2 MnO_4^-(aq) \rightarrow 5 UO_2^{2+}(aq) + 4 H^+(aq) + 2 Mn^{2+}(aq)$

22.64   (a) $Ni(s) + 4 CO(g) \rightarrow Ni(CO)_4(g)$

$\Delta H^\circ = \Delta H_f^\circ[Ni(CO)_4(g)] - 4 \Delta H_f^\circ[CO(g)]$

$\Delta H^\circ = 1 \text{ mol } (-602.9 \text{ kJ/mol}) - 4 \text{ mol } (-110.525 \text{ kJ/mol}) = -160.8 \text{ kJ}$

$\Delta S^\circ = S^\circ[Ni(CO)_4(g)] - \{S^\circ[Ni(s)] + 4 S^\circ[CO(g)]\}$

$\Delta S^\circ = 1 \text{ mol } (410.6 \text{ J/K·mol}) - [1 \text{ mol } (29.87 \text{ J/K·mol}) + 4 \text{ mol } (197.674 \text{ J/K·mol})] = -410.0 \text{ J/K}$

$\Delta G^\circ = \Delta H^\circ - T\Delta S^\circ = -160.8 \text{ kJ} - (298 \text{ K})(-410.0 \text{ J/K})(1 \text{ kJ}/10^3 \text{ J}) = -38.6 \text{ kJ}$

$-38.6 \text{ kJ/mol} = -(8.3145 \times 10^{-3} \text{ kJ/K·mol})(298 \text{ K}) \ln K$

$\ln K = 15.6$

$K = 6 \times 10^6$

   (b) $\Delta G^\circ = 0 = \Delta H^\circ - T\Delta S^\circ = -160.8 \text{ kJ} - T(-410.0 \text{ J/K})(1 \text{ kJ}/10^3 \text{ J})$

$T = 392 \text{ K or greater}$

   (c)   React impure nickel with excess CO gas to form $Ni(CO)_4(g)$ in a product-favored reaction. Heating the carbonyl complex above 392 K will reverse the formation reaction, isolating pure nickel metal.

22.65
ion	$K_{formation}$ (NH$_3$ complex)
Co^{2+}	7.7×10^4
Ni^{2+}	5.6×10^8
Cu^{2+}	6.8×10^{12}
Zn^{2+}	2.9×10^9

22.66   Substituting 10^8 and 10^{18} into the expression ($-RT \ln K$) produces ΔG values of -45.6 kJ (ammine) and -102.7 kJ (en). Since the differences in ΔH values are much less than this (~8 kJ), entropy must play a role. While there are fewer molecules in the second reaction, the change in entropy (as the much larger bidentate ethylenediamine ligands form the complex) is greater.

Chapter 23
Nuclear Chemistry

INSTRUCTOR'S NOTES

For this edition of the text, the discussion of nuclear chemistry has again been placed as the final chapter. However, we believe that reactor accidents in the United States and the Soviet Union, and the ongoing debate in the United States concerning nuclear waste disposal, make it desirable to give this topic more prominence. In addition, its importance is indicated by the fact that about 20% of the papers abstracted in *Chemical Abstracts* annually in the general areas of physical, inorganic, and analytical chemistry concern nuclear chemistry. It is our hope that the material will be discussed in class to some extent, or that students will read the chapter out of interest in the subject.

Because almost everyone knows or thinks they know something about nuclear chemistry, you may find it useful to begin the study of this material with a pre-quiz to identify existing knowledge and misconceptions. The topics could include nuclear chemistry-based medicine, power and weapons. Such an exercise could provide a means of getting started in order to clarify some concepts, history and potential for this chemistry. Students can be encouraged to search for news stories in print or on the web in order for them to get a picture of what related topics are current.

SUGGESTED DEMONSTRATIONS

1. The Nature of Radioactivity

    *   Fortman, J. J. "An Overhead Projector Demonstration of Nuclear Beta Emission," *Journal of Chemical Education* **1992**, *69*, 162.

    *   Para, A. F.; Lazzarini, E. "Some Simple Classroom Experiments on the Monte Carlo Method," *Journal of Chemical Education* **1974**, *51*, 336.

    *   Herber, R. H. "General Chemistry Demonstrations Based on Nuclear and Radiochemical Phenomena," *Journal of Chemical Education* **1969**, *46*, 665.

    *   Smith, W. T.; Wood, J. H. "A Half-life Experiment for General Chemistry Students," (measurement of the half-life of bismuth-210), *Journal of Chemical Education* **1959**, *36*, 492.

2. Radiation Effects and Units of Radiation

    *   Because radon in homes is very much in the news, it might be interesting to have the class test some area of the chemistry building or campus dormitories for radon using a home testing kit available at most hardware stores.

3. Nuclear Synthesis and Decay

    *   Olbris, D. J.; Herzfeld, J. "Nucleogenesis! A Game with Natural Rules for Teaching Nuclear Synthesis and Decay," *Journal of Chemical Education* **1999**, *76*, 349.

SOLUTIONS TO STUDY QUESTIONS

23.1   See sections 2.1, 23.1, 23.2, 23.5, and 23.6

23.2   The mass of a nucleus is not equal to the sum of the mass of the constituent particles. The mass difference, called the mass defect, is equated with the energy holding the nuclear particles together. For ^{2}H, the nuclear mass (2.01410 g/mol) is less than the sum of the mass of a proton (1.007825 g/mol) and a neutron (1.008665 g/mol).

23.3   Binding energy per nucleon is calculated by first calculating mass defect for an isotope, converting the mass defect to binding energy (using the equation $E = mc^2$), and then dividing binding energy by the number of nuclear particles for that isotope.

23.4   Isotopes that fall to the left of the band of stability (high n/p ratio) undergo beta emission, and isotopes that fall to the right of the band of stability (low n/p ratio) undergo positron emission or beta capture to become more stable. Isotopes beyond Z = 83 are unstable and undergo alpha emission.

23.5   See section 23.5

23.6   Radioactive decay follows first-order kinetics. A (activity) $= kN$ (number of atoms)

$\ln(N/N_0) = \ln(A/A_0) = -kt$

23.7   See the description of carbon-14 dating in section 23.4.

23.8   See section 23.4

23.9   Several naturally occurring radioactive isotopes are found to decay to form a product that is also radioactive. When this happens, the initial nuclear reaction is followed by a second nuclear reaction, and if the situation is repeated, a third and a fourth, and so on. Eventually, a nonradioactive isotope is formed to end the series. Uranium ore contains trace quantities of the radioactive elements formed in the radioactive decay series, including radium and polonium.

23.10   See sections 23.8 and 23.9

23.11   Curies (Ci) measure the number of decompositions per second; 1 Ci $= 3.7 \times 10^{10}$ dps. The amount of energy absorbed by living tissue is measured in rads. One rad represents 0.01 J of energy absorbed per kilogram of tissue. Biological damage is quantified in rems. A dose of radiation in rem is determined by multiplying the energy absorbed in rads by the quality factor for that kind of radiation.

23.12   (a) $^{56}_{28}Ni$ (d) $^{97}_{43}Tc$

        (b) $^{1}_{0}n$ (e) $^{0}_{-1}\beta$

        (c) $^{32}_{15}P$ (f) $^{0}_{+1}\beta$

23.13   (a) $^{1}_{1}H$ (d) $2\ ^{1}_{0}n$

        (b) $^{27}_{13}Al$ (e) $^{254}_{102}No$

        (c) $^{1}_{0}n$ (f) $^{16}_{8}O$

23.14   (a) $^{0}_{-1}\beta$ (d) $^{226}_{88}Ra$

        (b) $^{87}_{37}Rb$ (e) $^{0}_{-1}\beta$

        (c) $^{4}_{2}He$ (f) $^{24}_{11}Na$

23.15   (a) $^{19}_{9}F$ (d) $^{37}_{17}Cl$

        (b) $^{59}_{27}Co$ (e) $^{55}_{25}Mn$

        (c) $^{40}_{20}Ca$ (f) $^{1}_{1}H$

23.16 $^{235}_{92}U \rightarrow\ ^{231}_{90}Th + ^{4}_{2}\alpha$

        $^{231}_{90}Th \rightarrow\ ^{231}_{91}Pa + ^{0}_{-1}\beta$

        $^{231}_{91}Pa \rightarrow\ ^{227}_{89}Ac + ^{4}_{2}\alpha$

        $^{227}_{89}Ac \rightarrow\ ^{227}_{90}Th + ^{0}_{-1}\beta$

        $^{227}_{90}Th \rightarrow\ ^{223}_{88}Ra + ^{4}_{2}\alpha$

        $^{223}_{88}Ra \rightarrow\ ^{219}_{86}Rn + ^{4}_{2}\alpha$

        $^{219}_{86}Rn \rightarrow\ ^{215}_{84}Po + ^{4}_{2}\alpha$

        $^{215}_{84}Po \rightarrow\ ^{211}_{82}Pb + ^{4}_{2}\alpha$

        $^{211}_{82}Pb \rightarrow\ ^{211}_{83}Bi + ^{0}_{-1}\beta$

        $^{211}_{83}Bi \rightarrow\ ^{211}_{84}Po + ^{0}_{-1}\beta$

        $^{211}_{84}Po \rightarrow\ ^{207}_{82}Pb + ^{4}_{2}\alpha$

23.17 $^{232}_{90}Th \rightarrow\ ^{228}_{88}Ra + ^{4}_{2}\alpha$

        $^{228}_{88}Ra \rightarrow\ ^{228}_{89}Ac + ^{0}_{-1}\beta$

        $^{228}_{89}Ac \rightarrow\ ^{228}_{90}Th + ^{0}_{-1}\beta$

        $^{228}_{90}Th \rightarrow\ ^{224}_{88}Ra + ^{4}_{2}\alpha$

        $^{224}_{88}Ra \rightarrow\ ^{220}_{86}Rn + ^{4}_{2}\alpha$

        $^{220}_{86}Rn \rightarrow\ ^{216}_{84}Po + ^{4}_{2}\alpha$

        $^{216}_{84}Po \rightarrow\ ^{212}_{82}Pb + ^{4}_{2}\alpha$

        $^{212}_{82}Pb \rightarrow\ ^{212}_{83}Bi + ^{0}_{-1}\beta$

        $^{212}_{83}Bi \rightarrow\ ^{212}_{84}Po + ^{0}_{-1}\beta$

        $^{212}_{84}Po \rightarrow\ ^{208}_{82}Pb + ^{4}_{2}\alpha$

23.18   (a) $^{198}_{79}\text{Au} \rightarrow {}^{198}_{80}\text{Hg} + {}^{0}_{-1}\beta$

          (b) $^{222}_{86}\text{Rn} \rightarrow {}^{218}_{84}\text{Po} + {}^{4}_{2}\alpha$

          (c) $^{137}_{55}\text{Cs} \rightarrow {}^{137}_{56}\text{Ba} + {}^{0}_{-1}\beta$

          (d) $^{110}_{49}\text{In} \rightarrow {}^{110}_{48}\text{Cd} + {}^{0}_{+1}\beta$

23.19   (a) $^{67}_{31}\text{Ga} + {}^{0}_{-1}\text{e} \rightarrow {}^{67}_{30}\text{Zn}$

          (b) $^{38}_{19}\text{K} \rightarrow {}^{38}_{18}\text{Ar} + {}^{0}_{+1}\beta$

          (c) $^{99m}_{43}\text{Tc} \rightarrow {}^{99}_{43}\text{Tc} + \gamma$

          (d) $^{56}_{25}\text{Mn} \rightarrow {}^{56}_{26}\text{Fe} + {}^{0}_{-1}\beta$

23.20   (a) $^{80m}_{35}\text{Br} \rightarrow {}^{80}_{35}\text{Br} + \gamma$

          (b) $^{240}_{98}\text{Cf} \rightarrow {}^{4}_{2}\alpha + {}^{236}_{96}\text{Cm}$

          (c) $^{61}_{27}\text{Co} \rightarrow {}^{0}_{-1}\beta + {}^{61}_{28}\text{Ni}$

          (d) $^{11}_{6}\text{C} \rightarrow {}^{0}_{+1}\beta + {}^{11}_{5}\text{B}$

23.21   (a) $^{54}_{25}\text{Mn} \rightarrow {}^{0}_{+1}\beta + {}^{54}_{24}\text{Cr}$

          (b) $^{241}_{95}\text{Am} \rightarrow {}^{4}_{2}\alpha + {}^{237}_{93}\text{Np}$

          (c) $^{110}_{47}\text{Ag} \rightarrow {}^{0}_{-1}\beta + {}^{110}_{48}\text{Cd}$

          (d) $^{197m}_{80}\text{Hg} \rightarrow {}^{197}_{80}\text{Hg} + \gamma$

23.22   (a) Both ^{3}H and ^{20}F have a high n/p ratio and will likely decay by beta emission

          (b) ^{22}Na has a low n/p ratio and will likely decay by positron emission

23.23   (a) ^{32}P has a high n/p ratio and will likely decay by beta emission

          (b) ^{38}K has a low n/p ratio and will likely decay by positron emission

23.24 $^{10}_{5}\text{B} \rightarrow 5\,{}^{1}_{1}\text{H} + 5\,{}^{1}_{0}\text{n}$

          $\Delta m = [(5 \times 1.00783) + (5 \times 1.00867)] - 10.01294 = 0.06956$ g/mol nuclei

          $E_b = (\Delta m)c^2 = (0.06956 \times 10^{-3}\ \text{kg/mol})(3.00 \times 10^8\ \text{m/s})^2 = 6.26 \times 10^{12}$ J/mol nuclei $(= 6.26 \times 10^9$ kJ/mol$)$

          $\dfrac{E_b}{n} = \dfrac{6.26 \times 10^9\ \text{kJ/mol nuclei}}{10\ \text{mol nucleons/mol nuclei}} = 6.26 \times 10^8$ kJ/mol nucleons

          $^{11}_{5}\text{B} \rightarrow 5\,{}^{1}_{1}\text{H} + 6\,{}^{1}_{0}\text{n}$

          $\Delta m = [(5 \times 1.00783) + (6 \times 1.00867)] - 11.00931 = 0.08186$ g/mol nuclei

          $E_b = (\Delta m)c^2 = (0.08186 \times 10^{-3}\ \text{kg/mol})(3.00 \times 10^8\ \text{m/s})^2 = 7.37 \times 10^{12}$ J/mol nuclei $(= 7.37 \times 10^9$ kJ/mol$)$

          $\dfrac{E_b}{n} = \dfrac{7.37 \times 10^9\ \text{kJ/mol nuclei}}{11\ \text{mol nucleons/mol nuclei}} = 6.70 \times 10^8$ kJ/mol nucleons

23.25 $^{30}_{15}P \rightarrow 15\ ^1_1H + 15\ ^1_0n$

$\Delta m = [(15 \times 1.00783) + (15 \times 1.00867)] - 29.97832 = 0.26918$ g/mol nuclei

$E_b = (\Delta m)c^2 = (0.26918 \times 10^{-3}$ kg$)(3.00 \times 10^8$ m/s$)^2 = 2.42 \times 10^{13}$ J/mol nuclei $(= 2.42 \times 10^{10}$ kJ/mol$)$

$\dfrac{E_b}{n} = \dfrac{2.42\ \times\ 10^{10}\ \text{kJ/mol nuclei}}{30\ \text{mol nucleons/mol nuclei}} = 8.08\ \times\ 10^8$ kJ/mol nucleons

$^{31}_{15}P \rightarrow 15\ ^1_1H + 16\ ^1_0n$

$\Delta m = [(15 \times 1.00783) + (16 \times 1.00867)] - 30.97376 = 0.28241$ g/mol

$E_b = (\Delta m)c^2 = (0.28241 \times 10^{-3}$ kg$)(3.00 \times 10^8$ m/s$)^2 = 2.54 \times 10^{13}$ J/mol nuclei $(= 2.54 \times 10^{10}$ kJ/mol$)$

$\dfrac{E_b}{n} = \dfrac{2.54\ \times\ 10^{10}\ \text{kJ/mol nuclei}}{31\ \text{mol nucleons/mol nuclei}} = 8.20\ \times\ 10^8$ kJ/mol nucleons

23.26 $^{40}_{20}Ca \rightarrow 20\ ^1_1H + 20\ ^1_0n$

$\Delta m = [(20 \times 1.00783) + (20 \times 1.00867)] - 39.96259 = 0.36741$ g/mol nuclei

$E_b = (\Delta m)c^2 = (0.36741 \times 10^{-3}$ kg$)(3.00 \times 10^8$ m/s$)^2 = 3.31 \times 10^{13}$ J/mol nuclei $(= 3.31 \times 10^{10}$ kJ/mol$)$

$\dfrac{E_b}{n} = \dfrac{3.31\ \times\ 10^{10}\ \text{kJ/mol nuclei}}{40\ \text{mol nucleons/mol nuclei}} = 8.27\ \times\ 10^8$ kJ/mol nucleons

23.27 $^{56}_{26}Fe \rightarrow 26\ ^1_1H + 30\ ^1_0n$

$\Delta m = [(26 \times 1.00783) + (30 \times 1.00867)] - 55.9349 = 0.5288$ g/mol nuclei

$E_b = (\Delta m)c^2 = (0.5288 \times 10^{-3}$ kg$)(3.00 \times 10^8$ m/s$)^2 = 4.76 \times 10^{13}$ J/mol nuclei $(= 4.76 \times 10^{10}$ kJ/mol$)$

$\dfrac{E_b}{n} = \dfrac{4.76\ \times\ 10^{10}\ \text{kJ/mol nuclei}}{56\ \text{mol nucleons/mol nuclei}} = 8.50\ \times\ 10^8$ kJ/mol nucleons

23.28 $^{16}_8O \rightarrow 8\ ^1_1H + 8\ ^1_0n$

$\Delta m = [(8 \times 1.00783) + (8 \times 1.00867)] - 15.99492 = 0.13708$ g/mol nuclei

$E_b = (\Delta m)c^2 = (0.13708 \times 10^{-3}$ kg$)(3.00 \times 10^8$ m/s$)^2 = 1.23 \times 10^{13}$ J/mol nuclei $(= 1.23 \times 10^{10}$ kJ/mol$)$

$\dfrac{E_b}{n} = \dfrac{1.23\ \times\ 10^{10}\ \text{kJ/mol nuclei}}{16\ \text{mol nucleons/mol nuclei}} = 7.71\ \times\ 10^8$ kJ/mol nucleons

23.29 $^{14}_7N \rightarrow 7\ ^1_1H + 7\ ^1_0n$

$\Delta m = [(7 \times 1.00783) + (7 \times 1.00867)] - 14.003074 = 0.11243$ g/mol nuclei

$E_b = (\Delta m)c^2 = (0.11243 \times 10^{-3}$ kg$)(3.00 \times 10^8$ m/s$)^2 = 1.01 \times 10^{13}$ J/mol nuclei $(= 1.01 \times 10^{10}$ kJ/mol$)$

$\dfrac{E_b}{n} = \dfrac{1.01\ \times\ 10^{10}\ \text{kJ/mol nuclei}}{14\ \text{mol nucleons/mol nuclei}} = 7.23\ \times\ 10^8$ kJ/mol nucleons

23.30   64 h/12.7 h = 5 half-lives

Amount remaining = 25.0 µg $\times\ (^1/_2)^5 = 0.781$ µg

23.31   10.8 d/2.69 d = 4 half-lives

Amount remaining = 2.8 µg $\times\ (^1/_2)^4 = 0.18$ µg

23.32   (a) $^{131}_{53}\text{I} \rightarrow \ ^{0}_{-1}\beta + \ ^{131}_{54}\text{Xe}$

        (b)   40.2 d/8.04 d = 5 half-lives

             $2.4 \ \mu\text{g} \times (^1/_2)^5 = 0.075 \ \mu\text{g}$

23.33   (a) $^{32}_{15}\text{P} \rightarrow \ ^{0}_{-1}\beta + \ ^{32}_{16}\text{S}$

        (b)   28.6 d/14.3 d = 2 half-lives

             $4.8 \ \mu\text{g} \times (^1/_2)^2 = 1.2 \ \mu\text{g}$

23.34 $k = \dfrac{0.693}{t_{1/2}} = \dfrac{0.693}{78.25 \ \text{h}} = 0.008856 \ \text{h}^{-1}$

       $\ln \dfrac{N}{N_0} = -kt$

       $\ln \dfrac{x}{0.015} = -(0.008856 \ \text{h}^{-1})(13 \ \text{d})(24 \ \text{h}/1 \ \text{d})$

       $x = 9.5 \times 10^{-4} \ \text{mg}$

23.35   (a) $^{131}_{53}\text{I} \rightarrow \ ^{0}_{-1}\beta + \ ^{131}_{54}\text{Xe}$

        (b) $k = \dfrac{0.693}{t_{1/2}} = \dfrac{0.693}{8.04 \ \text{d}} = 0.0862 \ \text{d}^{-1}$

            $\ln \dfrac{N}{N_0} = -kt$

            $\ln \dfrac{35.0}{100.0} = -(0.0862 \ \text{d}^{-1})t$

            $t = 12.2 \ \text{days}$

23.36   (a) $^{222}_{86}\text{Rn} \rightarrow \ ^{4}_{2}\alpha + \ ^{218}_{84}\text{Po}$

        (b) $k = \dfrac{0.693}{t_{1/2}} = \dfrac{0.693}{3.82 \ \text{d}} = 0.181 \ \text{d}^{-1}$

            $\ln \dfrac{N}{N_0} = -kt$

            $\ln \dfrac{20.0}{100.0} = -(0.181 \ \text{d}^{-1})t$

            $t = 8.87 \ \text{days}$

23.37 $k = \dfrac{0.693}{t_{1/2}} = \dfrac{0.693}{5.73 \times 10^3 \ \text{y}} = 1.21 \times 10^{-4} \ \text{y}^{-1}$

       $\ln \left(\dfrac{11.2}{14.0} \right) = -(1.21 \times 10^{-4} \ \text{y}^{-1})t$

       $t = 1850 \ \text{years old}$

       Year made = 1998 − 1850 = 150 AD

23.38 $k = \dfrac{0.693}{t_{1/2}} = \dfrac{0.693}{5.73 \times 10^3 \text{ y}} = 1.21 \times 10^{-4} \text{ y}^{-1}$

$\ln\left(\dfrac{72}{100}\right) = -(1.21 \times 10^{-4} \text{ y}^{-1})t$

$t = 2700$ years old

23.39   (a) $\ln\left(\dfrac{975}{1.0 \times 10^3}\right) = -k(1 \text{ y})$

$k = 0.025 \text{ y}^{-1}$

$t_{1/2} = \dfrac{0.693}{k} = \dfrac{0.693}{0.025 \text{ y}^{-1}} = 27 \text{ y}$

(b) $\ln\left(\dfrac{1.0}{100.0}\right) = -(0.025 \text{ y}^{-1})t$

$t = 180$ years

23.40   (a) $^1/_8 = (^1/_2)^3$ or three half-lives

$(5.27 \text{ y}) \times 3 = 15.8 \text{ y}$

(b) $k = \dfrac{0.693}{t_{1/2}} = \dfrac{0.693}{5.27 \text{ y}} = 0.131 \text{ y}^{-1}$

$\ln\left(\dfrac{A}{A_0}\right) = -(0.131 \text{ y}^{-1})(1 \text{ y})$

$\dfrac{A}{A_0}$ = fraction of activity = 0.88

23.41

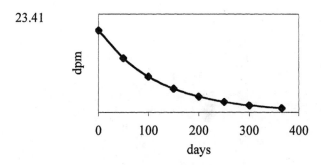

23.42

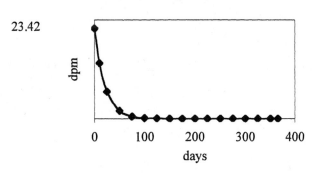

23.43   (a) $^{23}_{11}\text{Na} + ^{1}_{0}\text{n} \rightarrow ^{24}_{11}\text{Na}$

$^{24}_{11}\text{Na} \rightarrow ^{0}_{-1}\beta + ^{24}_{12}\text{Mg}$

(b) $\ln\left(\dfrac{1.01 \times 10^4}{2.54 \times 10^4}\right) = -k(20\ \text{h})$

$k = 0.046\ \text{h}^{-1}$

$t_{1/2} = \dfrac{0.693}{k} = \dfrac{0.693}{0.046\ \text{h}^{-1}} = 15\ \text{h}$

23.44 $\ln\left(\dfrac{5470}{7840}\right) = -k(72\ \text{d})$

$k = 0.0050\ \text{d}^{-1}$

$t_{1/2} = \dfrac{0.693}{k} = \dfrac{0.693}{0.0050\ \text{d}^{-1}} = 140\ \text{days}$

23.45 $^{239}_{94}\text{Pu} + 2\,^{1}_{0}\text{n} \rightarrow ^{241}_{94}\text{Pu}$

$^{241}_{94}\text{Pu} \rightarrow ^{0}_{-1}\beta + ^{241}_{95}\text{Am}$

23.46 $^{239}_{94}\text{Pu} + ^{4}_{2}\text{He} \rightarrow ^{240}_{95}\text{Am} + ^{1}_{1}\text{H} + 2\,^{1}_{0}\text{n}$

23.47 $^{238}_{92}\text{U} + ^{12}_{6}\text{C} \rightarrow ^{246}_{98}\text{Cf} + 4\,^{1}_{0}\text{n}$

23.48 $^{48}_{20}\text{Ca} + ^{242}_{94}\text{Pu} \rightarrow ^{287}_{114}114 + 3\,^{1}_{0}\text{n}$

23.49 $^{287}_{114}114 \rightarrow ^{4}_{2}\alpha + ^{283}_{112}112$

23.50   (a) $^{115}_{48}\text{Cd}$

(b) $^{7}_{4}\text{Be}$

(c) $^{4}_{2}\alpha$

(d) $^{63}_{29}\text{Cu}$

23.51   (a) $^{1}_{1}\text{H}$

(b) $^{12}_{6}\text{C}$

(c) $^{27}_{13}\text{Al}$

(d) $^{242}_{96}\text{Cm}$

23.52 $^{10}_{5}\text{B} + ^{1}_{0}\text{n} \rightarrow ^{4}_{2}\alpha + ^{7}_{3}\text{Li}$

23.53 $^{6}_{3}\text{Li} + ^{1}_{0}\text{n} \rightarrow ^{3}_{1}\text{H} + ^{4}_{2}\alpha$

23.54 $\quad k = \dfrac{0.693}{t_{1/2}} = \dfrac{0.693}{4.8 \times 10^{10} \text{ y}} = 1.4 \times 10^{-11} \text{ y}^{-1}$

$\ln\left(\dfrac{1.8}{1.6 + 1.8}\right) = -(1.4 \times 10^{-11} \text{ y}^{-1})t$

$t = 4.4 \times 10^{10}$ years old

23.55 $\quad k = \dfrac{0.693}{t_{1/2}} = \dfrac{0.693}{4.8 \times 10^{10} \text{ y}} = 1.4 \times 10^{-11} \text{ y}^{-1}$

$\ln(0.951) = -(1.4 \times 10^{-11} \text{ y}^{-1})t$

$t = 3.5 \times 10^{9}$ years old

23.56 $\quad$ When the ratio $^{206}\text{Pb}/^{238}\text{U} = {}^{1}/_{3}$, $^{1}/_{4}$ of the ^{238}U has decayed to ^{206}Pb and $^{3}/_{4}$ remains as ^{238}U

$k = \dfrac{0.693}{t_{1/2}} = \dfrac{0.693}{4.5 \times 10^{9} \text{ y}} = 1.5 \times 10^{-10} \text{ y}^{-1}$

$\ln\left(\dfrac{3}{4}\right) = -(1.5 \times 10^{-10} \text{ y}^{-1})t$

$t = 1.9 \times 10^{9}$ years old

23.57 $\quad k = \dfrac{0.693}{t_{1/2}} = \dfrac{0.693}{7.04 \times 10^{8} \text{ y}} = 9.8 \times 10^{-10} \text{ y}^{-1}$

$\ln\left(\dfrac{0.72}{3.0}\right) = -(9.8 \times 10^{-10} \text{ y}^{-1})t$

$t = 1.5 \times 10^{9}$ years ago

23.58 $\quad$ (a) $\quad ^{238}_{92}\text{U} + {}^{1}_{0}\text{n} \;\rightarrow\; ^{239}_{92}\text{U} + \gamma$

$\qquad$ (b) $\quad ^{239}_{92}\text{U} \;\rightarrow\; ^{239}_{93}\text{Np} + {}^{0}_{-1}\beta$

$\qquad$ (c) $\quad ^{239}_{93}\text{Np} \;\rightarrow\; ^{239}_{94}\text{Pu} + {}^{0}_{-1}\beta$

$\qquad$ (d) $\quad ^{239}_{94}\text{Pu} + {}^{1}_{0}\text{n} \;\rightarrow\; 2\,{}^{1}_{0}\text{n} + \text{energy} + \text{other nuclei}$

23.59 $\quad$ (a) $\quad \Delta m = 7.01600 - [6.01512 + 1.00867] = -0.00779$ g/mol

$\qquad \Delta E = (\Delta m)c^2 = (-0.00779 \times 10^{-3} \text{ kg/mol})(3.00 \times 10^{8} \text{ m/s})^2 = -7.01 \times 10^{11}$ J/mol

$\qquad \dfrac{-7.01 \times 10^{11} \text{ J}}{1 \text{ mol}} \cdot \dfrac{1 \text{ mol}}{6.022 \times 10^{23} \text{ atoms}} = -1.16 \times 10^{-12}$ J/atom

$\qquad$ (b) $\quad \lambda = \dfrac{hc}{E} = \dfrac{(2.998 \times 10^{8} \text{ m/s})(6.626 \times 10^{-34} \text{ J} \cdot \text{s})}{1.16 \times 10^{-12} \text{ J}} = 1.71 \times 10^{-13}$ m $= 0.171$ pm

23.60 $\quad 1 \text{ lb} \cdot \dfrac{453.59 \text{ g}}{1 \text{ lb}} \cdot \dfrac{1 \text{ mol } ^{235}\text{U}}{235 \text{ g}} \cdot \dfrac{2.1 \times 10^{10} \text{ kJ}}{1 \text{ mol } ^{235}\text{U}} = 4.1 \times 10^{10}$ kJ

$\dfrac{4.1 \times 10^{10} \text{ kJ}}{2.6 \times 10^{7} \text{ kJ/ton coal}} = 1600$ tons of coal

23.61   (a) $_{-1}^{0}e + _{+1}^{0}\beta \rightarrow 2\,\gamma$

        mass of electron = mass of proton

        $\Delta E = (\Delta m)c^2 = [2(9.109 \times 10^{-28}\text{ g})](1\text{ kg}/10^3\text{ g})(3.00 \times 10^8\text{ m/s})^2 = 1.64 \times 10^{-13}\text{ J} = 1.64 \times 10^{-16}\text{ kJ}$

  (b) $v = \dfrac{E}{h} = \dfrac{1.64 \times 10^{-13}\text{ J}/2\ \gamma\text{-rays}}{6.626 \times 10^{-34}\text{ J}\cdot\text{s}} = 1.24 \times 10^{17}\text{ s}^{-1}$

23.62 $(2.0 \times 10^6\text{ dps})(1.0\text{ mL}) = (1.5 \times 10^4\text{ dps})(x)$

       x = volume of circulatory system = 130 mL

23.63   fraction separated = (550 dpm)/(1950 dpm) = 0.28

       (0.28)(2.80 mg) = 0.79 mg threonine in sample

23.64 $\dfrac{27\text{ tagged fish}}{5250\text{ fish}} = \dfrac{1000\text{ tagged fish}}{x}$

       $x = 1.9 \times 10^5$ fish

23.65   Assume that the O atom of the alcohol is "tagged" with radioactive oxygen (^{15}O). If the O in the water comes from the —OH of the acid, the water is free of the radioactive ^{15}O isotope.

       If the O in the water comes from the alcohol, however, then the water will contain radioactive oxygen.

23.66   (a) The mass decreases by 4 units (with $_2^4\alpha$ emission) or is unchanged (with $_{-1}^0\beta$ emission) so the only masses possible are 4 units apart.

  (b) ^{232}Th series, m = 4n; ^{235}U series, m = 4n + 3

  (c)

Isotope	Series
^{226}Ra	^{238}U
^{215}At	^{235}U
^{228}Th	^{232}Th
^{210}Bi	^{238}U

  (d) Each series is headed by a long-lived isotope (in the order of 10^9 years, the age of the earth). The 4n + 1 series is missing because there is no long-lived isotope in this series. Over geologic time, all the members of this series have decayed completely.

23.67 $\dfrac{\Delta N}{\Delta t} = kN$

$N = \dfrac{1.0 \times 10^{-3} \text{ g}}{238 \text{ g/mol}} \cdot \dfrac{6.02 \times 10^{23} \text{ nuclei}}{1 \text{ mol}} = 2.5 \times 10^{18} \text{ nuclei}$

12 dps $= k(2.5 \times 10^{18} \text{ nuclei})$

$k = 4.7 \times 10^{-18} \text{ s}^{-1}$

$t_{1/2} = \dfrac{0.693}{k} = \dfrac{0.693}{4.7 \times 10^{-18} \text{ s}^{-1}} \cdot \dfrac{1 \text{ hr}}{3600 \text{ s}} \cdot \dfrac{1 \text{ day}}{24 \text{ hr}} \cdot \dfrac{1 \text{ year}}{365 \text{ day}} = 4.7 \times 10^{9} \text{ years}$

23.68   (a) ^{235}U series

(b) $^{235}_{92}\text{U} \rightarrow {}^{231}_{90}\text{Th} + {}^{4}_{2}\alpha$

$^{231}_{90}\text{Th} \rightarrow {}^{231}_{91}\text{Pa} + {}^{0}_{-1}\beta$

(c) The concentration of ^{231}Pa in pitchblende is 1 ppm, or $1.0 \text{ g}/10^{6}$ g. To isolate 1.0 g of ^{231}Pa you need 10^{6} g of the ore.

(d) $^{231}_{91}\text{Pa} \rightarrow {}^{227}_{89}\text{Ac} + {}^{4}_{2}\alpha$

INTERCHAPTER
The Chemistry of Fuels and Energy Sources

INSTRUCTOR'S NOTES

In this edition of the text four topics are included as dedicated interchapter units. This provides a high degree of flexibility in how the subjects can be taught.

This first interchapter on fuels and energy sources is a natural progression from the study of thermodynamics applied to chemistry in Chapter 6. The high degree of public interest in these topics should stimulate students to study the topic. This interchapter includes a wide range of subjects and multiple aspects of each. The content will give serious students a great deal of authoritative information for them to consider.

SUGGESTED DEMONSTRATIONS

1.   Fuel Cells

- Zerbinati, O. "A Direct Methanol Fuel Cell," *Journal of Chemical Education* **2002**, *79*, 829.

2.   Biosources of Energy

- Choi, M. M. F.; Wong, P. S.; Yiu, T. P. "Application of a Datalogger in Observing Photosynthesis," *Journal of Chemical Education* **2002**, *79*, 980.

SOLUTIONS TO STUDY QUESTIONS

1. $CH_4(g) + H_2O(g) \rightarrow 3\ H_2(g) + CO(g)$

   $100.\ g \cdot \dfrac{1\ mol\ CH_4}{16.04\ g} \cdot \dfrac{3\ mol\ H_2}{1\ mol\ CH_4} \cdot \dfrac{2.016\ g}{1\ mol\ H_2} = 37.7\ g\ H_2$

   $CH_2(\ell) + H_2O(g) \rightarrow 2\ H_2(g) + CO(g)$

   $100.\ g \cdot \dfrac{1\ mol\ CH_2}{14.03\ g} \cdot \dfrac{2\ mol\ H_2}{1\ mol\ CH_4} \cdot \dfrac{2.016\ g}{1\ mol\ H_2} = 28.7\ g\ H_2$

   $C(s) + H_2O(g) \rightarrow H_2(g) + CO(g)$

   $100.\ g \cdot \dfrac{1\ mol\ C}{12.01\ g} \cdot \dfrac{1\ mol\ H_2}{1\ mol\ CH_4} \cdot \dfrac{2.016\ g}{1\ mol\ H_2} = 16.8\ g\ H_2$

2.   Burning gasoline releases 47 kJ/g, burning C releases 32.8 kJ/g, and burning H_2 releases 119.9 kJ/g.

   fraction of C in gasoline + fraction of H in gasoline = 1

   47 kJ/g = 32.8 kJ/g (fraction of C in gasoline) + 119.9 kJ/g (fraction of H in gasoline)

   47 kJ/g = 32.8 kJ/g (x) + 119.9 kJ/g $(1 - x)$

   $x = 0.84$

   84% C and 16% H

3. $70.\ lb \cdot \dfrac{453.6\ g}{1\ lb} \cdot \dfrac{33\ kJ}{1\ g} = 1.0 \times 10^6\ kJ$

4.   Ethanol: $C_2H_5OH(\ell) + 3\ O_2(g) \rightarrow 3\ H_2O(g) + 2\ CO_2(g)$

   $\Delta H_f^\circ[O_2(g)] = 0$ kJ/mol

   $\Delta H^\circ_{rxn} = 2\ \Delta H_f^\circ[CO_2(g)] + 3\ \Delta H_f^\circ[H_2O(g)] - \Delta H_f^\circ[C_2H_5OH(\ell)]$

   $\Delta H^\circ_{rxn} = 2$ mol $(-393.509$ kJ/mol$) + 3$ mol $(-241.83$ kJ/mol$) - 1$ mol $(-277.0$ kJ/mol$)$

   $\Delta H^\circ_{rxn} = -1235.5$ kJ

   $\dfrac{-1367.5\ kJ}{1\ mol\ C_2H_5OH} \cdot \dfrac{1\ mol\ C_2H_5OH}{46.0688\ g} = -29.684$ kJ/g

   Ethane: $2\ C_2H_6(g) + 7\ O_2(g) \rightarrow 4\ CO_2(g) + 6\ H_2O(g)$

   $\Delta H_f^\circ[O_2(g)] = 0$ kJ/mol

   $\Delta H^\circ_{rxn} = 4\ \Delta H_f^\circ[CO_2(g)] + 6\ \Delta H_f^\circ[H_2O(g)] - 2\ \Delta H_f^\circ[C_2H_6(g)]$

   $\Delta H^\circ_{rxn} = 4$ mol $(-393.509$ kJ/mol$) + 6$ mol $(-241.83$ kJ/mol$) - 2$ mol $(-83.85$ kJ/mol$)$

   $\Delta H^\circ_{rxn} = -2857.3$ kJ

   $\dfrac{-2857.3\ kJ}{2\ mol\ C_2H_6} \cdot \dfrac{1\ mol\ C_2H_6}{30.0694\ g} = -47.512$ kJ/g

   Less energy evolved with combustion of ethanol because hydrogen bonding is stronger, so some energy is

   lost to overcoming intermolecular attractive forces.

5.   Burning 70. lb of coal produces 1.0×10^6 kJ/day (see problem 3).

$$7.0 \text{ gal} \cdot \frac{4 \text{ qt}}{1 \text{ gal}} \cdot \frac{1 \text{ L}}{1.06 \text{ qt}} \cdot \frac{1000 \text{ mL}}{1 \text{ L}} \cdot \frac{0.8 \text{ g}}{1 \text{ mL}} \cdot \frac{45 \text{ kJ}}{1 \text{ g}} = 9.5 \times 10^5 \text{ kJ}$$

Burning 7.0 gal of oil produces about 14% less heat than burning 70. lb of coal.

6. $Al_2O_3(s) \rightarrow 2 \text{ Al}(s) + {}^3/_2 \text{ O}_2(g)$

$\Delta H^{\circ} = \Delta H_f^{\circ}[Al_2O_3(s)] = -[1 \text{ mol} \cdot (-1675.7 \text{ kJ/mol})] = 1675.7 \text{ kJ}$

$$1.0 \text{ lb} \cdot \frac{454 \text{ g}}{1 \text{ lb}} \cdot \frac{1 \text{ mol Al}}{27.0 \text{ g}} \cdot \frac{1675.7 \text{ kJ}}{2 \text{ mol Al}} = 1.4 \times 10^4 \text{ kJ}$$

Energy to recycle 1.0 lb aluminum = $({}^1/_3)(1.4 \times 10^4 \text{ kJ}) = 4.7 \times 10^3 \text{ kJ}$

7. $$\frac{5.45 \times 10^3 \text{ kJ}}{1 \text{ mol C}_8\text{H}_{18}} \cdot \frac{1 \text{ mol C}_8\text{H}_{18}}{114.2 \text{ g}} = 47.7 \text{ kJ/g}$$

$$\frac{5.45 \times 10^3 \text{ kJ}}{1 \text{ mol C}_8\text{H}_{18}} \cdot \frac{1 \text{ mol C}_8\text{H}_{18}}{114.2 \text{ g}} \cdot \frac{0.688 \text{ g}}{1 \text{ mL}} \cdot \frac{1000 \text{ mL}}{1 \text{ L}} = 3.28 \times 10^4 \text{ kJ/L}$$

8. $$100 \text{ W} \cdot \frac{1 \text{ J/s}}{1 \text{ W}} \cdot \frac{1 \text{ kJ}}{1000 \text{ J}} \cdot \frac{3600 \text{ s}}{1 \text{ hr}} \cdot \frac{24 \text{ hr}}{1 \text{ day}} = 8640 \text{ kJ/day}$$

$$\frac{8640 \text{ kJ}}{1 \text{ day}} \cdot \frac{1 \text{ g coal}}{33 \text{ kJ}} = 260 \text{ g coal}$$

9. $$\frac{940 \text{ kW-hr}}{1 \text{ year}} \cdot \frac{1 \text{ kJ/s}}{1 \text{ kW}} \cdot \frac{3600 \text{ s}}{1 \text{ hr}} = 3.4 \times 10^6 \text{ kJ/year}$$

10.   Non-renewable: The energy source is not replenished after it is consumed.

coal, natural gas

Renewable: The energy is derived in some way from the Sun's energy, so it is replenished after use.

solar energy, geothermal energy, wind power

11. $2 \text{ CH}_3\text{OH}(\ell) + 3 \text{ O}_2(g) \rightarrow 2 \text{ CO}_2(g) + 4 \text{ H}_2\text{O}(\ell)$

$\Delta H^{\circ}_{\text{rxn}} = 2 \Delta H_f^{\circ}[\text{CO}_2(g)] + 4 \Delta H_f^{\circ}[\text{H}_2\text{O}(\ell)] - 2 \Delta H_f^{\circ}[\text{CH}_3\text{OH}(\ell)]$

$\Delta H^{\circ}_{\text{rxn}} = 2 \text{ mol} (-393.509 \text{ kJ/mol}) + 4 \text{ mol} (-285.83 \text{ kJ/mol}) - 2 \text{ mol} (-238.4 \text{ kJ/mol})$

$\Delta H^{\circ}_{\text{rxn}} = -1453.5 \text{ kJ}$

$$\frac{1453.5 \text{ kJ}}{2 \text{ mol CH}_3\text{OH}} \cdot \frac{1 \text{ mol CH}_3\text{OH}}{32.042 \text{ g}} \cdot \frac{0.787 \text{ g}}{1 \text{ mL}} \cdot \frac{1000 \text{ mL}}{1.0 \text{ L}} \cdot \frac{1 \text{ kW}}{1 \text{ kJ/s}} \cdot \frac{1 \text{ hr}}{3600 \text{ s}} = 5.0 \text{ kW-hr}$$

12. C_8H_{18} (5.45×10^3 kJ/mol) > CH_4 (882 kJ/mol) > C(s) (393.5 kJ/mol) > H_2 (241.83 kJ/mol)

13. $$325 \text{ m} \cdot 50.0 \text{ m} \cdot \frac{2.6 \times 10^7 \text{ J}}{\text{m}^2} \cdot \frac{1 \text{ kJ}}{1000 \text{ J}} = 4.2 \times 10^8 \text{ kJ/day}$$

14. $1 \text{ day} \cdot \dfrac{24 \text{ h}}{1 \text{ day}} \cdot \dfrac{1.0 \times 10^6 \text{ J}}{1 \text{ h}} \cdot \dfrac{1 \text{ kJ}}{10^3 \text{ J}} = 2.4 \times 10^4 \text{ kJ/day}$

$2.4 \times 10^4 \text{ kJ/day} \cdot \dfrac{10^3 \text{ J}}{1 \text{ kJ}} \cdot \dfrac{1 \text{ kW-h}}{3.60 \times 10^6 \text{ J}} = 6.7 \text{ kW-h/day}$

15. $1.0 \text{ cm}^3 \cdot \dfrac{12.0 \text{ g}}{1 \text{ cm}^3} \cdot \dfrac{1 \text{ mol Pd}}{106.4 \text{ g}} = 0.113 \text{ mol Pd}$

$0.084 \text{ g} \cdot \dfrac{1 \text{ mol H}_2}{2.02 \text{ g}} \cdot \dfrac{2 \text{ mol H}}{1 \text{ mol H}_2} = 0.083 \text{ mol H}$

$\dfrac{0.113 \text{ mol Pd}}{0.083 \text{ mol H}} = \dfrac{1.4 \text{ mol Pd}}{1 \text{ mol H}}$ The formula is $Pd_{1.4}H$

16. Assume the density of water is 1.00 g/mL

$q_{water} = (225 \text{ g})(4.184 \text{ J/g·K})(340. \text{ K} - 293 \text{ K}) = 4.4 \times 10^4 \text{ J}$

$1100 \text{ W} \cdot 90 \text{ s} \cdot \dfrac{1 \text{ J/s}}{1 \text{ W}} = 9.9 \times 10^4 \text{ J}$

Efficiency $= \dfrac{4.4 \times 10^4 \text{ J}}{9.9 \times 10^4 \text{ J}} \cdot 100\% = 44\%$ efficient

17. $1.00 \text{ mile} \cdot \dfrac{1 \text{ gal}}{55.0 \text{ miles}} \cdot \dfrac{4 \text{ qt}}{1 \text{ gal}} \cdot \dfrac{1 \text{ L}}{1.057 \text{ qt}} \cdot \dfrac{1000 \text{ mL}}{1 \text{ L}} \cdot \dfrac{1 \text{ cm}^3}{1 \text{ mL}} \cdot \dfrac{0.737 \text{ g}}{1 \text{ cm}^3} \cdot \dfrac{48.0 \text{ kJ}}{1 \text{ g}} = 2.43 \times 10^3 \text{ kJ}$

INTERCHAPTER
The Chemistry of Life: Biochemistry

INSTRUCTOR'S NOTES

This second interchapter on biochemistry naturally follows the organic chemistry chapter.

This information will bring together what students have learned and perhaps are learning in biology class with their understanding of chemistry.

In addition to organic chemistry, topics from previous chapters which are used for biochemical applications include:

- Hybridization and molecular structure (peptide bonds)
- Thermochemistry (energy and ATP)
- Oxidation and reduction (NADH)

SUGGESTED DEMONSTRATIONS

1.   Photosynthesis

- Choi, M. M. F.; Wong, P. S.; Yiu, T. P. "Application of a Datalogger in Observing Photosynthesis," *Journal of Chemical Education* **2002**, *79*, 980.

2.   Web-Based Tutorial

- Casiday, R. E.; Holten, D.; Krathen, R.; Frey, R. F. "Blood-Chemistry Tutorials: Teaching Biological Applications of General Chemistry Material," *Journal of Chemical Education* **2001**, *78*, 1210.

SOLUTIONS TO STUDY QUESTIONS

1.   (a) 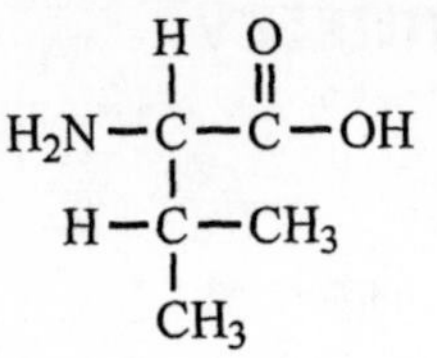
$$H_2N-\underset{\underset{\displaystyle CH_3}{|}}{\overset{\overset{\displaystyle H}{|}}{C}}-\overset{\overset{\displaystyle O}{||}}{C}-OH$$
$$\qquad\quad \underset{\displaystyle CH_3}{|}$$
$$H-\overset{|}{C}-CH_3$$

(b) 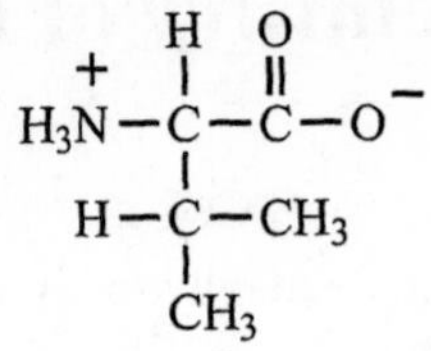
$$H_3\overset{+}{N}-\underset{}{\overset{\overset{\displaystyle H}{|}}{C}}-\overset{\overset{\displaystyle O}{||}}{C}-O^-$$
$$H-\overset{|}{C}-CH_3$$
$$\underset{\displaystyle CH_3}{|}$$

(c) The zwitterionic form will be the predominant form at physiological pH.

2,   Polar: serine, lysine, aspartic acid

Nonpolar: alanine, leucine, phenylalanine

3.

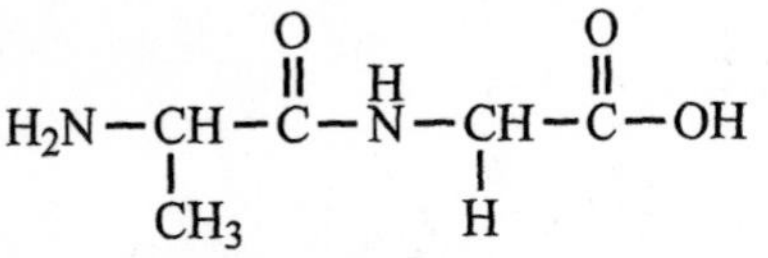

alanine-glycine 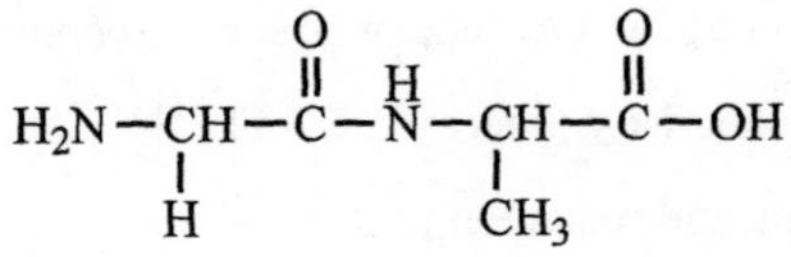   glycine-alanine

4.

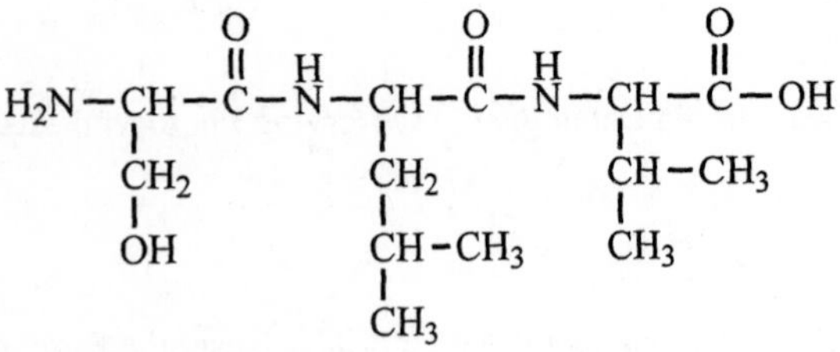

5.

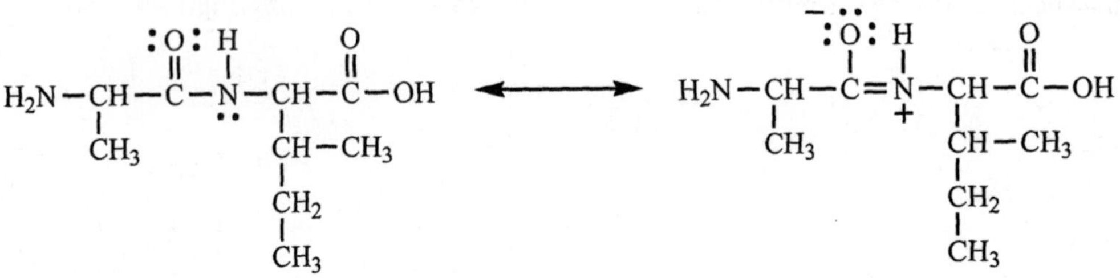

6.   (a) primary structure

(b) quaternary structure

(c) tertiary structure

(d) secondary structure

7.   The quaternary structure would tell us how the two subunits are arranged with respect to each other.

8. (a)

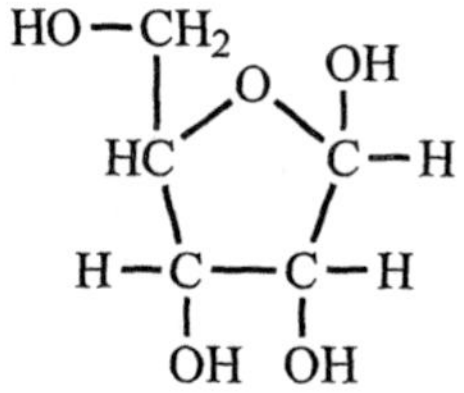

(b)

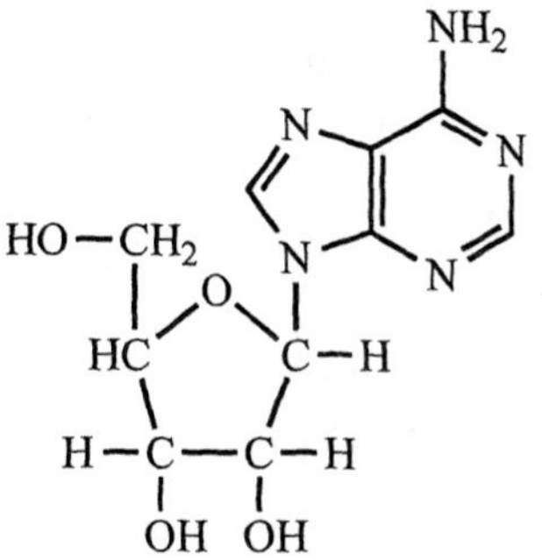

(c)

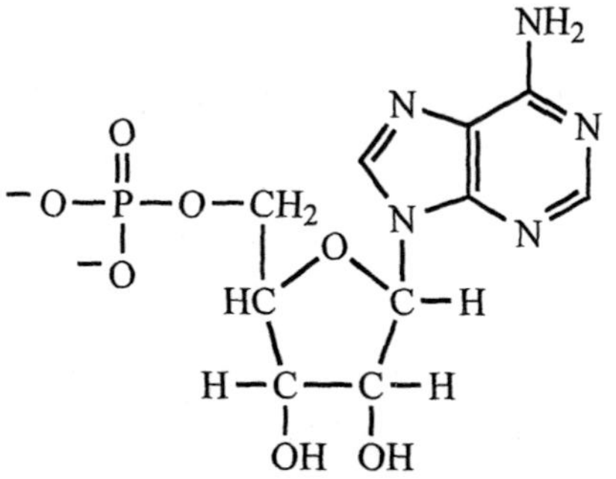

9.

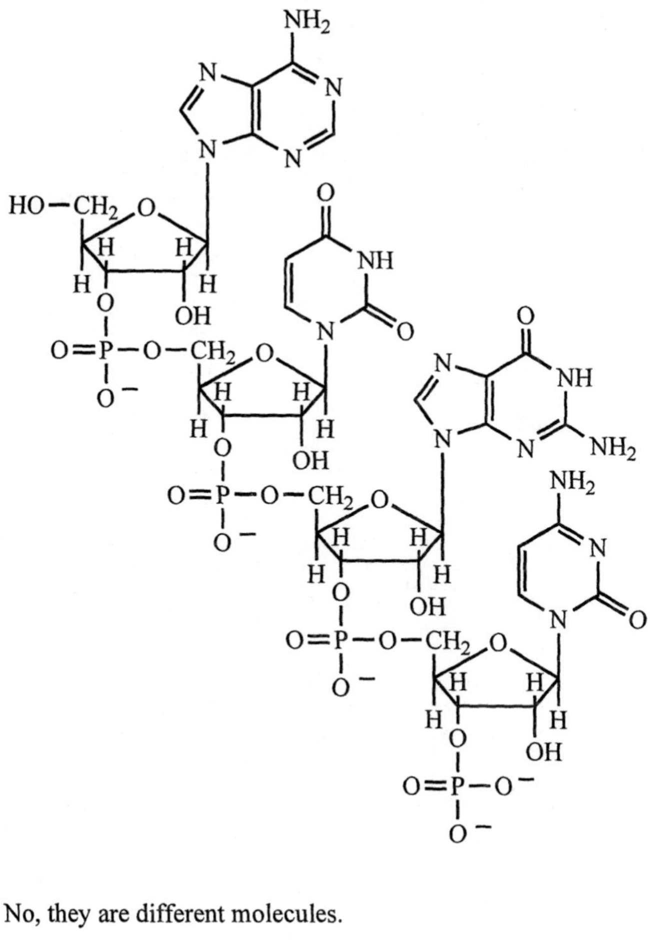

10.   No, they are different molecules.

11.   They proposed A–T base pairs and C–G base pairs. There are two hydrogen bonds in an A–T pair and three in a C–G pair.

12.   (a) Hydrogen bonds.

(b) In order for replication to take place, the two strands must be able to separate from each other.
If they were joined by covalent bonds, it would take much more energy to separate them.   Other bonds in the molecule might also break with this input of energy.

13.   (a) 5'-GAATCGCGT-3'

(b) 5'-GAAUCGCGU-3'

(c) 5'-UUC-3', 5'-CGA-3', and 5'-ACG-3'

(d) glutamic acid, serine, and arginine

14.   (a) glutamic acid

(b) 5'- TTC-3'

(c) The DNA sequence would now be 5'-TGC-3'. This would lead to an mRNA codon of 5'-GCA-3'. This codes for the amino acid alanine.

15.   (a) In transcription, a strand of RNA complementary to the segment of DNA is constructed.

(b) In translation, an amino acid sequence is constructed based on the information in an mRNA sequence.

16. $\Delta H_f°[O_2(g)] = 0$ kJ/mol

$\Delta H°_{rxn} = 6 \Delta H_f°[CO_2(g)] + 6 \Delta H_f°[H_2O(\ell)] - \Delta H_f°[C_6H_{12}O_6(s)]$

$\Delta H°_{rxn} = 6$ mol $(-393.509$ kJ/mol$) + 6$ mol $(-285.83$ kJ/mol$) - 1$ mol $(-1273.3$ kJ/mol$)$

$\Delta H°_{rxn} = -2802.7$ kJ

17.   (a) false

(b) true

(c) true

(d) true

18.   (a) NADH is oxidized

(b) O_2 is reduced

(c) O_2 is the oxidizing agent

(d) NADH is the reducing agent

19.   (a) $\Delta H_f^{\circ}[O_2(g)] = 0$ kJ/mol

       $\Delta H^{\circ}_{rxn} = \Delta H_f^{\circ}[C_6H_{12}O_6(s)] - \{6 \Delta H_f^{\circ}[CO_2(g)] + 6 \Delta H_f^{\circ}[H_2O(\ell)]\}$

       $\Delta H^{\circ}_{rxn} = 1$ mol $(-1273.3$ kJ/mol$) - [6$ mol $(-393.509$ kJ/mol$) + 6$ mol $(-285.83$ kJ/mol$)]$

       $\Delta H^{\circ}_{rxn} = 2802.7$ kJ

       (b) $\dfrac{2802.7 \text{ kJ}}{1 \text{ mol glucose}} \cdot \dfrac{1 \text{ mol}}{6.02214 \times 10^{23} \text{ atoms glucose}} \cdot \dfrac{1000 \text{ J}}{1 \text{ kJ}} = 4.6540 \times 10^{-18}$ J/glucose molecule

       (c) $E = \dfrac{hc}{\lambda} = \dfrac{(6.626 \times 10^{-34} \text{ J} \cdot \text{s})(2.998 \times 10^8 \text{ m/s})}{650 \text{ nm} \cdot \dfrac{1 \text{ m}}{10^9 \text{ nm}}} = 3.1 \times 10^{-19}$ J/photon

       (d) The amount of energy per photon is less than the amount of required per molecule of glucose, therefore multiple photons must be absorbed.

20.   1   B
       2   F
       3   I
       4   G
       5   D
       6   H
       7   E
       8   A
       9   C

451

INTERCHAPTER
The Chemistry of Modern Materials

INSTRUCTOR'S NOTES

This third interchapter on modern materials naturally follows the chemistry of liquids and solids.

Students in engineering and related fields should recognize the importance of the topics included in this interchapter. All students will have heard of several materials described, such as semiconductors, ceramics, glass, cements and superconductors.

SUGGESTED DEMONSTRATIONS

- For examples of polymer demonstrations see Chapter 11.

SOLUTIONS TO STUDY QUESTIONS

1. The GaAs band gap is 140 kJ/mol.

    $$\frac{140 \text{ kJ}}{\text{mol}} \cdot \frac{1000 \text{ J}}{1 \text{ kJ}} \cdot \frac{1 \text{ mol}}{6.022 \times 10^{23} \text{ photons}} = 2.3 \times 10^{-19} \text{ J/photon}$$

    $$\lambda = \frac{hc}{E} = \frac{(6.626 \times 10^{-34} \text{ J} \cdot \text{s})(2.998 \times 10^{8} \text{ m/s})}{2.3 \times 10^{-19} \text{ J}} = 8.5 \times 10^{-7} \text{ m}$$

    This is in the infrared portion of the spectrum.

2. Substitutional impurities should be similar in size and, for a solid solution, should have similar electronegativities.

    Al atom radius=143 pm, electronegativity (χ)=1.5

    (a) Sn   r = 141 pm χ = 1.8   Sn could be a substitutional impurity

    (b) P   r = 115 pm χ = 2.1   P could not be a substitutional impurity

    (c) K   r = 227 pm χ = 0.8   K could not be a substitutional impurity

    (d) Pb   r = 154 pm χ = 1.8   Pb could be a substitutional impurity, but it would not be as good as Sn

3. $$1.0 \text{ cm}^2 \cdot \left(\frac{1 \text{ m}}{100 \text{ cm}}\right)^2 \cdot \frac{925 \text{ W}}{1 \text{ m}^2} \cdot \frac{1 \text{ J}}{1 \text{ W} \cdot \text{s}} \cdot \frac{60 \text{ s}}{1 \text{ min}} \cdot 0.25 = 1.4 \text{ J/min}$$

4. $$1.0 \text{ cm}^2 \cdot \left(\frac{1 \text{ m}}{100 \text{ cm}}\right)^2 \cdot \frac{925 \text{ W}}{1 \text{ m}^2} = 0.093 \text{ W/solar cell}$$

    $$700 \text{ W} \cdot \frac{1 \text{ solar cell}}{0.093 \text{ W}} = 7600 \text{ solar cells}$$

    Each cell has an area of 1.0 cm^2, so the area of the panel is 7600 cm^2.

5. In the photo, there are approximately 3 gears across for the width of the spider mite. Because the spider mite is about 0.4 mm wide, then each of these gears measures approximately 0.1 to 0.13 mm in diameter, or 100 to 130 μm in diameter. A typical red blood cell is about 6 to 8 mm in diameter. This means that the gears are about 12 to 18 times bigger than a red blood cell.

6. Pewter is 91% Sn, 7.5% Sb, and 1.5% Cu.

    Density = (0.91)(7.265 g/cm^3) + (0.075)(6.697 g/cm^3) + (0.015)(8.95 g/cm^3) = 7.2 g/cm^3

7. Air has a density of 1.29×10^{-3} g/cm^3 at STP, and the density of SiO$_2$ is 2.3 g/cm^3.

    (0.01)(2.3 g/cm^3) + (0.99)(1.29×10^{-3} g/cm^3) = 0.024 g/cm^3

    A 1 cm^3 piece of aerogel will weigh 0.024 g

INTERCHAPTER
The Chemistry of the Environment

INSTRUCTOR'S NOTES

This fourth interchapter on environmental chemistry reviews several topics that should be of general interest to the student. The chemistry important to the processing of drinking water is an excellent application of some topics recently covered, such as the solubility product and pH. Air pollution is readily recognized by students as a potential cause for concern, so their study of some aspects of air quality should be easily accepted. Most students will probably not be able to define the term green chemistry at this point, so the discussion in this interchapter will provide them with a basic background in a field which will become more important during their professional lives.

SUGGESTED DEMONSTRATIONS

- Gani, N.; Khanam, J. "Are Surfactant Molecules Really Oriented in the Interface?" *Journal of Chemical Education* **2002**, *79*, 332.

- Najdoski, M.; Petrusevski, V. M. "A Novel Experiment for Fast and Simple Determination of the Oxygen Content in Air," *Journal of Chemical Education* **2000**, *77*, 1447.

- Wilmer, B. K.; Poziomek, E. J.; Orzechowska, G. E. "Environmental Chemistry Using Ultrasound," *Journal of Chemical Education* **1999**, *76*, 1657.

SOLUTIONS TO STUDY QUESTIONS

1 $Ca(OH)_2(s) \rightleftharpoons Ca^{2+}(aq) + 2\ OH^-(aq)$ $K_{sp} = 5.5 \times 10^{-5}$

     $Mg^{2+}(aq) + 2\ OH^-(aq) \rightleftharpoons Mg(OH)_2(s)$ $K = 1/K_{sp} = 1/(5.6 \times 10^{-12})$

———

     $Ca(OH)_2(s) + Mg^{2+}(aq) \rightleftharpoons Ca^{2+}(aq) + Mg(OH)_2(s)$ $K_{net} = 9.8 \times 10^6$

2. $Al(H_2O)_6^{3+}(aq) + H_2O(\ell) \rightleftharpoons Al(H_2O)_5(OH)^{2+}(aq) + H_3O^+(aq)$ $K_a = 7.9 \times 10^{-6}$

     $K_a = 7.9 \times 10^{-6} = \dfrac{[Al(H_2O)_5OH^{2+}][H_3O^+]}{[Al(H_2O)_6]} = \dfrac{x^2}{0.015 - x}$

Assume that x is much smaller than 0.015

$7.9 \times 10^{-6} = \dfrac{x^2}{0.015}$

$x = [H_3O^+] = 3.4 \times 10^{-4}\ M$

$pH = -\log[H_3O^+] = 3.46$

3. $Ca^{2+}(aq) + 2\ HCO_3^-(aq) + CaO(s) \rightarrow 2\ CaCO_3(s) + H_2O\ell)$

     $[Ca^{2+}] = \dfrac{175\ mg}{1\ L} \cdot \dfrac{1\ g}{1000\ mg} \cdot \dfrac{1\ mol\ Ca^{2+}}{40.08\ g} = 0.00437\ mol/L$

     $\dfrac{0.00437\ mol\ Ca^{2+}}{1\ L} \cdot \dfrac{1\ mol\ CaO}{1\ mol\ Ca^{2+}} \cdot \dfrac{56.08\ g}{1\ mol\ CaO} \cdot 1.5 \times 10^6\ L = 3.7 \times 10^5\ g\ CaO$

4.   (a) Assume that a sequence of reactions occurs in solution.

     (1) Precipitation of Ca^{2+} using CaO:

     $Ca^{2+}(aq) + 2\ HCO_3^-(aq) + CaO(s) \rightarrow 2\ CaCO_3(s) + H_2O(\ell)$

     $1.0\ L \cdot \dfrac{0.050\ mol\ Ca^{2+}}{1\ L} \cdot \dfrac{1\ mol\ CaO}{1\ mol\ Ca^{2+}} \cdot \dfrac{56.1\ g}{1\ mol\ CaO} = 2.8\ g\ CaO$

     (2) Precipitation of Mg^{2+} using CaO:

     $Mg^{2+}(aq) + 2\ HCO_3^-(aq) + CaO(s) \rightarrow CaCO_3(s) + MgCO_3(s) + H_2O(\ell)$

     $Mg^2(aq) + CO_3^{2-}(aq) + CaO(s) + H_2O(\ell) \rightarrow CaCO_3(s) + Mg(OH)_2(s)$

     $Mg^{2+}(aq) + CaO(s) + H_2O(\ell) \rightarrow Ca^{2+}(aq) + Mg(OH)_2(s)$

———

     $3\ Mg^{2+}(aq) + 3\ CaO(s) + 2\ HCO_3^-(aq) + CO_3^{2-}(aq) + H_2O(\ell)$

                     $\rightarrow MgCO_3(s) + 2\ Mg(OH)_2(s) + 2\ CaCO_3(s) + Ca^{2+}(aq)$

     $1.0\ L \cdot \dfrac{0.0010\ mol\ Mg^{2+}}{1\ L} \cdot \dfrac{3\ mol\ CaO}{3\ mol\ Mg^{2+}} \cdot \dfrac{56.1\ g}{1\ mol\ CaO} = 0.056\ g\ CaO$

     (3) Precipitation of Mg^{2+} produces additional Ca^{2+}, remove with Na_2CO_3:

     $Ca^{2+}(aq) + Na_2CO_3(aq) \rightarrow 2\ Na^+(aq) + CaCO_3(s)$

     $1.0\ L \cdot \dfrac{0.0010\ mol\ Mg^{2+}}{1\ L} \cdot \dfrac{1\ mol\ Ca^{2+}}{3\ mol\ Mg^{2+}} \cdot \dfrac{1\ mol\ Na_2CO_3}{1\ mol\ Ca^{2+}} \cdot \dfrac{83.0\ g}{1\ mol\ Na_2CO_3} = 0.028\ g\ Na_2CO_3$

(b) $CaCO_3$:

$$1.0 \text{ L} \cdot \frac{0.050 \text{ mol Ca}^{2+}}{1 \text{ L}} \cdot \frac{2 \text{ mol CaCO}_3}{1 \text{ mol Ca}^{2+}} \cdot \frac{100.1 \text{ g}}{1 \text{ mol CaCO}_3} = 10. \text{ g CaCO}_3$$

$$1.0 \text{ L} \cdot \frac{0.0010 \text{ mol Mg}^{2+}}{1 \text{ L}} \cdot \frac{2 \text{ mol CaCO}_3}{3 \text{ mol Mg}^{2+}} \cdot \frac{100.1 \text{ g}}{1 \text{ mol CaCO}_3} = 0.067 \text{ g CaCO}_3$$

$$1.0 \text{ L} \cdot \frac{0.0010 \text{ mol Mg}^{2+}}{1 \text{ L}} \cdot \frac{1 \text{ mol Ca}^{2+}}{3 \text{ mol Mg}^{2+}} \cdot \frac{1 \text{ mol CaCO}_3}{1 \text{ mol Ca}^{2+}} \cdot \frac{100.1 \text{ g}}{1 \text{ mol CaCO}_3} = 0.033 \text{ g CaCO}_3$$

Total mass = 10. g + 0.067 g + 0.033 g = 10. g $CaCO_3$

$MgCO_3$:

$$1.0 \text{ L} \cdot \frac{0.0010 \text{ mol Mg}^{2+}}{1 \text{ L}} \cdot \frac{1 \text{ mol MgCO}_3}{3 \text{ mol Mg}^{2+}} \cdot \frac{84.3 \text{ g}}{1 \text{ mol MgCO}_3} = 0.028 \text{ g MgCO}_3$$

$Mg(OH)_2$:

$$1.0 \text{ L} \cdot \frac{0.0010 \text{ mol Mg}^{2+}}{1 \text{ L}} \cdot \frac{2 \text{ mol Mg(OH)}_2}{3 \text{ mol Mg}^{2+}} \cdot \frac{58.3 \text{ g}}{1 \text{ mol Mg(OH)}_2} = 0.039 \text{ g Mg(OH)}_2$$

5. $HClO(aq) + NH_3(aq) \rightarrow NH_2Cl(aq) + H_2O(\ell)$

acid-base reaction, oxidation-reduction reaction

$HClO(aq) + NH_2Cl(aq) \rightarrow NHCl_2(aq) + H_2O(\ell)$

acid-base reaction, oxidation-reduction reaction

$HClO(aq) + NHCl_2(aq) \rightarrow NCl_3(aq) + H_2O(\ell)$

acid-base reaction, oxidation-reduction reaction

$H_2SO_4(aq) + 2 NH_3(aq) \rightarrow (NH_4)_2SO_4(aq)$

acid-base reaction

$HNO_3(aq) + NH_3(aq) \rightarrow NH_4NO_3(aq)$

acid-base reaction

6.   The answer to this question will depend on where you live. The water quality report for New York City is found at http://www.nyc.gov/html/dep/html/wsstate.html.

7.   The answer to this question will depend on where you live. The air quality of various locations within New York City is found at http://www.dec.state.ny.us/website/dar/bts/airmon/aqipage2.htm. Current concentrations of sulfur dioxide, carbon monoxide, formaldehyde, and ozone are reported at various locations within New York City.

8.   The winners of the President's Green Chemistry Awards are found at http://www.epa.gov/greenchemistry.

9. PM_{10} is the sum of the concentration of all particles greater than or equal to 10 micrometers in diameter.

   $PM_{10} = 0.001 + 0.001 + 0.009 + 0.012 + 0.012 = 0.035 \ \mu g/m^3$

   $PM_{2.5} = 0.065 \ \mu g/m^3$

Personal Response System and In-Class Worksheets

PERSONAL RESPONSE SYSTEM IS GENERAL CHEMISTRY

John Kotz has been using a Personal Response System (PRS) in his General Chemistry I and II classes at SUNY-Oneonta for the past two and one-half years. The systems, which are designed for the collection and display of real-time polling data in classrooms, are becoming widely used in the U. S. in large lecture sections in introductory courses for chemistry, physics, biology, and geology.

The system consists of a set of receivers permanently mounted on the walls. Each student purchases a transmitter with a unique code number to communicate with the system. At SUNY-Oneonta, questions are handed out to each student on paper before class begins. Questions can be imbedded in Powerpoint or could be written on the board, but

An Interwrite PRS transmitter

given the room and computer configuration at Oneonta, it is more convenient to hand out the questions. This also provides students with a record of the questions asked in class.

At what point in the class the questions are asked depends on the material being covered. The usual practice is to take the last 10 minutes of class and use the questions as review. At times, however, it is best to use the questions in the beginning as a review of previous material. Alternatively, one can use a series of questions to lead the students through a new topic. Finally, animations and videos from the General ChemistryNOW CD-ROM can be used to illuminate the questions being asked. The system is currently used in almost every lecture in General Chemistry, and questions are posed that probe student understanding of concepts or that are meant to uncover common student errors.

When a student responds to a question, a box on a grid on the screen in the front of the room lights up to show that an answer has been submitted. The computer also records the student's number and response, but the student's name or response is not shown on the screen; that is, student responses are anonymous. Students have more than one

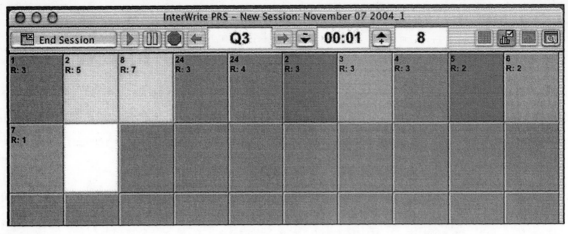

The PRS student response grid

chance to answer a question, but only the last response is saved by the system. When all of the responses have been collected, the PC analyzes and displays the response data, usually in the form of a bar graph. Students then see how their answer compares with the responses submitted by the entire class.

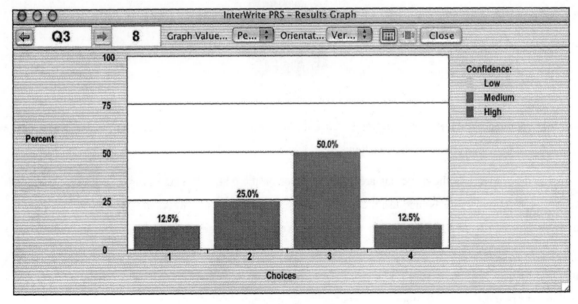

A PRS results graph

The responses of each student can be saved in a database and analyzed at a later time. One could also use it as a quizzing device or simply use it to take attendance. At Oneonta students can accumulate "participation" credit, worth a portion of one examination, by responding in lecture and by handing work in during recitation.

The system has been quite successful, chiefly because it gives an immediate picture of the class's understanding and because it allows students to see where they stand. It also allows the instructor to point out where common errors have been made while the question is fresh in the minds of the students.

Student acceptance has been high. In a year-end survey in May 2004, some student comments were:

- They helped me feel like I was participating in lecture more.
- They encourage students to participate.
- You can get the wrong answer and not have everyone know.
- Valuable for us to see how we are understanding things or not.

In that same survey, 33 out of 41 students said that the system was "valuable," "very valuable," or "extremely valuable."

The PRS Question sheets that follow in this manual are taken from a complete set that can be found on the website that accompanies the textbook or by contacting your Thompson/Brooks-Cole representative.

CHAPTER 1

Student Name_____Date_____

A. Which of the following is NOT an element?
 1. hydrogen
 2. lithium
 3. iron
 4. water
 5. silver

B. Which of the following is NOT a compound?
 1. salt
 2. water
 3. potassium
 4. sugar
 5. alcohol

C. Which of the following might best describe the particulate nature of a gas like helium, He?

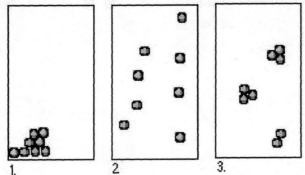

D. Which of the following is NOT a physical change?
 1. the freezing of a liquid to form a solid
 2. dissolving a solid in water to form a solution
 3. burning a piece of paper
 4. evaporating water to steam
 5. sublimation of ice to water vapor

E. A piece of a polypropylene rope (used for water skiing) floats on water, whereas a terephthalate polymer from a soda bottle sinks in water. What is the order of *increasing* density of these substances?
 1. water <polypropylene <soda bottle plastic
 2. polypropylene <water <soda bottle plastic
 3. polypropylene <soda bottle plastic <water
 4. soda bottle plastic <polypropylene <water
 5. soda bottle plastic <water <polypropylene

F.   A piece of metal with a mass of 33.2 g is immersed in 10.0 mL of water in a graduated cylinder. Determine the identity of the metal. (*General ChemistryNow CD-ROM*, Screen 1.8)

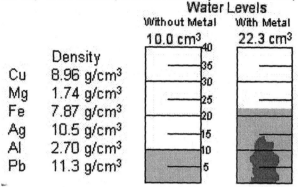

G.   Four balloons are each filled with a different gas of varying density:

Helium, $d = 0.164$ g/L   Argon, $d = 1.633$ g/L

Neon, $d = 0.825$ g/L   Krypton, $d = 4.425$ g/L

If the density of dry air is 1.12 g/L, which balloon or balloons float in air?

1.   All four
2.   helium and neon
3.   helium, neon, and argon
4.   helium, argon, and krypton
5.   argon and krypton

H.   You are given temperature readings at three locations on Earth: 29 °C, 45 °F, and 256 K. What is the order of increasing temperature?

1.   29 °C < 45 °F < 256 K
2.   45 °F < 29 °C < 256 K
3.   256 K < 29 °C < 45 °F
4.   256 K < 45 °F < 29 °C
5.   45 °F < 256 K < 29 °C

I.   Screen 1.12 of the *General ChemistryNow CD-ROM* illustrates the reaction of the elements phosphorus (P, gray) and chlorine (Cl, green) to produce the compound phosphorus trichloride.

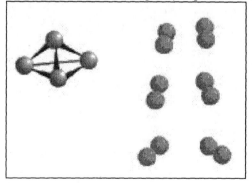

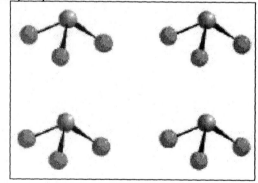

Reactants   Products

1.   The reaction involves 1 P atom and 6 Cl atoms and give 1 PCl_3 molecule
2.   The reaction involves 4 P atoms and 12 Cl atoms and give 4 PCl_3 molecules
3.   The reaction involves 1 P atom and 6 Cl atoms and give 4 PCl_3 molecule

J. Place the following in order of increasing size: 215 mm, 9 cm, 2.3 m, and 0.125 m
   1. 215 mm < 9 cm < 2.3 m < 0.125 m
   2. 215 mm < 9 cm < 0.125 m < 2.3 m
   3. 9 cm < 215 mm < 0.125 m < 2.3 m
   4. 9 cm < 215 mm < 0.125 m < 2.3 m
   5. 0.125 m < 9 cm < 215 mm < 2.3 m

K. A sample has a mass of 1245 g. Which number below is NOT equivalent to 1245 g?
   1. 1.245×10^6 mg
   2. 1.245 kg
   3. 1.245×10^3 g
   4. 1.245×10^3 kg

L. A sample has a volume of 2250 mL. Which of the following is NOT equivalent to this volume?
   1. 2.250×10^3 mL
   2. 2250 L
   3. 2.250×10^{-3} L
   4. 2.250 L

M. A sample of gold ($d = 19.32$ g/cm^3) has a mass of 1.25 kg. What is the correct setup to calculate its volume in liters?

   1. $\text{Volume(L)} = 1.25 \text{ kg} \left(\dfrac{1000 \text{ g}}{1 \text{ kg}} \right) \left(\dfrac{19.32 \text{ g}}{1 \text{ cm}^3} \right) \left(\dfrac{1 \text{ mL}}{1 \text{ cm}^3} \right) \left(\dfrac{1 \text{ L}}{1000 \text{ mL}} \right)$

   2. $\text{Volume(L)} = 1.25 \text{ kg} \left(\dfrac{1000 \text{ g}}{1 \text{ kg}} \right) \left(\dfrac{1 \text{ cm}^3}{19.32 \text{ g}} \right) \left(\dfrac{1 \text{ mL}}{1 \text{ cm}^3} \right) \left(\dfrac{1 \text{ L}}{1000 \text{ mL}} \right)$

   3. $\text{Volume(L)} = 1.25 \text{ kg} \left(\dfrac{1 \text{ cm}^3}{19.32 \text{ g}} \right) \left(\dfrac{1 \text{ mL}}{1 \text{ cm}^3} \right) \left(\dfrac{1 \text{ L}}{1000 \text{ mL}} \right)$

   4. $\text{Volume(L)} = 1.25 \text{ kg} \left(\dfrac{1000 \text{ g}}{1 \text{ kg}} \right) \left(\dfrac{1 \text{ cm}^3}{19.32 \text{ g}} \right) \left(\dfrac{1 \text{ L}}{1000 \text{ mL}} \right)$

   5. $\text{Volume(L)} = 1.25 \text{ kg} \left(\dfrac{19.32 \text{ g}}{1 \text{ cm}^3} \right) \left(\dfrac{1 \text{ mL}}{1 \text{ cm}^3} \right) \left(\dfrac{1 \text{ L}}{1000 \text{ mL}} \right)$

CHAPTER 2

Student Name_____Date_____

A. Which of the following is NOT an isotope of element X, the atomic number for which is 9?

1. $^{19}_{9}X$

2. $^{20}_{9}X$

3. $^{9}_{18}X$

4. $^{21}_{9}X$

B. Which statement describes the composition of an isotope of iron, ^{58}Fe?
   1. 26 neutrons, 32 protons, and 26 electrons
   2. 32 neutrons, 26 protons, and 26 electrons
   3. 26 neutrons, 26 protons, and 32 electrons
   4. 26 neutrons, 26 protons, and 26 electrons

C. An element (E) has several naturally occurring isotopes, with the following abundances:
^{72}E, 54.5% ^{73}E, 15.6% ^{74}E, 29.9%

The most reasonable atomic weight for this element would be
   1. 72.1
   2. 72.6
   3. 73.1
   4. 73.8
   5. 74.0

D. Which list of elements includes those in the same periodic group?
   1. Mg, Fe, Al
   2. Ti, B, Ge
   3. B, Al, Tl
   4. Cl, Si, Sn
   5. Fe, Co, Ni

E. Which list of elements includes those in the same period or row of the periodic table.?
   1. Mg, Fe, Al
   2. Ti, S, Ge
   3. B, Al, Tl
   4. Cl, Si, Sn
   5. Fe, Co, Ni

F. Which of the following elements has the largest molar mass?
   1. K
   2. Ne
   3. As
   4. Fe
   5. Si

G. You have 0.25 mol of each of the following elements. Which one has the largest mass?

1. Fe
2. Al
3. Zn
4. Ca
5. C

H. Which sample has the largest number of atoms?

1. 0.10 mol Al
2. 1.3 g Si
3. 0.090 mol Fe
4. 10.5 g Fe
5. 3.2 g S

CHAPTER 3

Student Name_____ Date_____

A. The molecule pictured here is one of the essential amino acids.
   What is the molecular formula of the acid?

   1. C_2H_5NO
   2. C_3H_5NO
   3. $C_3H_5NO_2$
   4. $C_3H_6NO_2$
   5. $C_3H_7NO_2$

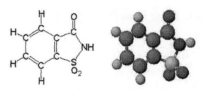

B. The molecule pictured here is saccharin, an artificial sweetener. The molecular formula for saccharin is

   1. C_6H_4NOS
   2. $C_6H_4NO_3S$
   3. $C_6H_5NO_3S$
   4. $C_7H_5NO_3S$
   5. C_7H_5NOS

C. What ion in the following list is NOT likely to form?

   1. Na^+
   2. Mg^{3+}
   3. Al^{3+}
   4. Fe^{2+}
   5. Zn^{2+}

D. When the ion Sr^{2+} forms,

   1. the Sr atom loses 1 electron and now has the same number of electrons as Kr
   2. the Sr atom loses 1 electron and now has the same number of electrons as Xe
   3. the Sr atom loses 2 electron and now has the same number of electrons as Kr
   4. the Sr atom gains 2 electrons and now has the same number of electrons as Kr
   5. the Sr atom loses 3 electrons and now has the same number of electrons as Kr

E. Which of the following series contains only *known nonmetal anions*?

   1. S^{2-}, Br^-, Al^{3+} 4. Cl^-, Fe^{3+}, S^{2-}
   2. N^{2-}, I^-, O^{2-} 5. In^+, Br^{2-}, Te^{2-}
   3. P^{3-}, F^-, Se^{2-}

F. The ion ClO^- has

   1. 25 protons and 25 electrons
   2. 25 protons and 26 electrons
   3. 25 protons and 24 electrons
   4. 26 protons and 25 electrons
   5. 26 protons and 26 electrons

G. Which compound in the following list is NOT possible?
 1. $CaBr_2$
 2. KI
 3. Al_2O
 4. $LiCl$
 5. MgO

H. Which compound in the list below is NOT possible?
 1. K_2NO_3
 2. $CaSO_4$
 3. $Fe(ClO_4)_2$
 4. Na_3PO_4
 5. $LiHSO_4$

I. Which compound formula and name in the list is NOT correct?
 1. $CaSO_4$, calcium sulfate
 2. $NaNO_3$, sodium nitrate
 3. MgI_2, magnesium iodide
 4. NH_4PO_4, ammonium phosphate
 5. $Ca(ClO)_2$, calcium hypochlorite

J. Which compound formula and name in the list is NOT correct?
 1. $NaHSO_4$, sodium hydrogen sulfate
 2. $CaHPO_4$, calcium hydrogen phosphate
 3. $FeCl_3$, iron(III) chloride
 4. NiO, nickel(III) oxide
 5. $Cu(CH_3CO_2)_2$, copper(II) acetate

K. Which compound in the list is NOT ionic? That is, which one in the list is a molecular compound?
 1. $LiCl$, lithium chloride
 2. SO_2, sulfur dioxide
 3. AlF_3, aluminum fluoride
 4. $Ba(NO_3)_2$, barium nitrate
 5. $NaHCO_3$, sodium hydrogen carbonate

L. Which compound formula and name for a molecular compound in the list is NOT correct?
 1. CH_4, methane
 2. SF_4, sulfur tetrafluoride
 3. N_2O, dinitrogen oxide
 4. N_2O_4, nitrogen oxide
 5. NH_3, ammonia

M. All of the formulas below are correct EXCEPT
 1. $Ba(NO_3)_2$ 4. $Al_2(SO_4)_3$
 2. $KClO_4$ 5. Ca_2HPO_4
 3. Na_3N

N. Sodium oxalate has the formula $Na_2C_2O_4$. Based on this information, the formula for iron(III) oxalate is
   1. FeC_2O_4 4. $Fe_2(C_2O_4)_3$
   2. $Fe(C_2O_4)_2$ 5. $Fe_3(C_2O_4)_2$
   3. $Fe(C_2O_4)_3$

O. All of the following statements concerning ionic compounds are correct EXCEPT
   1. as the ion charges increase, the attraction between the ions increases.
   2. ionic compounds form extended 3-dimensional networks called crystal lattices.
   3. ionic crystals tend to be rigid, and they cleave along planes.
   4. positive and negative ions are attracted to each other by electrostatic forces.
   5. the electrostatic forces are weaker in CaO than in NaCl.

P. What is the *approximate* molar mass of FeO, iron(II) oxide?
   1. 72 g/mol
   2. 56 g/mol
   3. 896 g/mol

Q. The molar mass of CH_4 is 16 g/mol. Which represents the greatest number of molecules of CH_4?
   1. 32 g
   2. 1.8 mol
   3. 12 g

R. The molar mass of CO_2 is 44 g/mol. Which answer best represents the percent composition of the compound?
   1. 50.0% C and 50.0% O
   2. 12.0% C and 88.0% O
   3. 27.3% C and 72.7% O
   4. 12.0% C and 32.0% O

S. The formula of the hydrocarbon decane is $C_{10}H_{22}$. The empirical formula is
   1. CH_2
   2. C_2H_4
   3. C_5H_{11}
   4. $C_{10}H_{22}$

T. The simplest carbohydrate is glyceraldehyde. Its empirical formula is CH_2O, and its molar mass is 90.08 g/mol. The **molecular formula** is
   1. CH_2O
   2. $C_2H_4O_2$
   3. $C_3H_6O_3$
   4. $C_4H_8O_4$

U. Nitrogen and oxygen form a series of oxides with the general formula N_xO_y. One of them has 46.67% N. The *empirical formula* for this oxide is
   1. N_2O
   2. NO
   3. NO_2
   4. N_2O_3
   5. N_2O_5

V. You combine 6.54 g of Zn with oxygen and find a white powder, Zn_xO_y, with a mass of 8.14 g. The empirical formula of the product is
   1. ZnO
   2. Zn_2O
   3. ZnO_2
   4. Zn_2O_3

CHAPTER 4 (1)

Student Name_____Date_____

A. Dinitrogen pentaoxide can be produced by the reaction between nitrogen and oxygen. Write a balanced equation for the reaction.
   1. $NO \rightarrow N + O$
   2. $2 N + 5 O \rightarrow N_2O_5$
   3. $N_2 + 5 O_2 \rightarrow N_2O_5$
   4. $2 N_2 + 5 O_2 \rightarrow 2 N_2O_5$

B. _____ $H_2S(g)$ + _____ $SO_2(g)$ $\rightarrow$ _____ $S(s)$ + _____ $H_2O(g)$
   Which statement(s) regarding this reaction is (are) true?
   1. 3 moles of S are produced per mole of H_2S.
   2. 1 mole of SO_2 is consumed per mole of H_2S.
   3. 1 mole of H_2O is produced per mole of H_2S.
   4. The total number of moles of products is always equal to the total number of moles of reactants used.

C. In the reaction of 2.0 mol of CCl_4 with an excess of HF, 1.7 mol of CCl_2F_2 is obtained.
   $CCl_4(\ell) + 2 HF(g) \rightarrow CCl_2F_2(\ell) + 2 HCl(g)$
   1. The theoretical yield for CCl_2F_2 is 1.7 mol.
   2. The actual yield for CCl_2F_2 is 1.0 mol.
   3. The actual yield for the reaction is 85%.
   4. Theoretical yield cannot be determined unless the exact amount of HF used in known.

CHAPTER 4 (2)

Student Name_____Date_____

A. _____ $H_2S(g)$ + _____ $SO_2(g)$ → _____ $S(s)$ + _____ $H_2O(g)$
   Which statement(s) regarding this reaction is (are) true?
   1. 3 moles of S are produced per mole of H_2S.
   2. 1 mole of SO_2 is consumed per mole of H_2S.
   3. 1 mole of H_2O is produced per mole of H_2S.
   4. The total number of moles of products is always equal to the total number of moles of reactants used.

B. In the reaction of 2.0 mol of CCl_4 with an excess of HF, 1.7 mol of CCl_2F_2 is obtained.
   $CCl_4(\ell)$ + 2 HF(g) → $CCl_2F_2(\ell)$ + 2 HCl(g)
   1. The theoretical yield for CCl_2F_2 is 1.7 mol.
   2. The actual yield for CCl_2F_2 is 1.0 mol.
   3. The actual yield for the reaction is 85%.
   4. Theoretical yield cannot be determined unless the exact amount of HF used in known.

C. Ammonia is prepared by the reaction
   $N_2(g)$ + 3 $H_2(g)$ → 2 $NH_3(g)$
   If you mix 10.0 mol of H_2 with excess N_2, the stoichiometric factor used to calculate the amount (moles) of NH_3 produced is
   1. 1 mol H_2/2 mol NH_3
   2. 3 mol H_2/1 mol NH_3
   3. 3 mol H_2/2 mol NH_3
   4. 2 mol NH_3/3 mol H_2

D. If you mix 10.0 mol of N_2 with 25.0 mol of H_2,
   $N_2(g)$ + 3 $H_2(g)$ → 2 $NH_3(g)$
   the limiting reactant is
   1. N_2
   2. H_2
   and the amount of NH_3 produced will be
   1. 20.0 mol NH_3
   2. 16.7 mol NH_3
   3. 37.5 mol NH_3
   4. 25.0 mol NH_3
   5. 35.0 mol NH_3

E. Iron(III)oxide is reduced to iron with CO, carbon monoxide

$Fe_2O_3(s) + 3\ CO(g) \rightarrow 2\ Fe(s) + 3\ CO_2(g)$

You combine 25 mol of Fe_2O_3 with 65 mol of CO.

The limiting reactant is

1. Fe
2. CO

The amount of Fe produced will be

1. 25 mol
2. 40 mol
3. 43 mol
4. 50 mol
5. 65 mol
6. 98 mol

CHAPTER 5 (1)

Student Name_____Date_____

A. Solubility: Which of the following is the only INSOLUBLE salt in water?
    1. NH_4NO_3
    2. NaOH
    3. PbI_2
    4. K_2CO_3
    5. LiCl

B. Solubility: Which of the following is the only SOLUBLE salt in water?
    1. $NiCO_3$
    2. CaF_2
    3. NiS
    4. $CuBr_2$
    5. $Fe_3(PO_4)_2$

C. Writing net ionic equations:*(not a "clicker" question)*
    Write the net ionic equation for the reaction of copper(II)sulfate and sodium hydroxide to produce copper(II)hydroxide and sodium sulfate.
    Step 1: Write the overall balanced equation

    Step 2: Decide on the water solubility of each product and reactant

    Step 3: Remove spectator ions and write the net ionic equation

CHAPTER 5 (2)

Student Name_____Date_____

A. You have 60.0 mL of 0.25 M HCl. How many moles of HCl are present?
   1. 0.25 mol
   2. 0.60 mol
   3. 0.15 mol
   4. 0.025 mol
   5. 0.015 mol

B. You add 60.0 mL of 0.25 M HCl to a 500 mL volumetric flask and then add water to the mark on the flask. What is the concentration of HCl in the diluted solution?
   1. 0.030 M
   2. 0.015 M
   3. 0.025 M
   4. 0.060 M
   5. 0.050 M

C. What is the pH of the dilute solution prepared in part B?
   1. 2.50
   2. 1.82
   3. 3.00
   4. 1.52
   5. 5.50

CHAPTER 5 (3)

Student Name_____Date_____

A. In the demonstration of the reaction of Zn with VO_2^+, the oxidation number of V in VO_2^+ is
   1. −5
   2. −3
   3. 0
   4. +3
   5. +5

B. Which of the following statements is correct regarding the demonstration of the reaction of Zn with VO_2^+?
   1. Zn is oxidized and VO_2^+ is the reducing agent
   2. Zn is reduced and VO_2^+ is the reducing agent
   3. Zn is oxidized and VO_2^+ is the oxidizing agent
   4. Zn is reduced and VO_2^+ is the oxidizing agent

C. In the demonstration of the electrolysis of KI in water, the half-reactions are
   $$2\, I^-(aq) \rightarrow I_2(aq) + 2\, e^-$$
   $$2e^- + 2\, H_2O(\ell) \rightarrow H_2(g) + 2\, OH^-(aq)$$
   Which of the following describes this process?
   1. I^- is reduced and H_2O is oxidized
   2. I^- is oxidized and H_2O is reduced
   3. I^- is reduced and H_2O is reduced
   4. I^- is oxidized and H_2O is oxidized

D. Copper metal reacts with HNO_3 to give Cu^{2+} ions and NO_2 gas.
   1. Copper is the reducing agent and HNO_3 is the oxidizing agent
   2. Copper is the oxidizing agent and HNO_3 is oxidized
   3. Copper is the reducing agent and HNO_3 is reduced
   4. Copper is the oxidizing agent and HNO_3 is the reducing agent

CHAPTER 6 (1)

Student Name_____Date_____

These questions use the Simulation on CD-ROM Screen 6.9, Heat Capacity of Pure Substances

When a piece of copper (5.0 g) is heated for 2.0 seconds, and 100 J of heat energy is transferred to the copper, the temperature increases from 20.0 ˚C to 71.9 °C.

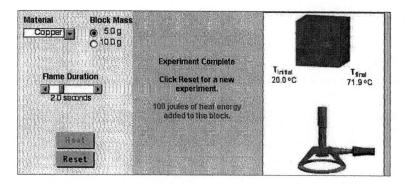

A. If 10.0 g of Cu is heated for 2.0 seconds(and 100 J are transferred), what is the final temperature of the block?
   1. 71.9 °C
   2. 100 °C
   3. 46 °C
   4. 123.9 °C
   5. 719 °C

B. If 5.0 g of Cu is heated for 4.0 seconds(and 200 J are transferred), what is the final temperature of the block?
   1. 71.9 °C
   2. 100 °C
   3. 46 °C
   4. 123.9 °C
   5. 719 °C

C. Use the data above to calculate the specific heat capacity, C, of copper.
   1. 0.278 J/g·K
   2. 0.385 J/g·K
   3. 1.93 J/g·K
   4. 2.60 J/g·K

CHAPTER 6 (2)

Student Name_____Date_____

A. Which equation below defines the standard molar enthalpy of formation of gaseous methanol, CH_3OH?
   1. $CH_4(g) + 1/2\ O_2(g) \rightarrow CH_3OH(g)$
   2. $C(s) + 2\ H_2(g) + 1/2\ O_2(g) \rightarrow CH_3OH(g)$
   3. $CO(g) + 2\ H_2(g) \rightarrow CH_3OH(g)$
   4. $H_2O(g) + C(s) + H_2(g) \rightarrow CH_3OH(g)$

B. You wish to know the enthalpy change for the following reaction.

   $P_4(s) + 6\ Cl_2(g) \rightarrow 4\ PCl_3(\ell)$ $\Delta H° = ?$

   Use Hess's law and the following information to find this $\Delta H°$.

   $P_4(s) + 10\ Cl_2(g) \rightarrow 4\ PCl_5(s)$ $\Delta H° = -1774.0$ kJ

   $PCl_3(\ell) + Cl_2(g) \rightarrow PCl_5(s)$ $\Delta H° = -123.8$ kJ

   1. -1898.8 kJ
   2. -1650.2 kJ
   3. $+1897.8$ kJ
   4. $+1650.2$ kJ
   5. -1278.8 kJ

C. Using the answer to the preceding question, decide on the value of $\Delta H°$ for the formation of 1 mol of $PCl_3(\ell)$.

   1. -1898.8 kJ
   2. -474.7 kJ
   3. -1650.2 kJ
   4. -6600.8 kJ
   5. -319.7 kJ
   6. $+412.5$ kJ
   7. $+474.7$ kJ

CHAPTER 6 (3)

Student Name_____Date_____

A. *See CD-ROM, Screen 6.11, Simulation.* Equal masses of liquid A, initially at 100 °C, and liquid B, initially at 50 °C, are combined in an insulated container. The final temperature of the mixture is 80 °C. Which has the larger specific heat capacity, A or B?
  1. A
  2. B
  3. A and B have the same specific heat capacity.

B. What is the specific heat capacity of an unknown metal if 195 joules of heat are required to raise the temperature of 12.1 g by 34.6 °C?
  1. 0.466 J/g·K
  2. 0.335 J/g·K
  3. 0.714 J/g·K
  4. 0.816 J/g·K

C. How many joules of heat are required to heat 1.00 g of lead from 25 °C to the melting point (327 °C) and melt all of it?
  Specific heat capacity for lead = 0.159 J/g·K   Heat of fusion of lead = 24.7 J/g
  1. 2.47 J
  2. 39.4 J
  3. 48.0 J
  4. 72.7 J

CHAPTER 7 (1)

Student Name_____Date_____

A. Which of the following is NOT a valid set of quantum numbers?
1. $n = 4$, $\ell = 1$, and $m_\ell = -1$
2. $n = 6$, $\ell = 5$, and $m_\ell = 0$
3. $n = 2$, $\ell = 2$, and $m_\ell = +1$
4. $n = 3$, $\ell = 2$, and $m_\ell = -2$

B. For a certain orbital, $n = 3$, $\ell = 1$, and $m_\ell = -1$. What type of orbital is this?
1. 3d
2. 3s
3. 3p
4. 4d

C. If an electron subshell has 7 orbitals, what is the ℓ value for this subshell?
1. two
2. three
3. four
4. five

CHAPTER 7 (2)

Student Name_____Date_____

Consider only the following quantum levels for the H atom. Assume the emission spectrum of an excited H atom will consist of transitions only between these levels.

_____$n = 5$
_____$n = 4$

_____$n = 3$

_____$n = 2$

_____$n = 1$

A. How many emission lines are possible, considering only the five quantum levels above?

1.	1	4.	8
2.	3	5.	7
3.	4	6.	10

B. Photons of the highest frequency will be emitted in a transition from the level with $n =$ _____ to the level with the $n =$ _____.

1. from $n = 1$ to $n = 2$
2. from $n = 2$ to $n = 1$
3. from $n = 3$ to $n = 1$
4. from $n = 4$ to $n = 1$
5. from $n = 5$ to $n = 1$
6. from $n = 5$ to $n = 4$

C. The emission line having the longest wavelength corresponds to a transition from the level with $n =$ _____ to the level with $n =$ _____ .

1. from $n = 1$ to $n = 2$
2. from $n = 2$ to $n = 1$
3. from $n = 3$ to $n = 1$
4. from $n = 4$ to $n = 1$
5. from $n = 5$ to $n = 1$
6. from $n = 5$ to $n = 4$

CHAPTER 7 (3)

Student Name_____Date_____

A. A local radio station has a frequency of 98.6 megahertz (MHz). What is the wavelength of this station in centimeters? (1 MHz $= 1.00 \times 10^6$ cycles per second)
    1. 304 cm
    2. 37.1 cm
    2. 0.329 cm
    4. 0.00289 cm

B. Which of the following produces radiation having the highest frequency?
    1. microwave oven
    2. AM radio
    3. radar
    4. FM radio

C. Which of the following types of radiation has the longest wavelength?
    1. gamma rays
    2. visible
    3. ultraviolet
    4. radar

D. Which of the following types of radiation has the highest energy?
    1. gamma rays
    2. visible
    3. ultraviolet
    4. radar

CHAPTER 8 (1)

Student Name_____Date_____

A. What element has the following electron configuration?

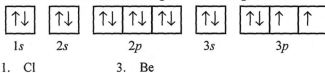

1. Cl   3. Be
2. S   4. Ti

B. Write out the electron configuration for Tc, element 43, using the ***noble gas and box notations***.

C. Write out the electron configuration for Pu, plutonium, element 94, using the ***noble gas and spdf notations***.

D. What element has the electron configuration $[Xe]\ 4f^{14}\ 5d^{10}\ 6s^2\ 6p^2$?
1. Hf   3. Pb
2. Lu   4. Sn

E. What is the electronic configuration of P^{3-}?
1. $[Ne]\ 3s^2\ 3p^6$ 3. $[Ne]\ 3s^2$
2. $[Ne]\ 3s^2\ 3p^3$ 4. $[Ne]\ 3p^6$

F. What ion corresponds to the following electron configuration?

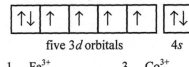

five $3d$ orbitals $4s$

1. Fe^{3+} 3. Co^{3+}
2. Rh^{3+} 4. Ni^{2+}

G. Write out the electron configuration for V^{3+} (the vanadium +3 ion)using the ***noble gas and box notations.***

483

H. Which of the following is the correct electronic configuration for the zirconium(II) ion?
   1. $[Ar]\,4d^2$ 3. $[Ar]\,5s^2$
   2. $[Kr]\,5s^2$ 4. $[Kr]\,4d^2$

I. Which of the following ions is paramagnetic?
   1. Ca^{2+} 3. Zn^{2+}
   2. Sc^{3+} 4. Zr^{2+}

J. Which of the following elements has two unpaired electrons when it is a +3 ion?
   1. vanadium   3. aluminum
   2. cadmium   4. antimony

K. Which of the following ions is diamagnetic?
   1. Ti^{2+} 3. Mg^{2+}
   2. V^{2+} 4. Cr^{2+}

L. Which of the following is the correct electronic configuration for the nickel(II) ion?
   1. $[Ar]\,3d^8$ 3. $[Ar]\,4s^2\,3d^6$
   2. $[Kr]\,4s^2\,3d^6$ 4. $[Kr]\,3d^8$

M Which of the following elements has three unpaired electrons when it is a +2 ion?
   1. zinc   3. strontium
   2. zirconium   4. cobalt

N. What is the electronic configuration of Br^-?
   1. $[Ar]\,4s^2\,4p^5$ 3. $[Ar]\,4s^2\,4p^6$
   2. $[Kr]\,4s^2\,4p^6$ 4. $[Kr]$

CHAPTER 8 (2)

Student Name_____Date_____

A. Compare the elements Na, B, Al, and C with regard to the following properties:

Which has the largest atomic radius?
1. Na
2. B
3. Al
4. C

Which has the largest (most negative) electron affinity?
1. Na
2. B
3. Al
4. C

Which has the largest (most positive) ionization energy?
1. Na
2. B
3. Al
4. C

B. Which of the following groups of elements is arranged correctly in order of increasing first ionization energy?
1. $Mg < C < N < F$
2. $N < Mg < C < F$
3. $Mg < N < C < F$
4. $F < C < Mg < N$

C. Which of the following elements would have the greatest difference between the first and the second ionization energy?
1. lithium
2. carbon
3. fluorine
4. nitrogen

CHAPTER 15 (1)

Student Name_____Date_____

A few drops of blue food dye were added to water followed by a solution of bleach. (Initially, the concentration of dye was about 3.4×10^{-5} M, and the bleach (NaOCl) concentration was about 0.034 M.) The dye faded as it reacted with the bleach. The color change was followed by a spectrophotometer, and the data are plotted below.

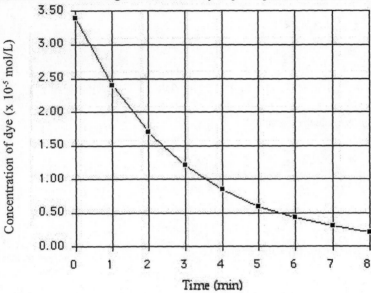

A. What is the average rate of reaction over the first 2 minutes?
   1. −1.7 mol/L·min
   2. −2.4 mol/L·min
   3. −0.85 mol/L·min

B. Over the time from 4 to 6 minutes?
   1. −0.18 mol/L·min
   2. −0.55 mol/L·min
   3. −0.80 mol/L·min

C. With time the rate of reaction
   1. declines
   2. stays the same
   3. increases

D. Why does the rate behave as it does?
   1. [Dye] increases
   2. [Dye] stays same
   3. [Dye] decreases

CHAPTER 15 (2)

Student Name_____Date_____

Consider the data below for the reaction

$$N_2H_4 + 2\,H_2O \rightarrow N_2 + 4\,H_2O$$

in the presence of Cu^{2+} ion. Derive the rate law from the data given below.

Experimental Data				
Experiment	$[N_2H_4]$ $\times 10^3$ M	$[H_2O]$ $\times 10^3$ M	$[Cu^{2+}]$ $\times 10^6$ M	Initial Rate of N_2 Gas Evolution (mL N_2/min)
1	16	65	1.23	7.3
2	33	65	1.23	7.4
3	33	33	1.23	3.6
4	33	131	1.23	15.0
5	33	65	1.30	8.3
6	33	65	2.46	16.2

The rate law is
1. Rate = $k[N_2H_4][H_2O][Cu^{2+}]$
2. Rate = $k[N_2H_4][H_2O]^2[Cu^{2+}]$
3. Rate = $k[N_2H_4][H_2O]^2$
4. Rate = $k[H_2O][Cu^{2+}]$
5. Rate = $k[H_2O]^2[Cu^{2+}]$

CHAPTER 15 (3)

Student Name_____Date_____

A. The decomposition of SO_2Cl_2 is first-order in SO_2Cl_2 and it has a half-life of 4.1 hours. If you begin with 1.6×10^{-3} mol of SO_2Cl_2, how many hours elapse before the quantity of SO_2Cl_2 has decreased to 2.00×10^{-4} mol?

1. 4.1 hours
2. 8.2 hours
3. 12.3 hours
4. 16.4 hours
5. 20.5 hours

B. The radioactive isotope copper-64 (^{64}Cu) is used in the form of copper(II) acetate to study Wilson's disease. The isotope has a half-life of 12.70 hours.

Part I. What is the value of k for this process?
1. 12.70 h^{-1}
2. 0.0787 h^{-1}
3. 0.0546 h^{-1}

Part II. What fraction of copper(II)acetate remains after 2.0 days?
1. 0.50
2. 0.21
3. 0.073

CHAPTER 15 (4)

Student Name_____Date_____

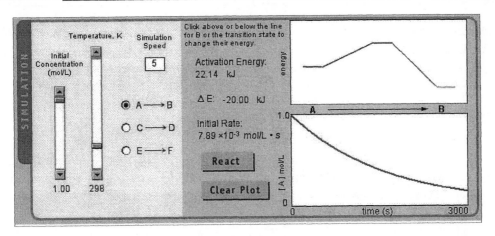

A. The reaction of A → B is

   1. exothermic

   2. endothermic

B. Which diagram shows an activation energy of 22.14 kJ?

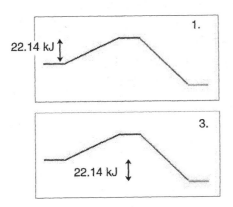

C. If the activation energy is kept at 22.14 kJ but the temperature is increased to 400 K, the reaction rate is

   1. faster   2. slower   3. unchanged

D. Which diagram shows the effect of increasing temperature?

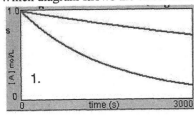

   (Note: The original concentration-time curve shown above is still shown in the diagram.)

E. If the activation energy is increased (at a constant temperature), the reaction rate is

   1. faster   2.   slower 3.   unchanged

CHAPTER 18 (1)

Student Name_____Date_____

1. You titrate 100. mL of a 0.025 M solution of benzoic acid with 0.100 M NaOH to the equivalence point. What is the pH of the final solution?

$$C_6H_5CO_2H(aq) + NaOH(aq) \rightarrow Na^+(aq) + C_6H_5CO_2^-(aq) + H_2O(\ell)$$

The pH of the final solution will be

1. less than 7
2. equal to 7
3. greater than 7

2. You titrate 100. mL of a 0.025 M solution of benzoic acid with 0.100 M NaOH to the equivalence point. What is the pH when half of the benzoic acid has been consumed?

$$C_6H_5CO_2H(aq) + NaOH(aq) \rightarrow Na^+(aq) + C_6H_5CO_2^-(aq) + H_2O(\ell)$$

The pH of the final solution will be

1. less than 7
2. equal to 7
3. greater than 7

3. What is being titrated in the diagram below? What is being used to titrate the substance?

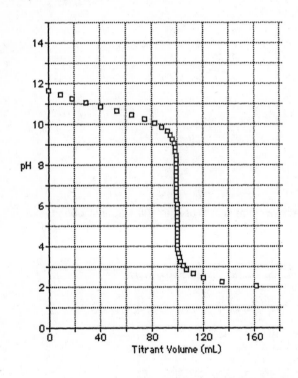

Titration of a
1. strong acid with strong base
2. weak acid with strong base
3. strong base with weak acid
4. weak base with strong acid
5. weak base with weak acid
6. weak acid with weak base

CHAPTER 18 (2)

Student Name_____Date_____

A. Which choice would be an ideal buffer solution?
   1. 0.20 M HCN and 0.10 M KCN
   2. 0.20 M HCl and 0.10 M KOH
   3. 0.20 M CH_3CO_2H and 0.10 M HCO_2H
   4. 0.10 M HCl and 0.010 M KCl

B. A buffer has 0.1 MNH_4Cl and 0.10 MNH_3. Knowing that K_a for $NH_4^+ = 5.6 \times 10^{-10}$ (and $pK_a = 9.25$) the pH of this buffer will be about
   1. 4.75
   2. 9.25
   3. 7.00
   4. 5.60

C. Acetic acid has $K_a = 1.8 \times 10^{-5}$ ($pK_a = 4.74$). To prepare a buffer containing CH_3CO_2H and $NaCH_3CO_2$ and having a pH of 5, the ratio
   $$\frac{[CH_3CO_2H]}{[NaCH_3CO_2]}$$
   should be about
   1. 1/1
   2. 1.8/1
   3. 1/1.8
   4. 5.0/1

CHAPTER 20 (1)

Student Name_____Date_____

A cell is set up and the following reaction is observed:

$$Ni^{2+}(aq) + Cd(s) \rightarrow Ni(s) + Cd^{2+}(aq)$$

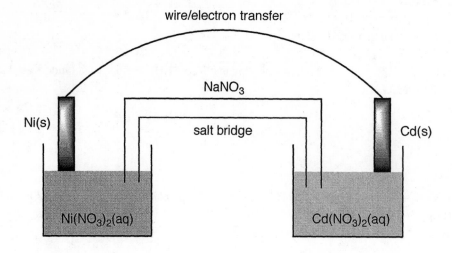

A. Electron transfer
    1. Electrons transfer from Ni to Cd
    2. Electrons transfer from Cd to Ni

B. Redox
    1. Ni^{2+} is oxidized and is the reducing agent
    2. Cd is oxidized and is the reducing agent

C. Electrodes
    1. Cd is the anode and is negative
    2. Cd is the anode and is positive
    3. Cd is the cathode and is negative
    4. Cd is the cathode and is positive

D. In the salt bridge (which contains Na^+ and NO_3^- ions)
    1. NO_3^- ions move from the Cd side to the Ni side and Na^+ ions move from the Ni side to the Cd side.
    2. NO_3^- ions move from the Ni side to the Cd side and Na^+ ions move from the Cd side to the Ni side.

CHAPTER 20 (2)

Student Name_____Date_____

The cell below uses the reaction $Zn(s) + 2\ H^+(aq) \rightarrow Zn^{2+}(aq) + H_2(g)$

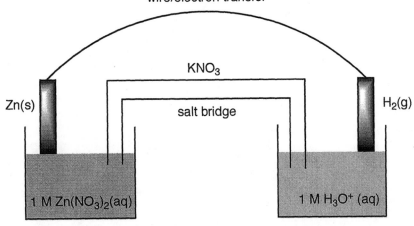

A. Electron transfer
   1. Electrons transfer from Zn to hydrogen electrode
   2. Electrons transfer from hydrogen electrode to Zn

B. Redox
   1. Zn is oxidized and is the reducing agent
   2. H_2 is oxidized and is the reducing agent

C. Electrodes
   1. Zn is the anode and is negative
   2. H_2 is the anode and is positive
   3. Zn is the cathode and is negative
   4. H_2 is the cathode and is positive

D. In the salt bridge (which contains K^+ and NO_3^- ions)
   1. NO_3^- ions move from the Zn side to the H_2 side and K^+ ions move from the H_2 side to the Zn side.
   2. NO_3^- ions move from the H_2 side to the Zn side and K^+ ions move from the Zn side to the H_2 side.

CHAPTER 20 (3)

Student Name_____Date_____

Use Table 20.1, Table of Reduction Potentials

A. What is the best oxidizing agent in the following list?
   1. O_2
   2. H_2O_2
   3. Cl_2

B. What is the best reducing agent in the following list?
   1. Hg
   2. Al
   3. Sn

C. Considering only the half-reactions involving Cu, H_2, and Zn:
   1. H_2 can reduce both Zn^{2+} and Cu^{2+}
   2. H_2 can reduce Zn but not Cu^{2+}
   3. Zn can reduce H^+ but not Cu^{2+}
   4. Zn can reduce H^+ and Cu^{2+}

D. What is E° for the following reaction? $2\ Fe^{3+}(aq) + Sn(s) \rightarrow 2\ Fe^{2+}(aq) + Sn^{2+}(aq)$
   1. 0.911 V
   2. 0.631 V
   3. 1.682 V
   4. 0.771 V
   5. 0.14 V

General ChemistryNOW CD-ROM and Website

The technology associated with this textbook is designed to offer both students and faculty tools they can use to aid student learning. The textbook comes with the *General ChemistryNOW* CD-ROM, which provides a local version of the material on the textbook website. The electronic content is completely and seamlessly integrated with material and treatment in the textbook.

ORGANIZATION

The content on the *General ChemistryNOW* CD-ROM is organized by chapter. Within a chapter, the student is offered an Exam Preparation Quiz, the chapter content, and a set of useful tools. The *General ChemistryNOW* CD-ROM and the content on the textbook website are identical with exception that the Exam Preparation Quiz may only be performed online.

CONTENT

The electronic materials in *General ChemistryNOW* take a variety of forms.

- **Description Screens** are edited versions of the original *General Chemistry Interactive* CD-ROM screens. The material is presented using videos and animations to tie together macroscopic experimental observations with nanoscale chemical interpretations.

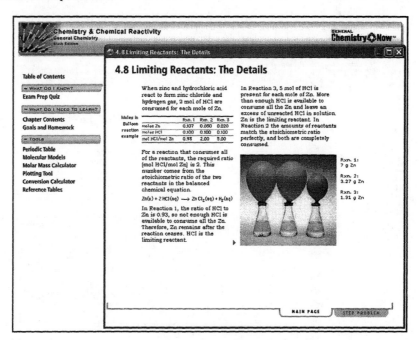

A content screen in Chapter 4

- **Tutorial** modules cover all important problem types. Most work by asking a question and then leading the student through the solution step-by-step if the student has trouble answering the problem. Others are more graphical in nature, asking the student to construct a diagram on-screen and then analyzing it and offering advice on how to correctly complete it. Tutorials are intended to aid students with basic skills as well as with problem solving.

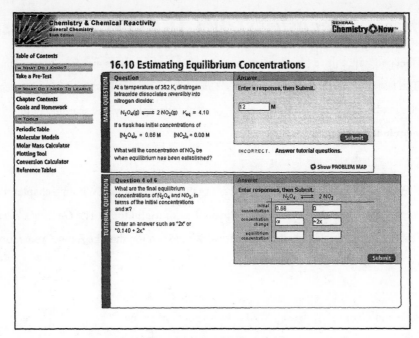

A Tutorial screen in Chapter 16

- **Homework Study Question Tutorials** are tutorial modules based on end-of-chapter study questions from the textbook. These questions contain randomized content and offer step-by-step problem solving advice. A minimum of 20 questions from each chapter have been converted to tutorial form. These tutorial questions are identified in the textbook by a blue square.

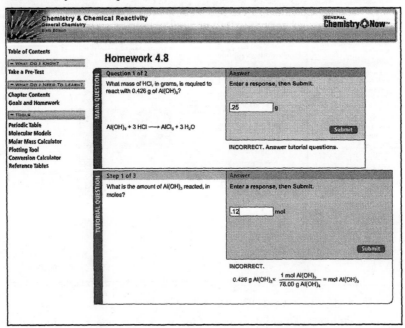

A Homework Study Question screen in Chapter 4

- **Simulations** are experiment- or theory-based interactive modules where the student manipulates parameters and observes how the chemical system responds. Each of these includes a set of leading questions to complete the guided inquiry experience. These modules are intended to enhance the student's conceptual understanding of chemical systems and relationships. Each simulation has an instructor version intended for use in the classroom that is large format and does not include any guiding questions (available on the website).

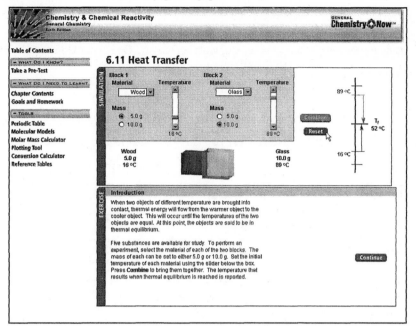

A Simulation screen in Chapter 6

- **Exercises** are multimedia-based modules that lead students to closely examine videos, animations, and, especially, active versions of text figures. These are referred to as Active Figures in the text. Each module presents the image, video, or animation and leads the students through an exploration using a set of questions and answers. Like simulations, exercises are intended to aid conceptual understanding and to enhance the usefulness of text figures.

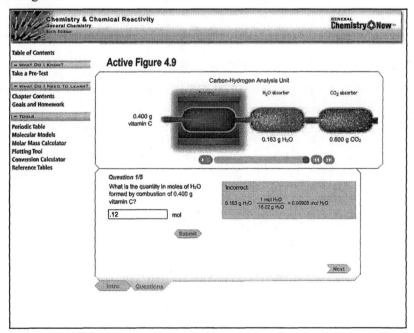

An Active Figure in Chapter 4

- **Exam Preparation Quiz** questions are multiple choice questions that are intended as the final self-test by the student to determine if they are proficient in the course material.

ACCESS TO CONTENT

The chapter content can be accessed by the Chapter Contents screen, the Goals and Homework screen, or by the follow-up materials seen after taking a Exam Preparation Quiz.

- The **Goals and Homework** screen connects the electronic resources with chapter learning goals from the textbook. Each goal and subgoal is linked to appropriate content screens, interactive modules, and homework study question tutorials materials on the *General ChemistryNOW* CD-ROM and website.

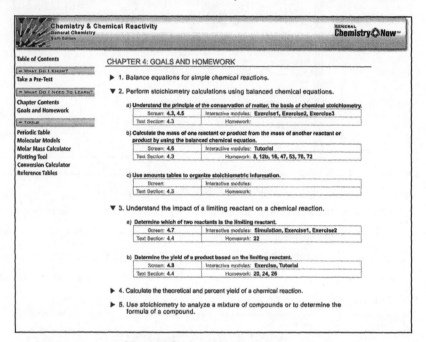

Chapter 4 Goals and Homework screen

- The **Chapter Contents** screen presents the content screens in order of the textbook sections, associating interactive modules such as simulations and tutorials with the appropriate content screen. The Homework Study Questions and Active Figures are listed on this contents screen.

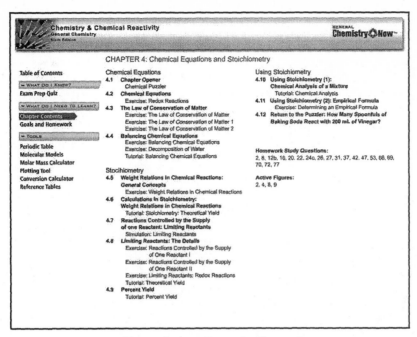

Chapter Contents Screen for Chapter 4

- After the student takes an Exam Preparation Quiz, they are presented with a **Learning Plan**. This plan identifies the goals and subgoals that the student should focus on and the associated content screens, tutorials, simulations, and/or homework study questions.

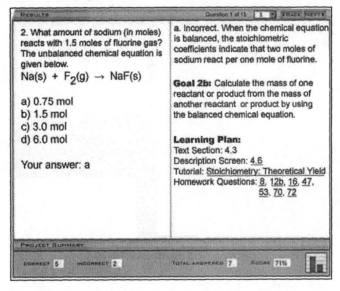